WATSON
The Smartest Dog in the U.S.A.

by

Karla Kuskin

Harper & Row, Publishers · New York, Evanston, and London

For Nicholas
who reads as well
as Watson does

WATSON
The Smartest Dog in the U.S.A.

Copyright © 1968 by Karla Kuskin
Printed in the United States of America. All rights reserved. No part of this book may be used or reproduced in any manner whatsoever without written permission except in the case of brief quotations embodied in critical articles and reviews. For information address Harper & Row, Publishers, Incorporated, 49 East 33rd Street, New York, N.Y. 10016.
Library of Congress
Catalog Card Number:
68-10370

WATSON
The Smartest Dog in the U.S.A.

Watson, who is a dog, told me this story and asked me to write it down for you. He would write the story himself, but he buried his pen in the garden and now he cannot find it.

There was, and is, a dog named Watson, who is handsome, intelligent, and has, so everyone says, winning ways.

He can run like the wind, dance a nice dog trot, juggle, play pretty good clarinet, make blueberry pancakes, and read. He likes to read best of all.

Watson lives with Huey Middle, who is four, and his parents, Joan and Arnold Middle. Joan is twenty-nine. Arnold is thirty and a half.

Watson and Huey are good friends. Every morning they go for a walk. They often go to the library, and Watson takes out a book. Huey is too young to have a library card. In the afternoon Watson reads the book to Huey.

Books are meat and drink to Watson. He loves them. He laughs so hard at the funny parts that he falls on his nose. The sad parts make him so sad that tears come to his eyes and splash onto his paws. Watson thinks that every story he reads is about himself. When he reads about a mouse, he becomes that mouse. When he reads about a lion, he turns into that lion.

On Thursday Watson and Huey got a new book from the library. They looked at it as they walked home through the park. It looked so good that instead of waiting until after lunch to read it they sat down on a bench in the sun. Watson put on his reading glasses and began:

"Once there was a long, thin, mean, lean witch, who lived on top of a hill of green ice at the end of the world."

That's when Watson became the witch. He picked up the branch of a tree. It was his broomstick. Watson flew around making faces. He laughed a mean laugh and frightened some pigeons. He cackled at babies and stamped all over the grass where it said KEEP OFF.

Then Huey threw an acorn and hit him. Watson remembered that he was a dog and began to read again:

"The witch had the biggest dragon in the world for protection. He had sharp, shiny teeth, a long tail with an arrow on the end of it, and he blew smoke out of his nose. For two cents he would eat up anybody who set one tiny foot on the hill of green ice at the end of the world."

That's when Watson became the dragon. He growled horribly and waved his snaky tail. He bellowed and snorted smoke out of his nose. He opened his huge mouth and took a great big bite out of a giant.

The giant was a water fountain. Watson bumped his nose and splashed his reading glasses. Then he remembered that he was a dog and began to read again:

"Now at the other end of the world on a grass-green, flower-flecked, sweet-smelling hill lived a wise old king, who was as nice as pie and as rich as hard sauce. All day long this dear man sat in his palace and gave away pearls and cup-cakes."

That's when Watson became the king. He picked up a scepter, put on a crown, and smiled sweetly at everyone. And he was so generous. He gave away everything he could find—stones, grass, sticks, old chewing gum, broken pieces of chalk, and skate keys. He was going to give

the book away when Huey pushed him so hard that Watson's crown fell off, and he remembered that he was a dog and began to read again:

"The king had a daughter. She was shy as a breeze and as fair as early May. She had long yellow hair, sea-blue eyes, and a smile that lighted the room. She loved one of the royal cowboys with all her heart."

That's when Watson became the royal cowboy. He galloped his glorious horse, *yippied* and *yahooed,* shot his silver pistols in the air, and lassoed a steer.

The steer was a little girl on a tricycle, and she rang the bell so loudly that Watson remembered he was a dog and began to read again:

"Everybody liked the cowboy except the witch. She was so mean that she hated him. She put him in a dungeon in the middle of the earth. 'You will never get out of there,' she cackled. The cowboy sat on the cold ground and watched the spiders build webs around him. He thought of how much he missed the princess and his horse and he cried and cried."

That's when Watson began to cry. He sniffed, he bit his lip, and then he wept and the tears ran down his nose and splashed onto his paws. Huey spoke to him softly. He yelled at him. He pushed and pulled him, but Watson kept on crying. Huey picked up the book, shook some tears off the pages, and led Watson home.

Mrs. Middle came to the door. She held a handkerchief for
Watson and said, "Blow." He blew and kept on crying.
"What are we going to do?" said Mrs. Middle as she served
lunch. Huey shook his head. The tablecloth was damp from
Watson's tears and the tunafish salad turned into soup. After
lunch Watson and Huey lay down for their nap, but Watson
got the pillow so wet that they couldn't sleep.

In the afternoon Huey and his mother tried everything they could think of. They brought out his clarinet, but Watson wouldn't play. They put a record on the phonograph, but Watson wouldn't dance. Huey found two oranges, a pear, and a walnut in the fruit bowl, but Watson wouldn't juggle. Huey and Mrs. Middle raced across the lawn, but Watson, who could beat them both, wouldn't run.

At last Mr. Middle came home for supper. He was the oldest, so they asked him what to do. "It is best to finish whatever you begin," he said, putting his coat in the closet.

They found the book, gave it to Watson, and waited. He began to read through his tears:

"The princess missed the cowboy as much as he missed her. She sat at a window, and her tears ran down like rain. The king saw this, and he got so angry at the witch that he paid the dragon one hundred dollars to run to the top of the green-ice hill and eat the long, thin, mean, lean witch up.

The dragon ate all of her except her buttonholes, and the magic spell broke into a thousand pieces. The royal cowboy got out of the dungeon. He was smiling as he rode up to the palace on his glorious horse. The princess laughed for joy, the king danced, and they all lived happily forever after."

That's when Watson began to smile. "There's nothing like a good book," he said and he laughed for joy. Then he danced.

And he was still dancing the next morning as he flipped the blueberry pancakes and juggled the juice.

N E U R O L O G Y
for the Speech-Language Pathologist

Sixth Edition

NEUROLOGY

for the Speech-Language Pathologist

WANDA G. WEBB, PhD, CCC-SLP
Assistant Professor
Department of Hearing and Speech Sciences
School of Medicine
Vanderbilt University
Nashville, Tennessee

ELSEVIER

ELSEVIER

3251 Riverport Lane
St. Louis, Missouri 63043

NEUROLOGY FOR THE SPEECH-LANGUAGE PATHOLOGIST,
SIXTH EDITION   ISBN: 978-0-323-10027-4

Notices

Knowledge and best practice in this field are constantly changing. As new research and experience broaden our understanding, changes in research methods, professional practices, or medical treatment may become necessary.

Practitioners and researchers must always rely on their own experience and knowledge in evaluating and using any information, methods, compounds, or experiments described herein. In using such information or methods they should be mindful of their own safety and the safety of others, including parties for whom they have a professional responsibility.

With respect to any drug or pharmaceutical products identified, readers are advised to check the most current information provided (i) on procedures featured or (ii) by the manufacturer of each product to be administered, to verify the recommended dose or formula, the method and duration of administration, and contraindications. It is the responsibility of practitioners, relying on their own experience and knowledge of their patients, to make diagnoses, to determine dosages and the best treatment for each individual patient, and to take all appropriate safety precautions.

To the fullest extent of the law, neither the Publisher nor the authors, contributors, or editors, assume any liability for any injury and/or damage to persons or property as a matter of products liability, negligence or otherwise, or from any use or operation of any methods, products, instructions, or ideas contained in the material herein.

Library of Congress Cataloging-in-Publication Data

Names: Webb, Wanda G., author.
Title: Neurology for the speech-language pathologist / Wanda G. Webb, PhD,
  CCC-SLP, Assistant Professor, Department of Hearing and Speech Sciences,
  School of Medicine, Vanderbilt University, Nashville, Tennessee.
Description: Sixth edition. | St. Louis, Missouri : Elsevier Inc., [2017] |
  Originally published: Neurology for the speech-language pathologist /
  Russell J. Love, Wanda G. Webb ; illustrations by Donna B. Halliburton. |
  Includes bibliographical references and index.
Identifiers: LCCN 2016000517 | ISBN 9780323100274 (pbk.)
Subjects: LCSH: Language disorders–Pathophysiology. | Neurology.
Classification: LCC RC423 .L68 2017 | DDC 616.85/5–dc23 LC record
available at http://lccn.loc.gov/2016000517

Content Strategy Director: Penny S. Rudolph
Content Development Manager: Jolynn Gower
Senior Content Development Specialist: Brian Loehr
Publishing Services Manager: Hemamalini Rajendrababu
Senior Project Manager: Divya Krishna Kumar
Designer: Ashley Miner

Printed in the United States of America

Last digit is the print number: 9 8 7 6 5 4 3 2 1

This book is dedicated in loving memory to Dr. Russell J. Love,
former senior author, who passed away in March 2006 at the age of 75.

Russell J. Love was born in Chicago, attended Tulane University, and graduated with his master's degree and then later his PhD from Northwestern University. As a clinician, he served as a speech-language pathologist at the Moody School for Cerebral Palsied Children in Galveston, Texas; the VA hospital in Coral Gables, Florida; Michael Reese Hospital in Chicago, Illinois; and the Bill Wilkerson Center in Nashville, Tennessee. As a professor, he taught at DePaul University and at Vanderbilt University and retired as professor emeritus from Vanderbilt in 1995. Among other acknowledgments of his contribution, Dr. Love was awarded the Honors of the Tennessee Association of Audiologists and Speech-Language Pathologists and was made a fellow of the American Speech-Language-Hearing Association. He was most proud of his work as an advocate for the rights of persons with communication and physical disabilities.

Dr. Love's memory is cherished by his family, his friends, and his colleagues as a man of perseverance, intelligence, compassion, and quick wit. He was a caring and devoted husband, father, grandfather, teacher, collaborator, and friend. My wish for every student reading this text is that you will find a teacher or mentor who will guide you in your studies and your career as carefully and with as much respect and insight as Dr. Love guided me and so many others.

This book is also dedicated in loving memory to my husband, Joe C. Luttrell, who passed away suddenly in December 2007.

Joe and I had been married only 2 or 3 years when Russell Love and I began the work on the first edition of this text. He and Russell were friends and Barbara, Russell's wife, and Joe were the persons to whom the first edition was dedicated because of their unfailing support of our work. He continued with that kind of support for me through the next three editions, through Russell's death, and during the writing with Dr. Adler of the 5th edition. This new edition was done with only memories of the support and love he always gave me. He was my best friend and the love of my life. This book is dedicated to him with appreciation for the strength and spirit to "soldier on" that only a loving partnership like ours could engender.

My second wish for any student or anyone using this text is that your life will also be blessed with someone who provides you with such gifts.

Acknowledgments

For an author primarily trained in the field of speech-language pathology, rather than neurology, a project like this demands reliance on colleagues in neurology to assist in the development of the work. Howard S. Kirshner brought his expertise to bear on the earlier editions, which establish the foundation of the current text. I remain in his debt for that guidance.

I am indebted as well to several members of the editorial staff, past and present, of Butterworth-Heinemann and now Elsevier. In past editions, specific individuals of the Butterworth-Heinemann staff have been named in the acknowledgments, as have various people in Nashville who provided invaluable secretarial support for those earlier editions. I will not reiterate their names here, but that is not to detract from the value of their contributions. They will always be remembered as critical to the success this book has enjoyed. For this edition, I am most grateful for the guidance of Jolynn Gower and Penny Rudolph and for the editing expertise of Brian Loehr and Anna Schook.

During the best of times, no undertaking as complex as this revision is completed without the support of coworkers, family, and friends. I first want to express my appreciation to Dr. Richard Adler for initiating this project with me. He and I began planning the sixth edition; he did a great deal of early research and turned all of it over to me when we decided I would continue writing the sixth edition. He did much of this research during times of illness and through a horrible Minnesota winter and the melting of spring! I very much appreciate the early assistance he so willingly provided and, of course, much of the content for which he was responsible in the fifth edition continues in the sixth edition. Thank you, Richard.

I am most grateful to my students and my colleagues at Vanderbilt University for all they have taught me and continue to teach me. I sometimes cannot believe how fortunate I am to be teaching such bright inquisitive future professionals and to work with faculty and staff at Vanderbilt who model for them the highest quality of professionalism in research, teaching, and patient care.

And finally I wish to acknowledge and thank my family and friends who have been extremely supportive through these very difficult years since the death of my husband and through this writing project. I know they will celebrate as much as I will its publication as they have stuck with me and listened to my whining and excuses for almost 2 years of writing! There are so many who deserve my recognition, and I can name only a few here. Acknowledging that, appreciation and affection are extended here to all the POMS, Linda Meyer, Judy Luna, Penny Powers, Lee and Jim Huddleston, Victoria Webb, Joe Simpson, and Lisa and Gayle Crowe for all your faith in me and your encouragement. There would be no sixth edition without it.

Wanda G. Webb

Addendum, August 30, 2015: On the very day I am writing these acknowledgments and dedications, one of my "Neurology Heroes" passed away. Dr. Oliver Sachs was a giant among researchers, teachers, and clinicians who practice neurology. He possessed a fascination with the brain and an understanding of speech and language that surpassed most neurologists. In his writing he shared the stories of many of his patients with speech-language and other disorders, enabling the public to see the humanity in these patients. More than a million copies of his books, most of which are fascinating essays based on case histories, have been sold. If you are not familiar with his books, do yourself a favor and read one soon. The medical profession and the reading public in general will miss you, Dr. Sachs. Rest in Peace.

Foreword

Speech Pathology and Neurology: Intersecting Specialties

Neurology is the study of the effects of disease in the nervous system—brain, spinal cord, cerebellum, nerves, and muscles—on human behavior. The neurologist examines specific functions—including higher cortical functions; cranial nerve functions; and motor, sensory, and cerebellar functions—all to localize disorders to specific areas of the nervous system. These lesion localizations, along with the clinical history of how the deficit developed, allow for a precise diagnosis of the disease process. Laboratory and brain imaging tests may help to confirm the diagnosis, but the process should always start with localization and disease diagnosis in a clinical neurologic evaluation.

Speech and communication are among the most complicated functions of the human brain, involving myriad interactions among personality, cognitive processes, imagination, language, emotion, and lower sensory and motor systems necessary for articulation and comprehension. These functions involve brain pathways and mechanisms, some well understood and others only beginning to be conceptualized. The brain mechanisms underlying higher functions such as language are known largely through neurologic studies of human patients with acquired brain lesions. Animal models have shed only limited light on these complex disorders.

Stroke has historically been a great source of information because this "experiment of nature" damages one brain area while leaving the rest of the nervous system intact. For more than a century, patients with strokes and other brain diseases have been studied in life, and the clinical syndromes have then been correlated with brain lesions found at autopsy. New methods of brain imaging have made possible the simultaneous study of a lesion in the brain and a deficit of communication in the same patient. These advances in brain imaging, including computed tomography, magnetic resonance imaging (MRI), and positron emission tomography (PET), have brought about a burgeoning of knowledge in this area. Functional brain imaging modalities such as functional MRI and PET scanning now permit the visualization of brain activation in normal subjects during language tasks, and these studies have contributed further to our knowledge of the organization of language in the brain.

In this book, the factual groundwork has been laid for the understanding of the nervous system in terms of the organization of the brain, descending motor and ascending sensory pathways, and cranial nerves and muscles. Understanding these anatomic systems makes possible the understanding and classification of the syndromes of aphasia, alexia, dysarthria, and dysphonia, as well as the effects of specific, localized disease processes on human speech and communication. All these subjects are clearly and accurately reviewed. The speech-language pathologist who studies this book should have a much improved comprehension of the brain mechanisms disrupted in speech-impaired and language-impaired patients, and thereby a greater understanding of the disorders of speech and language themselves.

Perhaps the most important by-product of this book should be a closer interaction between neurologists and speech-language pathologists. Neurologists understand the anatomic relationships of the brain and its connections, but they often fail to use speech and language to their full limits in assessing the function of specific parts of the nervous system. A careful analysis of speech and language functions can supplement the more cursory portions of the standard neurologic examination devoted to these functions. Thus detailed aphasia testing supplements the neurologist's bedside mental status examination, and close observation of palatal, lingual, and facial motion during articulation supplements the neurologist's cranial nerve examination. The neurologist's diagnosis of the patient's disorder, on the other hand, should aid the speech-language pathologist in understanding the nature and prognosis of the speech and language disorder. The neurologist and speech-language pathologist should ideally function as a team, complementing each other. For this teamwork to occur, however, each specialist must comprehend the other's language. To this end, these authors have made the language of the neurologist understandable to the speech-language pathologist. As a neurologist who worked closely with Dr. Webb and Dr. Love, I applaud this important accomplishment.

I would like to end with a personal statement about Dr. Russell Love, one of the two original authors of this book. Dr. Love was an inspiring scientist and colleague who personified the relationship between speech-language pathologist and neurologist. In his long career, he taught generations of speech-language pathologists and neurologists. To the end, he was always gracious, optimistic, and informative in all of his interactions.

Howard S. Kirshner
Professor and Vice-Chair
Department of Neurology
Vanderbilt University Medical Center
Nashville, Tennessee

Preface

Introduction

It is indeed rare to find a speech-language pathologist in practice today who does not interact with the medical profession. The person practicing in hospitals, rehabilitation settings, nursing homes, or home health settings obviously will be a part of a medical team, whether formal or informal. The person practicing in the school systems, where the majority of speech-language pathologists and many educational audiologists are employed, also frequently will need to interact in some way with the medical profession, as will persons in private practice. In both of these settings, medically fragile children and adults are treated who have a communication disorder associated with a medical condition. This evolution in patient population has made it critical for the speech-language pathologist and audiologist to be well versed concerning anatomy and physiology of body systems related to speech, language, and hearing. Arguably the most important system is the nervous system—the foundation of all movement and thought associated with speech and language.

Background

The idea for this text was first conceived by Russel and I out of a frustration that there was, at that time (1986), no textbook written by speech-language pathologists for that profession that was devoted strictly to the neurology of "the human communication nervous system." Over the years, there have been several textbooks published that are devoted to this topic and written by practicing speech-language pathologists. However, most of these texts only emphasize the anatomy and physiology of the nervous system underlying normal communication. *Neurology for the Speech-Language Pathologist* is dedicated not only to the study of the normal system function, but also to an introduction to the disorders that occur when the nervous system is developmentally abnormal or becomes diseased or damaged.

Audience

The targeted audience for this book is, of course, students preparing to become practicing speech-language pathologists. Students intending to enter the profession of audiology frequently will be enrolled in a class on neurology of human communication. Although this text does not go into the depth of the auditory system that students will need later, they will find it useful for their future endeavors. The text is also written to serve as a reference for speech and hearing professionals already in practice who wish to update themselves in neurology or who may not have had a specific curriculum regarding the neurologic foundation of communication and its disorders.

Concept and Importance to the Profession

As Dr. Howard Kirshner states in the foreword to this book, the speech-language pathologist and the neurologist are able to work together more successfully for the patient's benefit when they "speak the same language." This was one of the initial thrusts of the creation of this textbook. Ultimate benefit is also achieved when speech-language pathologists can understand the terminology and the concerns of other professions involved in the habilitation and rehabilitation of patients. Thus the content has evolved over the years to help the speech-language pathologist obtain a better understanding of nervous system function in related systems often treated by other professionals, such as those in physical therapy, occupational therapy, and neuropsychology.

In this new century, there is a demand for evidence-based practice, meaning that there is a demand that the speech-language pathologist design and use diagnostic and treatment methodologies based on sound theory and research-based evidence that supports that theory and practice. Knowledge about nervous system function and how the brain develops, initiates, and maintains movement; learns and remembers; and recovers or changes after injury is critical to successful practice. This book is dedicated to enhancing that knowledge.

Organization

The sixth edition is organized a bit differently from previous editions, and a separate chapter on the developing brain has been added, effectively giving the text a three-chapter section on pediatrics. In regard to the entire text, the introductory chapter discusses the intertwining histories of the professions of speech-language pathology and neurology. Chapters 2 and 3 are foundation chapters, providing an overview of the anatomy of the central and peripheral nervous systems. Chapter 3 also includes a section on some of the more popular neurodiagnostic studies that are becoming increasingly important in our profession's research and clinical literature. Chapters 4 and 5 describe anatomy and physiology of neuronal function and the sensory systems of vision, hearing, and touch. Chapters 6 to 8 are devoted to anatomy and physiology of normal motor function, the cranial nerves, and the motor speech disorders that result from damage or disease affecting oral-motor function. Chapter 9 explores the neuroanatomy and neurophysiology underlying language and learning. Chapter 10 discusses various language and cognitive disorders in adults with neurologic damage. Chapter 11 is the new chapter reviewing the development of the human brain from conception through the early postnatal period. Chapter 11 also contains the section on the examination of primitive reflexes of the newborn, which those familiar with previous editions will recognize. Chapter 12 provides information on pediatric disorders of speech, and Chapter 13 examines pediatric language disorders.

The first four chapters provide the reader with anatomic terms and location and function of structures in an overview of the entire nervous system without getting too much into the details of the specific systems. The idea is to have a mental concept of the entire nervous system and the structural and functional relationships before studying in depth the systems most relevant to communication and related disorders.

Distinctive Features

- The text combines information concerning both neuroanatomy and neurophysiology with information about speech and language disorders associated with nervous system dysfunction.
- The disorder section of the text includes separate chapters on speech and language, which are further divided into pediatric and adult disorders.
- Included in the text is information designed to help the reader understand related disorders, such as disorders of visual processing and hearing and limb movement, that are treated by other members of the habilitation or rehabilitation team.
- The text also includes a description of a neurologist's typical bedside examination and assessment for adults and pediatric patients.

Learning Aids

- There are 170 photos, scans, illustrations, and diagrams, many of them highlighted with the second color for clarity, that depict anatomic structure and

function within the nervous system as well as characteristics of neurologic disease or injury.
- Detailed vocabulary listings are provided on the first page of each chapter, highlighted within the chapter discussion, and defined in the back-of-book glossary.
- Certain chapters contain a case history and description of a patient with a condition pertinent to the system or disorder discussed within that chapter. Cases are followed by questions for consideration and discussion.
- Detailed summary and application boxes appear at the end of each chapter and organize the information into bulleted listings for ease of reference.
- Appendices provide a listing and brief description of medical conditions related to communication disorders, an outline of a bedside neurologic examination, and a screening neurologic examination—all invaluable references for student clinicians and practitioners.

Ancillary Materials

An Evolve website has been created specifically to accompany this sixth edition of *Neurology for the Speech-Language Pathologist*. Resources are available free of cost to all students via the URL http://evolve.elsevier.com/Webb/neurology/. Instructor resources are available to all adopting instructors, who can register for free access via their sales representative. Following is a summary of the resources available online:

For Instructors

- A **test bank** features over 400 objective-style questions—multiple-choice, true/false, and fill-in-the-blank—each with an accompanying rationale for the correct answer and a page-number reference to direct the reader to the exact textbook page on which that content is discussed.
- An **image collection** featuring artwork from the textbook—two-color renderings, photographs, and brain-imaging scans—is available for download into PowerPoint or other presentations.

For Students

- **Flashcards** reproduce the book's glossary into a fun and interactive tool that helps readers practice terminology and ensure content mastery. The flashcards are excellent resources for examination preparation.

- **Answers to case study questions** are included to help readers test their knowledge and understand chapter content as it applies to realistic patient situations.
- Chapter reference lists are reproduced in a **bibliography** that contains Pubmed links, allowing readers to search quickly and easily for relevant

literature and connect directly to specific journal articles.
- **Animations** are also included, providing amazing views of various neuroanatomy and neurophysiology structures, concepts, and diseases and disorders.

Wanda G. Webb

Contents

1

Introduction to Speech-Language Neurology

We must admit that the divine banquet of the brain was, and still is, a feast with dishes that remain elusive in their blending, and with sauces whose ingredients are even now a secret.

MacDonald Critchley, *The Divine Banquet of the Brain*, 1979

KEY **TERMS**

agnosias
anterior
aphasia
apraxias
association fiber
   tracts
asymmetry
behavioral neurology
Carl Wernicke
cephalic
clinical neurology
computed
   tomography (CT)

dorsal
dysarthrias
inferior
localization of
   function
Noam Chomsky
Norman Geschwind
Pierre Paul Broca
plasticity
posterior
rostral
superior
ventral

Why Neurology?

The 1990s were labeled by the U.S. Congress as the Decade of the Brain. Likewise, 1990 was the year of the Americans with Disabilities Act (ADA). In 2006, American Speech-Language-Hearing Association (ASHA) members learned about the reauthorization of the IDEA (Individual Disability Education Act). Since the inception of the federal laws to help and protect Americans who have a variety of disabilities, including communication and hearing disorders, ASHA academic and clinical standards have undergone major changes as well. A tremendous expansion of knowledge has occurred in the neurosciences, including increased complexities of the types and severity of disorders treated by all speech-language pathologists (SLPs), from the school-based SLP and educational audiologist to the hospital-based certified SLP professional. ASHA has recognized these advances in neuroscience by realizing that an SLP or audiologist must have an expanded knowledge of neuroanatomy and physiology to remain a viable member of either the Individual Educational Plan (IEP) or the interdisciplinary team (IDT). That is why academic and clinical standards for all SLPs and audiologists underwent a major change in the early twenty-first century.

For the student of speech-language pathology and audiology, these governmental reform acts and advances in neuroscience have played a significant role in forming the current academic and clinical standards used by ASHA. The new certification standards required as of July 2004 mandate particular knowledge and skills for students to be prepared to serve a variety of communication and hearing disorders in children and adults. From an undergraduate's general education, which is now required to include biologic and physical sciences, to the graduate student's in-depth study of stroke, traumatic brain injury (TBI), or autism, academic programs have had to increase neuroscience offerings. The work of the linguist, the cognitive psychologist, and the neuroscientist, as well as the SLP and audiologist, has brought to the field of communication sciences and disorders an accelerated knowledge of the specialized brain mechanisms that underlie speech, language, and hearing and their disorders. Specialists now possess the knowledge and skills to understand, implement, analyze, and synthesize the neurologic bases of speech, language, and hearing, as well as the skills required to meet the ADA, IDEA, and new ASHA standards.

Widespread interest in the study of neurogenic issues has increased among speech and language students as opportunities for clinical experiences and employment in schools, hospitals, rehabilitation centers, and other health care agencies continue to increase. Increased longevity of human beings has caused a greater incidence of hearing, speech, and language disorders such as presbycusis, dementia, **aphasia**, dysarthria, and apraxia. With improving medical technology, traumatically brain-injured infants, children, and adults are now saved from death much more frequently than in the past. The speech and language disorders of these survivors present new and greater challenges to the SLP and audiologist.

In 1986, when the first edition of this text appeared, only half of undergraduate and graduate training programs in communication disorders offered specific coursework in neurology with an emphasis on speech and language mechanisms. As of this new edition, 30 years later, the majority of the 300 programs (*www.asha.org*) in the field provide such coursework. In 2004 Adler[2] surveyed all accredited ASHA programs in *Speech-Language Pathology and Audiology*. The survey consisted of questions asking academic programs to give information about the anatomy and physiology (A&P) and neuroanatomy and physiology (N&P) courses required in their undergraduate and master's degree course sequences. Results indicated that the A&P course is offered in every program, and more than 70% of the accredited programs offered N&P courses. Many of these courses in neuroanatomy are on the graduate level, and all respondents made it clear that the N&P course is quite relevant and is required for all students to meet the standards and prepare students for challenging SLP positions.

Accompanying a growing interest among neurologists in communication sciences and disorders has been a parallel increase in the number of practicing SLPs. In the past 4 decades, membership in ASHA has risen from 2203 in 1952 to more than 173,000 members and affiliates in 2013 (*www.asha.org*). Although not all of these individuals are interested in neurologic disorders, many are, and for those who wish to study and specialize in neurologic speech and language disorders, a certification body, the Academy of Neurologic Communication Disorders and Sciences, accepts qualified members. Specialization in adult neurologic impairment, child neurologic impairment, or both is possible. In the past 5 to 10 years, ASHA special interest divisions have begun the process of specialization certifications in many areas, including child language, swallowing, fluency, and intraoperative monitoring. Most SLPs and audiologists work in schools, hospitals, or medical center or university clinics. All settings currently use an IDT approach and call the team a variety of names, including IDT, IEP team, clinical rounds team, or interdisciplinary management team (IMT). Regardless of name, the main function is to assess the client, discuss results from all disciplines, write a treatment plan that includes goals and objectives, and ensure that all goals and objectives have one outcome—the improvement of speech and language functioning for that client.

The client might be seen in a school setting, a hospital, an outpatient clinic, a developmental center, through a home health agency, in a rehabilitation center, a university clinic, or in an office of a private practice. The SLP provides important information to what is usually a team of educational or medical professionals regarding a person's speech and language deficits and assets as related to brain functioning.

Recent Contributors to the Study of Neurologic Communication Disorders

During the past 4 decades, two towering figures have dominated the field of language and speech. One, a neurologist, was Norman Geschwind (1926-1984). He almost single-handedly resurrected the early neurologic literature of Europe focusing on language disorders and related deficits. Geschwind brought this body of knowledge to the attention of the American medical audience when interest in aphasia and related disorders was waning. He particularly highlighted the value of identifying lesions in the connective pathways of the brain, as well as diagnosing lesions in the traditional localized cortical areas of the brain that had been associated with language disorders for more than a century. His masterwork, "Disconnection Syndromes in Animals and Man," was published in *Brain* more than 49 years ago.[21]

Geschwind taught brilliantly at Harvard University Medical School for many years and inspired generations of students to pursue neurology as a specialty and to concentrate on disorders of higher cerebral function. This area is now known as behavioral neurology. Aphasia and other related disorders, such as agnosia and apraxia, were considered minor aspects of a general neurologic practice until Geschwind highlighted them in neurology and related fields.

Thanks to Geschwind's original and incisive thinking, the study of language and its disorders returned to its rightful place of importance among the vast range of neurologic diseases. His thinking was so innovative that it influenced many other scientific disciplines, particularly linguistics, psychology, and philosophy. Geschwind is one of the few physicians who has been honored by having their scientific papers collected and published before their death.[22]

The second towering figure in the latter half of the twentieth century in the field of neurology of speech and language has been Noam Chomsky, a linguist of international renown. Chomsky is credited with creating a scientific revolution in the understanding of syntax and other components of language,[28] and he has been called a major intellectual force, a "modern master" of creative and scientific thought.[42]

Beginning in 1957 with his monograph *Syntactic Structures*,[10] Chomsky developed a theory of grammar, stressing mental processes that replaced the structural analysis of language based on the mechanistic and behavioral viewpoint exemplified by the writings of Bloomfield.[4] Chomsky disputes the traditional idea that language is essentially a system of habits established by training and forcefully argues that every human being has the innate capacity to use language. Innate grammatical processes, he believes, are triggered by external stimuli but function autonomously. The concept of innateness implies a biologic, neurologic, and genetic basis for language.

Chomsky's definition of grammar differs from that of structuralist linguists in that it is concerned with a specific and formal description of language, as well as neurologic language processes as they work in the human brain. The details of these aspects of language, however, are not clearly explained in Chomsky's writings, and it can be difficult, even with knowledge of transformational-generative grammar, to reconcile the details of the newer linguistic theory of Chomsky with the older neurologic theory of Geschwind and his followers. Box 1-1

BOX 1-1

Two Key Leaders in Speech and Language

Norman Geschwind (1926-1984)

- Revitalized early neurologic literature focusing on language disorders and related deficits
- Brought body of knowledge to attention of American medical audience
- Highlighted the value of identification and diagnosis of lesions in areas associated with language disorders
- Published masterwork "Disconnection Syndromes in Animals and Man" (1965) in *Brain*
- Largely founded the field of behavioral neurology
- Influenced other disciplines such as linguistics, psychology, and philosophy

Noam Chomsky (1928-)

- Created scientific revolution in understanding syntax and other components of language
- Published *Syntactic Structures* in 1957, which outlined his theory of grammar
- Argued the revolutionary notion that the capacity for language learning and usage is innate, not learned
- Theorized that grammar includes neurologic language processes that parallel a formal description of language

summarizes the work of both Geschwind and Chomsky in speech-language neurology.

The more recent literature, however, is beginning to synthesize the linguistic and neurologic positions in explaining disordered communication. Steven Pinker, a cognitive psychologist and linguist, wrote that language may be considered an "instinct" in the same sense that Charles Darwin conceived of animal instincts. Pinker asserts that grammar is a perfect example of a biologic trait determined by the Darwinian principle of natural selection and that it is genetically based. In addition, Pinker stated that the intricately structured neural circuits that support language and speech are "laid down by a cascade of precisely timed genetic events."[45] A genetic nature of language is supported by cases of inherited disturbance that appear to be accompanied by specific defects of grammar.[25]Even earlier than Pinker's work, a biologic defense of Chomsky's concept of innateness appeared in a well-known but somewhat controversial book by Eric Lenneberg (1921-1975), *The Biological Foundations of Language.*[36] Lenneberg clearly placed language development in a developmental neurology context. One of the highlights of this book was Lenneberg's attempt to define a critical period for the acquisition of early language. Lenneberg maintained that the acquisition of syntax was paced by the rate of cerebral maturation and the lateralization of language mechanisms. He asserted that the rapid acquisition of language starts at approximately 2 years of age, as the brain begins to grow rapidly, and slows at puberty (at approximately 12 years of age), when cerebral growth reaches a plateau. Although often criticized, the concept of critical periods is consistent with the importance of biologic and neurologic mechanisms for language development, and some have supported Lenneberg's claims.[34]

Although the concepts of Lenneberg, Geschwind, and particularly Chomsky concerning neurologic aspects of language have been widely criticized, they have focused interest on the need to understand brain function in detail when studying speech and language disorders.

Not all biologic and neurologic theories of language have come from linguists or cognitive-behavioral psychologists. Harold Goodglass and Edith Kaplan were neuropsychologists and students of Geschwind who worked together at the Boston Veterans Administration Hospital to develop diagnostic theories of aphasia and assessment protocols for testing aphasic language behaviors,[24] thereby contributing to the SLP's knowledge of language and neuroanatomy and neurology.

SLPs have provided a vast amount of assessment and intervention insights into the field of neurologic communication disorders from the vantage point of the therapy room. Although many SLPs have collaborated with neurologists to make extremely important contributions, the work of Nancy Helm-Estabrooks serves as a focal model for clinicians. Helm-Estabrooks was employed at the Boston Veterans Administration Hospital for much of her career as an SLP. There she was strongly affected by the excitement generated by Norman Geschwind and his students as they developed the field of behavioral neurology. Helm-Estabrooks has worked closely with various neurologists and neuropsychologists and is recognized worldwide for her innovative contributions, particularly in testing and therapy techniques for patients with neurogenic disorders. An example of her work is the *Manual of Aphasia Therapy*[30] written with the internationally known neurologist Martin L. Albert.

The SLP must understand the results of speech and language assessment in terms of the underlying neurologic mechanisms. Further, the SLP should be able to be conversant with current methods of neurologic diagnosis and treatment as they apply to persons with communication disorders. The neurologist's point of view toward speech and language disorders should be familiar to every clinician. In turn, neurologists must be knowledgeable about the assessment methods and therapy procedures of the communication disorders specialist. The understanding of each other's work is particularly crucial because neurology and the study of speech and language disorders have developed independently for many years and are only now beginning to interact more closely. This increased interaction will certainly result in additional benefits for members of both professions and those they serve.

The clinical neurologist must work closely with the SLP in evaluating the communication disorders of the neurologic client. The SLP is clearly not responsible for making the final diagnosis of a neurologic disorder. Nevertheless, the SLP is responsible for assessing all relevant aspects of speech, language, and related disorders in clients with a known or suspected neurologic disorder.

Historic Roots: Development of Speech-Language Pathology as a Brain Science

Speech-language pathology traces many of its roots to clinical neurology. In 1861 the French physician Pierre Paul Broca (1824-1880) studied the brains of two patients who had sustained language loss and motor speech disorders.[5] This study allowed him to localize human language to a definite circumscribed area of the left hemisphere, thereby laying the foundation for a brain science of speech and language. Broca's discovery went far beyond the now-classic description of an interesting brain disorder called aphasia. Possibly foremost among his conclusions were the assertions that the two hemispheres of the brain are asymmetric in function and that the left cerebral hemisphere contains the language center in most human beings. Important implications of brain asymmetry are even now coming to light some 130 years later. Asymmetry of function is more pervasive than originally thought. It extends well beyond language to other brain areas and their functions.

Another conclusion that has had lasting importance for neurology since Broca's death is that specific behavioral functions appear to be associated with clearly localized sites in the brain. The corollary of this observation is that behavioral dysfunction can point to lesions at specific sites in the nervous system. The concept of localization of function in the nervous system has been repeatedly demonstrated by clinical and research methods since Broca first articulated it more than a century ago. This observation was so profound that it became a significant historic force in the establishment of the medical discipline of clinical neurology. Much of clinical neurology depends on the physician's ability to lateralize and localize a lesion in the nervous system.

An important fact for speech-language pathology was that Broca's discovery stimulated a period of intensive search for a workable explanation of the brain mechanisms of speech and language. Probably no period in the history of neurologic science has so advanced the understanding of communication and its disorders as those years between Broca's discovery and World War I. An overview of Broca's life work can be found in Box 1-2.

BOX 1-2

The Work of Pierre Paul Broca (1824-1880)

- Touchstone study in 1861 allowed Broca to localize human language to a specific region of the left hemisphere, suggesting that the two hemispheres of the brain are asymmetric in function
- First to identify the brain disorder aphasia
- Articulated localization of function, leading to the establishment of the medical discipline of clinical neurology
- Stimulated intensive research into a workable explanation of the brain mechanisms of speech and language

---

One of the first and foremost outcomes of this intensive study of speech-language brain mechanisms was the establishment of neurologic substrata for modalities of language deficit other than the expressive oral language described by Broca. In 1867 William Ogle published a case that demonstrated that a cerebral writing center was independent of Broca's center for oral language.[39] In 1874 Carl Wernicke (1848-1905) identified an auditory speech center in the temporal lobe associated with comprehension of speech, as opposed to Broca's area in the frontal lobe that was an expressive speech center.[50] In the terminology of that time, lesions in Broca's area produced a *motor* aphasia, and one in Wernicke's area produced a *sensory* aphasia. These terms are no longer used in medical terminology. The very general descriptor terms now used are *expressive* (motor) and *receptive* (sensory) aphasia. In 1892 Joseph Dejerine identified mechanisms underlying reading disorders.[16] Disorders of cortical sensory recognition, or the agnosias, were named by Sigmund Freud in 1891,[19] and in 1900 Hugo Liepmann comprehensively analyzed the apraxias, disorders of executing motor acts resulting from brain lesions.[37]

EARLY LANGUAGE MODELS

Of the many neurologic models of the cerebral language mechanisms generated soon after Broca's great discovery, Wernicke's 1874 model has best withstood the test of time. Wernicke stressed the importance of cortical language centers associated with the various language modalities, but he also emphasized the importance of association fiber tracts connecting areas or centers. Like his teacher Theodore Meynert (1833-1892), he understood that the connections in the brain were just as important as the centers for a complete picture of language performance.[38] In addition, Wernicke organized the symptoms of language disturbance in such a way that they could be used diagnostically to predict the lesion site in either connective pathways or centers in the language system. Ironically, the Wernicke model was eclipsed until the last half of the twentieth century, when it was revitalized and expanded by Norman Geschwind and his followers.[21]

Wernicke's model came under criticism by the English neurologist Henry Head in 1926.[29] He lumped Wernicke with a cadre of early neurologists he considered the more flagrant of the "diagram makers," implying that they constructed language models that were highly speculative and not supported by empirical evidence. Current methods of neurologic investigation, including electrical cortical stimulation, isotope localization of lesions, computed tomography (CT), and regional blood flow studies in the brain.

Neurologic speech mechanisms, as opposed to language mechanisms, also received attention in the late nineteenth century. In 1871 the famous French neurologist Jean Charcot (1825-1893) described the "scanning speech" that he associated with "disseminated sclerosis," now known as multiple sclerosis.[8] The term *scanning*, probably inappropriate, has also been widely used to describe speech with cerebellar or cerebellar pathway lesions (see Chapter 8). In 1888 an English neurologist, William Gowers (1846-1915), surveyed the neurologic speech disorders, known as dysarthrias, in a well-known book titled *A Manual of Diseases of the Nervous System*.[26]

WORLD WAR I

World War I had a profound influence on the study of speech and language mechanisms resulting from neurologic insult. With a large population of head-injured young men with penetrating skull wounds, some neurologists felt an urgency for treatment. A handful of dedicated neurologists provided therapy for these traumatic language disorders because the profession of speech pathology was not yet born. Not until the next decade did the profession really begin. Lee Edward Travis has the distinction of being the first individual in the United States to specialize in the field of speech and language disorders at the doctoral level. In 1927 he became the first director of the speech clinic at the University of Iowa. His special interest was in stuttering, which he began to study in a neurologic context. Influenced by the neuropsychiatrist Samuel Terry Orton (1879-1948), Travis researched the hypothesis that stuttering was the result of brain dysfunction,[47] specifically an imbalance or competition between the two cerebral hemispheres to control the normal bilateral functioning of the speech musculature. Orton's hypothesis of dysfunctioning neural control of the speech musculature[40] has generally been discredited, but his hemisphere competition theory of stuttering still surfaces from time to time in different guises to explain certain communication disorders.

Although several of the founders of speech-language pathology in the United States believed that psychological explanations were more rewarding for understanding speech and language problems, notable exceptions existed. In particular, Harold Westlake of Northwestern University; Robert West of the University of Wisconsin; Jon Eisenson, formerly of California State University; and Joseph Wepman of the University of Chicago were all advocates of neurologic principles in communication disorders.

MODERN TIMES

During World War II, which brought in its wake thousands of injured soldiers and other military personnel with traumatic aphasia, neurologists, psychologists, and SLPs were used in treatment programs for the first time. This effort produced a series of books and articles on aphasia rehabilitation; perhaps the most notable for the neurologically oriented SLP was Wepman's *Recovery from Aphasia* (1951).[49] It served as a textbook of language disorders for the growing number of students in the field and often served as their first introduction to the study of a major neurologic communication disorder.

The study of neurologic speech mechanisms was greatly advanced after World War II by the work of Wilder G. Penfield (1891-1976) and his colleagues in Canada. Penfield, a neurosurgeon, used the technique of electrical cortical stimulation to map cortical areas directly, particularly speech and language centers. In 1959 in *Speech and Brain Mechanisms*[41] (written with Lamar Roberts), he documented his observations on cerebral control of speech and language function and wrote on the concepts of subcortical speech mechanisms and infantile cerebral **plasticity**.

The 1960s and 1970s were marked by several advances of neurologic concepts in communication and its disorders. As already mentioned, newer linguistic theory, particularly that proposed by Noam Chomsky,[11,12] emphasized the universal features and innate mechanisms reflected in language. The biologic aspects of language and speech were highlighted by the linguist and psychologist Eric Lenneberg, who specifically placed language acquisition in the context of developmental neurology.[36] The split-brain studies reported by Roger Sperry and his colleagues,[44] in which the commissural tracts between the hemispheres were severed, indicated specific functions of the right hemisphere were different from the left.

Major anatomic differences in the right and left language centers were also demonstrated in the human brain. Most significant for SLPs and audiologists are larger areas in the left temporal lobe in the fetus, infant, and adult.[23,48,51] These differences suggest an anatomic basis for cerebral dominance for language and appear to contradict a theory of progressive lateralization of speech centers.

Throughout the 1960s and 1970s considerable attention was paid to neurologic speech disorders. Neurologists and SLPs in the Mayo Clinic Neurology Department[13-15] documented the acoustic-perceptual characteristics of the major **dysarthrias** in a viable classification scheme. This work has stimulated wide-spread study of the various adult dysarthrias in speech science laboratories around the country.

The 1960s and 1970s were also marked by the development of two psychometrically sound and widely used aphasia tests: the *Minnesota Test of Differential Diagnosis of Aphasia*[43] and the *Boston Diagnostic Aphasia Examination.*[24]

The 1980s found researchers talking about the importance of early stimulation and experience for brain and language development.[27] The 1980s also brought further advances in aphasia diagnostic testing when the *Western Aphasia Battery*[33] and the first edition of the *Communication Activities in Daily Living*[32] were published. By the 1990s further advances in assessment for aphasia, TBI, and, for the first time, language and communication problems caused by dementia produced the *Scales of Cognitive Abilities for Traumatic Brain Injury,*[1] the *Arizona Battery for Communication Disorders of Dementia,*[3] the third edition of *Examining for Aphasia,*[17] the *Burns Brief Inventory of Communication and Cognition,*[6] the second edition of the *Communication Activities in Daily Living,*[32] the *Comprehensive Aphasia Test,*[45] and the second edition of the *Frenchay Aphasia Screening Test.*[18]

The 1990s saw significant advances in knowledge about language development and the brain with the publication of *The Language Instinct.*[42] In 1997 Dr. Martha Taylor Sarno completed a 5-year study funded by National Institutes of Health on the effects of aphasia secondary to stroke on the quality of life in middle-aged and older people. Findings indicated that age was not a major factor in the recovery and quality of life of individuals with aphasia.[46] During the decade of the 1990s, research into the incidence, prevalence, and rehabilitation needs of persons with TBI proliferated, and in 1999 a report to Congress was made highlighting the need for further research and rehabilitation funding for persons affected by TBI.[7]

And now we find ourselves in the twenty-first century! A few of the more recent tests published related to neurologic basis of communication or disorders include the *Cognitive Linguistic Quick Test (CLQT)*[31] and the *Multimodal Communication Screening Test for Persons with Aphasia (MCST-A).*[35] Research and treatment have taken giant steps forward into the twenty-first century incorporating the use of advanced technology. Many SLPs are experimenting with, refining, and documenting positive outcomes of service delivery models that incorporate telehealth in treatment of patients with neurogenic communication disorders.[9] Research designs developed by SLPs such as Dr. Julius

Fridriksson, as well as many others, have resulted in collaboration with neurologists and radiologists to utilize advanced technology such as functional magnetic resonance imaging (fMRI) or transcranial stimulation to expand our knowledge of how neurodevelopmental problems or acquired brain damage alters language, speech, and/or swallowing.[20]

Directions and Planes

This text uses many drawings and photographs to aid in visualization. The human body itself may be defined in terms of a standard anatomic position, one in which the body is erect and the head, eyes, and toes are pointed forward. The limbs are at the side of the body, and the palms face forward (Fig. 1-1). When viewing drawings in texts or creating anatomic sketches, constantly orient yourself in terms of the standard anatomic positions and planes. From this fundamental position other positions, planes, and directions are defined (Fig. 1-2). Box 1-3 summarizes the major planes or sections used in anatomic drawings to orient the reader to the view that was used. The orienting directional terms that may be used when navigating around an illustration of the brain may be slightly different because the brain itself is tilted inside our skull. Figure 1-3 illustrates the anatomic planes of the brain.

To understand what you are reading as well as the drawings and pictures you will be seeing when studying neuroanatomy, it is imperative that you understand the directional terms and the different planes in which the views may be pictured. Conventional textbooks are only two-dimensional, and thus it is of excellent benefit to the student to use websites that are designed to picture anatomic structures with three-dimensional reconstruction technique.

Several terms are used to designate direction in neuroanatomy (Figs. 1-1 and 1-2). Some of these terms are used synonymously. **Anterior** and **ventral** mean toward the front or in front of when any part of the body (including the spinal cord) except the brain is illustrated. However, note in Figure 1-3 that if it is the brain that is being discussed or illustrated, ventral means **inferior**. When orienting in the brain, **rostral** is the synonymous term for anterior (Fig. 1-3). **Posterior** or **dorsal** indicates toward the back or behind for both. **Superior** refers to above or upward in both; inferior means below or downward in both but is synonymous with ventral in the brain. The terms *cranial* and **cephalic** can be used in place of superior when orienting direction in the body.

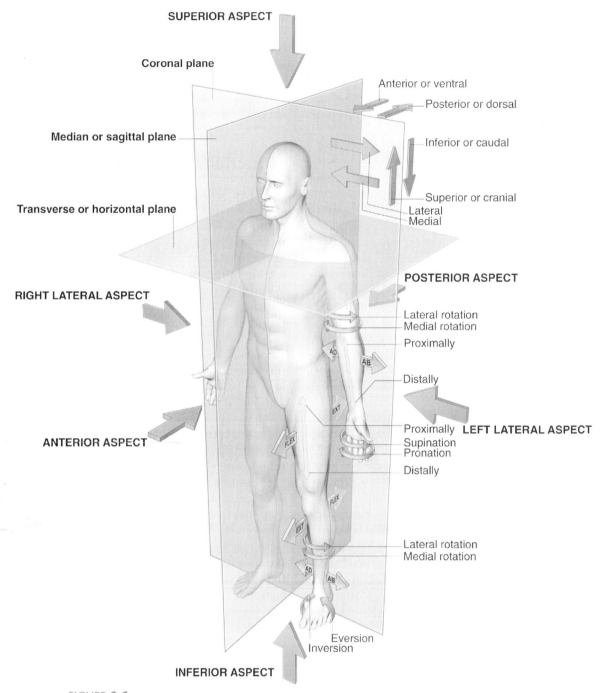

FIGURE **1-1**
Standard anatomic position for study of the human body with anatomic planes and terms for type or direction of movement included. (From Standring, S. [2016]. *Gray's Anatomy: The Anatomical Basis of Clinical Practice*, [41st ed.]. London: Churchill Livingstone.)

How to Study

Most students in speech-language pathology receive a limited introduction to the neurosciences in their undergraduate careers. The majority of students are enrolled in courses designed to acquaint them with the anatomy and physiology of speech, but these courses usually focus on speech musculature. Students often do not receive an adequate introduction to neuroanatomy and neurophysiology of speech and language.

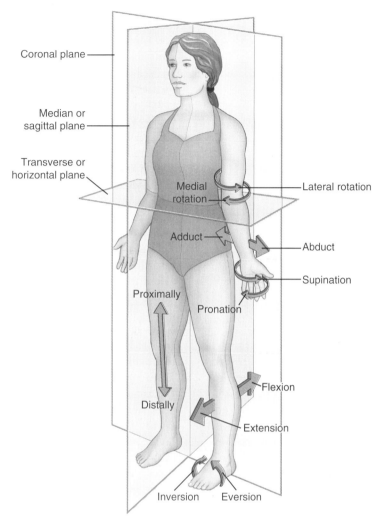

FIGURE **1-2**
Directional references for the human body. (Reprinted from Blaussen.com staff.
"Blaussen gallery 2014." Wikiversity Journal of Medicine. *https://en.wikiversity.org/wiki/*
Wikiversity_Journal_of_Medicine/Blausen_gallery_2014#Other_anatomy)

BOX 1-3

Standard Anatomic Positions and Planes

- The median plane, or section, passes longitudinally through the brain and divides the right hemisphere from the left hemisphere.
- The sagittal plane divides the brain vertically at any point and parallels the medial plane.
- A coronal, or frontal, section is any vertical cut that separates the brain into front and back halves.
- A horizontal plane divides the brain into upper and lower halves and is at right angles to the median and coronal planes.
- A transverse cut is any section that is at right angles to the longitudinal axis of the structure.

It is assumed that students will learn these details in courses in aphasia, adult dysarthria, and rehabilitation of speech in cerebral palsy. Students find that neuroscience courses taken as advanced undergraduates or beginning graduate students are difficult.

Students often say that neurology courses are difficult because they believe they must learn the technical term for each hill and valley in the complex anatomy of the brain. In addition, the technical terms are unfamiliar, usually derived from Greek and Roman word roots. This text concentrates on crucial terminology for an understanding of speech and language and the diseases and conditions that result in communication disorders. The number of terms

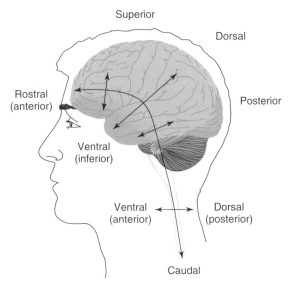

FIGURE **1-3**
Axes of the human brain. (Reprinted from Martin, J. G. [1989]. *Neuroanatomy.* New York: Elsevier.)

believed to be important has increased over the various editions of this text as the scope of practice for SLPs has expanded. Because of the crucial role that SLPs now play on many medical, rehabilitation, and educational teams, they also must be familiar with terminology used by other health professionals when discussing the client's condition. A glossary is provided at the end of the text.

Part of the strategy in mastering any text in the biologic sciences is to give the study of drawings, diagrams, and tables in the text as much time as the narrative sections. If the reader can come away from a study of this text with a set of working mental images of the structures and pathways of the nervous system that are important to communication and can recall them at critical times, then one of the purposes of the authors will be realized. With an emphasis on imagery as one of the better ways to learn neurology, it should be no surprise that the authors urge readers to use as a teaching aid their own drawings of structures and pathways. Even crude sketches, carefully labeled, teach the necessary anatomic relations and fix pathways, structures, and names in the mind. Students (and instructors!) are also encouraged to use the vast resource of the Internet. There are now literally thousands of photos, illustrations, and videos dealing with neuroanatomy, neuroscience, and neurology on various websites sponsored by universities, government agencies, and research institutes. I encourage you to be careful; choose sites that are well established in terms of the credentials for providing such technical information. Because of the

precipitous manner in which websites and the information contained on them changes, only a few sites are recommended or referenced in these chapters. Your instructor is likely to be able to recommend or help you find valuable sites to assist your exploration of the nervous system.

Chapters 2 and 3 provide an overview of the nervous system in total. Subsequent chapters often refer back to certain sections of these chapters to review the written information and the illustrations that provide a beginning foundation of knowledge regarding the neurologic characteristics of the communicative nervous system. Chapters 4, 5, and 6 expand teaching on the structure and physiology of neurons; the sensory systems of touch, vision, and hearing; and the motor system. Chapters 7 and 8 discuss cranial nerves and the disorders of speech production that SLPs commonly assess and treat in adults. Chapter 9 deals with the anatomy and physiology of the parts of the nervous system primarily concerned with language and learning, and Chapter 10 discusses acquired language disorders in adults. The last three chapters of this text are dedicated to learning how the brain develops from birth (Chapter 11), to pediatric speech (Chapter 12), and to language (Chapter 13) disorders.

A synopsis of facts and clinical applications important to the SLP are presented at the end of each chapter. Students should be aware that these are not the only important facts in the chapter! This synopsis should not be the only thing you study for your examinations because your task is not to memorize a lot of facts with little understanding as to how they relate to the human communication nervous system.

Chapters 5 through 8, 10, 12, and 13 also provide case studies, that is, a description of a patient and the signs and symptoms of his or her disorder. Questions are provided to consider regarding the patient's symptoms. Answers can be found on the Evolve website.

The reader is encouraged to attempt to integrate verbal material with eidetic imagery, as well as with thoughtful consideration of what patients with these conditions experience. Students must call on all their brainpower, bringing into play the special capacities of both the right and left hemispheres of the brain. The left hemisphere is specialized for its capacities of verbal analysis and reasoning, whereas the right hemisphere is specialized for its visual-spatial functions. However, it will become clear to you that, though this specialization exists, the right and the left hemispheres are integrated in communication and cognition. Both hemispheres also use subcortical areas to retrieve memories and empathize with others. Therefore, readers will use their whole brain to learn about the whole brain!

Synopsis of Clinical Information and Applications for the Speech-Language Pathologist

- The source of all speech and language behavior is the brain
- 1990: Americans with Disabilities Act
- 2004: New ASHA clinical and academic standards
- 2005: IDEA was reauthorized
- 2008: Revised ASHA clinical and academic standards
- ASHA membership, 2013 = more than 173,000
- Norman Geschwind: First neurologist to outline the literature focusing on language disorders and related deficits
- Geschwind influenced linguistics, psychology, and philosophy
- Noam Chomsky: First international linguist to correlate language and speech with brain functioning
- Chomsky: Language is innate and implies a biologic, neurologic, and genetic basis for language
- Pinker: Synthesized the linguistic and neurologic bases of language
- Lenneberg: Wrote *The Biological Foundations of Language*
- Goodglass and Kaplan: Neuropsychologists and students of Geschwind
- Broca: First to localize human language to the left hemisphere
- Behavioral functions are attributed to specific sites in the brain
- Ogle: Identified a writing center in the brain independent of Broca's area
- Carl Wernicke: Identified an auditory center for speech associated with comprehension of speech, opposing Broca, who identified the expressive center
- The temporal lobe has become identified with language and speech comprehension and the frontal lobe with language and speech expression
- Freud: First to identify cortical sensory areas or agnosias
- Liepmann: First to identify the apraxias of motor execution
- Travis: First identified stuttering to be the result of brain dysfunction, specifically the imbalance between the two hemispheres
- Neurologic aspects of communication disorders by Harold Westlake, Joseph Wepman, Robert West, and Jon Eisenson
- Wepman's *Recovery from Aphasia* served as the first textbook of language disorders in the field of speech pathology
- Penfield: First to use cortical mapping for identifying areas of language and speech functions in the brain
- Directions and planes help orient you to identify structures and site of lesions and injuries

REFERENCES

1. Adamovich, B., & Henderson, J. (1992). *Scales of Cognitive Abilities for Traumatic Brain Injury.* Austin, TX: Pro-Ed.
2. Adler, R. K. (2004). *The anatomy and physiology of speech and the neuroanatomy and physiology of speech courses: State of the art.* Chicago: ASHA Convention.
3. Bayles, K., & Tomoeda, C. (1993). *Arizona Battery for Communication Disorders of Dementia.* Austin, TX: Pro-Ed.
4. Bloomfield, L. (1933). *Language.* New York: Holt, Rinehart and Winston.
5. Broca, P. (1861). *Remarques sur le siége de la faculté du langage articulé, suivies d'une observation d'aphémie (perte de la parole).* Bulletin: Société.
6. Burns, M. (1997). *Burns Brief Inventory of Communication and Cognition.* San Antonio, TX: Psychological Corporation.
7. Centers for Disease Control and Prevention website. Traumatic brain injury in the United States: A report to Congress. Available at: http://www.cdc.gov/traumaticbraininjury/tbi_report_to_congress.html.
8. Charcot, J. M. (1890). *Oeuvres compléte de J. M. Charcot.* Paris: Lecrosnier et Babe.
9. Cherney, L. R., & van Vuuren, S. (2012). Telerehabilitation, virtual therapists and acquired neurologic speech and language disorders. *Seminars in Speech and Language, 33,* 243–257.
10. Chomsky, N. (1957). *Syntactic structures.* The Hague: Mouton.
11. Chomsky, N. (1972). *Language and mind.* New York: Harcourt and Brace.
12. Chomsky, N. (1975). *Reflections on language.* New York: Pantheon Books.
13. Darley, F. L., Aronson, A. E., & Brown, J. R. (1969a). Differential diagnostic patterns of dysarthria. *Journal of Speech and Hearing Research, 12,* 246–249.
14. Darley, F. L., Aronson, A. E., & Brown, J. R. (1969b). Clusters of deviant speech dimensions in the dysarthrias. *Journal of Speech and Hearing Research, 12,* 462–469.
15. Darley, F. L., Aronson, A. E., & Brown, J. R. (1975). *Motor speech disorders.* Philadelphia: W. B. Saunders.
16. Dejerine, J. (1892). Contribution a etude anatomopathologique et clinique des differentes varietes de cectie verbal. *Mémoires de la Société de Biologie, 27,* 1–330.
17. Eisenson, J. (1994). *Examining for aphasia* (3rd ed.). Austin, TX: Pro-Ed.
18. Enderby, P., Wood, V., & Wade, D. (2006). *Frenchay Aphasia Screening Test.* Hoboken, NJ: Wiley Publishers.
19. Freud, S. (1953). *On aphasia: A critical study.* Translated by F. Stengel. New York: International Universities Press.
20. Fridriksson, J. (2011). Measuring and inducing brain plasticity in chronic aphasia. *Journal of Communication Disorders, 44,* 557–563.

21. Geschwind, N. (1965). Disconnection syndromes in animals and man. *Brain, 88,* 237–294, 585–644.

22. Geschwind, N. (1974). *Selected papers on language and the brain.* Boston: D. Reidel.

23. Geschwind, N., & Levitsky, W. (1968). Human brain: Right-left asymmetries in temporal speech region. *Science, 168,* 186–187.

24. Goodglass, H., & Kaplan, E. (1972). *Assessment of aphasia and related disorders.* Philadelphia: Lea & Febiger.

25. Gopnik, M., & Crago, M. (1991). Family aggregation of developmental language disorder. *Cognition, 39,* 1–50.

26. Gowers, W. R. (1888). *A manual of diseases of the nervous system.* Philadelphia: Blakiston.

27. Greenough, W. T., Black, J. E., & Wallace, C. S. (1987). Experience and brain development. *Developmental Psychobiology, 22,* 727–252.

28. Harris, R. A. (1993). *The linguistics wars.* New York: Oxford University Press.

29. Head, H. (1926). *Aphasia and kindred disorders.* (2 vols). London: Cambridge University Press.

30. Helm-Estabrooks, N., & Albert, M. L. (1991). *Manual of aphasia therapy.* Austin, TX: Pro-Ed.

31. Helm-Estabrooks, N. (2001). *Cognitive Linguistic Quick Test.* Menlo Park, CA: Pearson.

32. Holland, A., Frattali, C., & Fromm, D. (1999). *Communication activities in daily living* (2nd ed.). Austin, TX: Pro-Ed.

33. Kertesz, A. (1982). *Western Aphasia Battery.* Austin, TX: Pro-Ed.

34. Kolb, B., & Gibb, R. (2011). Brain plasticity and behavior in the developing brain. *Journal of the Canadian Academy of Child and Adolescent Psychiatry, 20,* 265–277.

35. Lasker, J. P., & Garrett, K. L. (2006). Using the Multimodal Communication Screening Test for Persons with Aphasia (MCST-A) to guide the selection of alternative communication strategies for people with aphasia. *Aphasiology, 20,* 2–4.

36. Lenneberg, E. (1967). *Biological foundations of language.* New York: Wiley.

37. Liepmann, H. (1900). Das Krankheitbild der apraxie ("motorischen asymbolie"). *Monatsschrift fur Psychiatrie und Neurologie, 8,* 15–40.

38. Meynert, T. (1885). *Psychiatry.* Translated by B. Sachs. New York: Putnam.

39. Ogle, W. (1867). Aphasia and agraphia. *St. George's Hospital Reports, 2,* 83–122.

40. Orton, S. T. (1937). *Reading, writing and speech problems in children.* New York: W. W. Norton.

41. Penfield, W., & Roberts, L. (1959). *Speech and brain mechanisms.* Princeton, NJ: Princeton University Press.

42. Pinker, S. (1994). *The language instinct.* New York: William Morrow.

43. Schuell, H. (1965). *The Minnesota Test for Differential Diagnosis of Aphasia.* Minneapolis: University of Minnesota Press.

44. Sperry, R. W., Gazzaniga, M. S., & Bogen, J. E. (1969). Interhemispheric relationships: The neocortical commissures; syndromes of hemispheric disconnection. In P. J. Vinken, & G. W. Bruyn (Eds.), *Handbook of clinical neurology.* vol. 4. Amsterdam: North Holland.

45. Swinburn, K., Porter, G., & Howard, D. (2004). *Comprehensive Aphasia Test.* New York: Psychology Press.

46. Taylor-Sarno, M. (1997). Quality of life in the first poststroke year. *Aphasiology, 11*(7), 665–679.

47. Travis, L. E. (1931). *Speech pathology.* New York: Appleton-Century-Crofts.

48. Wada, J. A., Clark, R., & Hamm, A. (1975). Cerebral asymmetry in humans. *Archives of Neurology, 2,* 239–246.

49. Wepman, J. (1951). *Recovery from aphasia.* New York: The Ronald Press.

50. Wernicke, C. (1874). *Der aphasische symptomenkomplex. Breslau: Cohn and Weigert.* Translated in Eggert, G. H. (1977). Wernicke's works on aphasia. A sourcebook and review. The Hague: Mouton.

51. Whitelson, S. F., & Pallie, W. (1973). Left hemisphere specialization for language in the newborn: Neuroanatomical evidence of asymmetry. *Brain, 96,* 641–647.

2

Organization of the Nervous System I

The brain is the organ of destiny. It holds within its humming mechanism secrets that will determine the future of the human race.
Wilder Graves Penfield, *The Second Career*, 1963

KEY **TERMS**

angular gyrus
arcuate fasciculus
association cortex
astrocytes
ATP
axon
axon hillock
axoplasm
basal ganglia
blood-brain barrier
boutons
brainstem
Broca's area
cell respiration
CNS
cerebellum
cerebrum
choroid plexuses
cingulate gyrus
colliculi
corpus callosum
corpus striatum
dendrites
dendritic spines
diencephalon
ependymal cells
fasciculus
fissure
ganglia
glial
gray matter
Heschl's gyrus
homunculus
hypothalamus
innervate
insula
internal capsule
lentiform or lenticular
   nucleus
limbic system
medulla oblongata
mesencephalon
microglia
midbrain
myelin
neuroglial cells
neurons
neurotransmitters
nucleolus
occipital lobe
oligodendrocytes
parahippocampal
   gyrus
paralimbic areas
parietal lobe
PNS
perisylvian zone
pons
premotor area
primary cortical areas
reflex arc
Schwann cells
somatosensory
striatum
substantia nigra
subthalamus
sulcus
Supplementary or
   secondary motor
   area
supramarginal gyrus
synapse
tectum
temporal lobe
thalamus
uncus
Wernicke's area
white matter

13

Human Communication Nervous System

The nervous system is the source of all communication in human beings. Only human beings can express novel utterances to each other through oral or gestural language. Our highly advanced system of oral and gestural language identifies us as unique in the animal kingdom. This facility is the result of an aggregate of intricate nervous system mechanisms that have developed in the human brain through a series of dramatic evolutionary changes. Over a period of thousands of years, a novel representation and organization of neural structures and processes has been created in the human brain that results in what may be called the human communication nervous system. How does this nervous system differ from the communication nervous system of other animals? A clear answer to this question began to emerge from attempts to teach the great apes, particularly chimpanzees, different types of communication systems; attempts to teach *oral* speech to chimpanzees were notably unsuccessful. Only human beings have the specialized vocal tract enabling the potential for producing the complex acoustic signal known as speech or oral language. On the other hand, attempts to teach chimpanzees by using visual and gestural representations of human language have been somewhat successful. Chimpanzees have been taught to use colored plastic chips to represent morphemes and in other cases have learned to use some signs taken from American Sign Language to the extent that they can communicate adequately, and even creatively, in a rudimentary manner. Whether these nonverbal languages are characteristically human is open to question, but human beings and chimpanzees do share some characteristics of communication. The chimpanzee most likely uses cortical structures of the brain to master visual and gestural components of human language.

Some have suggested that overall brain size, which reflects the total volume of the cerebral cortex, the total number of nerve cells in the brain, and the degree of dendrite growth or proliferation of the processes of the nerve cell, is crucial to information processing and communication processing. Considering these factors, what are the differences between the human brain and that of the chimpanzee?

The chimpanzee's impressive but limited gestural language is reflected by its average brain weight of 450 g compared with an average weight of 1350 g for the human brain. Generally, a lack of uniqueness has been found in the parietal, occipital, and temporal lobes of both chimpanzees and human

beings. In the frontal lobe of the brain, however, human beings are distinguished by an area of cortex that has been named Broca's area. This specialized cortical area has been associated with the control of expressive language. With the exception of Broca's area, the primary difference between the human and chimpanzee cortex is quantitative, with the temporal lobe, inferior parietal lobe, and frontal lobe anterior to Broca's area being larger in human beings. These areas, as detailed in later chapters, are portions of the cerebral cortex that make an advanced language system possible. These particular species-specific brain structures, plus the human being's special vocal tract and the significant increase in the size of the information- and communication-processing cortex, account for the exceptional capability for communication.[23]

FOUNDATIONS OF THE NERVOUS SYSTEM

Chapters 2 and 3 provide an overview of the anatomy and physiology of the human nervous system. After discussing the "building blocks" of the nervous system, this text takes a "top-down" approach to the gross anatomy, beginning with the cortex and ending with the spinal cord anatomy. This organization was chosen because as human beings, cortical processing and control are vital to all but the most basic motor, cognitive, and emotional functions. It is not your ears that hear; it is really your brain. Your thoughts are initiated through cortical networks. Your memories and their associated emotions are stored in your brain. Therefore it seems appropriate to start with the "boss" and work our way down the organizational ladder of the nervous system in order to understand it better. Before we begin looking more closely at the individual structures of the brain and spinal cord, however, a study of the microstructure and foundation of this miraculous nervous system of ours will be helpful for understanding the complex function of the larger structures.

Anatomically, the human nervous system has two major divisions: the **central nervous system** (CNS) and the **peripheral nervous system** (PNS). The CNS, also called the neuraxis, consists of the brain and spinal cord. Two types of nerves are found within both systems, the cranial and the spinal nerves, and their **ganglia**. The term *ganglia* refers to the masses of nerve cell bodies associated with the particular nerve and located as an enlargement on that nerve or at the juncture or separation point of that nerve with another peripheral nerve. The nerves of the PNS connect the brain and spinal cord with peripheral structures such as muscles, glands, and organs. Both divisions of the nervous system contain somatic parts that control bodily movements and **innervate** sensory organs as well as autonomic parts that innervate visceral organs.

The Chemical Makeup of Nerve Cells

As taught in elementary science classes, all living things are composed of cells, the building blocks of life. The nervous system is no exception. It is a collection of two types of cells: nerve cells, also called **neurons**, and **neuroglial cells**. Recent research[1] found approximately 86 billion neurons with an almost equal number of neuroglial cells making up the human nervous system.

Although cells are the building blocks on which the human body is structured, they themselves are also composed of smaller units. These units are organelles, functional units within the cytoplasm that have their own bilipid membrane. Breaking down the organelles, we see that they, like all living matter, are composed of molecules. As is typical in living matter, nerve cells have four major classes of molecules: lipids, proteins, carbohydrates, and nucleic acid. There are two types of nucleic acid within each cell, deoxyribonucleic acid (DNA) and ribonucleic acid (RNA).

All cells contain an organelle called the nucleus. The nucleus contains most of the DNA of the cell and is bound by a bilipid membrane that has several openings or pores in it. DNA carries the genetic code of each living organism. It is helpful when studying genetic-based disorders in children to know at least basic facts about DNA, RNA, and the chromosomes that each carry a copy of the genetic code of a person.

The code stored in our DNA is made up of four chemical bases with the four chemicals typically referred to by the first letter: A, adenine; G, guanine; C, cytosine; and T, thymine. Each chemical base is attached to complex made up of a two-sugar molecule and a one-phosphate molecule. This combination of sugar molecules and phosphate molecule is referred to as a *nucleotide*. The nucleotide and its attached chemical base will pair up with another such structure and form a unit called a base pair; base pair units are formed by the pairing of A with T and the pairing of C with G. DNA is arranged in two long strands that form a spiral called a double helix. This double helix looks somewhat like a ladder with the base pairs forming the ladder's rungs and the sugar and phosphate molecules forming the vertical sides of the ladder (Fig. 2-1). In human beings, the human genome (the entire genetic set) is found in the 46 chromosomes duplicated in each cell of the body. This is possible because the DNA can make copies of itself. Within the double helix, each strand can duplicate the pattern and sequence of the bases. This

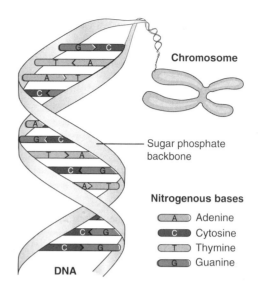

FIGURE **2-1**
The structure of DNA.

allows for exact copies of the DNA in the cell to be present in the new cell when cell division takes place in the embryo.

The genetic information contained in the DNA is encoded into proteins. Proteins are the "worker bees" of the cell, performing most of the various cellular reactions that constitute life. The other nucleic acid molecule in the cell, RNA, serves both storage and transcoder functions as an intermediary between the DNA and a targeted protein. The nucleus of the cell contains at least one prominent dense area, the **nucleolus**, where RNA is synthesized. RNA is only single stranded and is made up of four bases as well, but there is no thymine base; rather the chemical uracil (U) is present instead. There are different types of RNA in a cell: messenger (mRNA), ribosomal (rRNA), and transfer (tRNA). rRNA is the most abundant and works with proteins to form the ribosomes (discussed later in the chapter) of a cell. mRNA leaves the cell, moving to the cytoplasm where proteins are synthesized. In protein synthesis, the base sequence carried in the genetic code on the RNA is "read" by the ribosome and translated into corresponding amino acids. Cellular proteins are formed by the chemical linking of two or more amino acids, forming peptides. These peptides are then linked in a series becoming polypeptides. One or more polypeptides make up all cellular proteins. The tRNA transfers a particular amino acid to the polypeptide chain during protein synthesis

As alluded to earlier, surrounding the nucleus is a mass of cytoplasm containing organelles that serve to synthesize proteins and maintain cellular metabolic balance. Found in this cytoplasm are: rough and smooth endoplasmic reticulum, free ribosomes, Golgi apparatus, lysosomes, and mitochondria. The endoplasmic reticulum and the ribosomes are in abundance in neuronal cell bodies because of their key participation in lipid and protein synthesis, which is constantly needed for optimal nervous system function. Vesicles, which are little transporter membrane sacs, "bud" off from the endoplasmic reticulum and help deliver the proteins and lipids to the Golgi apparatus organelles. The Golgi apparatus organelle sorts the substances, and the vesicles eventually deliver them to the plasma membrane where they may fuse with the membrane delivering proteins to it or shed their contents to the outside of the cell. The vesicles may also carry digestive enzymes and become the organelles called lysosomes.[4]

Mitochondria are the power source of the cell, providing the energy a cell needs to function by converting the energy from food into a useable form for cellular function. The mitochondria produce adenosine triphosphate (ATP), the cell's main energy source. Cells in the nervous system have the highest metabolic rate of any cells in the human body and therefore must continually renew their energy source. Our bodies, through the action of ATP, convert energy from the sun into a usable form for cellular function. A process called cell respiration, which is driven by enzymes in the body regenerates ATP constantly. Only about 250 g of ATP are available at any one time in the body (about as much energy as provided by an AA battery), and this small amount is being used persistently in healthy cells.[20] Therefore, it must be reproduced repetitively by the cells.

Although most of your DNA is contained in chromosomes within the cell's nucleus, mitochondria have a small amount of their own DNA (37 genes) that is vital for normal mitochondria cell functioning. The mitochondrial DNA is, except in rare cases, inherited from maternal lineage, being provided by the egg rather than by the sperm. Thus this DNA changes much more slowly through the generations than nuclear DNA.

Because lipids do not dissolve in water, the bilipid membrane surrounding the nerve cell body forms a barrier between what is inside the cell (the intracellular material) and what surrounds it on the outside (the extracellular material). This membrane is also studded with globular proteins that serve as channels that allow molecules of certain chemicals (neurotransmitters) to pass through when the membrane is appropriately stimulated. These channels are usually specific to one type of molecule, barring others from entering the cell. Understanding the function of the channels becomes important when we study how neural impulses are generated and how neurons communicate within networks.

The Structure and Function of Neurons

Like other cells in your body, both neurons and neuroglial cells consist of a cell body, also known as a soma or perikaryon. Also, as with other cells in the body, cells of the nervous system maintain their defined structure with a cytoskeleton. A cytoskeleton is composed of microtubules, intermediate filaments (neurofilaments), and microfilaments. Neurons can also be seen microscopically to have processes extending from them; these processes include one axon per neuron and many dendrites. The axon and the dendrites are critical to neuronal communication between different parts of the nervous system. The cytoskeleton of these appendages provides scaffolding for transport of molecules along these structures. Cytoskeleton dysfunction has been linked to disorders affecting the human nervous system, such as neurofibromatosis and type 2 and Duchenne muscular dystrophy.

Figure 2-2 shows a multipolar neuron or nerve cell. Neurons are specialized to receive, conduct, and transmit nerve impulses. This transmission may be to or from a muscle, gland, or another nerve cell. Although nerve cells vary widely in terms of size and shape, they all have certain characteristics in common. They all have two types of processes extending from the cell body. The processes specialized to receive the impulses moving *toward* the cell are dendrites. They have a broad base, taper away from the cell body, and branch somewhere in the vicinity of the cell body. Most neurons are multipolar and have several dendrites extending from the cell body. Effectively, these dendrites expand the area of the neuron available for contact by other neurons, thus allowing *convergence* of neural impulses onto one neuron from many other neurons. Small protrusions, called dendritic spines, help expand the area of contact even farther. These dendritic spines appear as small hairlike or bulbous structures on the dendrite's membrane.

The other type of process extending from a neuron conducts the impulse *away from* the cell and is called the axon. Each neuron has only one axon, and it connects with the body of the neuron at a site called the axon hillock. Collateral branches, however, are frequently found coming off the axon itself. Because the axon carries all the neural information out of the cell, this branching increases the opportunity for *divergence* in the nervous system.

The cytoplasm of an axon contains structural elements called microtubules and neurofilaments that help maintain its cytoskeleton. These elements also help transport organelles and metabolic substances

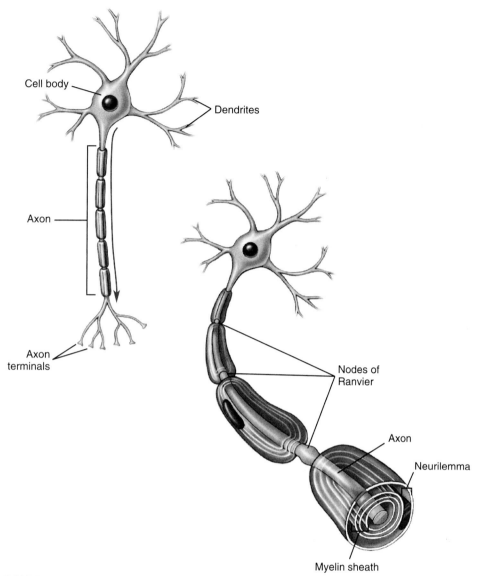

FIGURE **2-2**
Structure of a neuron. (From Herlihy, B. [2007]. *The human body in health and illness* [3rd ed.].
St. Louis: Saunders.)

along the axon. Axons come in different diameters and lengths. The thicker axons conduct impulses more rapidly than thinner ones because they are usually myelinated (i.e., covered by a white, glistening lipoprotein sheath called the myelin sheath). This fatty sheath of myelin insulates the axon and allows more rapid propagation of the impulse along the axon. Most axons (and some dendrites) are well myelinated, although some thinner axons are either unmyelinated or thinly myelinated. Figure 2-3 shows a longitudinal cut of a myelinated axon.

The axon loses any myelin sheath at its destination and divides into several small terminal branches. At the end of these branches there are usually swellings, referred to as axon terminals or boutons. The bouton establishes contact with another neuron or the cells of a muscle or gland. The site of this contact is a synapse or a synaptic junction. The synapse is the primary means by which the neuron elicits responses in target cells, typically by a release of a chemical known as a neurotransmitter. Chapter 4 provides a more in-depth discussion of the synapse.

Aside from the movement of neural impulses down an axon, proteins and other organelles move along the axon in its protoplasm (known as axoplasm), a process called axoplasmic transport. This helps maintain the structural and functional integrity of the axon. This transport may be anterograde, from the cell body

FIGURE **2-3**
Longitudinal view of a myelinated axon in the CNS. (Reprinted from Haines, D. [2006]. *Fundamental neuroscience* [3rd ed.]. Philadelphia: Churchill Livingstone.)

distally, and retrograde, back toward the cell body from the axon terminal. The retrograde transport mediates the movement of substances providing *trophic*, or nutritional, support for the neuron. An example of trophic support is substances known as nerve growth factors.

Clusters of interconnected neurons with specific functions can be found throughout the nervous system. These groups are called neuronal pools and are discussed in Chapter 4.

Neuroglia

Composing the majority of cells in the nervous system are the glial, or neuroglial, cells. The CNS contains four types of neuroglial cells: astrocytes, oligodendrocytes (called Schwann cells in the PNS), microglia, and ependyma.

Glial cells do not propagate neural impulses but provide extremely important supportive and facilitative functions to the nervous system. Although we spend a majority of our study looking at signals generated by the neurons and the ensuing activations (or lack thereof), you must understand that the neuroglia make it possible for neurons to function optimally. Many of the disorders you will study result from a breakdown in the neuroglial support for the nervous system. Brain tumors often form in the neuroglial cells (example: astrocytoma); diseases that affect children (example: mitochondrial disease) and adults (example: multiple sclerosis) involve neuroglia and affect central and/or peripheral nervous system functioning with consequent effect on speech and language. The following neuroglia are critical to optimal nervous system function.

Astrocytes provide the structural matrix surrounding neuron cell bodies in the CNS and modulate neuronal activity locally and regionally. Astrocytes of the CNS also play a major role in maintaining the extracellular environment around the neuron. Astrocytes are responsive to and may have specific receptors for certain neurotransmitters. They are now thought to take an active role in modulating neuronal activity and synaptic plasticity.[19]

In many tissues of the body, solutes can pass rather freely from the blood into the cells of that tissue by diffusing through gaps between the endothelial cells, those cells that line the interior surface of blood and lymphatic vessels. In the CNS, however, the astrocytes cause the walls of the capillaries to form tight endothelial junctions, forming what is called the blood-brain barrier. Therefore most solutes passing into neural tissue must go through the endothelial cells themselves. Water, gases, and small lipid-soluble molecules may pass easily across the endothelial cells, but most other substances must be carried across by transport systems. Consequently, the passage of substances into neural tissue from the blood is not always easily accomplished. Dysfunction of the astroglial cells or the complex surrounding particular neuronal networks is receiving more and more attention in research into neurogenerative diseases as a possible etiology or major contributor to the disease process. The astroglia are also being studied due to possibly serving a neuroprotective role.[22]

Oligodendrocytes are found within the central nervous system; here they form and maintain myelin, the white fatty sheath covering on the CNS axons. In the PNS, *Schwann cells* perform this function for nerves and nerve roots.

Microglia are numerous and perform "scavenger" functions. They may migrate to the site of injury in the brain, multiply, and become brain macrophages, cleaning out debris after neural cell death. They are sometimes referred to as the brain's immune system because the microglia mediate immune response to injury or infection.

As is further discussed in Chapter 3, there are cavities within the central nervous system through which cerebrospinal fluid circulates. These cavities within the brain are called ventricles. The spinal cord also contains a central cavity called a canal through which the fluid flows. Ependymal cells line these cavities in the brain and spinal cord. Specialized ependymal cells form structures called choroid plexuses, which are found in each ventricle of the brain. The choroidal epithelial cells on the surface of the choroid plexus structures are responsible for the manufacture of cerebrospinal fluid.

Glial cells called satellite cells are found in the PNS, forming thin sheaths that surround individual ganglia associated with sensory, sympathetic, and parasympathetic nerves. These cells surround the cell bodies, and although their specific physiologic role is not well understood, some current theories suggest that they may have a significant role in maintaining the microenvironment of the ganglion cells.[8]

Beyond the functions stated previously for glial cells, they are also important in the early development of the CNS. Study of the embryology of the nervous system indicates that glia serve to guide developing neurons in their migration to the correct location. Box 2-1 outlines the basic structure of neuroglial cells in the human nervous system.

Gray Matter

Some areas of the brain and spinal cord appear gray and others appear white. The white areas, called white matter, contain many myelinated axons, with the pearly white myelin covering responsible for the color of the area. The cortex is the superficial covering of gray matter found over the cerebral hemispheres and in the cerebellum. Gray matter contains aggregations of nerve cell bodies embedded in delicate nerve processes. The gray matter seen in the *interior* of the brain consists of large groups of nerve cell bodies; these are called subcortical nuclei. The thalamus and the structures making up the basal nuclei (also known as the basal ganglia) are composed of subcortical nuclei. Gray matter is also found in the spinal cord; the cell bodies aggregate as columns in the spinal cord and form the H-shaped midportion of the cord.

The cells of the cerebral cortex are horizontally organized into six cell layers. The organization of these layers is known as the cytoarchitecture of the brain. Each layer contains a different type of cell, with the pyramidal cells, the largest cells in the brain, found in layer 5. The cortex is organized vertically as well as horizontally. Vertical columns of interconnected neurons each hold a functional unit of cells that share a related purpose and a related location of the stimulus that drives their function. For example, the visual cortex has visual orientation columns.

ORGANIZATION

To comprehend the human communicative nervous system thoroughly, a basic understanding of the organization of the system as a whole is required. The nervous system should be thought of as separate from the other tissues and structures of the body. Imagine the major parts of the nervous system as if they were displayed on a dissection table spread out for study. On the table would be an oval-shaped brain with a tail-like appendage, called the spinal cord, hanging from its base. The cranial nerves, which we will study in the most depth, are attached to the base of the brain. Another set of nerves, the spinal nerves,

---

BOX 2-1

Summary of Glial (Neuroglial) Cells

- Provide supportive functions in the nervous system
- Do not propagate neural impulses
- Serve in early development of CNS, guiding developing neurons to their correct locations

Astrocytes

- Provide structural matrix for cell bodies in the CNS
- Cause capillary walls to form tight endothelial junctions to ensure that most solutes must pass through endothelial cells
- Help maintain appropriate environment for neuronal function
- Allow for neural plasticity and help brain adapt to injury

Oligodendrocytes

- Form and maintain myelin

Microglia

- Perform scavenger functions such as cleaning out debris after neural cell damage and forming brain macrophages
- Mediate immune response after injury or infection to the brain

Ependyma

- Line ventricles in the brain and spinal cord
- Specialized types form choroid plexus, which manufactures cerebrospinal fluid

Satellite Cells

- Found in CNS and PNS
- Surround neuron bodies but function unknown

---

project from both sides of the spinal cord (Fig. 2-4). Of all these parts—the brain, cord, and nerves—the brain is by far the most important for communication. Within the brain, evolutionary neural mechanisms of the communication nervous system are developed.

The nerves that exit the brain merely transmit sensory or motor information to and from the brain to control the speech, language, and hearing mechanisms. The nerves attached to the spinal cord innervate, or send nerve impulses to, muscles of the neck, trunk, and limbs and bring sensation from these parts to the brain.

From this oversimplified first mental image of the structure and function of the communication nervous system, a more precise and complex picture will be developed of the aspects of anatomy, physiology, and

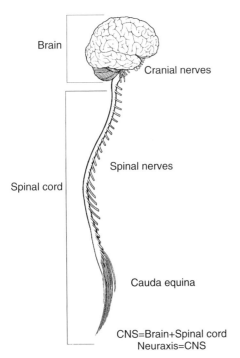

FIGURE **2-4**
The central nervous system (CNS), including the brain and spinal cord. The CNS is synonymous with the term *neuraxis*.

diagnosis of neurogenic speech, language, and hearing disorders. This chapter and the next take an in-depth look at the two major divisions of your nervous system, beginning with the CNS. Chapter 3 deals with the anatomy of the PNS and will also discuss a third system important to both the CNS and the PNS, called the autonomic nervous system. Chapter 3 also introduces you to the anatomic structures and the processes that nourish and protect these systems.

Central Nervous System

The brain is gray, shaped like an oval, and slightly soft to the touch. The average brain weighs approximately 1350 g, or roughly 3 pounds. The brain is housed in the part of the bony skull called the cranium. A synonym for brain is encephalon. The largest mass of brain tissue is identified as the **cerebrum**. The human cerebrum has evolved to include three parts: the cerebral hemispheres, limbic system (in earlier terminology, rhinencephalon), and basal nuclei (aka, basal ganglia).

The cerebral hemispheres are the two readily discernible large halves of the brain. The cerebral hemispheres are connected by a mass of white matter called the **corpus callosum**. During development the cerebral hemispheres become enormously enlarged

and overhang the structures deep in the brain called the diencephalon and brainstem. The cerebral hemispheres are crucial for communication, particularly the left hemisphere, where the major neurologic mechanisms of speech and language are found.

CORTICAL DIVISIONS

The cerebral hemispheres are identical twins in looks, but the functions of their parts dramatically differ. Each cortical mantle, or cover, of a hemisphere is anatomically divided into four different principal lobes: frontal, temporal, parietal, and occipital. These lobes can be located on the brain's outer and medial (between the hemispheres) surfaces by using certain landmarks, the gyri and sulci. A gyrus is formed from the enfolding of the cortex during development; a gyrus appears as a slight elevation on the surface. A **sulcus** is a groove-like depression that separates the gyri. Another name for a sulcus is **fissure**. The gyri and sulci seen on the surfaces of the two cerebral hemispheres serve as boundaries for the lobes (Figs. 2-4 and 2-5).

Cortical Localization Maps
For more than a century, neuroanatomists have divided and classified the human cortex into different areas. These tireless attempts to fractionate the cortex followed the unparalleled achievement of Paul Broca. In 1861 Broca demonstrated that different cortical regions were associated with different mental functions, one of which was expression of speech.[3] The localization systems that followed have most frequently been based on cell study of the cortex made by histologic methods. This allows the development of cytoarchitectural diagrams or maps based on the varied cell structures of the cortex. The most popular map, developed by the German neurologist Korbinian Brodmann (1868-1918), is represented in Figures 2-5 and 2-6. Note that each area of the cortex is numbered, providing a much more convenient way to specify a cortical site than by a complex description of gyri and sulci. Brodmann's map is open to criticism on the grounds that it chops the cortex into innumerable specific centers, implying that cortical areas have sharply defined limits, but it is a convenient tool in clinical practice for indicating cortical localization. Brodmann's classification numbers are sometimes provided in this text to orient the reader to Figures 2-5 and 2-6.

Cerebral Lobes
Why Is This important for Speech-Language Pathology?
Contemporary practice in speech-language pathology, regardless of where one practices, often requires medical record review and understanding. The cerebral

FIGURE **2-5**
Superior view of the cerebral hemispheres with cortical binding, according to Brodmann.
(Reprinted from Werner, J. J. [2001]. *Atlas of neuroanatomy.* Boston: Butterworth-Heinemann.)

hemispheres contain networks for information processing and contain the primary cortical areas that activate muscles and initially receive sensory input. When these mechanisms are underdeveloped or disrupted by disease or injury, speech, swallowing, hearing, and/or language deficits as well as cognitive deficits may occur. It is important as a practitioner to know the location in the cerebral hemispheres of the primary areas and to know the key processing functions thought to be associated with each of the principal lobes. I often recommend that in the beginning you "tag" the lobes in your memory as containing certain structures and performing certain critical functions for speech, language, or hearing (e.g., temporal lobe = Heschl's gyrus, Wernicke's area, hearing, auditory comprehension).

Frontal Lobe

The frontal lobe is bounded anteriorly by the lateral sulcus, or sylvian fissure, and posteriorly by the central

sulcus, or rolandic fissure. The frontal lobe accounts for approximately one third of the surface of the hemisphere. In the frontal lobe is a long gyrus immediately anterior to the central sulcus. This prominent gyrus is called the precentral gyrus, and it comprises the majority of what is known as the *primary* motor cortex (area 4). The term *motor strip* is also used for this area. Nerve fibers composing a large motor pathway called the pyramidal tract descend into the brain and spinal cord from starting points in the primary motor area. The cells in this area are responsible for voluntary control of skeletal muscles on the opposite, or contralateral, side of the body. This fact has important clinical significance, which is discussed later in the chapter.

The connections between the controlling area on the primary motor cortex and the voluntary muscles served are arranged so that a map of motor control can be drawn on the cerebral cortex to show the pattern of

FIGURE **2-6**
Medial view of the right hemisphere. (Reprinted from Werner, J. J. [2001]. *Atlas of neuro-anatomy.* Boston: Butterworth-Heinemann.)

cortical innervation (Fig. 2-7, *B*). This map is referred to as a **homunculus**, which is Latin for "little man." The areas are represented in an almost upside-down or inverted fashion. The area of cortical representation given to a particular part does not appear to be strongly related to the size of that part of the body, because the leg and arm are given a smaller area of cortical tissue than the hand or mouth. Rather, the body parts that require the most precision in motor control are apportioned the larger cortical areas. Shown in Figure 2-7, *A*, is the cortical sensory map or sensory homunculus, which is a mirror image of the motor map and represents the pattern of sensory input from the body to the somatosensory cortex on the post central gyrus which is located not in the frontal but in the parietal lobe.

Immediately anterior to the primary motor area are the premotor cortex and another area with motor assignment, the supplementary motor area. These ancillary motor areas (area 6) are important in motor learning and in the performance of routine and less-practiced motor sequences.

In the frontal lobe of the left hemisphere is an important region known as **Broca's area** (areas 44 and 45). Located in the inferior (third) frontal gyrus of the lobe

(2, 3, and 4), Broca's area in most people appears to be important for the production of fluent, well-articulated speech. The left hemisphere is the dominant hemisphere in most persons, meaning that this hemisphere controls language functions. Approximately 90% of the population is right handed with left hemisphere dominance for language. Even the majority of persons who are left handed show left dominance for language. If damage to Broca's area occurs in adults who are left hemisphere–dominant for language, a characteristic breakdown usually occurs in the normally fluent production of verbal language; if the damage is limited to Broca's area specifically, this breakdown is usually transient. If the damage results from a larger lesion that includes Broca's area but also surrounding cortical tissue in what is known as the **perisylvian zone**, a classic syndrome of acquired language disorders or *aphasia*, called Broca's aphasia, may be diagnosed (discussed further in Chapter 10). Ablation of the area in the nondominant hemisphere corresponding to Broca's area has an effect on language in only a small percentage of the population.

Another part of the frontal lobe also concerned with initiation of movement is the area devoted to control of the eyes. The frontal eye fields (area 8) lie just

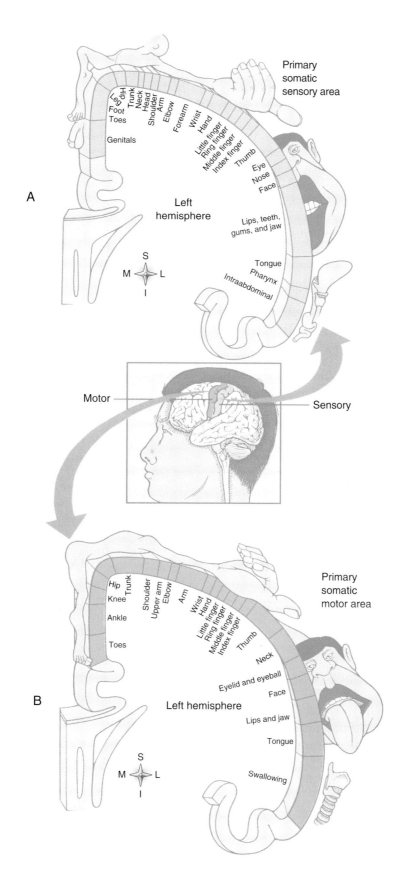

FIGURE **2-7**

Primary somatic sensory (**A**) and motor (**B**) areas of the cortex. The illustrations show which parts of the body are mapped to specific areas of the postcentral (sensory) and precentral (motor) gyri. The exaggerated face indicates that more cortical area is devoted to processing information to and from the face than, for example, the leg or arm. This disparity is due the precision of motor control and distinct sensory processing needed for speech and swallowing. (Reprinted from Thibodeau, G., & Patton, K. [2006]. *Anatomy & physiology* [6th ed.]. St. Louis: Mosby.)

anterior to the premotor cortical area. These areas are involved in initiating rapid eye movements and directing attention.

The rest of the frontal lobe is composed of **association cortex,** a different type of cortical tissue with less-defined functional assignment. This frontal area is often referred to as the prefrontal cortex (areas 9, 10, 11, 46, and 47) and contains the frontal association areas. Frontal association areas are vital to successful executive functioning. Appropriate and well-developed executive functioning allows the execution of nonroutine processes that require planning, analysis, feedback, self-regulation, and so forth. The ability to participate successfully in school, work, family, and social settings depends on these frontal association areas.

Parietal Lobe

The **parietal lobe** is bounded anteriorly by the central sulcus, inferiorly by the posterior end of the lateral sulcus, and posteriorly by an imaginary borderline. The primary sensory, also known as somatosensory or somesthetic, cortex is found in the parietal lobe (areas 1, 2, and 3), the major portion of which is the postcentral gyrus (see Fig. 2-5). It is also known as the *sensory strip,* but it is helpful to use the term **somatosensory** to help remember that bodily sensations, as opposed to visual and auditory sensations, are processed here. This gyrus lies directly posterior to the central sulcus, or rolandic fissure. On this sensory cortex can be mapped the sensory control of various parts of the body. Somesthetic sensations (e.g., pain, temperature, touch) are sent to the sensory cortex from the opposite side of the body. This arrangement is a mirror image of the motor strip (see Fig. 2-7).

Two gyri in the parietal lobe are important to locate and become familiar with in regard to language. The first is the **supramarginal gyrus** (area 40), which curves around the posterior end of the lateral sylvian fissure. The second, the **angular gyrus** (area 39), lies directly posterior to the supramarginal gyrus. It curves around the end of a prominent sulcus in the temporal lobe, the superior temporal sulcus (see Fig. 2-5). Damage in the area of the angular gyrus in the dominant left hemisphere may cause word-finding problems (anomia), reading and writing deficits (alexia with agraphia), as well as left-right disorientation, finger agnosia (inability to identify the fingers), and difficulty with arithmetic (acalculia).

The postcentral gyrus (somatosensory cortex) is a *primary* cortical area, whereas the majority of the remaining parietal lobe cortex is composed of association cortex, mostly concerned with somatosensory and visual association function. The parietal lobe has been characterized as the "association area of association areas" because of the multimodal processing that takes place there. As a whole, the parietal lobes may be the most lateralized in function of all the lobes in the cerebrum, although the specialization is not complete. Language functions tend to be concentrated in the left parietal lobe around the gyri just discussed. In the nondominant hemisphere, the parietal lobe association cortex primarily processes spatial information and related selective attention. Damage here may result in difficulty attending to or a complete neglect of the contralateral side of space. Visuospatial and constructional deficits (such as in drawing, building small models, and so on) may be found on testing the patient with right-hemisphere parietal lobe damage.

Temporal Lobe

The **temporal lobe** is the seat of auditory processing in the brain. It is bounded superiorly by the sylvian fissure and posteriorly by an imaginary line that forms the anterior border of the occipital lobe. Two gyri of the temporal lobe are prominent on the lateral surface of the brain: the superior and middle temporal gyri. The third important gyrus, the inferior gyrus, can be seen on the lateral surface but continues onto the interior surface of the lobe as well (see Fig. 2-5). Less visible on the lateral surface are the transverse temporal gyri (areas 41 and 42), which can be found on the upper edge of the temporal lobe, extending deep in the medial surface of the brain. The transverse gyrus of Heschl (most commonly called **Heschl's gyrus**), area 41, forms the primary auditory cortex, representing the cortical center for hearing in each hemisphere. There is bilateral representation of the auditory signal though more fibers terminate in the gyrus of the contralateral hemisphere than will terminate on the ipsilateral side of the brain. The ability to detect the presence of sound is a function of the peripheral hearing mechanism and the auditory nerves. The cortical area is the site of conscious processing of those impulses as "sound," allowing us to perceive these signals as sound and do what we call "hear."

Area 42 is adjacent to Heschl's gyrus and is an auditory association area, although it is frequently presented as part of the primary cortical area of hearing. It has been found to participate in the processing of harmonic and rhythmic patterns. Unilateral damage in areas 41 and/or 42 of the auditory cortex does not cause deafness in one ear but rather may result in difficulty interpreting a sound or locating a sound in space. Bilateral lesions in the auditory cortex cause what is known as cortical deafness (see Chapter 5).

The posterior part of the superior temporal gyrus in the left temporal lobe is the auditory association area, best known as **Wernicke's area** (area 22), which is important to the development and use of language. Damage to Wernicke's area may result in a particular classification of acquired language disorder called **Wernicke's aphasia** (see Chapter 10).

On the medial aspect of the temporal lobes, near the sagittal plane between the two hemispheres one can locate several important deep brain areas important to memory. These include the hippocampal region and the parahippocampal gyrus. On the parahippocampal gyrus can be found subcortical areas known as the perirhinal, parahippocampal and entorhinal cortices.

If the two borders of the lateral (Sylvian) fissure are pulled apart, a cortical structure called the **insula**, or the island of Reil, may be seen hidden under the area where the temporal, parietal, and frontal lobes come together. It includes some of the oldest cortical tissue in the brain. The insula is not part of the temporal lobe or any of the four major lobes but is considered a lobe unto itself. Fiber connections to the insula are not well defined and the functions are not well understood, but the insula is thought to receive input regarding pain and viscerosensory input. As discussed in Chapter 10, lesions involving the insula in the dominant hemisphere may also contribute to difficulty producing well-articulated, fluent speech.

Occipital Lobe

The **occipital lobe** occupies the small area behind the parietal lobe and is marked on the lateral surface by imaginary lines rather than prominent sulci. Two sulci that can be found on the medial surface of the brain that help locate the occipital lobe are the parietal-occipital sulcus and the calcarine sulcus (see Fig. 2-6). The occipital lobe is concerned with vision, with the primary visual area (area 17) located in gyri that border the calcarine sulcus.

Perisylvian Zone

The cortex surrounding the sylvian fissure in the dominant temporal lobe (left for the majority of the population) is identified as the perisylvian zone, where the major neurologic components for understanding and producing language are found. These components include Broca's area, Wernicke's area, the supramarginal and angular gyri, as well as major long association tracts that connect the components (Fig. 2-8). The central language mechanism and its disorders are discussed in depth in Chapters 9 and 10.

CEREBRAL CONNECTIONS

Why Is This Important for Speech-Language Pathology?

We have acknowledged that the cerebrum is the "boss" of the nervous system. This must mean that the connections between and within the cerebral hemispheres and with lower structures are a vital part of how the nervous system works. Knowledge of the nervous system must include the types of fibers found in these areas. This eventually leads you to an understanding of how the various structures are connected and form pathways for neural impulses to traverse. Figure 2-9 schematically depicts the different types of fibers discussed later in the chapter.

Projection Fibers

Projection fibers are long axons of neurons that send impulses to a distant structure in the CNS. The most notable projection fibers are the corticospinal fibers, which project from the primary motor cortex down to the spinal cord, and the corticobulbar fibers, which project from the primary motor cortex down to the cranial nerve nuclei. Corticopontine fibers are also projection fibers, projecting from the motor areas to the brainstem and then down to the cerebellum.

Association Fibers

Association fibers form association tracts, connecting areas within the hemisphere. Short association tracts

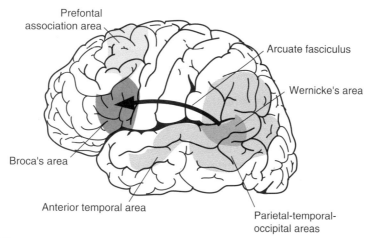

FIGURE **2-8**
Primary language and association areas of the cortex.

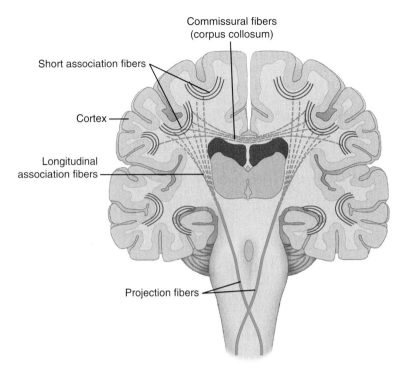

FIGURE **2-9**
Schematic representation of the types of connective fibers in the CNS.

are within lobes, and long tracts are between lobes. **Fasciculus**, meaning "little bundle," is the type of name given to many of these tracts important to language and speech. Figure 2-10, *A*, is a graphic depiction of some of these fiber tracts.

One important association tract is the **arcuate fasciculus** (AF). The AF is important to language because a large number of its fibers travel from the posterior temporal lobe forward by way of another set of fibers, the superior longitudinal fasciculus (SLF), to the motor association cortex in the frontal lobe. Lesions in the area of the arcuate fasciculus may cause a major syndrome of aphasia (an acquired language disorder caused by brain damage) called conduction aphasia. There are also indirect AF fiber connections between Broca's area and the parietal lobe as well as connecting the parietal lobe with Wernicke's area.[14]

The uncinate fasciculus (UF) gathers fibers from the temporal pole, uncus, hippocampal gyrus, and amygdala in the rostral portion of the temporal lobe. The UF follows a complicated path and eventually extends into the orbitofrontal cortex and prefrontal cortex. Thus it links areas of the temporal lobe important for sound recognition, object recognition, and recognition memory with areas of the frontal lobe involved in emotion, inhibition, and self-regulation.[14] The functional significance of this pathway is not totally understood, although it has been suggested that it allows the reward/

punishment biased association memories stored in the orbitofrontal cortex to access mnemonic associations (e.g., names, facial features, voice) stored in the temporal lobe, thus perhaps influencing decisions, learning, and memory as well as social behavior.[21]

The inferior longitudinal fasciculus (ILF) runs along with and lateral to a fasciculus known as the inferior fronto-occipital fasciculus (FOF) whose fibers eventually enter the frontal lobe. The ILF has vertical fibers arising in the occipital lobe outside the striate cortex (in extrastriate cortical areas). There are also horizontal fibers that run along the length of the temporal lobe, terminating in the anterior temporal region. The ILF appears to have a role in object recognition as well as memory and visual discrimination. Catani and Mesalum[5] propose a role for the ILF in linking object recognition with the lexical label. Table 2-1 describes some of the important fasciculi in the cerebral hemispheres.

Commissural Fibers

Commissural fibers connect an area in one hemisphere with an area in the opposite hemisphere. The corpus callosum is the largest set of commissural fibers in the brain and is a pathway of crucial importance to speech-language functions (Fig. 2-10, *B*). The corpus callosum serves as the major connection between the hemispheres and conveys neural information from one hemisphere to the other. The corpus callosum is the largest of the

FIGURE **2-10**
A, Association fiber tracts of the left cerebral hemisphere with particular emphasis on the arcuate fasciculus and the uncinate fasciculus. **B,** The corpus callosum in a medial view and transverse section. It is the largest of the commissures connecting the two hemispheres.

side-to-side interconnections between the two hemispheres and, in general, connects analogous areas in the two hemispheres.

The anterior and posterior commissures are other small bundles of interhemispheric fibers, located anteriorly and posteriorly to the corpus callosum. The anterior commissure connects the olfactory bulbs, amygdaloid nuclei, and the medial and inferior temporal lobes. The posterior commissure fibers connect areas in the occipital lobes, primarily areas concerned with pupillary response and eye movement control.

Split-Brain Research
The corpus callosum and its role in the transfer of information from one hemisphere to another

TABLE 2-1

White Matter Association Pathways, Location, and Function

ASSOCIATION FIBERS	MAIN PATHWAY(S)	FUNCTION
Superior longitudinal fasciculus	Posterior arm fanning out into parietal, occipital, and posterior temporal lobes; anterior arm recurves to the anterior temporal lobe	Interconnects frontal with the other three lobes Significant for initiation of motor activity, spatial attention, gesture, and orofacial memory
Arcuate fasciculus	Connects Wernicke's area with Broca's area. Different segments connect inferior parietal lobule with those two areas; connects Broca's with middle frontal and precentral gyri; connects Wernicke's with middle temporal gyrus	Ability to recognize language and respond to it appropriately
Uncinate fasciculus	Complex pathway from rostral temporal lobe (temporal pole, uncus, hippocampal gyrus, amygdala) to the white matter of the orbitofrontal cortex (may ascend and reach prefrontal areas)	Ventral limbic path; significant for processing novel information, self-regulation, and positive/negative evaluation of emotional information May be important for visual learning
Superior fronto-occipital fasciculus	Fibers from occipital and parietal lobes join and run horizontal and forward to prefrontal and premotor cortex	Significant for peripheral vision, visual motion perception, and visual-spatial processing
Inferior fronto-occipital fasciculus	Superior parietal, posterior temporal, and inferior occipital fibers follow complex dorsal and ventral paths to frontal and prefrontal cortical areas	May be important to object recognition and discrimination, semantic processing, and emotional-cognitive interaction
Inferior longitudinal fasciculus	From extrastriate visual association areas in occipital lobe to anterior temporal lobe, uncus, parahippocampal gyrus, and amygdala	Significant for its role in object recognition, visual discrimination, and memory May link visual object recognition to lexical label
Cingulum bundle	Forms most of white matter of the cingulate gyrus. Longer fibers connect multiple areas around corpus callosum	Major component of dorsal limbic pathway Involved in motivation and emotion as well as spatial working memory

Summarized from Nadich, T. P., Krayenbuhl, N., Kollias, S., Bou-Haidar, P., Bluestone, A. Y., & Carpenter D. M. (2010). White matter. In T. P. Nadich, M. Castillo, S. Cha, & J. G. Smirniotopoulos (Eds.), *Imaging of the brain* (pp. 205-244). Philadelphia: Elsevier Saunders.

attracted wide attention when split-brain operations were first performed on human beings in the 1960s.[15] This large bundle of commissural fibers may be cleanly and completely severed surgically without damage to other tissue. This operation, called a commissurotomy, has been performed on patients plagued by chronic and severe epileptic seizures that could not be controlled by massive doses of anticonvulsive medication. A seizure that begins in one cerebral hemisphere may easily travel across the corpus callosum to the other hemisphere, producing a bilateral generalized seizure. Neurosurgeons reasoned that sectioning the corpus callosum would contain the seizure to one hemisphere.

Results of the early commissurotomies were even more beneficial than had been anticipated. Not only did the surgery contain seizures to a single hemisphere, but it also reduced seizures overall because of the severing of apparent reciprocal actions between the hemispheres.

The surgery also provided information on the differing psychological functions of each hemisphere and on the role of the corpus callosum in the brain mechanisms for speech and language. The split-brain patients clearly showed asymmetry for speech and language functions, indicating that the corpus callosum plays a decisive role in transmitting language received at the right primary auditory area and heard in the right ear to the left hemisphere, where it is processed by the major mechanisms for speech and language.

Experiments on patients who underwent the split-brain procedure suggested that the right hemisphere was responsible for spatial, tactile, and constructional tasks. These experiments led to speculations that the two hemispheres function in different ways, each having its own cognitive style. The left hemisphere was characterized as logical, analytic, and verbal, the right as intuitive, holistic, and perceptual/spatial. However, as will become increasingly clear to you, they are unquestionably integrated in intact brain function.

SPECIFIC CORTICAL AREAS

The cortical areas can be divided into three major divisions: primary motor projection areas, primary sensory reception areas, and association areas. Association areas comprise the majority of the cortex, making up approximately 86% of it.

The primary motor projection cortices are found in the frontal lobes on the precentral gyri, the bilateral cortical strips from which voluntary movement patterns are initiated. The motor strip serves as a source of descending motor pathways, projecting to lower levels of the nervous system.

The primary sensory reception areas register sensory impulses relayed from the periphery to the thalamus and upward to the cortex. The pathways from thalamus to cortex are called thalamic radiations. The primary sensory reception areas of the cortex are (1) the primary auditory cortex (areas 41 and 42), located in Heschl's gyrus in the temporal lobes; (2) the primary somatosensory cortex in the postcentral gyri of the parietal lobes (areas 1, 2, and 3); and (3) the primary visual cortex (area 17) in the occipital lobes.

PRIMARY MOTOR PROJECTION CORTEX

The primary motor projection cortex is known as the motor area, or motor strip. In Brodmann's system, it is area 4. The motor area is located on the anterior wall of the central sulcus and the adjacent precentral gyrus. Figure 2-6 shows the areas devoted to the motor control of the different parts of the body. Recall that this area allows contralateral motor control of the limbs. Some of the muscles of the oral mechanism have contralateral control, but many are bilaterally innervated. The inverted arrangement of motor control areas on the bilateral motor cortices reveals that cortical control for the muscles and functions of the speech mechanism is represented at the lower end of the motor area on the lateral wall of the cerebrum. The large areas given over to motor control of the oral mechanism contribute to the coordination of its rapid and precise movements during talking, singing, and changing facial expression.

Anterior to the motor area is the **premotor area** (area 6), considered a supplement to the primary motor projection cortex and related to the extrapyramidal system. If areas 4 and 6 are ablated, spasticity in the limbs results. A third motor area, discovered by Wilder G. Penfield, is found on the ventral surface of the precentral and postcentral gyri. It is called the **supplementary**, or **secondary**, **motor area**.

In more recent years the supplementary motor area has received considerable attention. One of its primary functions appears to be to work in conjunction with other structures in the control of sequential movements, and speech production is a prime example of sequential movement. Research is also finding support for the supplementary area's involvement in the timing of speech for fluent speech production.[6]

PRIMARY SOMATOSENSORY CORTEX

The primary somatosensory cortex (areas 1, 2, and 3) is on the postcentral gyrus and is a primary receptor of general bodily sensation. Thalamic radiations relay sensory data from skin, muscles, tendons, and joints of the body to the primary somatosensory cortex. Lesions of this cortex produce partial sensory loss (paresthesia); rarely does complete sensory loss (anesthesia) occur. A lesion causes numbness and tingling in the opposite side of the body. Widespread destructive lesions produce gross sensory loss with an inability to localize sensation.

PRIMARY AUDITORY RECEPTOR CORTEX

Heschl's gyrus (areas 41 and 42), as previously described, is the primary auditory receptor cortex. The area is found in each temporal lobe, but the left Heschl's area appears to be somewhat larger in most individuals. The significance of this neuroanatomic difference is not completely clear, but it may be related to language dominance.

PRIMARY VISUAL RECEPTOR CORTEX

The primary visual receptor cortex is in the occipital lobe along the calcarine fissure, which can be seen from the medial surface of the hemisphere and is not obvious on the outside of the brain. The area, 17 in the Brodmann scheme, is also known as the striate area. It receives fibers from the optic tract. Lesions of the optic pathways cause various degrees of blindness. This partial blindness is considered a visual field defect.

PRIMARY OLFACTORY RECEPTOR CORTEX

The cortical area that allows appreciation of smell is deep in the temporal lobe and is called the primary olfactory receptor cortex (area 28, medial surface). It includes an area called the uncus and the nearby parts of the parahippocampal gyri of the temporal lobe. The olfactory nerves, the end organs for smell, lie in a bony structure in the nose. The nerves end in the olfactory bulb, which is an extension of brain tissue in the nasal area. The bulbs are supported by an olfactory stalk. Destruction of the olfactory system causes anosmia, or lack of smell. Irritative lesions produce olfactory hallucinations or uncinate fits.

Association Cortex
Specific Association Areas

Cortical Motor Speech Association Areas. Surrounding the foot of the motor and premotor cortices are areas considered motor association areas. These areas are numbered 44, 45, 46, and 47 in the Brodmann system. They are called the opercular gyri. Areas 44 and 45 include the pars opercularis, the pars triangularis, and the pars orbitalis. Areas 44 and 45 in the left hemisphere are sometimes called the frontal operculum. Area 44 is known best as Broca's area. Although its function is controversial, Broca's area usually is associated with the formation of motor speech plans for oral expression. The cytoarchitecture of the area is similar in both right and left hemispheres, but traditional theory maintains that only the left is involved with verbal formulation. Regional cerebral blood flow and metabolic rate studies have suggested that right cortical areas may also be activated during some speech and language activities.

Sensory Association Areas. The sensory association areas, where elaboration of sensation occurs, can best be considered as extensions of the primary sensory receptor areas. They are also known as secondary association areas or unimodal association areas because only one type of sensory input is processed there. Their margins are necessarily vague, and what the exact functions of certain areas are is controversial. The sensory association areas are richly connected to the receptor areas by a host of association fibers, but these association fibers are often difficult to follow because of the vast number of relays in the cortical association system. Areas 5 and 7 in the parietal lobe are related to general somesthetic sensation. Areas 42 (part of Heschl's gyrus) and 22 (Wernicke's area) are related to language comprehension. Areas 18 and 19 in the occipital lobe are visual association areas, important for visual perception and for some visual reflexes such as visual fixation. Lesions in this area may cause visual hallucinatory symptoms.

The function of the sensory association areas is that of gnosis, or knowing. A deficit in the sensory association function is known as agnosia, a perceptual-cognitive deficit presumed to follow a destructive cerebral lesion; agnosia means lack of recognition. Lesions in auditory association areas affecting the appreciation of incoming sound produce language disorders. Areas surrounding Heschl's gyrus are involved in adding meaning to sound and providing comprehension of language. Lesions in area 42 destroy the ability to appreciate the meaning of sound, and lesions in area 22 compromise the ability to understand spoken language. Lesions of visual association areas may cause different types of visual agnosia in which the patient cannot, through the visual modality alone, recognize certain visual patterns (e.g., objects or faces).

Categories of Association Cortex. The cytoarchitecture of association cortex is different for different areas and determines what kind of neural information can be processed by those cells. Generally, the association areas adjacent to primary motor and sensory areas are unimodal; that is, only one type of information is processed by those cells. These association areas elaborate on the information received at the specific primary motor and sensory areas to which they are adjacent.

Further removed from the primary motor or sensory cortical areas, other types of association cortices are found, termed polymodal and supramodal. Polymodal is sometimes referred to as multimodal, and supramodal may be referred to as heteromodal in some texts.

Polymodal association areas are found somewhat close to the unimodal areas near the primary reception cortex. Polymodal association cortex is linked to processing of two or more sensory modalities. For example, polymodal association cortex, processing both auditory and visual information, can be found in the temporal lobe and in the occipital lobe. The parahippocampal gyrus receives input from all areas of the cerebral cortex, processing several types of sensory information.

The association areas add meaning and significance to the sensory or motor information received in the primary motor or sensory areas. The matching of present sensory information with past sensory information drawn from memory probably takes place in the polymodal association areas, which are linked to several sensory modalities. Motor association areas are sites where motor plans, programs, and commands are formulated with input from auditory and somatosensory processing, particularly touch, as well as other modalities.

Certain sensory association areas blend and mingle sensory information from several association areas to establish a higher level of cortical sensory information. This type of processing results in a complex level of awareness that is above and beyond mere recognition of sensory data. This level of sensory awareness is known as perception, which is defined as the mental process of becoming aware of or recognizing an object or idea. The processes are primarily cognitive rather than affective or conative, although all three aspects are manifested.[17]

For example, if someone places a door key in your hand in the dark, you must recognize its shape and judge its size, weight, texture, and metallic surface to match this information with memories and concepts of keys. This is called stereognostic perception. Only when you can identify your perception of the key can you name the key and relate its function if asked. The everyday sensory recognition of objects relies on complex sensory integration of multiple sensations enhanced by memory and conceptual knowledge of objects with similar qualities. This complex activity of knowing is called gnosis. Other common kinds of perception are such skills as depth perception and visual-spatial perception. Intuition can be thought of as a type of perception.

The highest level of processing is carried on in association areas best described as supramodal, meaning that these cortical areas are concerned with neural processing that is not directly linked to sensory or motor functions. This kind of association cortex and cortical function can be found primarily in the following areas:

- The prefrontal area, for higher executive function
- Perisylvian cortex, subserving language
- Limbic lobe, subserving emotion and motivation

The prefrontal cortex and the perisylvian cortical area and function were previously outlined and are discussed in depth in Chapter 9. The limbic lobe, its structures, and probable association functions are examined next. A summary of categories of the association cortex is provided in Box 2-2.

The Limbic System

Why Is This Important for Speech-Language Pathology?

Speech-language pathologists (SLPs) will encounter disorders that have caused dysfunction of deeper structures of the cerebral hemispheres. This is especially true with more diffuse brain damage caused by a traumatic brain injury. A critical cognitive skill, memory, is often affected with damage to these structures, resulting in major alterations to the treatment plan. Emotional processing is an important function of some of these structures and the client's emotional state also impacts the treatment plan and the success of therapy. The SLP should be familiar with these structures and their functions so that this may be anticipated in planning.

Cortical-Like Tissue

The associative function of the structures of the limbic system have been discussed and supported by Mesulam[11] and Benson.[2] They indicate that these areas of the brain are architecturally considered cortical areas, although not named as part of the cortex in most instances. As most other anatomists do, these authors include in their overviews of association cortex what Mesulam

---

BOX 2-2

Categories of the Association Cortex

Unimodal

- Only one type of information is processed by the cells in these areas
- Areas elaborate on information received at adjacent primary motor and sensory areas
- Information can be related to either motor or sensory input

Polymodal

- Found in close proximity to unimodal areas, near the primary reception cortex
- Linked to processing two or more kinds of sensory information (e.g., auditory and visual information)
- Matches present sensory information with past sensory information

Supramodal

- Highest level of processing
- Areas concerned with neural processing not linked directly with sensory or motor functions
- Found primarily in prefrontal area, perisylvian cortex, and limbic lobe

---

calls heteromodal cortex, which is composed of the six-layer formation accepted as cortical tissue. These associative areas include the supramodal cortex previously discussed. This cortex has the six-layer formation found in 90% of cortex, including the primary motor and sensory areas as well as the multimodal and supramodal association areas. The six-cell-layer cortex is called neocortex or isocortex.

Cortical regions with tissue composed of fewer than six cell layers are functionally associated with the limbic system and are classified as allocortex. Allocortex can also be broken down into different types or regions. Cortical structures with three to five cellular layers are classified as paleocortex, whereas structures with only three cellular layers are classified as archicortex.

Mesulam's and Benson's discussions of these other types of associative cortices focus on patterns formed by regions sharing common functions. Beyond the primary association areas and the secondary motor and sensory association areas previously discussed, neuroanatomists of this school point to the higher level associative functions of the more primitive cortex found deep to the neocortex and best seen on the medial surface of the brain (Fig. 2-11). The cytoarchitecture of these structures reveals a composition of primarily three layers, rather than six layers, with some structures showing transition between the six- and three-layer formation. Thus these structures are cortical-like in nature because true cortex has six layers.

Parahippocampal and Hippocampal Gyri

The parahippocampal gyrus (see Fig. 2-11) is a transitional architecture representing a six-layer formation laterally with a change to a three-layer formation more medially. Folded within the parahippocampal gyrus is the hippocampus. The hippocampal gyrus is actually part of the hippocampal formation, which is a curved, rolled-in-and-under area of cortex bulging into the floor of the temporal (inferior) horn of the lateral ventricle. The hippocampal formation consists of the dentate gyrus, hippocampal gyrus, and white matter, called fimbria, that issues from this area and eventually forms the crus (or leg) of the fornix. Traditionally included as part of the limbic system, most anatomists now separate these hippocampal structures from the limbic system because of their involvement in encoding new memories.[13] For the sake of discussion of anatomic location, the hippocampal formation will be discussed with the limbic system here.

Limbic and Paralimbic Structures

The limbic system or limbic lobe (see Fig. 2-11) was named by Pierre Paul Broca, who thought of it as the fifth lobe of the brain. It is occasionally referred to as Broca's lobe because of this. The "lobe" is on the medial surfaces of the two hemispheres. An archlike

pattern of cortex surrounding the nonconvoluted central portions of the brain can be observed on the medial surfaces of the hemispheres with the brainstem removed. This internal circular arch is called the limbic lobe (or limbic system or formation). The limbic system includes the oldest or most primitive cortex, the rhinencephalon, also called the "smell brain." The prefix *rhino* means "nose"; the functions of the old animal brain dealt primarily with the sense of olfaction, or smell. Because smell is a much more crucial sense for animals in their adaptation to the environment than it is to human beings, the old brain is relatively large in animals, and the cerebral hemispheres are less well developed.

The histologic makeup of the rest of the limbic system is phylogenetically old in relation to the cerebral hemispheres (neocortex) but not as old as the olfactory brain tissue. The limbic system structures have many connections among themselves as well as connections to the hypothalamus (see "Diencephalon" later in this chapter) and to neocortical structures. In the evolution of the human brain, the older parts have come under the direction of the newer cortical systems, creating a hierarchy. Autonomic and hormonal responses caused by hypothalamic action are under the direction of the limbic structures, which in turn are under the direction of the higher cortical structures. Through these connections, the limbic area helps shape behavioral reaction to sensory input through analysis, reaction, and remembrance of stimuli, situations, reactions, and

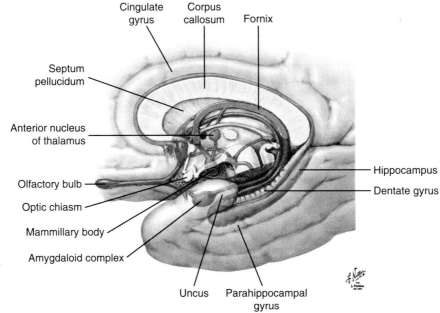

FIGURE **2-11**

The limbic system with limbic and paralimbic structures. (Netter illustrations from *www. netterimages.com* © Elsevier, Inc., All Rights Reserved.)

results.[12] Heimer[9] asserts that the anatomic and functional characteristics of some of the structures of this area are distinct enough to be considered apart from the others, and he questions the concept of a limbic system. For example, the amygdala is the key structure in emotional behavior and the hippocampus and related structures are of primary importance when discussing memory (see Chapter 9).

Mesulam[11] conceives of the limbic system as being formed by several smaller structures, including the subcallosal gyrus, cingulate gyrus, isthmus, hippocampal gyrus, and uncus. A medial view of the left hemisphere indicates some of these structures (see Fig. 2-11). The cingulate gyrus (gyrus cinguli) arches over the corpus callosum, beginning at the anterior subcallosal area and arching back to the junction with the parahippocampal gyrus. This juncture is called the isthmus. The *uncus* is the knob or hooklike area of the parahippocampal gyrus. Mesulam includes in the limbic system structures that are cortical-like in archetype. Cortical-like refers to the fact that their formations are part cortical and part subcortical nuclear in architecture. These structures are the amygdala (or amygdaloid body), substantia innominata, and septal area. They are formed by the simplest and most undifferentiated type of cortex in the forebrain.

A second associative area of cortex is composed of the paralimbic areas (see Fig. 2-11). Although some neuroanatomists include these areas as part of the limbic system rather than refer to them as paralimbic,[12] Mesulam[11] points out that gradual increases in complexity of the cortex can be found in these areas when compared with the previously mentioned limbic system formations. These structures form an uninterrupted girdle around the medial and basal aspects of the cerebral hemispheres. The paralimbic areas include the caudal orbitofrontal cortex, insula, temporal pole, parahippocampal gyrus (proper), and cingulate complex. The caudal orbitofrontal cortex includes Brodmann areas 10, 11, and 47[10] (see Fig. 2-5). The cingulate complex includes the tissue of the anterior cingulate and middle cingulate cortex. Studies of these areas have shown different functional connections for these anatomically close areas. Strong connections with limbic and autonomic functional areas have been traced for the anterior cingulate cortex. The middle cingulate cortex connections are primarily with cognitive processing and sensorimotor processing areas.[18]

The parahippocampal gyrus completes the C shape of the "limbic lobe." Most of the rostral part of the parahippocampal gyrus is occupied by an area known as the entorhinal area, which can be identified by its irregular surface (similar to an orange peel). The entorhinal cortex is closely related to the hippocampus.

If the premise is accepted that cortical functioning is hierarchical and a vast network of interrelated functional systems have different, but similar, neuroanatomic substrates, then the study of the functional systems (such as language, memory, emotion) and their disorders must be tempered with the knowledge that brain function is highly complex, with interdependent systems throughout, and only partially understood. While functional subunits of brain operations are studied, attempts to analyze and synthesize the integration of the neural systems that control human behavior continue at a rapid pace.

Other Structures of the Central Nervous System

Cell bodies of other structures are amassed into nuclei below the level of the cortex and appear gray in fresh dissection, although a large number of white matter tracts pass through these areas. The structures or areas of the CNS discussed in this section are the diencephalon (thalamus and related structures), basal ganglia, cerebellum, brainstem, and spinal cord.

Why Is This Important for Speech-Language Pathology?

The functions of the following structures are primarily associated with sensory and motor processing rather than information processing. Speech-language pathologists diagnose and treat a number of conditions in which information processing remains intact but sensory and/or motor systems are impaired affecting speech, voice, hearing, and swallowing. As discussion of these structures continues in this text, it also will be pointed out that connections with cortical and limbic areas that do contribute to cognitive and emotional processing are also found in these areas. Discussion of these important structures begins with the diencephalon and takes you down to the spinal cord.

Diencephalon

Buried deep within the cerebral hemispheres is a group of structures known collectively as the diencephalon (Fig. 2-12). This region is composed of the following four primary structures:

- Thalamus
- Hypothalamus
- Epithalamus
- Subthalamus

The pituitary gland is also considered part of the diencephalon.

Thalamus

The thalamus is located ventrally (toward the belly), and the hypothalamus is located dorsally (toward the back). The thalamus is a large, rounded structure consisting of gray matter. It is made up of two egglike masses that lie on either side of the third ventricle, one of the large openings in the brain through which cerebrospinal fluid flows. The posterior end of the thalamus expands in a large swelling, the pulvinar. Wilder G. Penfield, a famous twentieth-century neurosurgeon, was the first to ascribe special subcortical speech and language functions to this structure.

The thalamus integrates sensation in the nervous system. It brings together and organizes sensation from all the classic sensory systems except olfaction. Anatomists usually divide the thalamus into regions and discuss the important nuclei in a particular region. These nuclei act as thalamic relays, sending sensory information upward to sensory areas of the cerebral cortex. The to-and-fro sensory pathways between the thalamus and cerebral cortex are so numerous, and the two structures so interdependent, that assigning a sensory deficit to the thalamus versus the sensory cortical areas of the cerebrum is sometimes difficult. Relays from the cerebellar, limbic, and basal ganglia pathways are also found in the thalamus, subserving motor and autonomic functions as well. The thalamus in the left hemisphere may also play a role in speech and language (see Chapters 6 and 9).

Hypothalamus

The lower part of the lateral wall and the floor of the third ventricle make up the **hypothalamus** (see Fig. 2-12). Also on the floor of the third ventricle are two nipple-shaped protuberances called the mammillary bodies (see Fig. 2-11), containing nuclei important to hypothalamic function. The hypothalamus is a critical structure to autonomic and endocrine function (see Chapter 3). It controls several aspects of emotional behavior, such as rage and aggression, as well as escape behavior. In addition, it helps regulate body temperature, food and water intake, and sexual and sleep behavior. The hypothalamus exerts neural control over the pituitary gland, which releases hormones involved in many bodily functions.

Epithalamus and Subthalamus

The epithalamus is a small region of the diencephalon consisting of the pineal gland, habenular nuclei, and stria medullaris thalami. The pineal gland contains no true neurons, only glial cells. Through a complicated process involving the hormone melatonin, it participates in regulation of the body's circadian (24-hour) rhythms. The stria medullaris connects fibers from the habenular nuclei with the limbic system. The specific function of the habenular nuclei in human beings is unclear.

The **subthalamus** consists of a large subthalamic nucleus that is functionally considered a part of the basal ganglia, as discussed in the next section. The subthalamus also consists of a caudal area called the

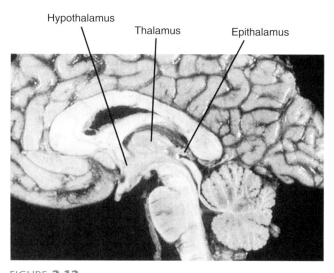

Hypothalamus   Thalamus   Epithalamus

FIGURE **2-12**

The structures of the diencephalon. (Modified from Lundy-Ekman, L. [2013]. *Neuroscience: Fundamentals for rehabilitation* [4th ed.; Fig. 1-12, p. 11] St. Louis: Saunders.)

zona incerta. Fibers from neurons in the zona incerta project to many areas, including the cerebral cortex, and may exert an inhibitory effect on the motor pathways.

Basal Ganglia

The **basal ganglia**, or basal nuclei as some texts use, are large masses of gray matter deep within the cerebrum, below its outer surface or cerebral cortex. The division of the structures known as basal ganglia has been confusing in the literature because various anatomists have categorized the structures differently. A review of current literature indicates that most neuroanatomists include the following structures as basal ganglia (or basal nuclei):

- Caudate nucleus
- Putamen
- Globus pallidus
- Substantia nigra
- Subthalamic nucleus

The putamen and globus pallidus are sometimes grouped and called the **lentiform** or **lenticular nucleus**. The caudate and the putamen grouped together are called the **striatum** (or neostriatum in some texts). These three main parts—caudate, putamen, and globus pallidus—when grouped together are referred to as the **corpus striatum**. Figure 2-13 illustrates the basal ganglia as seen in a coronal section with Figure 2-14 representing a medial view of the nuclei.

Squire et al.[16] also include nuclei that are not traditionally included as basal ganglia structures but which, they point out, are analogous to those traditionally discussed. This set of nuclei consists of the

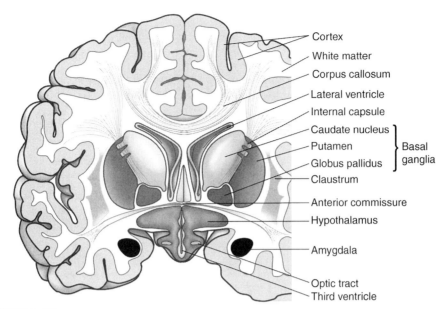

FIGURE **2-13**
The structures of the basal ganglia illustrated in a horizontal section through the cerebrum. (Redrawn from Guyton, A.C. [1991]. *Basic Neuroscience: Anatomy and Physiology* [2nd ed.]. Philadelphia: Saunders. In Drain, C. B. [2009]. *Perianesthesia nursing: A Critical Care Approach* [5th ed.]. St. Louis: Saunders.)

nucleus accumbens (see Fig. 2-14) and the olfactory tubercle, which they refer to collectively as the ventral striatum (as opposed to the neostriatum). Other nuclei corresponding to the globus pallidus are termed the ventral pallidum by these authors. These nuclei are mentioned because you may see these structures included in the basal ganglia in other texts or in articles. This text will not discuss the function of these structures as part of the basal ganglia. Research literature, particularly on motivation and emotion, may present you with more discussion on these structures and their relation to the basal ganglia.

The Striatum

Making up the striatum (or neostriatum) are the caudate nucleus and the putamen. The term *striatum* resulted from the striped appearance of the area due to the many axon fibers passing through it. The caudate nucleus is a C-shaped formation. Because of the C shape, a coronal view of the basal ganglia will reveal only a small portion of the caudate and may show part of the head, the body, or the tail. The head of the caudate is enlarged, and the structure tapers into a narrow tail. It lies close to the thalamus and adjacent to the wall of the lateral ventricle. The caudate is connected to the putamen by strands of gray matter but is separated physically from it by the anterior portion of the large white band of descending axons called the **internal capsule**. The striatum receives most of the excitatory input that

is provided to the basal ganglia from the cortex. In turn, the striatum transmits inhibitory impulses to the globus pallidus and the substantia nigra, using the neurotransmitter GABA (gamma-aminobutyric acid).

Substantia Nigra

The **substantia nigra** ("black substance" in Latin) is a long nucleus located in the midbrain but considered functionally a part of the basal ganglia because of its reciprocal connections with other brainstem nuclei. It consists of two components, the pars compacta and the pars reticulata, which have different connections and use different neurotransmitters. Degeneration of the pars compacta of the substantia nigra results in the reduction of the availability of the neurotransmitter dopamine. This lack of dopaminergic innervation to the striatum results in disorders associated with hypokinesia or reduced motor movements. Parkinson's disease is a result of reduced functioning of the substantia nigra.

Subthalamic Nucleus

The subthalamic nucleus is the large nucleus of the subthalamus, which is anatomically a part of the diencephalon. The subthalamic nucleus itself, however, is functionally considered a part of the basal ganglia. It receives projections from the globus pallidus, the cerebral cortex, the substantia nigra, and the reticular formation of the pons. The subthalamic nucleus sends projections to the globus pallidus and

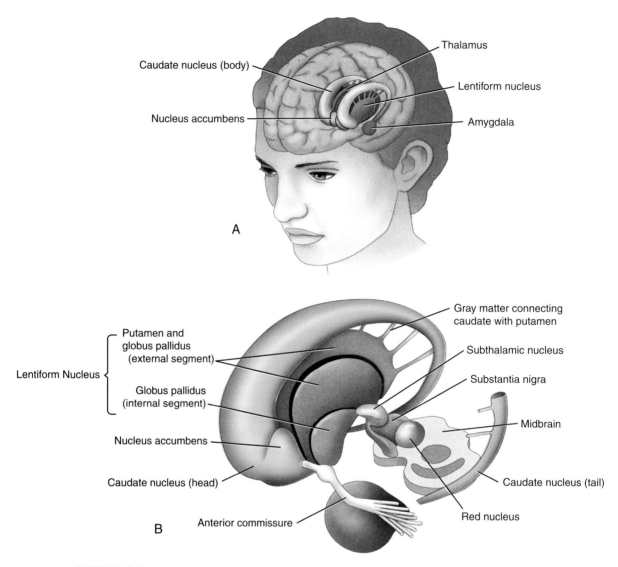

FIGURE 2-14
Basal ganglia: illustration of dissection allowing a medial view of the nuclei of the basal ganglia.

the substantia nigra. The neurons of this nucleus use an excitatory neurotransmitter, glutamate. The neurons of the subthalamic nucleus are, in normal motor function, usually inhibited from firing by thalamic override. When damage occurs to the basal ganglia pathways and subthalamic or related neurons are not inhibited from firing (i.e., disinhibition occurs), an abnormal increase in involuntary motor movements is seen. This results in disorders associated with hyperkinesia or increased motor movements, such as Huntington's chorea.

Input to the basal ganglia is generally considered to be through the caudate nucleus and the putamen, that is, the striatum. Received here are afferents from all four lobes of the cortex, thalamic nuclei, and part of the substantia nigra (the pars compacta). The output fibers of the basal ganglia usually are from the globus pallidus and another part of the substantia nigra (the pars reticulata). The output of these structures usually is projected to certain thalamic nuclei, the brainstem reticular formation, the superior colliculus, and cortical motor areas in the frontal lobe.

CEREBELLUM AND BRAINSTEM

The brain contains two other quickly identifiable parts in addition to the large cerebrum: the cerebellum and the brainstem. Both structures are extremely important to an understanding of the neurology of speech.

Cerebellum

The word cerebellum means "little brain," and the cerebellum is indeed a much smaller structure than the cerebrum, weighing approximately one eighth as much. The cerebellum is located at the rear of the brain, below and at the base of the cerebrum (Fig. 2-15). It resembles a small orange wedged in the juncture of the attachment of the spinal cord to the melon-shaped cerebrum. The cerebellum as it is understood is a relatively recent evolutionary addition to the nervous system. Initially it was found in fish and was almost solely related to vestibular functioning. As movement on four legs evolved, the cerebellum developed a rich mass of connections to the spinal cord. As upright posture developed and human beings continued to learn new physical skills, the cerebellum, particularly the posterior lobes, developed many linkages with the cerebrum.

Similar to the cerebrum, the cerebellum consists of two hemispheres. Each is primarily concerned with coordination of movements ipsilaterally, providing fine coordination of movement. The cerebellum plays an important role in postural stability and fixation, as well as in learning a novel motor act. Coordination of the extremely rapid and precise movements of normal articulation of speech also depends on intact cerebellar functioning. Damage may result in a particular type of motor speech disorder, one of the classic dysarthria types called ataxic dysarthria (see Chapter 8). The cerebellum may also have a role in cognitive processing with linkages found with the lateral prefrontal cortex. Cerebellar anatomy and function are discussed in Chapter 6.

Brainstem

The fourth major part of the brain is the brainstem (see Fig. 2-15). The brainstem and its subdivisions cannot be directly viewed unless the cerebral hemispheres are cut away to reveal the internal structures of the brain. The brainstem appears as a series of structures that seem to be an upward extension of the spinal cord, thrust upward into the brain between the cerebral hemispheres. Often the parts of the brainstem are depicted as extending as vertical segments one above the other, but the parts of the brainstem actually do not sit in a vertical plane. The upper structures are crowded together to fit within the cranium. In some texts and, in fact, previous editions of this text, the diencephalon is included as part of the brainstem. Contemporary neuroanatomy teaching separates the diencephalon and includes only three structures. Moving from the rostral (head) to the caudal (tail) segments, the three brainstem structures are as follows (Figs. 2-16 and 2-17):
- Mesencephalon (midbrain)
- Pons
- Medulla oblongata

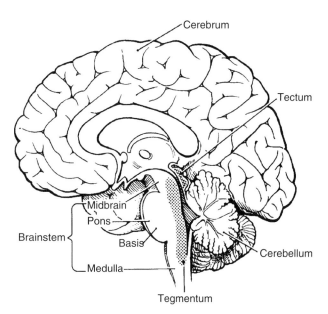

FIGURE **2-15**
Medial view of the right cerebrum, brainstem, and cerebellum.

Internal Anatomy of the Brainstem

The brainstem also has internal regions, with the presence and function of these regions depending on which structure is being examined. The midbrain has three regions: the tectum, tegmentum, and basis. The pons has a tegmentum and a basis. The tegmental regions are always found in the dorsal (posterior) aspect of the structures, whereas the basilar areas are on the anterior (ventral) aspect. The medulla is not considered to have a tegmental or basilar region as such, but the function of the areas of the medulla that are continuous with the tegmentum and the basis of the other two structures are quite similar in nature. Thus they are referred to as being contiguous areas with the tegmentum and the basilar regions of the midbrain and pons. Basically, the tegmental areas of the brainstem contain cranial nerve nuclei from which the axons of the cranial nerves exit the brain and become part of the PNS. The basilar areas of the brainstem structures all contain ascending and descending sensory and motor fibers. These regions are illustrated in Figures 2-15 and 2-17.

Midbrain. The midbrain (see Fig. 2-17), located immediately below the thalamus and hypothalamus, is also called the mesencephalon. The midbrain is the narrowest part of the brainstem and contains the tectum, or roof, one of the three longitudinal divisions of the brainstem. On the tectum are four swellings called colliculi ("little hills"): two inferior colliculi and two superior colliculi. The tectum and the four colliculi are known collectively as the corpus quadrigemina. The inferior colliculi serve as way stations in the central auditory nervous system, and the superior colliculi are way stations in the visual nervous system.

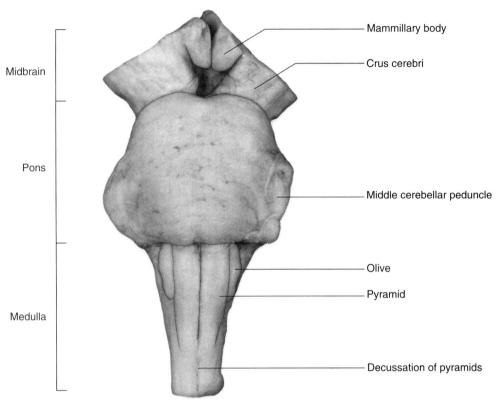

Mammillary body

Crus cerebri

Middle cerebellar peduncle

Olive

Pyramid

Decussation of pyramids

Midbrain

Pons

Medulla

FIGURE **2-16**
Ventral aspect of the brainstem. (From Crossman, A., & Neary, D. [2015]. *Neuroanatomy* [5th ed.]. Edinburgh: Churchill Livingstone.)

The crus cerebri is a massive fiber bundle found at the base of the midbrain. It includes fibers descending to the spine (corticospinal), the medulla (corticobulbar), and the pons (corticopontine). The tegmentum of the midbrain contains all the ascending and many of the descending systems of the spinal cord or lower brainstem. The term *cerebral peduncles* is often used interchangeably with the term *crus cerebri*, but according to Haines,[7] cerebral peduncle should be used to represent the area of the entire midbrain below the tectum. The base of the midbrain also contains the substantia nigra, which, as explained earlier, is a basal ganglia structure.

Pons. Just below the midbrain in the neuraxis is the **pons**, a massive rounded structure that serves in part as a connection to the hemispheres of the cerebellum (see Fig. 2-17). The connections to the cerebellum are made by a number of transverse fibers on the anterior surface of the pons, forming the cerebellar peduncles. The pons is aptly named; the Latin word for "bridge" is *pons*, and the pons is a bridge to the cerebellum. Several cranial nerves exit the brain from the pons, including three that are important to speech and hearing, cranial nerves V (trigeminal), VII (facial), and VIII (vestibulocochlear).

Medulla Oblongata. The **medulla oblongata** is the most caudal brainstem structure. Older terminology

identified it as the bulb. It is a rounded bulge that is an enlargement of the upper spinal cord (see Fig. 2-17). A median fissure (furrow) is present on the anterior surface. On either side of this fissure are landmark swellings called pyramids. The pyramids arise from the basilar pons and extend caudally to an area known as the pyramidal decussation. This area is formed by the decussation (crossing to the opposite side) of motor fibers traveling from the precentral gyrus in the frontal lobe to the spinal cord (corticospinal fibers of the pyramidal tract). Posterior to the pyramids are oval elevations, called olives, produced by the olivary nuclei. The olives are important way stations on the pathways of the auditory nervous system. The inferior cerebellar peduncles are also found on the medulla. The peduncles connect the cerebellum to the brainstem at the level of the medulla. The nuclei of several cranial nerves important to speech production can be found in the medulla, with their axons exiting the brain at this level. Because older terminology for the medulla was bulb, these motor fibers of cranial nerves that terminate in nuclei in brainstem structures are often referred to as corticobulbar fibers. These fibers are also sometimes referred to as corticonuclear fibers because their destination in the brainstem is the nuclei of the cranial nerves.

FIGURE **2-17**

Anterior (ventral; **A**), midsagittal (**B**), and posterior (dorsal; **C**) views of the brainstem, with cranial nerves referenced by Roman numerals. In **C**, the cerebellum is removed to expose the posterior surface of the brainstem and fourth ventricle. (Reprinted from Haines, D. [2006]. *Fundamental neuroscience* [3rd ed.]. Philadelphia: Churchill Livingstone.)

SPINAL CORD

Recall a mental image of the dissection of the nervous system. Looking at the brain, a long pigtail of flesh is visible hanging from its base; this is the spinal cord. It is normally found in an opening running through the center of the bony vertebral column. The spinal cord is strictly defined. It is caudal to the large opening at the base of the skull called the magnum foramen; the nervous tissue encased in the skull proper is the brain.

The spinal cord is divided into five regions. Each of these regions is named for a section of the 31 spinal vertebrae that surround the spinal cord itself. The regions of the cord are cervical, thoracic, lumbar, sacral, and coccygeal. The spinal cord does not extend the complete length of the vertebral column. In the adult it terminates at the level of the lower border of the first lumbar vertebra. In the child it is longer, ending at the upper border of the third lumbar vertebra. Figure 2-18 shows the segmental spinal nerve and the comparable vertebral levels.

A cross section of the spinal cord (Fig. 2-19) reveals an H-shaped mass of gray matter in the center of the spinal segment. As in other parts of the CNS, the gray matter contains neuronal and glial cell bodies, axons, and dendrites. Laminar organization is present in the gray matter, with 10 layers identified. Each layer is composed of neurons that respond to different sensory stimuli or innervate different muscle fibers.

The ventral, or anterior, portion of the cord mediates motor output. The anterior horn cell of the ventral gray matter is the point of synapse of the descending motor tracts (corticospinal) with the ventral roots of the spinal cord. The dorsal, or posterior, portion of the cord mediates sensory input coming into the spinal cord through the dorsal root of the spinal nerves.

Each lateral half of the spinal cord also has white matter columns: a dorsal or posterior column, a ventral or anterior column, and a lateral column. This white matter is composed of myelinated and unmyelinated nerve fibers as well as glial cells. The myelinated fibers form bundles or fasciculi that rapidly conduct nerve impulses that ascend or descend for varying distances. Bundles of white matter with a common function are called tracts. Major anatomic landmarks of a cross section of the spinal cord are shown in Figure 2-19. Refer often to this drawing when studying sensory and motor pathways.

Close inspection of the form and quantity of gray versus white matter reveals variations at the different levels of the spinal cord. The proportion of gray to white is

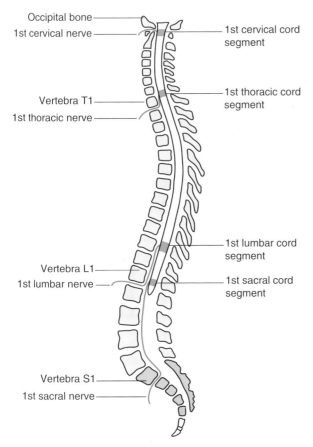

FIGURE **2-18**

Comparison of the level of the vertebral column and spinal cord. Spinal nerves C1-C7 emerge above the corresponding vertebrae, whereas the remaining nerves emerge below. (Reprinted from FitzGerald, M. J. T., & Folan-Curran, J. [2002]. *Clinical neuroanatomy and related neuroscience* [4th ed.]. Philadelphia: Saunders.)

greatest in the lumbar and cervical regions where the major motor and sensory neurons for the arms and legs are found. In the cervical regions the dorsal column (mediating sensory input) is somewhat narrow and the ventral column (mediating motor output) is broad and expansive. Both columns are broad and expansive in the lumbar region, and in the thoracic region both are narrow.

Combined with a careful sensory examination, testing of muscle functions can be most valuable to the physician in assessing the extent of a lesion. Most muscles are innervated by axons from several adjacent spinal roots. This peripheral nerve innervation pattern is discussed in Chapter 3.

Reflexes

Reflexes are subconscious automatic stimulus response mechanisms. The behavior of lower animals is primarily governed by reflexes. In human beings, reflexes are basic defense mechanisms to painful or potentially damaging sensory stimulation. If, for instance, you accidentally touch a hot stove, the sensation of pain does not need to be sent up the sensory tracts to the cortex. Motor commands from the cortex need not be sent down motor tracts to allow movement. The rapid response to noxious stimuli is processed quickly at the spinal level by a mechanism called the simple **reflex arc**. The reflex arc contains a receptor and an afferent neuron, which transmits an impulse along the peripheral nerve to the CNS, where the nerve synapses through an intercalated neuron with a lower motor or efferent neuron. From this point an impulse is sent to an efferent nerve, and then an efferent impulse passes outward in the nerve, which moves the effector (i.e., the muscle

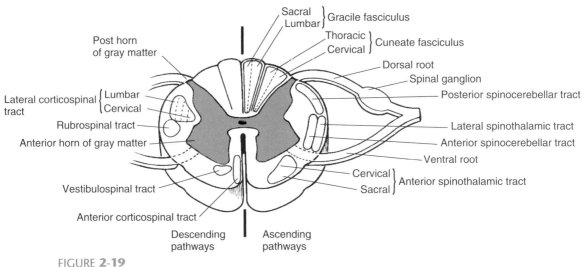

FIGURE **2-19**

Cross section of the spinal cord.

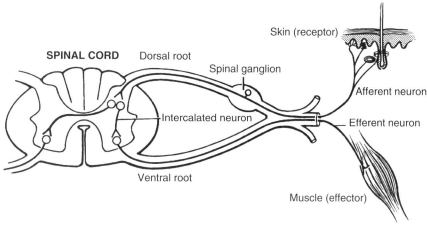

FIGURE **2-20**
A simple reflex arc.

or gland). A response is then elicited—you simply suddenly withdraw your finger (see Fig. 2-20).

There are several types of reflexes: superficial or skin reflexes, deep tendon or myotactic reflexes, visceral reflexes, and pathologic reflexes. Reflexes occur at different levels in the nervous system: spinal level, bulbar level, midbrain level, and cerebellar level. Reflex assessment is a vital tool for assessing the intactness of various sensory motor systems. Reflexes are discussed in more detail in Chapters 6 and 11.

Synopsis of Clinical Information and Applications for the Speech-Language Pathologist

- The uniqueness of Broca's area, a specialized vocal tract, and the expanse of information and communication processing areas give human beings their exceptional ability to communicate.
- The human communication nervous system consists of the CNS and the PNS. The autonomic nervous system is subsumed under both.
- Neurons are composed of organelles, which are composed of molecules. The four major classes of molecules in cells are lipids, proteins, carbohydrates, and nucleic acid.
- A bilipid layer surrounds the cell body of a neuron. The neuron has one axon, which typically carries impulses away from the cell body and may have many dendrites that carry information toward the cell body.
- Retrograde transport up the axon mediates movement of trophic substances, which provide nourishment for the cell.
- Astrocytes, oligodendrocytes, microglia, and ependyma cells are the main types of neuroglial cells. Each has its own specific purpose, primarily providing the structural support and environmental maintenance for the work of the neurons. For example, after cerebral injury, microglia clean up the debris caused by cellular deterioration.

- Gray-appearing areas of the brain contain the nuclei of cell bodies. White-appearing areas signal the presence of myelinated fiber tracts.
- The cortex is organized into six horizontal layers. The most recent (phylogenetically) cortical tissue is called neocortex. Cortical-like tissue with five to three layers is found in paralimbic and limbic system structures.
- The brain is divided into two hemispheres, left and right, with communication between the two primarily occurring through the commissural fiber pathway called the corpus callosum. In most people the left hemisphere is the dominant hemisphere for language.
- Gyri (elevations) and sulci (depressions) on the lateral and medial surfaces of the brain provide important landmarks for delineating the four lobes: frontal, temporal, parietal, and occipital. Particular types of language and other types of neurobehavioral disorders may result from developmental interruption or acquired injury to these areas.
- Important functional areas located in the frontal lobe are primary motor cortex, premotor cortex, supplementary motor area, Broca's area, and the prefrontal association cortex.
- Important functional areas in the temporal lobes are Heschl's gyrus (primary auditory cortex) and Wernicke's area.

Continued

Synopsis of Clinical Information and Applications for the Speech-Language Pathologist—cont'd

- Important functional areas of the parietal lobe are the primary sensory cortex, angular gyrus, and supramarginal gyrus.
- Important functional areas in the occipital lobes are the primary visual cortex and visual association cortex.
- The insula is an older area of cortex located deep to the sylvian fissure. It may have a role in motor programming for speech.
- The perisylvian area in the dominant hemisphere is the major area for understanding and producing language.
- Cerebral connections are made by projection fibers (to distant structures), association fibers (intrahemispheric), and commissural fibers (interhemispheric).
- Approximately 86% of cortex is categorized as association cortex. Some association areas are unimodal (process only one type of information) and some are polymodal (processing two or more types of information). The highest level of processing is carried on in supramodal association areas, which are not associated with any particular type of information. The prefrontal association area, perisylvian area, and the limbic areas have supramodal capability.
- Allocortex is composed of fewer than six layers, is inferior to the cortical mantle, and can be found in paralimbic and limbic system structures. Some of the limbic system structures are the rhinencephalon, cingulate gyrus, isthmus, hippocampal gyrus, and uncus. Paralimbic structures include the temporal pole, parahippocampal gyrus, and the cingulate complex. These paralimbic and limbic areas are primarily involved with emotion and memory.
- The diencephalon is composed of the thalamus, hypothalamus, epithalamus, and subthalamus, as well as the pituitary gland. The thalamus is the main relay structure of the brain. The hypothalamus is concerned with autonomic and endocrine functions.
- The brainstem consists of three divisions: midbrain, pons, and medulla. The tectum, tegmentum, and basis are longitudinal divisions of the three structures. The brainstem contains the nuclei of most of the cranial nerves, which control the sensory input and motor output of the oral and facial musculature.
- The basal ganglia or basal nuclei are groups of subcortical nuclei found deep within the brain. The structures of the basal ganglia are the caudate nucleus, putamen, globus pallidus, and substantia nigra. These function in regulation and control of motor movement, muscle tone, and planning for movement. Damage may result in hypokinesia or hyperkinesia and characteristic motor speech disorders.
- The cerebellum has two hemispheres and is located at the base of the cerebrum, connected through peduncles primarily to the pons. It plays an important part in postural stability and fixation and in learning a novel motor act. A specific motor speech disorder may follow damage to the cerebellum.
- The spinal cord is divided into five regions, each named for a section of the spinal vertebrae surrounding the cord: cervical, thoracic, lumbar, sacral, and coccygeal.
- The center of the spinal cord consists of gray matter. The ventral portion contains motor nuclei, and the anterior contains horn cells. The dorsal part mediates sensation through the dorsal nuclei. White matter tracts ascend from and descend to the spinal cord, mediating motor output and sensation to the limbs and trunk.

REFERENCES

1. Azevedo, F. A., Carvalho, L. R., Grinberg, L. T., Farfel, J. M., Ferretti, R. E., Leite, R. E., et al. (2009). Equal numbers of neuronal and non-neuronal cells make the human brain an isometrically scaled-up primate brain. *The Journal of Comparative Neurology, 513*, 532–541.
2. Benson, D. F. (1994). *The neurology of thinking.* New York: Oxford University Press.
3. Broca, P. (1861). Remarques sur le siège de la faculté du langage articulé suivis d'une observation d'aphemie. *Bulletin de la Société d'Anatomie, 6*, 330–364.
4. Cain, M., Damman, H., Lue, R. A., & Yoon, C. K. (2006). *Discover biology* (3rd ed.). New York: W. W. Norton; Sunderland, MA: Sinauer Associates.
5. Catani, M., & Mesalum, M. (2008). The arcuate fasciculus and the disconnection theme in language and aphasia. *Cortex, 44*, 953–961.
6. Etchell, A. C., Johnson, B. W., & Sowman, P. F. (2014). Behavioral and multimodal neuroimaging evidence for a deficit in brain timing networks in stuttering: a hypothesis and theory. *Frontiers in Neuroscience, 8*, 1–10. http://dx.doi.org/10.3389/fnhum.2014.00467.
7. Haines, D. (2006). *Fundamental neuroscience for basic and clinical applications* (3rd ed.). Philadelphia: Churchill Livingstone.
8. Hanani, M. (2010). Satellite glial cells: More than just "rings around the neuron." *Neuron Glia Biology, 6*, 1–2.
9. Heimer, L. (1995). *The human brain and spinal cord: Functional neuroanatomy and dissection guide* (2nd ed.). New York: Springer-Verlag.
10. Kringelbach, M. L. (2005). The orbitofrontal cortex: Linking reward to hedonic experience. *Nature Reviews Neuroscience, 6*, 691–702.

11. Mesulam, M. M. (1985). *Principles of behavioral neurology.* Boston: F. A. Davis.

12. Mosenthal, W. T. (1995). *A textbook of neuroanatomy with atlas and dissection guide.* New York: Parthenon Publishing Group.

13. Nadeau, S. E., Ferguson, T. S., Valenstein, E., Vierck, C. J., Petruska, J. C., Streit, W. J., & Ritz, L. A. (2005). *Medical neuroscience.* Philadelphia: Saunders.

14. Nadich, T. P., Krayenbuhl, N., Kollias, S., Bou-Haidar, Bluestone, A. Y., & Carpenter, D. M. (2010). White matter. In T. P. Nadich, M. Castillo, S. Cha, & J. G. Smirniotopoulos (Eds.), *Imaging of the brain.* Philadelphia: Elsevier Saunders.

15. Sperry, R. W., Gazzaniga, M. S., & Bogen, J. E. (1969). Interhemispheric relationships: The neocortical commissures; syndromes of hemispheric disconnection. In P. J. Vinken, & G. W. Bruyn (Eds.), *Handbook of clinical neurology* (Vol. 4). North Holland: Amsterdam.

16. Squire, L. R., Berg, D., Bloom, F. E., du Lac, S., Ghosh, A., & Spitzer, N. C. (2013). *Fundamental neuroscience* (4th ed.). Waltham, MA: Elsevier Academic Press.

17. *Stedman's Medical Dictionary for the Health Professions and Nursing* (7th ed.) (2011). Philadelphia: Lippincott Williams and Wilkins.

18. Stevens, F. L., Hurley, R. A., & Taber, K. H. (2011). Anterior cingulate cortex: Unique role in cognition and emotion. *Journal of Neuropsychiatry and Clinical Neuroscience, 23,* 121–125.

19. Taber, K. H., & Hurley, R. A. (2008). Astroglia: Not just glue. *Journal of Neuropsychiatry and Clinical Neuroscience, 20*(2), iv–129.

20. University of Leeds. (2010, May 25). "Nature's batteries" may have helped power early lifeforms. *Science Daily.* Retrieved from http://www.sciencedaily.com/releases/2010/05/100525094906.htm.

21. Von Der Heide, R. J., Skipper, L. M., Klobusicky, E., & Olson, I. R. (2013). Dissecting the uncinate fasciculus: Disorders, controversies and a hypothesis. *Brain, 136*(Pt 6), 1692–1707. http://dx.doi.org/10.1093/brain/awt094.

22. Verkhratsky, A., Rodriguez, J. J., & Parpura, V. (2013). Astroglia in neurological diseases. *Future Neurology, 8,* 149–158.

23. Wallman, J. (1992). *Aping language.* New York: Cambridge University Press.

3

Organization of the Nervous System II

The charm of neurology . . . lies in the way it forces us into daily contact with principles. A knowledge of the structure and function of the nervous system is necessary to explain the simplest phenomena of disease, and it can only be attained by thinking scientifically.

Henry Head

KEY TERMS

afferent
afferent fibers
anterior (ventral)
  horn cells
aqueduct of Sylvius
arachnoid
  granulations
arachnoid mater
autonomic nervous
  system
bilateral
Broca's (expressive)
  aphasia
cerebrospinal fluid
  (CSF)
choroid plexus
circle of Willis
constructional
  disturbances
contralateral
cranial nerves
diaphragma sella
dura mater
efferent fibers
encephalitis
enteric nervous
  system
falx cerebelli
falx cerebri
foramen
foramina
hemorrhage
homeostasis

internal carotid
  arteries
intervertebral
  foramina
ipsilateral
ischemia
lesion
meninges
motor fibers
nucleus solitarius
parasympathetic
  divisions
peripheral nervous
  system (PNS)
phrenic nerves
pia mater
postganglionic
preganglionic
sensory fibers
septa
somites
spinal peripheral
  nerves
subarachnoid space
sympathetic divisions
tentorium cerebelli
unilateral
venous sinuses
ventricular system
vertebral artery
Wernicke's
  (receptive) aphasia
x-ray

CHAPTER OUTLINE

Peripheral Nervous System
  Spinal Nerves
  Cranial Nerves
Autonomic Nervous System
Protection and Nourishment of the Brain
  Meninges
  Ventricular System
  Cerebrospinal Fluid
  Blood Supply of the Brain
General Principles of Neurologic Organization
  Contralateral Motor Control
  Ipsilateral Motor Control
  Bilateral Speech Motor Control
  Unilateral Language Mechanisms
  Scheme of Cortical Organization
Neurodiagnostic Studies in Speech and Language
  Static Brain Imaging
  Dynamic or Functional Brain Imaging
  Measures of Neural Connectivity
  Measures of Timing of Neural Activity
  Vascular Imaging
  Transcranial Doppler
  Cerebral Angiography and Magnetic Resonance
    Angiography
  Summary of Neuroimaging
  Overview of the Human Communication Nervous
    System
Appendix 3-1

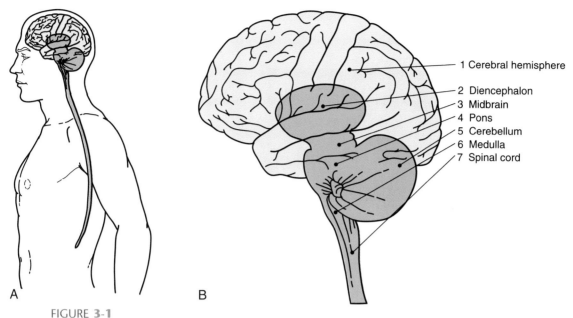

FIGURE **3-1**

A, Location of the central nervous system (CNS) in the body. **B,** Seven major divisions of the CNS: (1) cerebral hemisphere, (2) diencephalon, (3) midbrain, (4) pons, (5) cerebellum, (6) medulla, and (7) spinal cord. The midbrain, pons, and medulla comprise the brainstem. (Reprinted from Martin, J. H. [1996]. *Neuroanatomy text and atlas* [2nd ed.]. New York: McGraw-Hill.)

The central nervous system (CNS) with its vast network of neurons and neural connections is the controlling influence in the human communication nervous system. Glial cells reside within the CNS and provide structure and metabolic support for the neurons. tThe CNS, however, would not be functional, or necessary, without the lower level structures reviewed in this chapter. The nervous system consists of separate peripheral and central components organized into two parts—not independent from each other, but interdependent on each other. This chapter outlines the functions of the peripheral nervous system that allow this interdependence with the CNS (Fig. 3-1).

Peripheral Nervous System

The **peripheral nervous system (PNS)** includes (1) the cranial nerves with their roots and rami (branches), (2) the peripheral (spinal) nerves, and (3) the peripheral parts of the autonomic nervous system. The peripheral ganglia are groups of nerve cell bodies located outside the CNS forming an enlargement on a nerve or on two or more nerves at their junction. They are primarily sensory in nature, although motor ganglia are found particularly in the autonomic nervous system.

The cranial nerves exit from the neuraxis at various levels of the brainstem and the uppermost part of the spinal cord. When we use the term *peripheral nerves*, we are typically referring to the spinal nerves plus their branches.

Cranial nerves V (the trigeminal nerve), VII (the facial nerve), IX (the glossopharyngeal nerve), and X (the vagus nerve) have dedicated sensory ganglia originating from the neural crest during embryonic development. They contain pseudounipolar cell bodies. These sensory ganglia are classified as the trigeminal or semilunar ganglion (cranial nerve V); the geniculate ganglion of cranial nerve VII; the superior and inferior ganglia of cranial nerve IX, or the glossopharyngeal nerve; and the jugular and nodose ganglia of cranial nerve X, or the vagus nerve. The jugular and nodose ganglia are often referred to as the superior and inferior ganglia of the vagus nerve. Cranial nerve VIII, the vestibulocochlear nerve, primarily arises from the otic placodes. Figure 3-2 illustrates the cranial nerve nuclei and their juxtaposition within the brainstem.

SPINAL NERVES

Spinal peripheral nerves are described as mixed nerves, meaning they carry both sensory and motor fibers. Each spinal nerve is connected to the spinal cord by two roots: the anterior root and the posterior root. The anterior root of the spinal nerve consists of bundles of nerve fibers that transmit nerve impulses away from the CNS. These nerve fibers are called **efferent fibers**.

FIGURE **3-2**
An interior (ventral) view of the brainstem with particular emphasis on cranial nerves.
(Reprinted from Haines, D. [2006]. *Fundamental neuroscience* [3rd ed.]. Philadelphia:
Churchill Livingstone.)

Efferent fibers that go to the muscles and make them contract are also called **motor fibers**. The motor fibers of the spinal nerves originate from a group of cells or motor nuclei in the spinal cord called the **anterior (ventral) horn cells**. The anterior horn cells are the point of synapse, or connection, with the spinal nerves as they leave the neuraxis. When nerve impulses have left the neuraxis, they have reached what the great British neurophysiologist Charles Sherrington (1857-1952) called the *final common pathway*, or the terminal route of all neural impulses acting on the muscles.

The posterior root of the spinal nerve consists of **afferent fibers** that carry information about the sensations of touch, pain, temperature, and vibration into the CNS via the spinal cord. They are also called **sensory**

fibers. The cell bodies of the sensory fibers are a swelling on the posterior root of the spinal nerve called the posterior root ganglion.

The motor and sensory roots leave and enter the spinal cord at the **intervertebral foramina**, where the roots unite to form a spinal nerve. At this point the motor and sensory fibers mix together.

Clinical principles have been developed based on the organization of the spinal roots that can be used when damage occurs to the spinal cord or spinal nerves. First, recall that a generalization can be made that the anterior, or ventral, half of the spinal cord is devoted to motor or efferent activity, and the posterior, or dorsal, half is devoted to sensory or **afferent** activity. Which motor and sensory activities are impaired depends on the specific site

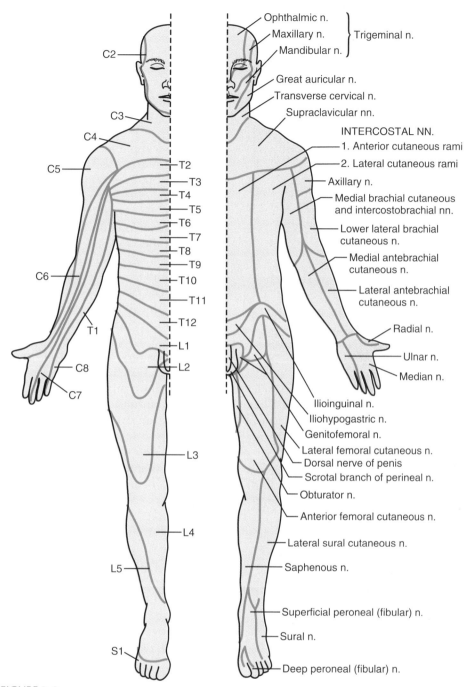

FIGURE **3-3**

Dermatomal patterns *(left)* and peripheral nerve fields *(right)*. (Modified from Gilman, S., & Newman, S. W. [2003]. *Manter and Gatz's essentials of clinical neuroanatomy and neurophysiology.* [10th ed.]. Philadelphia: F. A. Davis.)

of lesion in the spinal cord. A lesion, or damaged area, impairs motor and/or sensory activities at and below that cord level depending on the specific site of the lesion and the particular tracks interrupted. Naturally, large lesions in the spinal cord impair both sensory and motor functions.

As discussed later in this text, in early embryologic development, paired structures called somites are formed on the embryo. These somites differentiate into nonneural tissue (e.g., muscle, bone, and connective tissue). This somitic differentiation results in segmentally distributed zones called dermatomes. The dermatome region of each somite gives rise to a myotome, which is a muscle-forming body, and a skin plate, which is involved in formation of dermal tissue. The sensory component of each spinal nerve is distributed to a dermatome. Figure 3-3 shows the segmental distribution of cutaneous

Myotome Distributions of the Upper and Lower Extremity

C1/C2: neck flexion/extension
C3: neck lateral flexion
C4: shoulder elevation
C5: shoulder abduction
C6: elbow flexion/wrist extension
C7: elbow extension/wrist flexion
C8: finger flexion
T1: finger abduction
L2: hip flexion
L3: knee extension
L4: ankle dorsiflexion
L5: great toe extension
S1: ankle plantar flexion/ankle eversion/hip extension
S2: knee flexion
S3-S4: perineal reflex

(From Magee, D. J. [2009]. *Orthopaedic physical assessment* [4th ed., pp. 467-566]. St. Louis: Elsevier.)

innervation, showing on the left side of the figure which area of skin is supplied by which spinal nerve. The peripheral nerve field illustration on the right refers to an area of skin that is supplied by a particular peripheral nerve in that spinal nerve's distribution. Myotomes generally follow the same distribution as the dermatome, although there is more overlap of control. Box 3-1 lists the general myotome distribution for muscle innervation of upper and lower limbs by spinal nerves.

If there is a high spinal cord injury or lesion at the level of the cervical vertebrae, speech production may be affected because the respiratory muscles are controlled by spinal nerves exiting from the intervertebral foramina of the cervical and thoracic regions. The **phrenic nerves**, which supply motor signals to the diaphragm, originate mainly from C4, but contributions are also from C3 and C5. If respiration is stopped, death may follow with a lesion above the third, fourth, and fifth cervical nerves. Spinal cord injuries involving the caudal portion of the cord do not affect speech production but are of interest to the speech-language pathologist, who may work with spinal cord–injured patients on language or other related problems. These injuries are instructive in understanding the effect of lesions at various levels of the nervous system. Injuries in the spinal cord may produce partial or complete loss of function at the level of the lesion. Function is also completely or partially impaired below the level of the lesion. Spinal cord injuries must be considered very serious because they impair functions beyond those directly controlled at the lesion point.

CRANIAL NERVES

The **cranial nerves**, in contrast to the spinal nerves, are of more significance to the speech pathologist because most of the cranial nerves have some relation to the speech, language, and hearing process and seven of the 12 nerves are directly related to speech production and hearing.

On dissection, the 12 pairs of cranial nerves look like thin, gray-white cords. They consist of nerve fiber bundles surrounded by connective tissue. Like the spinal nerves, they are relatively unprotected and may be damaged by trauma. The cranial nerves leave the brain and pass through foramina of the skull to reach the sense organs or muscles of the head and neck with which they are associated. Some are associated with special senses such as vision, olfaction, and hearing. Cranial nerves innervate the muscles of the jaw, face, pharynx, larynx, tongue, and neck.

Unlike the spinal nerves, which attach to the cord at regular intervals, the cranial nerves are attached to the brain at irregular intervals. They do not all have dorsal (sensory) and ventral (motor) roots. Some have motor functions, some have sensory functions, and some have mixed functions. Their origin, distribution, brain and brainstem connections, functions, and evolution are complicated. (The cranial nerves are discussed in detail in Chapter 7.) They are traditionally designated by Roman numerals: cranial nerve I, olfactory; cranial nerve II, optic; cranial nerve III, oculomotor; cranial nerve IV, trochlear; cranial nerve V, trigeminal; cranial nerve VI, abducens; cranial nerve VII, facial; cranial nerve VIII, acoustic-vestibular; cranial nerve IX, glossopharyngeal; cranial nerve X, vagus; cranial nerve XI, spinal accessory; and cranial nerve XII, hypoglossal.

The cranial nerves from the brainstem are explicitly illustrated in Figure 3-2 and further outlined in Figure 3-4 regarding their location in the anterior (ventral) view and the anterolateral (ventrolateral) view of the brainstem.

Autonomic Nervous System

The innervation of involuntary structures such as the heart, smooth muscles, and glands is accomplished through the **autonomic nervous system**. Although this system has primarily indirect effects on speech, language, and hearing, the speech-language pathology and audiology student must be familiar with its contribution to total body function to understand how involuntary but vital functions such as hormonal secretions, visual reflexes, and blood pressure are controlled within the nervous system.

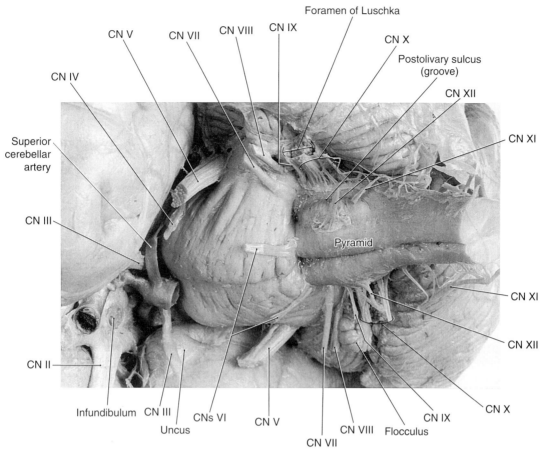

FIGURE **3-4**

An anterolateral (ventrolateral) view of the brainstem with special emphasis on cranial nerves. Note the position and relations of the foramen of Luschka. (Reprinted from Haines, D. [2006]. *Fundamental neuroscience* [3rd ed.]. Philadelphia: Churchill Livingstone.)

The autonomic nervous system is distributed throughout both the CNS and the PNS. The **enteric nervous system**, which is formed by neuronal plexus in the gastrointestinal tract, is considered a division of the autonomic nervous system. Enteric functioning has a direct effect on the deglutition and digestion of food.

Aside from the enteric system that deals directly with swallowing and digestion, the major divisions of the autonomic nervous system are the **sympathetic** and **parasympathetic divisions**, which have almost antagonistic functions. The sympathetic system is the body's alerting system, sometimes referred to as the fight-or-flight system. This part of the autonomic nervous system is responsible for such preparatory measures as accelerating the heart rate, causing constriction of the peripheral blood vessels, raising the blood pressure, and redistributing the blood so that it leaves the skin and intestines to be used in the brain, heart, and skeletal muscles if needed. It serves to raise the eyelids and dilate the pupils. The sympathetic part also decreases

peristalsis (the propelling contractions of the intestine) and closes the sphincters.

The parasympathetic part of the autonomic nervous system has an almost opposite calming effect on bodily function. It serves to conserve and restore energy by slowing the heart rate, increasing intestinal peristalsis, and opening the sphincters. As a result of parasympathetic action, other functions, such as increased salivation and increased secretion of the glands of the gastrointestinal tract, may take place.

The autonomic nervous system is composed of both efferent (conducting away from the CNS) and afferent (conducting toward the CNS) nerve fibers. Several similarities and differences exist between the neural control of skeletal muscle and visceral effectors such as smooth muscle. Lower motor neurons function as the final common pathway linking the CNS to skeletal muscle fibers. Similarly, the sympathetic and parasympathetic outflows serve as the final, but often dual, common neural pathway from the CNS to visceral effectors. However, unlike the somatic nervous system, the peripheral visceral motor pathway consists of two neurons. The first is the **preganglionic** neuron, which has its cell body in either the brainstem or the spinal cord. Its axons project as a thinly myelinated preganglionic fiber to an autonomic ganglion. The second, the **postganglionic** neuron, has its cell body in the ganglion and sends unmyelinated axon (postganglionic fiber) to visceral effector cells such as smooth muscle. Typically, parasympathetic ganglia are close to the effector tissue and sympathetic ganglia are close to the CNS. Consequently, parasympathetic pathways typically have long preganglionic fibers and short postganglionic fibers, whereas sympathetic pathways more often have short preganglionic and long postganglionic fibers.

The autonomic system also provides neural control of smooth muscle, cardiac muscle, glandular secretory cells, or a combination of these. For example, the gut wall is composed of smooth muscle and glandular epithelium. The sympathetic and parasympathetic systems have overlapping and, as stated previously, antagonistic influences on those viscera located in body cavities and on some structures of the head such as the iris. Visceral targets are also present in the body wall and limbs. These are found in skeletal muscle (blood vessels) and in the skin (blood vessels and sweat glands). Visceral structures of the body wall and extremities are generally regulated by the sympathetic division alone. Thus the sympathetic outflow has a global distribution in that it innervates visceral structures in all parts of the body, whereas the parasympathetic outflow serves only the head and body cavities.

Rarely is autonomic activity solely sympathetic or parasympathetic. Both parts work together in the autonomic nervous system along with the endocrine system to maintain the stability of the body's internal environment or **homeostasis**. The endocrine system is a group of glands and other structures that release internal secretions called hormones into the circulatory system. These hormones influence metabolism and other body processes. The endocrine system includes such organs as the pancreas, pineal gland, pituitary gland, gonads, thyroid, and adrenal glands. These work more slowly than the autonomic nervous system.

The integration of the autonomic activity with endocrine and somatic responses, allowing homeostasis to be maintained, is regulated by the hypothalamus. Evidence exists for a network of central neuronal circuits that includes the hypothalamus and the insula, the amygdala, and an area in the midbrain called the periaqueductal gray matter. These structures receive input from the **nucleus solitarius**, a prominent nucleus of the medulla that receives input from all visceral organs. Input is also received from other nuclei in the brainstem and spinal cord. This network is referred to as the central autonomic network and is probably responsible for adjustments to basic cardiovascular and respiratory functions as they relate to a range of body activities, such as food intake, emotional behavior, and mental activity.[13]

As stated earlier, the autonomic nervous system is of importance to the speech-language pathologist because of its indirect effect on communication functioning. A good example of the power of the autonomic nervous system is the sweaty palms, dry mouth, blushing, and upset stomach some people experience before delivering a speech. Those indirect effects may make a great deal of difference in how well one communicates.

Protection and Nourishment of the Brain

The brain and the spinal cord, which make up part of the CNS, PNS, and autonomic nervous system and house most of their mechanisms, must be protected and nourished to continue to function. Following is a discussion of the protection and nourishment of these structures.

MENINGES

The spinal cord and brain are the major coordinating and integrating structures for all physical and mental activities of the body and fortunately are well protected. The brain and spinal cord are covered by layers of tissue called the **meninges**. Within certain layers of these meninges is a cushioning layer of fluid called cerebrospinal fluid. The meninges are composed of three membranes; moving from the outermost to the innermost covering, they are known as the **dura mater** ("tough mother" in Latin), the **arachnoid mater**, and the **pia mater**.

The dura mater of the spinal cord is continuous with that of the brain through the opening in the skull called the **foramen** magnum. It consists of two layers that are closely united except where, in certain spots, they separate. In some parts of the dura mater of the brain they separate to form the **venous sinuses** (Fig. 3-5). In other parts of the brain, the inner layer also separates from the outer layer to reflect inward and form partitions, described as complex folds that divide the contents of the cranial cavity into different cerebral subdivisions. These infoldings or **septa** of the dura join with those formed in the opposite hemisphere to create three different double-layered partitions: the falx cerebri, the tentorium cerebelli, and the falx cerebelli (Fig. 3-6).

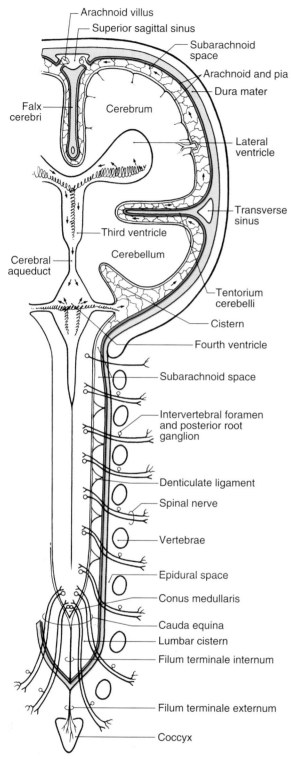

FIGURE **3-5**
The relation of the meninges to the brain and spinal cord and to their surrounding bony structures. The dura is represented in light green, the arachnoid in dark green. (Reprinted from Haines, D. E. [2000]. *Neuroanatomy: An atlas of structures, sections, and systems* [5th ed.]. Baltimore: Lippincott Williams & Wilkins.)

The falx cerebri develops first as two portions that become a single continuous structure later. It reflects downward between the hemispheres, attaching anteriorly and laterally to points on the skull and posteriorly to another partition, the tentorium cerebelli (also known simply as the tentorium). The falx cerebelli is located below the tentorium cerebelli on the middle of the occipital bone. This small dural infolding extends into the space between the cerebellar hemispheres, attaching to the occipital crest of the skull and the posterior portion of the tentorium. Part of it encloses the occipital venous sinuses. The tentorium cerebelli is the second largest of the dural folds. It attaches to bony walls of the skull in the temporal, occipital, and parietal regions. The tentorium cerebelli is the infolding found between the cerebral hemispheres above and the cerebellar hemispheres below. It is only found in mammals and birds, being absent in fish, amphibians, and reptiles.[11] There is another very small infolding of the dura, the diaphragma sella, which forms the roof of the sella turcica, the structure that encloses the pituitary gland. There is a tiny hole in the center of it, allowing the stalk (or infundibulum) of the pituitary to pass through. The anterior and posterior intercavernous sinuses are found in their respective edges of the diaphragma sella. These infoldings are illustrated in Figures 3-6 and 3-7. They are pictured as they appear on a magnetic resonance imaging scan.

When you consider the placement of these sturdy partitions being under and between the cerebral hemispheres as well as over and between the cerebellar hemispheres, it is fairly easy to understand how the dural infoldings brace the brain against rotary displacement.

There is no subdural space between the dura mater and the next layer of the meninges. When there is subdural space identified, it means that tissue damage has occurred to the deepest layer, creating a space.

Because there is no normal subdural space, the next meningeal layer can be found immediately below the dura. This second layer is the arachnoid mater. This membrane bridges over the sulci or folds of the brain. In some areas it projects into the venous sinuses to form arachnoid villi. The arachnoid villi aggregate to form the arachnoid granulations. The arachnoid granulations are from where the cerebrospinal fluid diffuses into the bloodstream.

Beneath the arachnoid mater layer is a space called the subarachnoid space, which is filled with cerebrospinal fluid. All cerebral arteries and veins, as well as the cranial nerves, pass through this space. This is why you often hear of subarachnoid hemorrhage or bleed because damage to the brain has resulted in artery or vein tears and blood is released into this subarachnoid space.

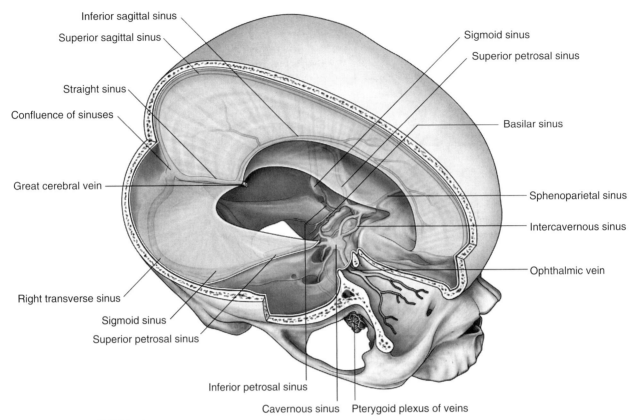

FIGURE **3-6**
Veins, meninges, and dural sinuses. (Reprinted from Drake, R., Vogl, W., & Mitchell [2006]. *Gray's anatomy for students* [2nd ed.]. Philadelphia: Churchill Livingstone.)

The third meningeal layer, the *pia mater*, closely adheres to the surface of the brain, covering the gyri (ridges) and going down into the sulci. The pia mater also fuses with the ependyma (a cellular membrane lining the ventricles) to form the choroid plexus of the ventricles. Figure 3-8 illustrates the meningeal layers.

VENTRICULAR SYSTEM

The **ventricular system** of the brain has three parts: the lateral ventricles, the third ventricle, and the fourth ventricle. These actually are small cavities within the brain joined to each other by small ducts and canals. Each ventricle contains a tuftlike structure called the **choroid plexus**, which mainly is concerned with the production of cerebrospinal fluid.

Figure 3-9 is an example of a midsagittal view of the brain showing the third and fourth ventricles in relation to the cerebral aqueduct and nearby structures.

The lateral ventricles are paired, one in each hemisphere. Each is a C-shaped cavity and can be divided into a body, located in the parietal lobe, and anterior, posterior, and inferior or temporal horns, extending into the frontal, occipital, and temporal lobes, respectively. The lateral ventricle is connected to the third ventricle by an opening called the intraventricular foramen, or the foramen of Munro. The choroid plexus of the lateral ventricle projects into the cavity on its medial aspect (see Fig. 3-9).

The third ventricle is a small slit between the thalami. It also is connected to the fourth ventricle through the cerebral aqueduct or the **aqueduct of Sylvius**. The choroid plexus is situated above the roof of the ventricle.

The fourth ventricle sits anterior to the cerebellum and posterior to the pons and the superior half of the medulla. It is continuous superiorly with the cerebral aqueduct and the central canal below. The fourth ventricle has a tent-shaped roof, two lateral walls, and a floor (see Fig. 3-9). It contains three small openings: the two lateral foramina of Luschka and the median foramen of Magendie. Through these openings the cerebrospinal fluid enters the subarachnoid space. The ventricular system serves as a pathway for the circulation of the cerebrospinal fluid. The choroid plexus of the ventricles appears to secrete cerebrospinal fluid actively, although some of the fluid may originate as tissue fluid formed in the brain substance.

Hemisphere in right supratentorial compartment

Falx cerebri

Hemisphere in left supratentorial compartment

Hemisphere in right supratentorial compartment

Hemisphere in left supratentorial compartment

Choroid plexus in atrium

Falx cerebri

Cerebellum in infratentorial compartment

Tentorium cerebelli

Hemisphere in supratentorial compartment

Choroid plexus in atrium

Tentorium cerebelli

Cerebellum in infratentorial compartment

FIGURE **3-7**

Axial (**A**), coronal (**B**), and sagittal (**C**) T1-weighted magnetic resonance images showing the relations of the falx cerebri (**A** and **B**) and the tentorium cerebelli (**B** and **C**). Note the positions of the right and left supratentorial compartments and the infratentorial compartment in relation to these large dural reflections in all three planes. (Reprinted from Haines, D. [2006]. *Fundamental neuroscience* [3rd ed.]. Philadelphia: Churchill Livingstone.)

CEREBROSPINAL FLUID

The brain and the spinal cord are suspended in a clear, colorless fluid called **cerebrospinal fluid (CSF)**, which serves as a cushion between the CNS and the surrounding bones, thereby protecting the brain against direct trauma. This fluid aids in regulation of intracranial pressure, nourishment of the nervous tissue, and removal of waste products.

The path of circulation of the CSF is illustrated in Figure 3-10. It flows from the lateral ventricles into the third ventricle, to the fourth ventricle, and into the subarachnoid space. It then travels to reach the inferior surface of the cerebrum and moves superiorly over the lateral aspect of each hemisphere. Some of it moves into the subarachnoid space around the spinal cord.

The CSF produced by the choroid plexus passes through the ventricular system to exit the fourth

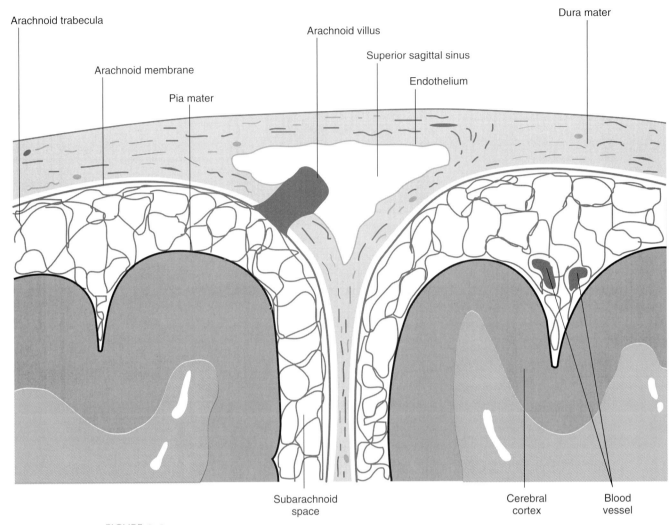

FIGURE **3-8**
Relation of the brain to the dura, arachnoid, and pia maters. (Redrawn from Bullock, T. H., Orkland, R., & Grinnel, A. [1977]. *Introduction to the nervous system.* San Francisco: W. H. Freeman.)

ventricle through the foramina of Luschka and Magendie. At this point, the CSF enters the subarachnoid space, which is continuous around the brain and spinal cord. The CSF in this subarachnoid space provides the buoyancy necessary to prevent the weight of the brain from crushing nerve roots and blood vessels against the internal surface of the skull. The weight of the brain, approximately 1400 g in air, is reduced to 45 g when it is suspended in CSF. Consequently, the tethers formed by delicate connective tissue strands traversing the subarachnoid space, the arachnoid trabeculae (see Fig. 3-8), are adequate to maintain the brain in a stable position.

The movement of the CSF through the ventricular system and the subarachnoid space is influenced by two major factors. A subtle pressure gradient exists between the points of production of CSF (the choroid plexus in the cerebral ventricles) and the points of transfer into the venous system (arachnoid villi). Because CSF is not compressible, it tends to move along this gradient. It also moves into the subarachnoid space by purely mechanical means, including gentle movements of the brain on its arachnoid trabecular tethers during normal activities and the pulsations of the numerous arteries found in the subarachnoid space.

Blockage of the CSF movement or a failure of the absorption mechanism results in the accumulation of fluid in the ventricles or around the brain tissue (Fig. 3-11). This results in hydrocephalus and is characterized by an increase in CSF volume enlargement of one or more of the ventricles, and usually an increase in CSF pressure.

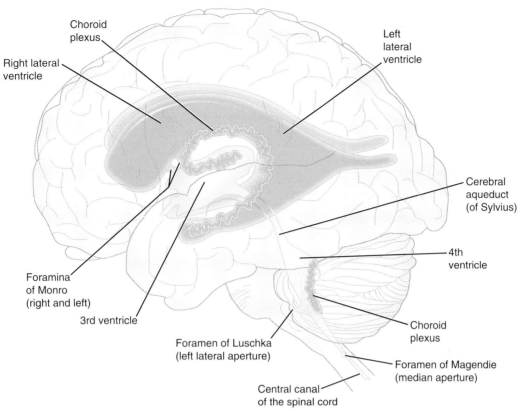

FIGURE **3-9**

The brain ventricles and the cerebrospinal fluid. This is a transparent view, looking from the left side of the brain. The two lateral ventricles communicate with the third ventricle, which in turn communicates with the fourth ventricle. (Modified from Boron, W., & Boulpaep, E. [2009]. *Medical Physiology* [2nd ed.]. St. Louis: Elsevier.)

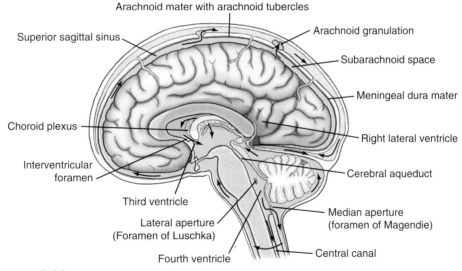

FIGURE **3-10**

CFS circulation.

Normal   Hydrocephalus

FIGURE **3-11**

Comparison of normal and hydrocephalic brains in sagittal (**A**), axial (**B**), and coronal (**C**) planes as seen on magnetic resonance images. (Reprinted from Haines, D. [2006]. *Fundamental neuroscience* [3rd ed.]. Philadelphia: Churchill Livingstone.)

The CSF is important in medical diagnostic procedures. The pressure of the fluid can be measured; if it is abnormally high, intracranial tumor, **hemorrhage**, hydrocephalus, meningitis, or **encephalitis** may be suspected. Chemical and cell studies may be made on CSF that is drawn out of the nervous system through a procedure called a lumbar puncture or spinal tap. This route also may be used to inject drugs to combat infection or induce anesthesia. Circulation of the CSF is illustrated in Figure 3-10.

BLOOD SUPPLY OF THE BRAIN

The blood serves the brain much as food serves the body; it nourishes it by supplying its most important element, oxygen. The brain uses approximately 20%

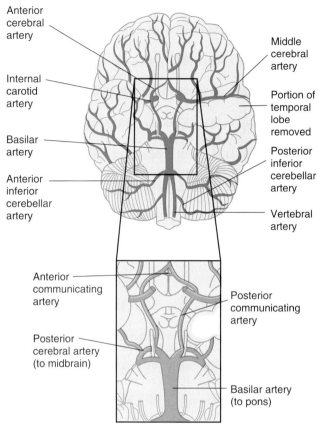

FIGURE **3-12**
The major arteries of the brain. Ventral view: the enlargement of the boxed area showing the circle of Willis. (From Aitken, L., Marshall, A., & Chaboyer, W. [2012]. *ACCCN's Critical Care Nursing* [2nd ed.]. Mosby Australia: Sydney.)

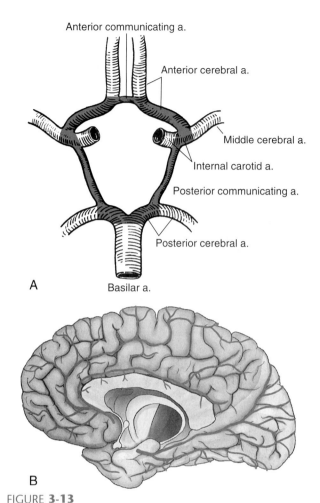

FIGURE **3-13**
The cerebral arterial circle (circle of Willis; **A**) The circle of Willis. (From Nolte, J. [2010]. *Essentials of the Human Brain*. St. Louis: Mosby.) (**B**) The large cerebral arteries: anterior, middle, and posterior. The area supplied by the anterior cerebral artery is green, the area supplied by the middle cerebral artery is pink, and the area supplied by the posterior cerebral artery is yellow. (From Lundy-Eckman, L. [2013]. *Neuroscience* [4th ed.]. Saunders: St. Louis.)

of the blood in the body at any given time and requires approximately 25% of the oxygen of the body to function maximally. Initially blood is delivered to the brain through four main arteries. Two large internal carotid arteries are on either side of the neck; these are a result of bifurcation, or splitting, of the common carotid artery from the heart. The other two main arteries supplying the brain are the vertebral arteries (Fig. 3-12).

Internal Carotid Arteries and Their Branches

The internal carotid arteries ascend in the neck and pass through the base of the skull at the carotid canal of the temporal bone. Each artery then runs horizontally forward and perforates the dura mater. After entering the subarachnoid space, the artery turns posteriorly and, at the medial end of the lateral sulcus, divides into the anterior and middle cerebral arteries. Other cerebral arteries are also given off by the internal carotid artery. The ophthalmic artery supplies the eye, the frontal area of the scalp,

the dorsum of the nose, and the ethmoid and frontal sinuses. The posterior communicating artery runs posteriorly above the oculomotor nerve and joins the posterior cerebral artery, forming part of the circle of Willis. The anterior communicating artery joins the two anterior cerebral arteries together in the circle of Willis (Fig. 3-13).

Through these cortical branches, the internal carotid artery provides the blood supply to a large portion of the cerebral hemisphere. The anterior cerebral artery supplies the medial surface of the cortex as far back as the parietal-temporal-occipital sulcus. It also supplies the so-called leg areas of the motor strip. Branches of this artery supply a small portion of the caudate nucleus, lentiform nucleus, and internal

FIGURE **3-14**
Middle cerebral artery. (From Kenyon, K., & Kenyon, J. [2010].
The Physiotherapist's Pocket Book [2nd ed.]. St. Louis.)

capsule. Following is a summary of the internal carotid artery branches (see Fig. 3-12):
- The ophthalmic artery gives rise to the central artery of the retina; damage to this artery (including ophthalmic aneurysms) causes ipsilateral visual loss.
- The posterior communicating artery joins the posterior cerebral artery and the anterior choroidal artery and follows along the optic tract.
- The anterior cerebral artery passes superiorly over the optic chiasm and is joined by its counterpart the anterior communicating artery; it supplies blood to the hypothalamus and the optic chiasm.
- The middle cerebral artery usually is the larger of the two terminal branches of the internal carotid artery (Fig. 3-14).

The middle cerebral artery is the largest branch of the internal carotid. Its branches supply the entire lateral surface of the hemisphere except for the small area of the motor strip supplied by the anterior cerebral artery, the occipital pole, and the inferolateral surface of the hemisphere, which is supplied by the posterior cerebral artery. The middle cerebral artery's central branches also provide the primary blood supply to the lentiform and caudate nuclei and the internal capsule.

Vertebral Artery and Its Branches

The vertebral artery passes through the foramina in the upper six cervical vertebrae and enters the skull through the foramen magnum. It passes upward and forward along the medulla and at the lower border of the pons and joins the vertebral artery from the opposite side to form the basilar artery. Before the formulation of the basilar artery, several branches are given off, including the following:
- The meningeal branches, which supply the bone and dura of the posterior cranial fossa
- The posterior spinal artery, which supplies the posterior third of the spinal cord

- The anterior spinal artery, which supplies the anterior two thirds of the spinal cord
- The posterior inferior cerebellar artery, which supplies part of the cerebellum, the medulla, and the choroid plexus of the fourth ventricle
- The medullary arteries, which are distributed to the medulla

After the basilar artery is formed by the union of the opposite vertebral arteries, it ascends and then divides at the upper border of the pons into the two posterior cerebral arteries. These arteries supply the inferolateral surface of the temporal lobe and the lateral and medial surfaces of the occipital lobe (i.e., the visual cortex). They also supply parts of the thalamus and other internal structures (see Fig. 3-13).

Other branches of the basilar artery include the following (see Fig. 3-12):
- The pontine arteries, which enter the pons
- The labyrinthine artery, which supplies the internal ear
- The anterior inferior cerebellar artery, which supplies the anterior and inferior parts of the cerebellum
- The superior cerebellar artery, which supplies the superior portion of the cerebellum

Circle of Willis

The circle of Willis, or the circulus arteriosus, is formed by the anastomosis of the two internal carotid arteries with the two vertebral arteries. The anterior communicating, anterior cerebral, internal carotid, posterior communicating, posterior cerebral, and basilar arteries are all part of the circle of Willis (see Fig. 3-13). This formation of arteries allows distribution of the blood entering from the internal carotid artery or vertebral artery to any part of both hemispheres. Cortical and central branches arise from the circle and further supply the brain.

The bloodstreams from the internal carotid artery and vertebral artery on both sides come together at a certain point in the posterior communicating artery. At that point the pressure is equal, and they do not mix. Should, however, the internal carotid artery or the vertebral artery be occluded or blocked, the blood will pass forward or backward across that point to compensate for the reduced flow. The circle of Willis also allows blood to flow across the midline of the brain if an artery on one side is occluded. The circle of Willis thereby serves a safety valve function for the brain, allowing collateral circulation (or flow of blood through an alternate route) to take place if the flow is reduced to one area. The state of a person's collateral circulation helps determine the outcome after a vascular insult, such as a stroke, occurs and affects blood flow to the brain.

General Principles of Neurologic Organization

Certain fundamental principles of neurologic organization are particularly crucial to the understanding and diagnosis of communication disorders. The following principles will also be built on in later chapters.

CONTRALATERAL MOTOR CONTROL

The first principle to remember is that major movement patterns in human beings have **contralateral** neurologic control in the brain. The arms and legs are represented in the motor strip of the cerebral cortex in a contralateral fashion. In other words, the cerebral hemisphere on one side of the body controls movements of the arm and leg on the other side of the body. This contralateral motor control is brought about by the crossing of the major voluntary motor pathway at the level of the lower brainstem. Auditory and visual sensory systems also have some contralateral organization, a fact that will become clinically important (see Chapters 5 and 6). The cranial nerves, as discussed subsequently, have mixed control so that you have to know which cranial nerve and/or muscle group considered in order to know the innervation pattern.

If a patient sent to the speech-language pathologist has a severe language disorder and some paralysis of the right arm and leg, these symptoms suggest that the brain lesion causing this motor deficit is probably in the left cerebral hemisphere (Fig. 3-15). The severe language disturbance accompanying the right limb paralysis serves as a confirming sign of left-sided brain lesion because in the majority of the population language dominance is located in the left hemisphere. Why the nervous system provides contralateral motor control of the limbs is not completely known, but the fact illustrates that knowledge of principles of neurologic organization can be used to posit the location of causative lesions seen in neurology and speech pathology.

IPSILATERAL MOTOR CONTROL

If a lesion occurs in the nervous system below the crossing of the major descending motor pathways, the effect is observed below the level of the lesion on the same side of the body where the lesion occurs. In many spinal cord injuries, paralysis and sensory loss occur below the point of injury. Thus a second important principle is to determine whether effects of lesions are **ipsilateral** or contralateral. An illustration of how the tongue might deviate ipsilateral to a lesion is shown in Figure 3-16. In

Patient's right   Patient's left

FIGURE **3-15**
Patient with a lesion of the internal capsule on the left side. This man exhibits a right hemiparesis, drooping of the lower part of the face on the right, and slight turning of the head to the left (weak left sternocleidomastoid muscle).

this figure, the tongue is paralyzed on the left side from surgery to remove a lymph node from the left side of the neck, resulting in damage to the ipsilateral hypoglossal nerve fibers.

BILATERAL SPEECH MOTOR CONTROL

For the most part, the midline muscles of the body in the head, neck, and trunk tend to be represented bilaterally, and the nerve fibers supplying these regions, with certain exceptions, descend from both cerebral hemispheres. This **bilateral** neural control provides smooth, symmetric movement for those muscles used in speaking: the lips, tongue, soft palate, jaw, abdominal muscles, and diaphragm. The principle of bilateral control of speech muscles suggests that serious involvement of the speech muscles usually results from diseases that affect bilateral neurologic mechanisms. With **unilateral** damage to the nervous system, effects on speech are generally less serious, and compensatory mechanisms are made available from the other side of the midline speech system.

Representation of the body is found in an inverted fashion on the motor areas of the cerebral cortex. Pathways concerned with movements of the lower limbs originate in the upper parts of the motor strip, whereas movements of the head and neck originate at the lower end of the motor strip, just above the sylvian fissure. The area surrounding the left sylvian fissure contains major areas for language processing. The anatomic relations of motor speech areas and language suggest that speech and language disturbances may commonly coexist because of the close proximity of their control areas on the cortex.

An example of bilateral damage effects of motor speech lesions may be seen in spastic dysarthria. When damage to the upper motor neurons occurs, spasticity results. With spasticity, affected muscles (in this case, those dealing with articulation, respiration, and phonation) show an increased resistance to passive movements or movement manipulation. The more rapidly the individual tries to move the articulators (or even an upper or lower extremity, as in cerebral palsy) the greater is the resistance to the movement. In spastic dysarthria, bilateral damage to the upper motor neurons usually is caused by stroke, head trauma, or a degenerative disease (see Chapter 8). The bilateral damage is within both direct activation pathways (corticobulbar and corticospinal tracts) and indirect pathways (extrapyramidal tract).

UNILATERAL LANGUAGE MECHANISMS

An impressive facet of cerebral asymmetry is that language mechanisms, for the most part, are unilaterally controlled in the brain, in contrast to the bilateral speech muscle mechanism. Handedness usually appears between 18 and 48 months of age. Among the adult population, more than 95% of right-handed people have their language mechanisms in the left cerebral hemisphere. Language dominance the world over is primarily in the left brain. Left-handed people are more variable. Some are right brained for language; others have bilateral representation of language. Figure 3-17 illustrates the left hemisphere and its relation to the motor and sensory (receptive) language areas. The obvious clinical principle suggested by these facts is that major language disturbance is a neurologic sign of left cerebral injury and that the left hemisphere has special anatomic properties for language.

FIGURE **3-16**
Paralysis of the tongue on the left side. Removal of a lymph node from the left side of the neck (**A**, *arrow*) inadvertently resulted in damage to peripheral fibers of the hypoglossal nerve on that side. The tongue deviates to the left (side of the lesion) on protrusion (**B**). (Reprinted from Haines, D. [2006]. *Fundamental neuroscience* [3rd ed.]. Philadelphia: Churchill Livingstone.)

FIGURE **3-17**
Motor and sensory language areas. (Reprinted from Castro, A., Merchut, M. P., Neafsey, E. J., & Wurster, R. D. [2002]. *Neuroscience: An outline approach.* Philadelphia: Mosby.)

SCHEME OF CORTICAL ORGANIZATION

Students and clinicians should have in mind a general scheme of organization of the cortex because it is the site of most language functions. Although any such scheme is oversimplified and exaggerated, it nevertheless provides a crude but workable framework for conceptualizing functional localization. Later chapters in this text detail the specifics of cortical localization.

The right and left hemispheres may be designated as nonverbal and verbal, and the anterior and posterior portions may be characterized as motor and sensory areas. The central sulcus divides the cerebral hemispheres into

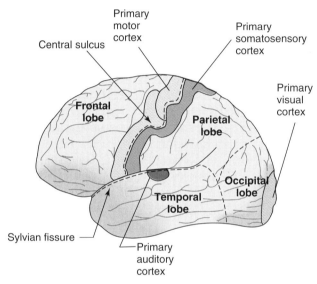

FIGURE **3-18**
Lateral view of the cerebral hemisphere. *Dashed lines* demarcate major lobes. (Reprinted from Castro, A., Merchut, M. P., Neafsey, E. J., & Wurster, R. D. [2002]. *Neuroscience: An outline approach.* Philadelphia: Mosby.)

anterior and posterior regions. Figure 3-18 provides a lateral view of the cerebral hemisphere, showing lobes and the sensory and motor cortices. In human beings, approximately half of the volume of the cerebral cortex is taken up by the frontal cortex. The frontal lobe contains the primary motor cortex, the premotor cortex, and Broca's area, the primary motor speech association area. In the anterior portion of the frontal lobes are the prefrontal areas, which are generally concerned with behavioral control of both cognitive and emotional functions.

Castro et al.[5] described lesions in the prefrontal cortex that may produce an "internal agnosia or the inability to communicate with one's limbic system as though suffering from an impairment of the 'sixth sense' that distinguishes appropriate from inappropriate behaviors and right from wrong." Mental shifts become difficult, and perseveration and rigidity are observed, as are a lack of self-awareness and a tendency toward concreteness. In brief, the frontal lobe appears to excel in the control, integration, and regulation of emotional and cognitive behavior. Cortical areas of the left hemisphere that mediate the processing of language are shown in Figure 3-19. Lesions in the inferior frontal lobe may result in **Broca's**, or **expressive**, **aphasia**, whereas damage to the angular gyrus, the supramarginal gyrus, and the superior temporal gyrus may result in **Wernicke's**, or **receptive**, **aphasia**.

In contrast, the posterior cortex appears to dominate the control, integration, and regulation of sensory behavior. The defects arising from the posterior cortex are related to the specific sensory association areas implicated by a lesion.

The occipital lobe, as previously noted, contains the primary visual cortex and visual association areas. Deficits in the primary cortex result in blind spots in the visual field, and total destruction of the cortex produces

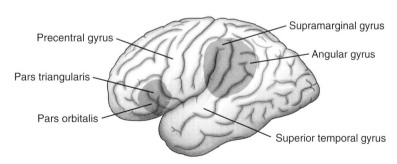

FIGURE **3-19**
Cortical areas that mediate the processing of language. Lesions in the pars orbitalis and pars triangularis of the inferior frontal lobe result in Broca's aphasia, whereas damage in the supramarginal and angular gyri and adjacent superior temporal gyrus results in Wernicke's aphasia.

complete blindness. Visual imperception and agnosias (see Chapter 5) are associated with the visual association areas.

The left parietal lobe is associated with **constructional disturbances** and visuospatial defects. Disorders of recognition, called agnosias, are common. The inferior parietal lobe is concerned with language association tasks, and lesions there cause defects in reading and writing. Contralateral neglect is associated with hemispheric lesions of the nondominant parietal association cortex. Such patients usually neglect stimuli on their left, as illustrated in Figure 3-20. In extreme cases the patient does not recognize the left side of his or her own body, a condition termed asomatognosia. An example is when a patient

has a left neglect and ignores the left side when getting dressed or grooming.

The temporal lobe on the left is concerned with hearing and related functions. It contains the primary auditory and auditory association areas. Auditory memory storage and complex auditory perception are among the functions of the temporal lobe. An area known as the speech zone surrounds the sylvian fissure and appears to contain the major components of the language mechanism. Damage in the speech zone produces Wernicke's aphasia (see Fig. 3-19).

With a clinical knowledge of primary sensory and related association areas and behavioral correlates to these areas, the speech-language pathologist is able to infer the approximate location of a lesion from the

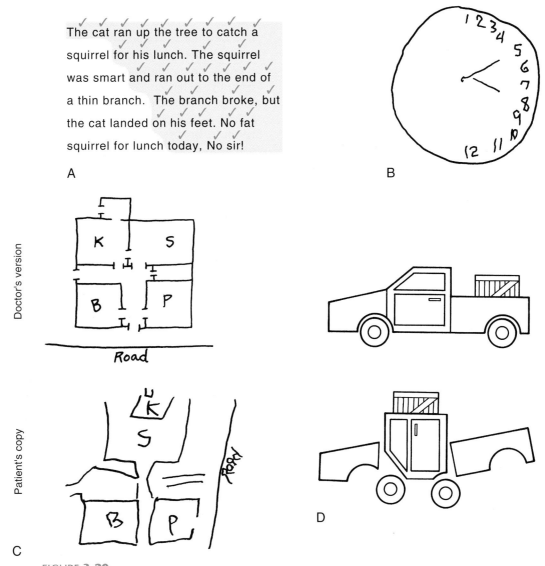

FIGURE **3-20**

Signs (A to D) of damage to the nondominant parietal association cortex. (Reprinted from Haines, D. [2006]. *Fundamental neuroscience* [3rd ed.]. Philadelphia: Churchill Livingstone.)

patient's behavioral symptoms and to recognize the well-known speech-language syndromes associated with cortical dysfunction. The general clinical principle is that specific cortical deficits can be associated with specific behavioral syndromes. A major exception to this is difficulty with word-finding or naming which is typically a non-localizable symptom.

Neurodiagnostic Studies in Speech and Language

The structures of the brain believed to be critical for speech and language function have been established by what is called the clinicopathologic method in neurology. Developed into a powerful technique by the great French neurologist Jean Charcot, this method establishes a relation between the site of a lesion and the behavioral functions that are lost or modified. The underlying assumption is that the area of lesion is related to the lost or disordered function. This simple logic is important in clinical neurology; it forms the basis of neurologic diagnosis and is the foundation of the historically traditional neurologic examination. Some of these neurobehavioral signs have been discussed in Chapter 2 and in this chapter.

Fortunately for the evolution of medical science and clinical treatment, the field of neurology has been advanced through the years by technology that has vastly clarified the actual sites of lesions and made diagnoses more valid and reliable, now through relatively noninvasive means. Objective neurodiagnostic tests, such as computed tomography (CT), magnetic resonance imaging (MRI), electroencephalography (EEG), and evoked related potentials (ERPs) as well as other clinical neurodiagnostic tests, have established the value of the clinicopathologic method in medicine yet dramatically enhanced the identification and treatment of neurologic disorders, including those which impact communication. Speech-language pathologists (SLPs) are expected to be somewhat familiar with these types of studies and use the reported information (if available) to plan diagnostic and treatment procedures. Use of the information provided by these studies can also help the SLP to identify inconsistencies between the behaviorally based diagnostic findings and the findings of the reported study. Speech and language function is quite vulnerable to neurologic changes; the results of the imaging or electrophysiologic study may not be consistent, perhaps warranting more exploration by one or both. Therefore, as we come to the end of our overview of the communicative nervous system, a brief discussion of some of the more commonly used neurodiagnostic methodologies that the SLP might find reported in

the medical record or research articles seems fitting to include at this point.

STATIC BRAIN IMAGING

CT and MRI were the foundation tools of early neurologic imaging, permitting study of the structure of the human brain with a degree of detail that is occasionally comparable with the detail revealed by postmortem examination. In fact, MRI, which generates fine cross sections of brain structure without penetrating radiation, may even go beyond postmortem examination because it allows views of multiple slices of the brain.

The CT scan yields a three-dimensional representation of the brain (Fig. 3-21), unlike the conventional radiograph, which provides a two-dimensional projection of a three-dimensional object. On a radiograph, the body appears on x-ray films as overlapping structures that are sometimes difficult to distinguish. The CT scanner uses an **x-ray** beam that is passed through the brain from one side of the head, and the radiation not absorbed by the intervening tissue is absorbed by a series of detectors revolving around the subject's head. The data from the radiation detectors allow a calculation of the density of tissue in a particular slice of brain. A computer then reconstructs a two-dimensional cross-sectional picture of the brain observed by the camera. Several cross sections may be printed corresponding to different planes through the head. Contrast substances are sometimes injected in the patient to increase the density of damaged tissue. This enhancement technique allows clearer visualization and more accurate diagnosis. Spiral CT, in which the x-ray tube rotates continuously around the patients while the table moves, was developed in the early 1990s along with a computational method that would eliminate the motion artifact this introduced. Spiral CT allowed much more flexible and rapid study. Because CT studies are quicker and less expensive to perform than MRI, the technology is more widely available in general medical settings. CT is frequently used in the emergency department and other acute settings. It is more sensitive to skull fracture and can detect the presence of foreign bodies, such as glass and metal, that are radiopaque. It can reveal the presence of blood in the linings and parenchyma of the brain and, therefore, is the first study of choice in a vascular event of unknown etiology so that hemorrhage could be ruled out first. Because MRI uses a magnetic field, CT is the study that would be chosen for patients with pacemakers, defibrillators, and other such devices.

MRI, probably the most widely used diagnostic imaging technique in neurology, generates cross-sectional images by using radio waves, a strong magnetic field, and gradient coils to detect the distribution of water

FIGURE **3-21**

Computed tomography (CT) scans of a 2-month-old infant with shaken baby syndrome (**A** and **B**) and magnetic resonance (MR) images of a normal 20-year-old woman (**C** and **D**). On the CT study, note that the brain detail is less than on the MR images but that the presence of blood (**A**, in the interhemispheric fissure between the hemisphere and the brain substance) is obvious. In the same patient, the bone window (**B**) clearly illustrates the outline of the skull but also clearly shows skull fractures (*arrows* in **A** and **B**). In this infant, the ventricles on the left are largely compressed, and the gyri have largely disappeared because of pressure from bleeding into the hemisphere. The pressure results in the effacement of the sulci and gyri on the left side. In the T2-weighted image (**C**), cerebrospinal fluid is white, internal brain structures are seen in excellent detail, and vessels are obvious. In the T1-weighted image (**D**), cerebrospinal fluid is dark and internal structures of the brain are somewhat less obvious. (Reprinted from Haines, D. [2006]. *Fundamental neuroscience* [3rd ed.]. Philadelphia: Churchill Livingstone.)

FIGURE **3-22**

The relation of imaging planes to the brain. The diagram shows the usual orientation of a patient in an MRI machine and the planes of the four scans (T1-weighted images) that are shown. **A** and **B**, Coronal scans; **C** and **D**, axial scans. (Reprinted from Haines, D. [2006]. *Fundamental neuroscience* [3rd ed.]. Philadelphia: Churchill Livingstone.)

molecules in living tissue (Figs. 3-22 and 3-23). The technique allows accurate assessment of brain tissue densities, and an excellent pictorial image can be generated by the computer. The explanation of the technology is beyond the scope of this text but it is helpful to know what "tissue weighting," which you will see as T1, T2, or proton density (PDW), does for an image. These parameters determine the contrast between tissues, allowing certain tissues to be more easily seen in an image. A T1-weighted image highlights tissues such

FIGURE **3-23**

MRI of the brain in the median sagittal plane (**A**) and in the sagittal plane but off the midline (**B**). The frontal lobe is to the left, and the occipital lobe is to the right. (Reprinted from Haines, D. [2006]. *Fundamental neuroscience* [3rd ed.]. Philadelphia: Churchill Livingstone.)

as fat (like white matter) and proteins, whereas CSF will appear dark. A T2-weighted image makes CSF lighter and fat appears darker, which may make this weighting more useful for identifying pathologies. If the contrast between these T1 tissues and CSF is not what is of interest, a PDW will be used, which will highlight differences in the proton densities of the two tissues with the denser tissue emphasized in the image and gray matter appearing brighter than white matter.[12]

Generally, MRI is more sensitive to abnormalities than CT. However, it is significantly more expensive to generate the image. Damasio and Damasio[7] pointed out that the analysis of CT and MRI images is sometimes difficult in that the number of brain slices provided for viewing may vary from institution to institution and from patient to patient. The number of slices may even vary in the same patient as scanning devices are improved over time.

Diffusion-weighted imaging (DWI) is another way of enhancing the usefulness of MRI in some cases. DWI allows the imaging of molecular motion or diffusion of water protons within tissue. DWI which highlights reduced diffusion has been found to be very useful to rapidly identify acute cerebral **ischemia** or loss of blood flow to an area. MRI study using DWI can be positive for reduced diffusion in these cases as early as 30 minutes after onset.[12] Figure 3-24 shows the usefulness of DWI in identifying axonal shearing which has been typically difficult to verify in traumatic injury.

Another advance in imaging to better see the white and gray matter in the brain is through voxel-based morphometry (VBM). This is primarily a research tool in which statistical methods originally applied to positron emission tomography (PET) scans are used on MRI scans. A *voxel* is the basic unit of computed tomography measurement, and the term comes from a combination of the words *volume* and *pixel*. It is essentially an imaged "slab" of tissue that has been divided into small volume elements called voxels with each voxel having an *x*, *y*, and *z* dimension on which statistical and other manipulations can be studied.[1] VBM has been used to study changes in gray matter volume in normal development, aging, and disease.[16] It also has been employed in anatomic studies of speech and language disorders.[15] Comparing the images of MRI, functional MRI (fMRI), and VBM has made it possible for advances in VBM for future research and clinical assessment.

DYNAMIC OR FUNCTIONAL BRAIN IMAGING

CT and MRI are unable to detect certain forms of cellular and subcellular brain pathology directly. Dynamic neuroimaging procedures that use emission tomography (PET and single-photon emission computed tomography [SPECT]) are helpful in cases in which imaging of brain structures alone is not decisive. For instance, in some cases of early dementia, CT and MRI scans appear normal, but language and neuropsychological testing reveals serious cerebral dysfunction.

Functional MRI (fMRI) uses an MRI scanner to measure regional blood flow, cerebral blood volume, and the change in blood oxygenation. fMRI study results in inferences about the location of brain activity. The most common fMRI study is a BOLD study, which stands for *blood oxygenation level–dependent* contrast. This study tracks the hemodynamic response to neural activity. This means that changes in blood flow and blood oxygenation are traced. fMRI has begun to be a popular technology for research by SLPs in collaboration with neurology and radiology. Brain activity in such areas as acquired language disorders, autism, and other communication disorders have been investigated with BOLD MRI.[6,8,10]

FIGURE **3-24**
Axonal shearing injury. **A,** Axial T2-weighted image shows a subtle area of reduced diffusion within the right paramedian corpus callosum *(arrow).* **B,** Axial diffusion-weighted image more clearly demonstrates abnormal reduced diffusion within the callosal lesion *(arrow).* (From Nadich, T.P., Krayenbuhl, N., Kollias, S., et al. [2013]. White Matter. In T.P. Nadich, M. Castillo, S. Cha, & Smirniotopoulos (Eds.), *Imaging of the brain,* Philadelphia: Elsevier/Saunders.

Positron emission tomograpy (PET) is a visual technique in which the subject is given a radioactively labeled form of glucose, which is metabolized by the brain. The radioactivity is later recorded by a special detector. Unlike CT and MRI scans, a PET scan measures

metabolic activity in different brain areas. More active areas metabolize more glucose, focusing more radioactivity in these areas. Thus regional three-dimensional quantification of glucose and oxygen metabolism or blood flow in the human brain is achieved. This technique is advantageous in that glucose metabolism is a more direct measure of the function of neural tissue than is cerebral blood flow, particularly in patients whose regulatory vascular mechanisms are affected by cerebral injury or disease. PET scan studies have been used to research higher mental functions during different cognitive and language tasks and appear to offer an excellent tool for the study of language in the human brain. This technology is expensive because it requires a cyclotron or atomic accelerator. Because of the color limitations of this text, an example PET scan cannot be displayed, but many can be found through a search of web images. One interesting example is found from the Berkeley Labs site *(www.lbl.gov).*

Single-photon emission computed tomography (SPECT) uses the mechanism of CT scan reconstruction, but instead of detecting x-rays, the instrument detects single photons emitted from an external tracer. Radioactive compounds that emit gamma rays are injected into the subject. As these biochemicals reach the brain, emissions are picked up that are converted into patterns of metabolism or blood flow in three-dimensional cross sections of the brain. SPECT has somewhat better temporal resolution than PET but its spatial resolution is less than PET or MRI and it is more invasive. The equipment is less expensive because a cyclotron is not required and it therefore may be used at small medical centers.

MEASURES OF NEURAL CONNECTIVITY

Diffusion tensor imaging (DTI) is the preferred method used to study white matter as is VBM for gray matter. DTI is a recently developed technique that is an extended version of DWI. It can measure neuronal activity and, in particular, the white matter neuronal cell networks (including the directionality of the actual tracts). Diffusion of water can be described as *isotropic* which means that diffusion occurs in the same degree in all directions or *anisotropic,* meaning that diffusion pattern is dependent on the direction being viewed. Because diffusion of water molecules occurs in the brain much more easily along lines that are parallel to axon bundles rather than perpendicular to them, the diffusion is anisotropic. Therefore this diffusion in the brain tissue has to be assessed in multiple directions with the resulting images then combined into an isotropic map, imaging the integrity of white matter tracts. DTI considers three factors in constructing the final image. One of these factors is the fractional anisotropy (FA); this results in essentially a gray scale representing the degree of variation of fiber direction at any point. The other two factors considered are (1) the mean diffusivity (MD), or overall displacement of the molecules in that voxel, and (2) the direction of greatest water mobility or the principal eigenvector (PE). FA values have been established for the normal brain, which will allow differentiation between gray and white matter. Intensity (FA) and directionality (PE) data can be combined into spectacular images called DTI color maps. In these maps, red signifies diffusion in a left-right direction, blue predominantly in a superior-inferior direction, and green represents diffusion in the anterior-posterior plane. Diffusion tensor tractography uses the data from DTI to construct a 3-D image of axon bundles. The Human Connectome Project is a large, National Institutes of Health–funded research project to map the human brain. Breathtaking images made from DTI studies can be found at the project's website gallery.[18]

A promising recent functional imaging technique that has been put to use both clinically and in research protocols is that of optical imaging, which uses the technology called near infrared spectroscopy (NIRS)[14] to assess response to brain activation. It is similar to fMRI in its objective, but unlike fMRI, which measures changes in deoxygenated hemoglobin, NIRS can monitor changes in deoxygenated and oxygenated hemoglobin plus changes in localized blood volume. Optical imaging is based on measuring the light absorption of different tissue properties through use of various infrared sources and detectors. It is noninvasive and can be done during motor, sensory, and cognitive tasks. Zeller et al.[17] used optical imaging in a visual-spatial task with patients with Alzheimer's disease and found decreased activation in the parietal lobe compared with control subjects.

MEASURES OF TIMING OF NEURAL ACTIVITY

It is well known that neurons emit small currents of electrical activity. In 1924 Hans Berger developed the first method to capture this activity. Other methods evolved from his early invention of the electroencephalogram (EEG).

Electroencephalography

An older diagnostic technique, electroencephalography (EEG), has been used for decades to diagnose lesions of the brain and help clarify their nature. EEG measures voltage fluctuations resulting from ionic currents between neurons in the brain. It measures these changes with the use of noninvasive scalp electrodes.

EEG is used to study seizure activity and diagnose epilepsy and its subtypes. The temporal resolution of EEG is excellent, but the limitation is that it is not correlated with any specific brain activity.

Another current use of EEG technology is the prediction of outcomes from patients with coma-related injuries. According to Boccagni and colleagues,[3] standard EEG has been proven to be a predictor of recovery of cognitive functioning in patients after coma caused by cerebral anoxia.

Evoked Potentials

Measurement of evoked potentials is a derivative of EEG. Rather than measuring spontaneous potentials detected from nervous system activity, this study reveals specific electrical potentials evoked and time-locked to the presentation of a known stimulus. The stimuli used are usually sensory (visual, auditory, somatosensory). If a stimulus is repeated enough times and each repetition produces a circumscribed electrical response, computer averaging can establish the onset of a response and its termination. Measurement called event-related potentials (ERPs) involves using an averaging computer to separate the electrical activity surrounding more complex processing events from the ongoing electrical background activity of the brain. It may be a response to internal or external stimulation of the nervous system. ERPs are often used in cognitive research. Although this technique has been used widely by some speech and psychological researchers, it is not without problems.[4] Both its validity and reliability can be questioned. Whether an electrical potential that occurs after a stimulus is of cerebral origin or is brought about by a motor act is not always certain. When a language stimulus evokes a cerebral potential, brain activity is not always present, and the absence of an electrical potential to a language stimulus does not mean no electrical activity occurred. Many electrical currents simply do not reach the surface electrodes; some are too small and erratic. In addition, the waveforms derived from stimulation are highly complex; therefore determining which section of the waveform that was generated in response to the language stimulus has psychological meaning is sometimes difficult.

Despite these limitations, event-related potential has the capacity to measure events in the brain millisecond by millisecond. A research paradigm frequently used in language studies yields a readiness potential. The subject is asked to repeat a word or phrase or speak freely with pauses of 3 or 4 seconds between portions of an utterance. The continuous EEG recording that precedes the onset of speech is analyzed by averaging waveforms across several utterances to discover what is termed the *readiness potential.*

Audiology has made good use of evoked potentials with a study known as an auditory brainstem response (ABR) or brainstem auditory evoked response (BAER). For this study, electrodes are placed on the scalp and electrical activity is recorded in response to click stimuli. The recordings from an ABR are displayed in vertical waves and waves I through V can be used to evaluate the integrity of the brainstem's response following the response from the cranial nerve to the upper brainstem.

Magnetoencephalography

Those electrical currents inside the head also produce magnetic field oscillations around active neurons. The strength and orientation of these magnetic fields can be detected from above the scalp by use of a magnetometer (MEG), which marks spontaneous or event-related activity (event-related magnetic fields or ERFs). The MEG locates the sources of the neural activity and the locations are superimposed on anatomic images such as MRI. MEG has been used to map the brain prior to surgical intervention, such as for epilepsy, and can be a useful research tool for mapping language.[9]

VASCULAR IMAGING

Noncontrast CT, contrast-enhanced CT, and MRI are the most frequently used studies at this time to identify the presence and extent of vascular infarction or disease. For the acute stroke, the most important task of the physician is to exclude hemorrhage. Hemorrhage would be a contraindication to any procedure introducing blood thinners or to the use of thrombolytic drugs or "clot busters" to perfuse an area of the brain deprived of blood flow by the presence of a thrombus or an embolus. The noncontrast CT is the most frequently used study for this purpose if the patient is seen early in the progression of the stroke. If it is available and there are no contraindications MRI is somewhat superior to CT for the acute-stage studies. Contrast-enhanced CT presents more risk to the patient but may better identify lesions.

It may be important for the physician to know the patency of the vascular system of a patient with suspected neurologic disease or injury. Once it is determined by a functional study that there is reduced blood flow to an area, it will be necessary to determine where the vascular perfusion has been interrupted or which vasculature is at risk of future occlusion, hemorrhage, or spasm.

TRANSCRANIAL DOPPLER

A transcranial Doppler study is a noninvasive procedure done by passing inaudible low frequency sound waves to the base of the brain. This is done by placing the probes over areas where thin bones are located: above the cheekbone, beneath the jaw, at the orbit of the eyes, or at the back of the head. It depends on where the best signal is found. The Doppler analyzes reflected sound waves coming from the major blood vessels. It can reveal disruption of blood flow and identify the affected vessels. Doppler studies of the carotid arteries are often done after a transient ischemic attack (TIA) to assess the patency of the major vessel from the heart to the brain.

CEREBRAL ANGIOGRAPHY AND MAGNETIC RESONANCE ANGIOGRAPHY

Conventional cerebral angiography is an invasive procedure because it involves the injection of a contrast media into the carotid artery. Once this dye is injected, a radiographic study is done while it works its way through the circulation paths of the brain, providing a radiographic picture of the vascular distribution to the brain. The risks of this procedure, especially in the acute stages of possible vascular compromise, are obvious. A plaque on the wall on the artery could be dislodged by the catheter carrying the dye resulting in an embolism, causing further deprivation of blood to the brain. In addition, allergic reaction to the contrast is possible. Therefore conventional angiography is used now only in selected patients and has been replaced, especially in the case of cerebrovascular accident, with magnetic resonance angiography (MRA).[2]

SUMMARY OF NEUROIMAGING

As pointed out in the beginning of this section, it is clinically useful for the practicing SLP to have knowledge of different types of neuroimaging studies that may be used by the physicians in the care of their patient. This familiarity will also be quite useful in reading research in speech-language pathology and audiology. Increasing collaboration is seen between SLPs and medical researchers using the various neuroimaging methods to understand normal brain function underlying communication and to identify brain differences related to acquired or developmental problems with communication. In addition to the techniques discussed in this section, additional neuroimaging methods are briefly described in Box 3-2.

OVERVIEW OF THE HUMAN COMMUNICATION NERVOUS SYSTEM

The organization of the human communication nervous system is fundamental to understand and recall. In the first three chapters of this text, you have been introduced to the history of the interaction between neurology and speech-language pathology, to structural

BOX 3-2

Additional Neuroimaging Technologies

Type	Description
Magnetic resonance microscopy	Uses high-field scanners and specific scanning technique to display information about internal composition of the cortex: Differing thickness of the cortical layers, definition of the layers (agranular vs. granular), variation in myelination of regions of brain.
CT perfusion (CTP)	Computed tomography study using intervenous injection of a contrast agent, cinefluoroscopy, and rapid temporal sampling methodology. Higher spatial resolution than MRP but limited by spatial issues.
Magnetic resonance perfusion (MRP)	MR study using a paramagnetic contrast agent (gadolinium). Yields information about vascularity of a region of interest. Vulnerable to patient motion and leakage across blood-brain barrier.
Arterial spin labeling (ASL)	A noninvasive MRI study quantifying CBF without the use of an exogenous agent. Uses "tagging" of endogenous arterial spinning through a complicated post-study comparison technique. Study largely limited to large research centers at present.
Magnetization transfer imaging	MRI technique sensitive to the exchange of magnetization between a liquid pool of free protons and a semi-solid pool of restricted protons. A magnetization transfer ratio (MTR) will quantify transfer between free and restricted water molecules. Used to study white matter and gray matter. Has been found to be useful in studies of patients with multiple sclerosis and other progressive diseases where brain tissue may appear normal in other studies.

anatomy and functionality of the main components of the central and peripheral nervous systems, and to some typical methods of imaging those structures in static images and in functional studies. From this point on, we further explore various aspects of this complex nervous system of ours. We will look at how neurons communicate with each other, briefly explore sensory systems intimately involved in communication (touch and vision), and then, in more depth, explore the structures and their function that are primarily responsible for our miraculous ability to hear, speak, and process

information in order to communicate with each other efficiently and effectively. The outline in Appendix 3-1 is a summary figure of the levels and an outline of the most important structures of the CNS. You may wish to quiz yourself at this point and, if necessary, review the preliminary information from this and the previous chapter on these structures. We go into more depth about them and the disorders associated with breakdown in their various systems in later chapters, and at times you will be reminded to review some of the information in these chapters.

Synopsis of Clinical Information or Applications for the Speech-Language Pathologist

- The CNS is the controlling influence for the human communication nervous system.
- The PNS is composed of the cranial nerves, peripheral nerves, and peripheral parts of the autonomic nervous system.
- Mixed nerves carry both sensory and motor fibers.
- Sensory and motor nerves exit at the intervertebral foramina.
- Roots unite to form a spinal nerve, whereas sensory and motor fibers mix.
- A lesion is a damaged area in the brain.
- Injury at the cervical cord (C1-C8) could affect speech production because of respiratory weakness.
- Cranial nerves have some relation to the speech, language, and hearing process.
- Seven of the 12 cranial nerves are directly related to speech production.

- Cranial nerves are unprotected and are vulnerable to trauma damage due to their point of exit from the brainstem.
- Some cranial nerves are motor, some are sensory, and some are mixed.
- Cranial nerve I, olfactory: Sensory/afferent; smell
- Cranial nerve II, optic: Sensory/afferent; vision
- Cranial nerve III, oculomotor: Motor/efferent; eye movement
- Cranial nerve IV, trochlear: Motor/efferent; eye
- Cranial nerve V, trigeminal: Mixed; pharynx, mastication, mandible, maxillary, eye, teeth, upper lip, scalp
- Cranial nerve VI, abducens: Motor/efferent; eye
- Cranial nerve VII, facial: Mixed; tongue/taste, oral cavity, facial movement, expression, salivary glands, Bell's palsy
- Cranial nerve VIII, vestibulocochlear: Sensory/afferent; hearing and balance

- Cranial nerve IX, glossopharyngeal: Mixed; gag reflex, swallowing, taste, external ear
- Cranial nerve X, vagus: Mixed; larynx, pharynx, taste buds, heart
- Cranial nerve XI, spinal, accessory: Motor/efferent; sternocleidomastoid muscles, trapezius muscles
- Cranial nerve XII, hypoglossal: Motor/efferent; intrinsic muscles of the tongue, movement, fasciculations, fibrillations of tongue
- The enteric nervous system is part of the autonomic nervous system and controls digestion and deglutition.
- The autonomic nervous system is composed of the sympathetic (flight or fight reaction) and parasympathetic (calming effect of bodily functions) systems.
- The autonomic nervous system involves neural control of smooth and cardiac muscles and gland secretions.
- The autonomic nervous system allows homeostasis to be maintained.
- The brain and spinal cord are protected and covered by meninges and a cushioning layer of tissue from CSF.
- Dura mater is the outermost layer of protection for the brain from rotary displacement.
- Arachnoid mater and subarachnoid space compose the middle layer in the meninges; all cranial nerves and cerebral arteries and veins pass through this space.
- Pia mater is the most internal layer of meninges; it adheres to the surface of the brain and contains blood supply.
- The brain has a three-part ventricle system: the lateral (two), third, and fourth ventricles.
- The ventricles are connected by small ducts and canals.
- Each ventricle contains a choroid plexus, which is responsible for the production of CSF.
- CSF is a clear, colorless fluid that cushions the CNS from the surrounding bones and protects against direct trauma.
- CSF helps regulate intracranial pressure, remove waste products, and nourish the nervous tissues.
- Hydrocephalus is a blockage of CSF or failure to absorb CSF.
- Elevated intracranial pressure may also be indicative of a tumor, hemorrhage, meningitis, or encephalitis.
- The brain requires approximately 25% of the body's oxygen.

- Two large internal carotid arteries and two vertebral arteries are the main suppliers of blood to the brain.
- The internal carotid divides into the anterior and middle cerebral arteries.
- The internal carotid also divides into the ophthalmic artery, and the posterior communicating artery, posterior cerebral artery, which are part of the circle of Willis.
- The anterior communicating artery joins anterior cerebral arteries at the circle of Willis.
- The internal carotid supplies much of the cerebral hemisphere.
- The middle cerebral artery is the largest branch of the internal carotid.
- The vertebral artery divides into the meningeal branch, posterior spinal branch, anterior spinal branch, posterior inferior cerebellar artery, and medullary branches.
- The basilar artery divides in the pontine arteries, labyrinthine artery, anterior inferior cerebellar artery, and superior cerebellar artery.
- The circle of Willis is formed by the anastomosis of the two internal carotids with the two vertebral arteries and its branches.
- Contralateral refers to a lesion affecting the opposite side of the body.
- Ipsilateral refers to a lesion affecting the same side of the body.
- Major movements in human beings have contralateral neurologic control because of fiber decussation (crossing) at the medullary location.
- Left cerebrovascular accident (stroke) results in contralateral (right side) paralysis or paresis (weakness).
- Right cerebrovascular accident (stroke) results in contralateral (left side) paralysis or paresis (weakness).
- If a lesion occurs after decussation, the affected side is ipsilateral.
- Bilateral damage to cortical areas (upper motor neurons) controlling speech musculature results in spastic dysarthria.
- In general, the right hemisphere of the brain governs nonverbal activity, and the left hemisphere of the brain governs verbal activity.
- In general, the anterior portions of the brain govern motor activity, and posterior portions of the brain govern sensory activity.
- Neuroimaging studies are used frequently in current practice with the most common being variations of computed tomography, magnetic resonance imaging, and evoked potentials.

REFERENCES

1. Ashburner, J., & Friston, K. J. (2000). Voxel-based morphometry—The methods. *Neuroimage, 11,* 805–821.
2. Avin, R. I., Bitar, R., Letourneau-Guillion, L., Young, R., Symons, S. P., & Fox, A. J. (2013). Atherosclerosis and the chronology of infarction. In T. P. Nadich, M. Castillo, S. Cha, & J. G. Smirniotopoulos (Eds.), *Imaging of the brain* (pp. 399–450). Philadelphia: Elsevier Saunders.
3. Boccagni, C., Bagnato, S. S. A., Prestandrea, C., & Galardi, G. (2011). Usefulness of standard EEG in predicting the outcome of patients with disorders of consciousness after anoxic coma. *Journal of Clinical Neurophysiology, 28,* 489–492.
4. Caplan, D. (1987). Cerebral evoked potentials and language. In D. Caplan (Ed.), *Neurolinguistics and linguistic aphasiology: An introduction.* New York: Cambridge University Press.
5. Castro, A. J., Merchut, M. P., Neafsey, E. J., & Wurster, R. D. (2002). *Neuroscience: An outline approach.* St. Louis: Mosby.
6. Crosson, B., McGregor, K., Kaundinva, S. G., Conway, T. W., Benjamin, M., Chang, Y., Moore, A. B., & White, K. D. (2007). Functional MRI of language in aphasia: A review of the literature and the methodological challenges. *Neuropsychological Review, 17,* 157–177.
7. Damasio, H., & Damasio, A. R. (1989). *Lesion analysis in neuropsychology.* New York: Oxford University Press.
8. Dichter, G. S. (2012). Functional magnetic resonance imaging of autism spectrum disorders. *Dialogues in Clinical Neuroscience, 14,* 319–351.
9. Frye, R. E., Rezaie, R., & Papanicolaou, A. C. (2009). Functional neuroimaging of language using magnetoencephalography. *Physics of Life Reviews, 6,* 1–10.
10. Gaillard, W. D., Balsamo, L., Xu, B., McKinney, C., Papero, P. H., Weinstein, S., et al. (2004). fMRI language tasks panel improves determination of language dominance. *Neurology, 63,* 1403–1408.
11. Galper, M. W., Nadich, T. P., Kleinman, G. M., Stein, E. G., & Lento, P. A. (2013). Cranial meninges. In T. P. Nadich, M. Castillo, S. Cha, & J. G. Smirniotopoulos (Eds.), *Imaging of the brain* (pp. 101–125). Philadelphia: Elsevier Saunders.
12. Kim, J. J., & Mukherjee, P. (2013). Static anatomic techniques. In T. P. Nadich, M. Castillo, S. Cha, & J. G. Smirniotopoulos (Eds.), *Imaging of the brain* (pp. 3–22). Philadelphia: Elsevier Saunders.
13. Mummery, C. J., Patterson, K., Price, C. J., Ashburner, J., Frackowiak, R. S. J., & Hodges, J. R. (2000). A voxel-based morphometry study of semantic dementia: Relationship between temporal lobe atrophy and semantic memory. *Annals of Neurology, 47,* 36–45.
14. Taber, K. H., Hillman, E. M., & Hurley, R. A. Optical imaging: A new window to the adult brain. *Journal of Neuropsychiatry and Clinical Neuroscience, 22,* 4.
15. Watkins, F., Vargha-Khadem, J., Ashburner, R. E., Passingham, A. C., Friston, K. J., Frackowiak, R. S. J., et al. (2002). MRI analysis of an inherited speech and language disorder: Structural brain abnormalities. *Brain, 125,* 465–478.
16. Wright, I. C., McGuire, P. K., Poline, J. B., Travere, J. M., Murray, R. M., Frith, C. D., et al. (1995). A voxel-based method for the statistical analysis of gray and white matter density applied to schizophrenia. *Neuroimage, 2,* 244–252.
17. Zeller, J. B., Herrmann, M. J., Ehlis, A. C., Polak, T., & Fallgatter, A. J. (2010). Altered parietal brain oxygenation in Alzheimer's disease as assessed with near infrared spectroscopy. *American Journal of Geriatric Psychiatry, 18,* 433–441.
18. Human Connectome Project (n.d.). Gallery. Retrieved from www.humanconnectomeproject.org/gallery

Appendix 3-1

A vast amount of information is provided in Chapters 2 and 3. Figure 3-25 is a summary drawing of the levels of the CNS to organize the information in Chapter 2. Referring to this figure while reading subsequent chapters will be helpful. An outline of the most important structures discussed in these chapters is also provided for review and organization. For each item, ask the following questions:

• What is it?
• Where is it?
• What does it do?

When appropriate, attempt to label drawings of some of the various structures for which illustrations were used. The effort put into doing this will be rewarded in understanding subsequent chapters.

I. The human nervous system
  A. Central nervous system
    1. Brain
  B. Cerebral hemispheres
    1. Four lobes
    2. Fissures
    3. Sulci
    4. Gyri
    5. Association cortex
    6. Connecting fibers
  C. Basal ganglia
    1. Corpus striatum
      (a) Caudate nucleus
      (b) Lentiform nucleus: putamen, globus pallidus
    2. Claustrum
  D. Limbic system

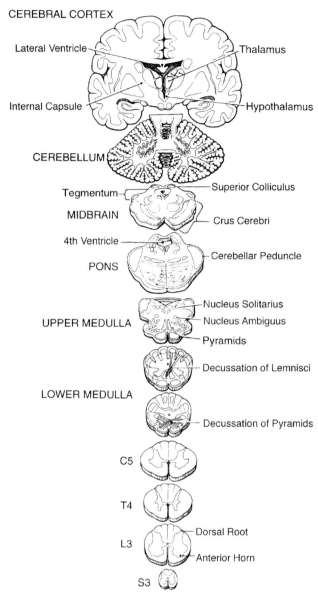

CEREBRAL CORTEX

Lateral Ventricle — Thalamus

Internal Capsule — Hypothalamus

CEREBELLUM

Tegmentum — Superior Colliculus

MIDBRAIN

Crus Cerebri

4th Ventricle — Cerebellar Peduncle

PONS

Nucleus Solitarius

UPPER MEDULLA — Nucleus Ambiguus

Pyramids

Decussation of Lemnisci

LOWER MEDULLA

Decussation of Pyramids

C5

T4

L3 — Dorsal Root

Anterior Horn

S3

FIGURE **3-25**
The levels of the central nervous system.

E. Cerebellum
F. Brainstem
  1. Medulla oblongata
   (a) Pyramids
   (b) Olives
   (c) Peduncles
  2. Pons
  3. Mesencephalon
   (a) Tectum
   (b) Colliculi
  4. Spinal cord
II. Spinal nerves
III. Peripheral nerves
IV. Five regions
  A. Meninges
V. Dura mater
VI. Arachnoid mater
VII. Pia mater
  A. Ventricles
VIII. Choroid plexus
IX. CSF
  A. Blood supply
X. Internal carotid artery and its branch
XI. Vertebral artery and its branches
XII. Circle of Willis
  A. PNS
   1. Spinal peripheral nerves
XIII. Anterior horn cell
XIV. Efferent fibers
XV. Afferent fibers
  Cranial nerves
XVI. Twelve pairs
  A. Autonomic nervous system
   1. Parasympathetic division
   2. Sympathetic division
   3. Enteric division (deglutition and peristalsis)
XVII. Clinical principles of neurologic organization
  A. Contralateral motor control
  B. Ipsilateral motor control
  C. Bilateral speech motor control
  D. Unilateral language mechanisms
  E. Scheme of cortical organization

4

Neuronal Function in the Nervous System

But strange that I was not told
That the brain can hold
In a tiny ivory cage
God's heaven and hell.

Oscar Wilde, *Poems and Fairy Tales of Oscar Wilde*, 1932

KEY TERMS

absolute refractory
  period
action potential (AP)
adequate stimulus
anastomosis
anion
anterograde
axon
axoplasm
bipolar cell
bouton
cations
cerebrovascular
  accident (CVA)
concentration
  gradient
convergence
dendrites
depolarization
distal
divergence
excitatory postsynaptic
  potential (EPSP)
graded potential
hyperpolarization
inhibitory
  postsynaptic
  potential (IPSP)
interstitial fluid
irritability
ligand-sensitive
microtubules
motor endplate
multipolar cell

myasthenia gravis
myelin
necrose
neurofilaments
neuron
neurotransmitters
orthograde
  transneuronal
  atrophy
osmotic force
perikaryon
postsynaptic
  terminal (receptor
  membrane)
potential
presynaptic terminal
proximal
pseudounipolar cell
relative refractory
  period
resting potential
retrograde
retrograde
  transneuronal
  degeneration
saltatory transmission
sodium-potassium
  pump
soma
spatial summation
summation
synapse
synaptic cleft
temporal summation

Neuronal Physiology

NEURON

The neuron, or nerve cell, is the basic anatomic and functional unit of the nervous system, underlying all neural behavior, including speech, language, and hearing. Each neuron consists of a cell body known as a soma, or perikaryon. These cell bodies actively synthesize proteins, illustrated by the large size of the cell nucleus of diffuse chromatin and at least one nucleolus where RNA is synthesized. In the cell's cytoplasm, ribosomes are abundant, and the endoplasmic reticulum and Golgi apparatus are extensive. (Review Fig. 2-2 for a refresher of the basic structure of the neuron.)

Neurons vary greatly in size, but most of the billions of neurons of the central nervous system (CNS) are small. Classifying on the basis of shape, three types of neurons may be identified: multipolar, pseudounipolar, and bipolar cells. Figure 4-1 outlines diagrammatically the various types of neurons. Each nerve cell contains a nucleus and one to a dozen projections of varying length. These projections receive neural signals and conduct neural impulses. Those receiving neural stimuli are called dendrites and are the shorter and more numerous projections of the nerve cell. The dendrites of a neuron generally are no more than a few millimeters in length.

Dendrites usually branch extensively, giving an appearance similar to a tree branch configuration. The dendrites have specialized receptors through which they receive signals from other neurons at the synapse (the contact point with another neuron). Information travels from a distal to a proximal point along dendrites to the cell body.

Dendrites often display several thorn-like protuberances called dendritic spines (see Fig. 4-1), usually on the most distal branches of the dendrite "tree." They are most prolific in the central nervous system (CNS) and are typically the sites of the synaptic contacts, forming an anastomosis, or connection.

The other process of a neuron is the axon, a longer single fiber that conducts nerve impulses away from the neuron to other parts of the nervous system, glands, or muscle (see Fig. 4-1). Axons arise from the cell body at an area called the axon initial segment or the axon hillock. Axons do not contain ribosomes, which is how scientists distinguish them from dendrites at the ultrastructural level. Axons range in length from several micrometers to more than 2 m. The diameter of individual axons varies greatly, and conduction velocity along the axon ranges from 2 to 100 m/s depending on the fiber size. The larger the diameter, the greater is the conduction velocity. In a physiologic sense, the term *axon* refers to a nerve fiber that conducts impulses away

from a nerve cell body. Any long nerve fiber, however, may be referred to as an axon regardless of the direction of the flow of nervous impulses.

The cytoplasm of the axon, called axoplasm, contains dense bundles of microtubules and neurofilaments. Each axon ends at a terminal button, or bouton, which is the point of contact with another neuron.

The site at which this bouton, or axon terminal, communicates with another neuron is called the synapse. The synapse is usually the point of contact between one neuron (typically the axon of that neuron) with another neuron's cell body, dendrites, dendritic spines, or axon. Axonal transport occurs either slowly or fast. If the transport occurs from the cell body toward the axon terminal, it is known as anterograde. Transport up the axon from the terminal toward the cell is also possible and is called retrograde. Figure 4-2 shows anterograde and retrograde axonal transport.

Neurons do the work of the nervous system by transmitting electrical signals or neural impulses to glands, muscles, and other neurons. Basically, the purpose of the neuron is to *communicate*, to send a "neural message." In the peripheral nervous system (PNS) many neuromuscular (i.e., neuron to muscle fiber) transmissions take place. In the brain itself, most of the neurons conduct neural impulses to other neurons, which are clustered quite close together, providing a high neuronal density in the cerebrum. This high density creates an almost unlimited capacity for complex neuronal activity. This neuronal activity, or brain activation, produces sensations, perceptions and thoughts as well as nerve signals eventually resulting in voluntary muscle movement. Activation is the result of rapid biochemical and biophysical changes at the cellular level and in the neurons and glial cells of the brain.[6]

In this chapter we examine this process very simplistically, looking at a basic communication process of neurons: the generation of an action potential (AP) for the types of neurons that conduct this straightforward type of firing pattern, an AP generated one spike at a time. We concentrate on learning the process through which this occurs. Once you understand the properties of neurons that enable this basic transmission, you will be better able to understand how other neurons may be different in their firing patterns. These other patterns are mentioned in this chapter, but further elucidation of these patterns is beyond the scope of this text. If you understand the cellular properties of neurons and how basic communication between neurons occurs, you will be on your way to exploring more advanced material should you choose to do so.

To begin looking at this process, we need to step back and look at the macro level to answer the larger question: How does a neuron communicate with another

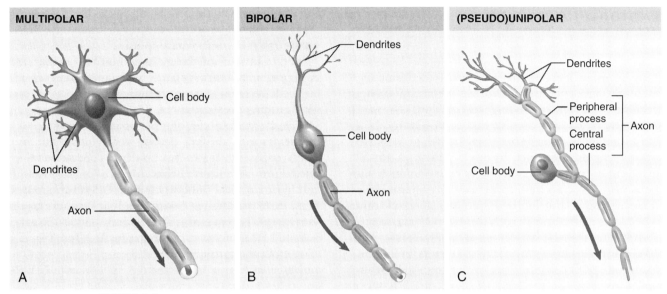

FIGURE **4-1**

Structural classification of neurons A, Multipolar neuron: neuron with multiple extensions from the cell body. B, Bipolar neuron: neuron with exactly two extensions from the cell body. C, (Pseudo) unipolar neuron: neuron with only one extension from the cell body. The central process is an axon; the peripheral process is a modified axon with branched dendrites at its extremity. (The red arrows show the direction of impulse travel.) (Courtesy of Dr. Huxley H.E. [1988]. In C.R. Leeson, T. Leeson, & A. Paparo (Eds.). *Text/Atlas of Histology.* St. Louis: Saunders.)

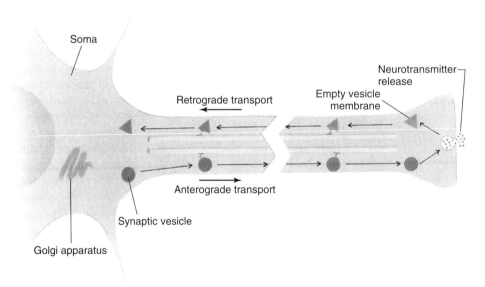

FIGURE **4-2**

Axoplasmic transport. Substances required by the axon are delivered from the soma via anterograde transport. Retrograde transport moves substances from the axon to the soma. The proteins that "walk" the vesicles along the microtubules are shown in red. (From Lundy-Eckman, L. [2013]. *Neuroscience* [4th ed.]. St. Louis: Saunders.)

cell? To begin the discussion, the process is first summarized and then we will break it down into details.

The neural "message" is a chemical or electrical signal sent to another neuron or another cell (such as a muscle cell). This neural message is most often chemical in nature, though there are electrical-only transmissions in the brain as well. The following 10 steps summarize the generation of an AP (the neural impulse propagated down an axon) resulting in a basic chemical synaptic transmission. Following the summary, details of the process are discussed and illustrated and an electrical transmission will also be described.

Steps in the neural transmission process: a summary:

1. Neurons contain fluid inside the cell (intracellular) and are bathed in fluid outside (extracellular fluid). These fluids are made up of water molecules and of chemicals that are ionic in nature, that is, they carry a positive or negative electrical charge.

2. The membrane surrounding the neuron and its extensions is an "excitable" membrane. When inactive, or not "firing," the neuron is at rest. This resting state is a result of the maintenance of a particular polarity or relative charge across that membrane. This resting polarity is obtained when the intracellular fluid surrounding the point of the axon hillock (initial segment of the axon) is approximately 70 mV more negative (–70 mV) than the fluid outside the cell membrane.

3. Due to this excitable state, the polarity at different points along the membrane is constantly being changed because there are neural signals being sent throughout your nervous system all the time. There is a certain threshold of change in polarity that will cause the neuron to "fire" or generate a neural electrical "spike" called an AP. An AP can be generated *only* at the axon hillock. However, most of the singular neural signals that reach the membrane of a neuron are not strong enough to generate movement around the membrane of the cell to the axon hillock to generate an AP. These signals do cause a change in polarity at a point on the cell membrane, resulting in what is called a **graded potential**. The changes in polarity can either depolarize (excitatory) or hyperpolarize (inhibitory) that section of the cell's membrane. Thus neural firing (an AP) most often results not from a single transmission but from the summative effect of many signals resulting in a **spatial** and/or a **temporal summation** of signaling effects on the membrane. This summation will result in a strong enough change in polarity at the axon hillock to generate an AP.

4. The threshold for an AP is reached through a depolarization causing the intracellular fluid to become more positive (or less negative) relative to the outside. This occurs through an influx of sodium (Na^+) ions. At the point of the axon hillock, this threshold for depolarization is approximately –55 mV.

5. Once generated, an AP (in a healthy neuron with a normal axon) is propagated in an "all-or-nothing" fashion down the axon to the end of it, the terminal bouton (the presynaptic terminal).

6. The AP triggers calcium channels in the presynaptic terminal to open and release calcium. The calcium influx causes synaptic vesicles in the presynaptic terminal to fuse with the membrane and release neurotransmitters that have been synthesized and stored in them.

7. The neurotransmitters diffuse out into a small space, the *synaptic cleft*, between the presynaptic terminal and the membrane of a postsynaptic terminal (e.g., the membrane of a receiving dendrite).

8. The postsynaptic membrane usually contains specialized receptor proteins for the neurotransmitters involved. With channel activation, the transmitter molecules will bind with the membrane. Binding of the principal neurotransmitters allows an exchange of ions across the postsynaptic membrane. Ionic transfer will result in either a brief *excitatory* postsynaptic potential (EPSP) or an *inhibitory* postsynaptic potential (IPSP).

9. Other neurotransmitters may be released at the same time and bind with their receptor proteins but serve as *neuromodulators* of the effect of the principal chemical. This occurs through a longer response called a second messenger system. The action that occurs in the receiving neuron or cell depends on whether the overall summation of the transmissions to it (the EPSPs, IPSPs, and second messenger action) results in another AP being generated, cell activity enhancement, or overall inhibition of activity.

10. The excess neurotransmitter substance left in the space of the synaptic cleft will be either taken up (reuptake) by the presynaptic membrane to be recycled or will be inactivated by enzymes.

CHEMICAL AND ELECTRICAL PROPERTIES OF CELLS

As discussed in Chapter 2, the neuron is enclosed by a membrane composed of protein channels and a bilipid layer. Water makes up a large percentage of our body (an estimated 55%-65% of an adult's body weight), and the brain contains more water than many other parts. A well-functioning nervous system depends on an appropriate volume of water content in the cells of the CNS and PNS. Too much water cannot be tolerated inside the cell, however, because an excess will cause swelling and cell integrity may be compromised. The chemical composition of the fluid inside and outside the cell membrane of the neuron ensures that this balance will be maintained. This chemical makeup of the intracellular and extracellular fluid also adapts the nervous system for both the chemical (primarily) and electrical signaling that must take place for neural transfer of information to occur.

What is this chemical composition? As noted earlier, the membrane of the neuron is permeable to the diffusion of the small molecules that compose water. The chemical composition of the other fluids of the cell is such that the diffusion across the membrane is not so simple. The other chemical molecules found in the intracellular and extracellular fluid are ions. Ions are atoms or molecules in which the number of electrons and protons are not equal, resulting in an excess positive or negative electrical charge. A positively charged ion is a cation, and a negatively charged ion is known as an anion. The intracellular fluid of a neuron contains a number of large protein anions. The membrane of the neuron is not permeable to these anions, and they cannot pass out of the cell. These large proteins, carrying a negative electrical charge, displace space that would be taken up by water if they were not there.

The fluid in and outside the nerve cell also contains solutions of sodium, potassium, calcium, and chloride ions. Chloride (Cl^-) ions carry a negative charge, and sodium (Na^+) and potassium (K^+) carry a positive charge. Calcium (Ca^{++}) ions are also present and carry two positive charges. The extracellular fluid (or **interstitial fluid**) bathing the cells of the brain and spinal cord is cerebrospinal fluid, which contains the same chemical ions and a much higher concentration of water than the intracellular fluid. Therefore the fluid inside the cell is said to be less dilute (a lower concentration of water molecules) than the fluid in the extracellular space. The dilution ratio of fluid inside the cell to that present outside the cell can be said to be a **concentration gradient**. Laws governing movement along a concentration gradient dictate that normal movement is from a region of higher concentration to a region of lower concentration (movement by **osmotic force**). To counteract this force and maintain stability for nerve cell functioning, there must be a mechanism to change the concentration gradient across this permeable membrane. The presence of a high concentration of sodium in the extracellular fluid provides this balance.

The membrane of the neuron ordinarily is impermeable to sodium ions; they cannot diffuse freely across the membrane, although they can be transported through selective channel proteins on the membrane (Box 4-1). Because the sodium ions do not easily move across the membrane and they are in high concentration in the extracellular space, the extracellular fluid becomes less dilute and more like that inside the cell. The concentration gradient is more balanced so that water volume is not excessive outside the cell and osmotic forces are counteracted.

BOX 4-1

Key Protein Membrane Channels and Pumps

Channel Proteins

- Allow small molecules to pass back and forth through a membrane; selective to one ion only.
- Sodium, potassium, and chloride channels in membrane of neuron important to neuronal function.
- Nongated: channels that are always open.
- Gated: channels that open and close conditionally and quickly.
- Voltage-gated: channels that open and close by voltage-sensitive mechanisms.
- Ligand-sensitive: channels that open and close in the presence of chemicals or neurotransmitters.

Protein Pumps

- Pumps open one side of a membrane at a time.
- Sodium-potassium pump: most important neuronal pump; provides energy to a cell along an electrical gradient powered by positively charged ions (cations) and negatively charged ions (anions).

Although these forces are essentially balanced, the relative electrical charge across the membrane that results from the ionic composition of the two fluids must be unbalanced for a neuron to be in a "resting" state. As is true of your own resting state, this does not mean that there is no activity at all. For a neuron, it means that it is not firing a neural impulse at that moment. At rest, there is a net negative charge of about 70 mV (–70 mV) with the fluid inside the cell being the more negative. In the intracellular fluid, there are many potassium ions contributing a positive ionic charge but the negative charge of those large protein anions helps maintain the overall net negative charge inside that is necessary for the resting state. The lack of anions outside the cell combined with the high number of sodium ions helps maintain a net positive charge relative to the inside; thus there is an unbalanced electrical charge across the membrane, and the cell is "at rest." For "activity" or neural firing, the inside of the cell has to become less negative relative to the outside, reaching a certain threshold to break the state of rest. This will be discussed soon, but first we must further elucidate how these extracellular and intracellular ionic differences are maintained.

IONIC CONCENTRATION GRADIENTS

The concentration gradient required for the appropriate ion ratio across the membrane is primarily maintained

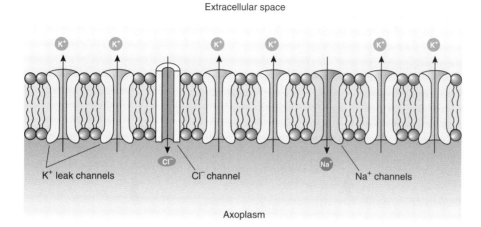

Extracellular space

K⁺ leak channels   Cl⁻ channel   Na⁺ channels

Axoplasm

FIGURE **4-3**

Schematic diagram of the establishment of the resting potential in a typical neuron. Observe that the potassium ion (K⁺) leak channels outnumber the sodium ion (Na⁺) and calcium ion (Cl⁻) channels; consequently, more K⁺ can leave the cell than Na⁺ or Cl⁻ can enter. Because there are more positive ions outside than inside the cell, the outside is more positive than the inside, establishing a potential difference across the membrane. Ion channels and ion pumps not directly responsible for the establishment of resting membrane potential are not shown. (From Gartner, L.P., & Hiatt, J.L. [2007]. *Color Textbook of Histology*, [3rd ed.]. Philadelphia: Saunders.)

by channels and pumps in the cell membrane (Fig. 4-3). Channels in the cell membrane consist of water-filled proteins that allow small molecules of a certain ion to pass back and forth depending on the need. The channels are selective to one ion only. Important to neuronal function are sodium, potassium, chloride, and calcium channels in the membrane of a neuron. The channels are classified according to the way that they open:

- Nongated channels—always open
- Gated channels—open under certain conditions and can close and open quickly
  - Voltage-gated—open and close at specific membrane potentials; operated by a voltage sensor mechanism in the protein.
  - Chemical or **ligand-sensitive**—open or close in the presence of certain chemicals or neurotransmitters.
  - Voltage-gated ligand-sensitive—opening of chemical-gated channels depends on depolarization caused by the voltage gating before the chemical can affect an opening.

As stated, the channels in the membrane of a nerve cell are selective to one ion only, these being sodium, potassium, chloride, or calcium. These chemicals are found inside and outside the cell, but potassium (K⁺) is much more concentrated inside the cell (along with those anions), whereas sodium (Na⁺), chloride (Cl⁻), and calcium (Ca⁺⁺) are more concentrated in the extracellular fluid. The exchange of sodium and potassium

across the membrane is the most important to initiation of an AP, basic to neural activity. Sodium is more likely to *enter* the cell through its channel; potassium is more likely to *leave* the cell through its dedicated channel. Because of this tendency and the need to maintain the proper ionic gradient across the membrane, it is important to have an extra mechanism to ensure the sodium and potassium levels can be in correct ratio. The **sodium-potassium pump** is the most important to the neuron, helping maintain the steep gradient of sodium to potassium and providing energy to a cell by increasing sodium transport into the cell.

Like the channels, the pumps in the membrane are water-filled proteins, but unlike the channels, which are completely open passages, the pump will open only on one side of the membrane at a time. The energy fueling this pump is adenosine triphosphate or ATP (review in Chapter 2 if needed). The interaction of the ATP results in a phosphate ion group binding with the transport channel protein. This *phosphorylation* changes the shape of the transport channel (the pump channel), driving out three sodium ions. That change in shape results in the transport channel now attracting potassium ions in the extracellular fluid. Two potassium ions then bind with the newly inviting channel and are pumped through the opening to the intracellular fluid. It is always a "3 sodium out, 2 potassium in" mechanism. Thereby, the excess of sodium in

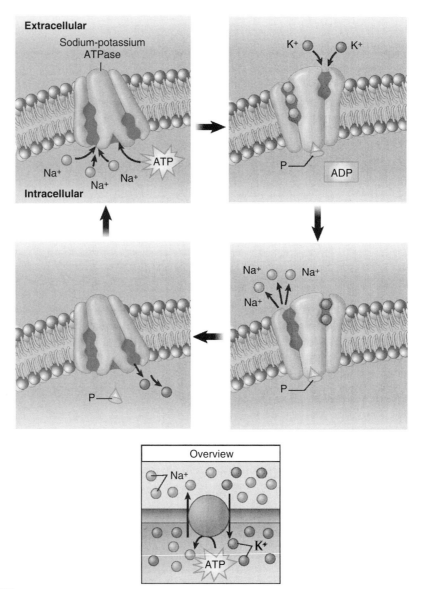

FIGURE **4-4**

Sodium-potassium pump. Three sodium ions (Na$^+$) bind to sodium binding sites on the pump's inner face. At the same time, an energy-containing adenosine triphosphate (ATP) molecule produced by the cell's mitochondria binds to the pump. The ATP breaks apart, and its stored energy is transferred to the pump. The pump then changes shape, releases the three Na$^+$ ions to the outside of the cell, and attracts two potassium ions (K$^+$) to its potassium binding sites. The pump then returns to its original shape, and the two K$^+$ ions and the remnant of the ATP molecule are released to the inside of the cell. The pump is now ready for another pumping cycle. *ATPase,* Adenosine triphosphatase. The small inset is a simplified view of Na$^+$-K$^+$ pump activity. (Adapted from McCance, K., & Huether, S. [2002]. *Pathophysiology* [4th ed.]. St. Louis: Mosby.)

the extracellular fluid is maintained. The concentration of sodium to potassium will also play an important part in the generation of chemical and electrical signals in the nervous system. An illustrated summary of membrane channels is shown in Figure 4-3. An illustration of the mechanisms of the sodium-potassium pump is shown in Figure 4-4.

ELECTRICAL FORCES

Neurons, like other cells, must exist at a steady state; that is, they must at times be at rest, without neural firing. As previously mentioned, osmotic forces are balanced so that the steady state is partially reached in healthy cells. Electrical forces across a cell membrane also must be balanced so that this steady or resting state can be maintained in all cells at some time. Positively charged ions are called cations, and any negatively charged ion is called an anion. The sodium, potassium, and chloride ions that make up the solute inside and outside the cell all carry a particular electrical charge. Chloride ions carry a negative charge and sodium and potassium carry a positive charge. Calcium ions are also present and carry two positive charges. Their particular role is discussed later in this chapter.

The intracellular portion of the neuron contains a high concentration of potassium and a low concentration of sodium and chloride in relation to the extracellular fluid. Also remember that large, negatively charged protein anions are found in the intracellular fluid, but not in the extracellular fluid. Outside the cell, sodium and chloride are found in high concentrations, approximately 10 times greater than inside the cell, and potassium is found in low concentration. The difference in chemical concentration produces ionic differences across the membrane of the cell. Because ions are charged molecules, these ionic differences create small electrical potentials across the surface membrane of the neuron.

Cellular Potential

Potential is defined as the relative amount of voltage in an electrical field. Think of the neuron as having two electrical fields, one outside and one inside the cell. At rest the electrical charge within the nerve cell is negative (dominated by the presence of the protein anions) relative to the outside of the cell (dominated by sodium ions).

The importance of ions to nervous system functioning may be understood through a discussion of their electrical properties and movements. The major functions of neurons, including integration (i.e., cognition or thinking), always depend on their electrical properties and how the ions move, eventually resulting in the firing of neural impulses or the inhibition of neural firing. Because of their critical role in neural messaging, most of the energy consumed by the nervous system is used for ionic movement. Ion currents are responsible for the creation of electrical events in biologic systems. During stimulation of some part of the body (e.g., oral mechanism for speaking, brain cells for thinking), negative ions attract positive ions and repel other negative ions; the opposite occurs for a positive ion. Ions move because of voltage gradients (opposite ions attract and same ions repel), chemical gradients, and metabolic activity (sodium and potassium ions expending high-energy phosphates [ATP → adenosine diphosphate], thus producing what is known as metabolic energy).

The ionic difference across the membrane at steady state is called the cell's resting potential. At resting potential, the difference in potential, or the separation of electrical charge, across the cell membrane is calculated to be approximately –70 mV. This means that a probe inserted into the cytoplasm inside the cell would find its charge to be 70 mV more negative than the charge measured in the fluid outside the cell. The resting potential is one aspect of the cell's characteristic irritability, or ability to respond to outside influences. At the resting potential the cell is not responding to any outside influences and it is not firing an impulse. An adequate stimulus is required, one that is capable of changing the cell's potential, to change the resting state. An adequate stimulus may be mechanical, thermal, electrical, or chemical in nature.

NEURAL MESSAGING

What an adequate stimulus may do to the membrane of a neuron is perturb it enough to (1) cause ion channels to open and (2) allow movement of the ions across the cell membrane, effecting a change in the relative charge, or polarization, across the membrane. An influx of the positively charged sodium ions causes a depolarization of the cell. Depolarization means that the inside of the cell has become less negative (or, if you prefer, more positive) relative to the outside of the cell. If that change in potential reaches a certain threshold (approximately –55 mV) at a certain point on the cell, the axon hillock, the generation of a neural impulse down the axon of the cell will begin. The neural impulse is in reality a trail of depolarization or spikes in electrical current traveling down the axon membrane. This brief spike is called an AP. There are few instances in which only one stimulation or neural signal to the membrane of a neuron will be of adequate strength to depolarize the membrane all on its own. This is why we must look at graded potentials before we get to the AP.

GRADED POTENTIALS

Graded potentials are primarily generated by sensory input, causing a change in the conductance of the membrane of the sensory receptor cell. Graded potentials also are those generated at a localized place on the cell membrane where an excitatory or inhibitory synapse has taken place. Graded potentials (also called local, or generator, potentials), which are excitatory in nature, are generated in the same way an AP is generated at the axon hillock, that is, by the influx of positively charged sodium ions into the intracellular fluid, decreasing the negativity of the charge inside relative to the outside of the cell. If this change in difference across the membrane reaches a certain threshold, a graded potential is generated at a segment of the cell membrane of the neuron or dendrite at which the stimulation occurred; that is, the change in the positive to negative ratio causes a *local* flow of current.

Unlike an AP, which is an all-or-nothing phenomenon, a graded potential is not likely to be fully propagated along the membrane; rather, the voltage will tend to decrease as the current spreads due to leakage of sodium ions through the resistance and capacitance of the membrane. The current may remain more localized, and potential may decrease in strength the further along the membrane it spreads. If the graded, or generator, potential initially is not strong enough to reach the threshold required for generation of an AP, it likely will decrease by the time it travels along the membrane to the axon hillock and an AP will not be generated at that time. Because of this decrement, graded potentials usually must summate either in time (a number of graded potentials occurring on the cell membrane at once) or in space (a number of graded potentials occurring at the same point on the membrane) to generate a signal strong enough to generate an AP.

HYPERPOLARIZATION

The ionic exchange that takes place as the cell's resting potential is changed may also result in a state called **hyperpolarization**. In this case the inside of the cell at the point of signaling to the membrane has become more negative relative to the outside of the cell. This occurs because of the influx of chloride anions.

ACTION POTENTIAL

APs are brief electrical transients visible when recorded as intracellular voltages or extracellular currents (Fig. 4-5).[4] If a neural signal is strong enough or the temporal or spatial summation of electrical signals is strong enough to depolarize the receiving cell at the point called the axon hillock, the result will be this electrical impulse, or action current (the AP), sent down the axon of that cell.

APs occur throughout the body's tissues, regulating secretions of hormones and even signaling fertilization of the egg by the sperm. In a nervous system, APs serve to integrate neural messages sent to cell bodies from sense organs and from other parts of the nervous system.

Once an AP is initiated at the axon hillock, a series of these depolarizations along the cell membrane of the axon is begun. The action current is thus propagated along an axon for long distances without a change in the waveform and at a constant velocity. This means that all the neuronal signals of coded information transmitted along axons in the nervous system are conveyed by a series of uniformly sized impulses. The information transmitted is therefore signaled by the frequency of APs generated rather than by their amplitude. The AP functions in an all-or-nothing manner. A stimulus sets up either a full-sized impulse or nothing.

FIGURE **4-5**

An example of a cholinergic neuron in the laterodorsal tegmental nucleus whose firing during REM sleep is correlated with fluctuations in blood pressure. BP, blood pressure; EEG electroencephalogram; EMG, electromyogram of neck muscle; rate, firing rate of the neuron; spike, trace of action potentials; SWS, slow wave sleep; W, wake. (From Séi, H. [2012]. *Blood pressure surges in REM sleep: A mini review, Pathophysiology*,19:4, 233–241. September.)

During the passage of an AP across a nerve cell membrane, that part of the membrane becomes briefly incapable of responding to another stimulus. This period of unresponsiveness is called an absolute refractory period. The absolute refractory period is relatively short, lasting approximately 0.8 ms. The absolute refractory period prevents an AP from traveling back up the axon, thus forcing the impulse down the fiber toward the terminal bouton of the axon. After the absolute refractory period, there is a relative refractory period during which an AP may be produced by an intense stimulus and then by stimuli of less intensity (Fig. 4-6).

Myelin

Nerve fibers, or axons, may be classified as myelinated or unmyelinated. Large peripheral nerves and the large axons of the CNS acquire a white fatty sheath of wrapping as the brain develops. Layers of myelin are incorporated in the cells that produce myelin—oligodendrocytes in the CNS and Schwann cells in the PNS. Myelin is white, contrasting these nerves sharply with the gray unmyelinated nerves, and the myelin sheet is thick. It can be revealed by a special myelin stain. The thick insulation of myelin is interrupted at intervals by structures called the nodes of Ranvier. Because of how the myelin sheaths are designed, these nodes enhance rapid propagation of the electrical impulse along the nerve fiber. The APs necessary to propagate a signal down a myelinated axon develop only at these nodes (Fig. 4-7). The impulse is vastly increased in speed by hopping from node to node on a myelinated axon without any active contribution from the long internodal spaces.

This mode of transmission is extremely efficient compared with the slow gliding along of the nerve impulses on unmyelinated fibers. The type of transmission in myelinated fibers is called saltatory transmission. The efficiency of saltatory transmission is achieved because of the insulation that prevents current flow between nodes; in addition, little leakage of current from the fibers occurs. The conduction velocity of a myelinated fiber is directly proportional to the diameter of the fiber, whereas in an unmyelinated fiber the velocity is approximately proportional to the square root of the diameter. On average, transmission along a myelinated fiber is roughly 50 times as fast as one along an unmyelinated fiber.

Unmyelinated fibers are more common in the smaller nerve fibers of the PNS, although the cranial nerves, which are part of the PNS, are relatively large in diameter and are myelinated. Six of the cranial nerves innervate the speech muscles and provide neuromotor control for talking. The rapid muscular movements underlying speech would require the fastest mode of transmission of neural impulses.

MYELIN DISORDERS

In demyelinating diseases, such as multiple sclerosis, groups of oligodendrocytes and their myelin segments degenerate and are replaced by astrocytic plaques. This loss of myelin results in an interruption of the propagation of the AP. The axons that become demyelinized survive temporarily, and some may even regenerate. The particular variety of motor, visual, or general sensory losses in multiple sclerosis reflects the location of the demyelization processes. Multiple sclerosis is caused by an autoimmune inflammatory response that damages the myelin sheath. If this inflammatory reaction is intense, the axons, too, may be damaged, producing irreversible neurologic deficits that show irregular fluctuating periods of exacerbation and remission.

Impairment of speech is found in approximately half of the population afflicted with multiple sclerosis. A speech disorder resulting from involvement of the neuromuscular aspect of the nervous system is called dysarthria. Clinical symptoms of dysarthria are detailed in Chapter 8.

The Synapse

As the electrical nerve impulse, in the form of an AP, moves along an axon, it comes to a point where it must be transmitted to another neuron, a gland, or a muscle. This point is known as a synapse. Until the discovery that small junctures occur at the synapse, researchers assumed that neurons were connected in one continuous network. Science now knows that between the membrane at the end of the axon (called the presynaptic terminal) and the membrane of the receiving cell (called the postsynaptic terminal or receptor membrane) is a small space called the synaptic cleft.

The transmission of a neural impulse across this synaptic juncture or gap is primarily a chemical process, sometimes an electrical process, and occasionally a combination of both. Electrical synapses will be discussed later in this chapter.

Most neural transmission is carried out through chemical messaging accomplished at the synapse. The transmission of nerve impulses to muscle in the PNS was the first well-established example of chemical synaptic transmission and remains the best understood. As recently as the twentieth century, many neurophysiologists believed that the impulse transmission of one thousandth of a second was too fast for any type of chemical mediation. An electrical nerve impulse was believed to excite the muscle fiber directly. The large electrical mismatch, however,

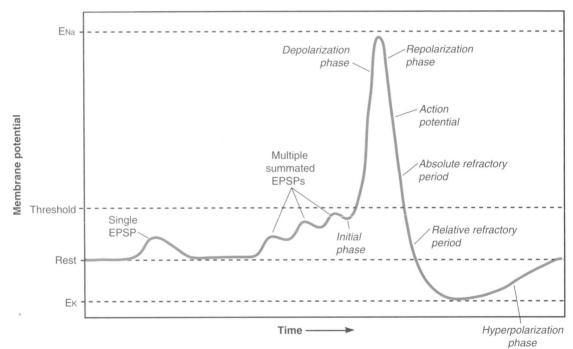

FIGURE **4-6**

Response of the neuron to the release of excitatory neurotransmitter by presynaptic neurons. The membrane potential (ordinate) becomes more positive as the binding of neurotransmitter released by firing of the presynaptic neuron increases sodium permeability through chemical-gated sodium channels, producing an EPSP. One EPSP of exaggerated amplitude is shown, after which sufficient EPSPs occur in quick succession to summate and elicit enough membrane depolarization to open up voltage-sensitive sodium channels. This reaches the threshold of depolarization necessary to generate an AP. The AP is terminated as the various sodium channels are inactivated, and voltage-sensitive potassium channels open and repolarize the membrane and, in this example, actually hyperpolarize it through efflux of potassium through opened potassium channels. (Reprinted from Nadeau, S., Ferguson, T. S., Valenstein, E., Vierck, C. J., Petruska, J. C., Streit, W. J., & Ritz, L. A. [2004]. *Medical neuroscience.* Philadelphia: Saunders/Elsevier.)

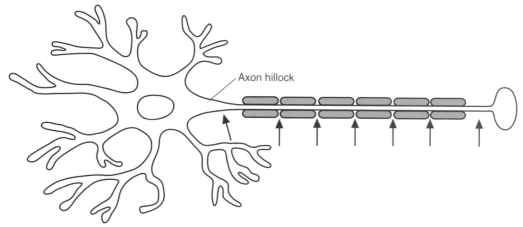

Axon hillock

FIGURE **4-7**

A neuron with myelin sheathing of its axon. The interruptions in the myelin sheath are the nodes of Ranvier. The *arrows* indicate regions of high-density, voltage-sensitive sodium channels; current flow; and action potential generation. (Reprinted from Nadeau S., Ferguson T. S., Valenstein E., Vierck C. J., Petruska J. C., Streit W. J., & Ritz L. A. [2004]. *Medical neuroscience.* Philadelphia: Saunders.)

between the tiny nerve fiber and the large muscle fiber indicated that an electrical explanation would be faulty by at least two orders of magnitude. In the 1930s researchers established that synaptic transmission in nerve-to-muscle synapses was entirely attributable to chemical mediation by a substance called acetylcholine.

Neurons primarily communicate with each other by a special type of junction called the synapse. The synapse includes a presynaptic terminal membrane, a postsynaptic receptor membrane, and a tiny space between called the synaptic cleft. When a neural impulse is generated down the axon by an AP, it travels to a point on the presynaptic membrane called the terminal bouton. At this point the AP causes opening of special voltage-gated calcium channels, allowing calcium to rush into the nerve terminal. This calcium release triggers synaptic vesicles in the axon to fuse with the presynaptic membrane and release chemicals called neurotransmitters, which have been synthesized and stored in those vesicles. These neurotransmitters are what determine whether the sending neuron is an excitatory neuron or an inhibitory neuron. Neurons are either one or the other, never both.

Looking through a powerful microscope, each neurotransmitter can be differentiated by molecular shape; no two are the same. Likewise, protein receptors dedicated to particular neurotransmitters also can be differentiated in the same manner. At the synapse the released transmitter chemical diffuses across the synaptic cleft. Slightly protruding from the surface membrane of a receiving neuron will be a part of each receptor molecule associated with that neuron. This protruding part can "sense" the presence of its neurotransmitter and bind it to the membrane. This binding is described as similar

to a key (the molecular shape of the neurotransmitter molecule) fitting into a lock (the matching shape of the receptor molecule). What happens after the binding to the receptor depends on the effect of that particular neurotransmitter and the type of receptor to which it binds.

Because the transmitter does effect a change in the target membrane, it must be rapidly inactivated so that too much is not released at one time. This inactivation may occur through action of an enzyme within the synaptic cleft (catabolism), a combination of enzyme action and reuptake, or a mix of diffusion out of the cleft and reuptake. The steps in neurotransmitter processing are shown in Figure 4-8.

The most frequently used example of neurotransmitter action is that of a neurotransmitter such as glutamate, which is excitatory to the postsynaptic cell. In this kind of transmission (and in many others), the transmitter release changes the potential of the receptor membrane to a receptor potential by opening ionic channels. In an **excitatory postsynaptic potential (EPSP)**, the neurotransmitter binds to chemical-gated sodium channel receptors. The conductance of these channels is briefly increased, and sodium is allowed to flow into the cell. This partially depolarizes the membrane. If a sufficient number of EPSPs arrive at the membrane in a synchronous fashion, the depolarization is larger in strength. If strong enough, the threshold to open the voltage-gated sodium channels at the axon hillock is reached and an AP is generated. If the EPSP is not strong enough and does not summate with others, it decreases and an AP is not generated at that time.

A neurotransmitter such as gamma-aminobutyric acid (GABA), the primary inhibitory transmitter substance in the nervous system, has the opposite effect on

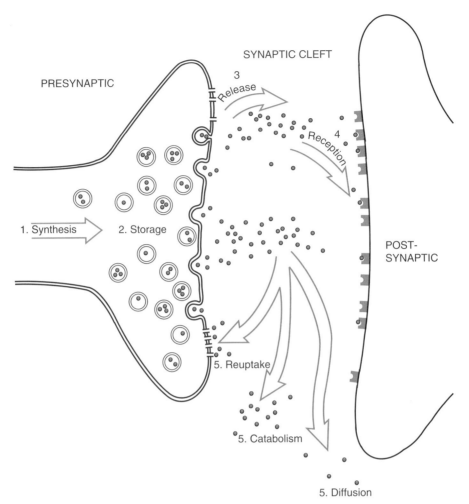

FIGURE **4-8**
The major steps in neurotransmitter processing. (Reprinted from Nadeau, S., Ferguson, T. S., Valenstein, E., Vierck, C. J., Petruska, J. C., Streit, W. J., & Ritz, L. A. [2004]. *Medical neuroscience.* Philadelphia: Saunders/Elsevier.)

the postsynaptic membrane. The binding of GABA with the membrane results in the influx of chloride ions or the efflux of potassium ions, either of which result in hyperpolarization of the membrane and an **inhibitory postsynaptic potential (IPSP)**. With this, the receptor neuron becomes somewhat less likely to generate a neural impulse or spike.

It is the summation of all the EPSPs, the IPSPs, and the modulating effects of postsynaptic activity that will eventually determine whether neural firing occurs at that particular moment. The action of the protein receptors on the receiving neuron may make a great deal of difference as to how the neuron reacts to the signaling of a particular neuron or group of neurons. Receptor proteins can be classified into two broad categories.[4] Ionotropic receptors work to form ion channels or pores through which ions may easily move into the receptor neuron and alter the electric

properties of the cell. Metabotropic receptors work by coupling with intracellular proteins called G-protein coupled receptors (GPCR). These G-proteins may have direct effects on the membrane ion channels or may regulate enzymes that work as *second messenger* molecules to alter cell properties. There are other postsynaptic actions that may occur, such as the influx of calcium through ion channels or the activation of receptors through membrane permeable substances such as nitric oxide.

In the next section we discuss some basic information about neurotransmitters. Elaboration on second messenger or other neuromodulation actions is beyond the scope of this text. It should be understood, however, that these events serve as neuromodulators and work with neurotransmitters, both natural and designed, to possibly alter properties of neurons and their synapses. These alterations might include changes in the firing rate, spike duration, ion channel selectivity, synaptic strength, and synaptic plasticity to mention a few. Obviously we have only scratched the surface of what is to be understood about how neurons communicate with each other, but the understanding of this basic information will enable you to explore further if you wish.

NEUROTRANSMITTERS

Neurotransmitters are the fundamental basis for chemical action in the nervous system. Table 4-1 illustrates the criteria generally agreed on as necessary to define a substance as a neurotransmitter.

There are many different neurotransmitters in the nervous system. Squire et al.[9] classified them into three broad categories: Classical, Nonclassical, and Unconventional neurotransmitters. See Box 4-2 for a list of some of the neurotransmitters in each of these classifications. Early studies of neurons presented them as containing only one neurotransmitter, but it is now known that a single neuron usually contains more than one and sometimes as many as three neurotransmitters.[4] Neurotransmitters carry information about and provide stimulation for changes in the functional state of a presynaptic or postsynaptic neuron. The effect on the postsynaptic membrane can be excitatory or inhibitory, but most serve to modulate the excitability of the neuron. For classification purposes, neurotransmitter specificity also can be used to describe neurons and their axons. For example, cells that contain the neurotransmitter dopamine are called dopaminergic neurons. If they contain glutamate, they are called glutamatergic.

Speech-language pathologists and audiologists often are confronted with patients who are diagnosed with disorders of neurotransmitter metabolism. Parkinson's disease results from a decrease in dopamine production in the substantia nigra. The decreased dopamine production accounts for the characteristic tremor and the inability to control movements. Research in Parkinson's disease is striving to determine what triggers the rapid death of the dopaminergic cells.

The original treatment for Parkinson's disease included administration of a form of L-dopa, a precursor of dopamine. This helped the nervous system increase dopamine synthesis, but it did not last long. More current pharmacologic therapy includes a combination of L-dopa with carbidopa because carbidopa cannot cross the blood-brain barrier (see Chapter 2). Carbidopa decreases L-dopa metabolism in the peripheral tissues, thus making it more readily available for the CNS to increase dopamine synthesis in the healthy neurons that are left.

TABLE 4-1 **What Makes a Chemical Substance a Neurotransmitter?**	
Production	A neurotransmitter must be synthesized by the neuron and released from the neuron. The presynaptic terminal should therefore contain the neurotransmitter and the enzymes necessary to synthesize it.
Identification	The substance should be released in a form that can be chemically or pharmacologically identified. Therefore it should be possible to isolate it and know its structure.
Reproduction capability	The events that occur on stimulation of the presynaptic terminal should be reproduced by the effect of this substance on the postsynaptic cell.
Blocking	The effects of the substance should be blocked by a competitive antagonist of the receptor in a dose-dependent manner. Treatments that inhibit the synthesis of the substance should block the effect of presynaptic stimulation as well.
Termination	There should be a mechanism that will terminate the action of the substance on the cell, such as uptake, enzymatic inactivation, etc.

Modified from Squire, L. R., Berg, D., Bloom, F. E., du Lac, S., Ghosh, A., & Spitzer, N. C. (2013). *Fundamental neuroscience* (4th ed.). Oxford, England: Academic Press.

Patients with seizures experience the effects of abnormal activity of glutamatergic neurons. Because it is an excitatory neurotransmitter, rapid and sustained firing of even a small group of these neurons in one area of the brain may lead to successive excitation of other similar neurons until a region, or in the case of a grand mal seizure, the entire brain, experiences a paroxysmal discharge, which is the seizure activity. Pharmacologic treatment is targeted toward utilization of GABA transmitters to inhibit neural firing. Drugs such as phenobarbital are used for long-term management of seizures.

CHEMICAL TRANSMISSION IN THE MOTOR SYSTEM

In peripheral nerve-to-muscle transmission, or neuromuscular transmission, the nerve is known to be a structure on the muscle surface, making contact with the muscle fiber but not fusing with it. A special

---

BOX 4-2

Classical, Non-classical, and Unconventional Neurotransmitters

Classical

GABA
Glycine
Glutamate
Aspartate
Homocysteine
Taurine
Acetylcholine
Monoamines
Catecholamines
Dopamine
Norepinephrine
Epinephrine
Serotonin
Adenosine
Adenosine triphosphate
Nitric oxide

Non-classical: Neuropeptides

β-Endorphin
Dynorphin

Neoendorphin
Arginine vasopressin
Oxytocin
Substance P
Kassinin
Neurokinin A
Neurokinin B
Eledoisin
Vasoactive intestinal peptide
Glucagon
Secretin
Growth hormone-releasing hormone
Methionine enkephalin
Leucine enkephalin

Unconventional

Endocannabinoids
Nitric oxide

---

structural enlargement of the muscle fiber called the motor endplate is at the synaptic junction. In the PNS, electrical currents generated by the action of the transmitter substance acetylcholine flow across the synapse to the postsynaptic membrane. In nerve-to-muscle impulses, this is the membrane of the motor endplate. An impulse is then generated along the muscle fiber, which sets off a complex series of events for muscle contraction.

Myasthenia gravis is an unusual disorder of neurotransmitter transmission in the motor system. With this neuromuscular disease, the patient shows muscle weakness on sustained effort. Neuromuscular transmission appears to fail after continuous muscle contraction as a result of reduced availability of acetylcholine at the synapse between nerve and muscle. Antibodies interfere with the transmission of the acetylcholine. These antibodies are an autoimmune disease reaction to postsynaptic receptor protein, with an involvement of the postsynaptic membranes. In the earlier stages, if the muscle is allowed to rest, normal function is restored until further use again depletes the acetylcholine.

The primary symptom of weakness often affects the speech muscles. The nerves innervating the larynx and velum are sometimes the first to be affected

by the disease. The weakened vocal folds do not close appropriately, and the voice becomes breathy and weak in intensity. A hypernasal voice quality may develop after sustained speaking because of weakness of the soft palate. As the speech deteriorates, the tongue, lips, and respiratory muscles may be involved. Speech symptoms are discussed further in Chapter 8.

Certain drugs (e.g., neostigmine [Prostigmin] and edrophonium [Tensilon]) temporarily and promptly relieve the symptoms and help the neurologist diagnose the disease. Treatment to reduce the antibodies blocking the acetylcholine transmission is effective in reversing the neuromuscular problem in the muscles of the body, as well as the speech muscles.

ELECTRICAL SYNAPSES (GAP JUNCTIONS)

Although chemical synapses are by far the most common signaling mechanism in the nervous system, electrical synapses occur more frequently than once thought. In vertebrates, they occur often at sensory synapses (for example, in the retina), in some nuclei of the thalamus, and also in some cortical-cortical neuron transmissions. They allow more rapid signaling because there is no electrical-to-chemical-to-electrical transition necessary. When they do occur, it is primarily at what are called gap junctions, rather than synaptic clefts, between dendrites or between two closely adjacent neuron cell bodies. Electrical synapses are excitatory only; there are no inhibitory electrical synapses. No neurotransmitter is involved, and no delay at the synapse occurs. Thus no modulation of the transmission would be possible. According to Fitzgerald and Folan-Curran,[3] electrical synapses occur to ensure that neurons that must participate in a common activity fire in synchrony. An example of this occurs in the medulla for synchronous discharge during inspiration.

Principles of Neuronal Operation

The CNS is constantly bombarded by volleys of sensory nerve impulses. Both excitation and inhibition play a large role in the nervous system. The excitatory and inhibitory influences provide a process of selectivity of impulses for transmission at the level of the synapse. This selectivity of transmission of nerve impulse may be the basic function of the synapse. The synapse also allows transmission in an all-or-nothing manner. In other words, all that can be transmitted is either a full-sized response for the condition of the axon or nothing.

Furthermore, the CNS is characterized by the principle of divergence. Charles Sherrington[7] observed that within the human nervous system are numerous branchings of all axons with a great opportunity for wide dispersal of impulses because the impulses discharged by a neuron travel along its branches to activate all its synapses. Synaptic divergence means that an AP can trigger multiple excitatory postsynaptic potentials simultaneously, affecting many dendritic terminals at once. This amplifies the activity of a single axon. This kind of divergent synaptic action is found, for example, in the cerebellum, which demonstrates great divergence, and in the sensory afferents of the thalamus. Another method of achieving divergence, involving axons, is also found in the nervous system. Axons branch into collaterals and give rise to multiple terminals, thus resulting in numerous synaptic contacts. This kind of divergence is common in the cortical cells. Thus the CNS is composed of an almost infinite series of sources and routes for widespread or accessory neuronal activity. This accessory neuronal activity forms what may be considered *neuronal pools* of activity.

A complementary principle of convergence exists in the nervous system. This principle, also enumerated by Sherrington, implies that all neurons receive synaptic information from many other neurons, some of an excitatory nature and some of an inhibitory nature. Synaptic convergence occurs when multiple synapses occur on one postsynaptic dendrite. The number of synapses on individual neurons is generally large, measured in hundreds or thousands, with the largest being approximately 80,000. When convergence occurs, two kinds of summation, or additive effects, may take place. *Temporal summation* may occur in which the effect of the neurotransmitters may be enhanced, for example, if the additive effect of all synapses is excitatory. The convergence could also summate in time with the excitatory and inhibitory potentials canceling each other out, resulting in the resting potential being maintained. The integration of the excitatory and inhibitory synapses usually functions, however, to *modulate* action. With modulation, there is a change in potential, but it is not as great a change as it would have been without the convergence.

Another kind of convergence summation is *spatial summation*. During this, the varied sites of synapse along the dendritic surface of the neuron cause responses to rise in the different parts of the neuron (graded potentials). The summation may increase the possibility of more local mechanisms during activation from the site on one dendritic tree to another.

Principles of divergence and convergence also suggest that certain neuronal systems can act primarily as either excitatory or inhibitory mechanisms for effective overall neuronal functioning. An example is the large excitatory and inhibitory neuronal system in the reticular formation deep within the brain, which both activates and suppresses levels of consciousness during wakefulness and sleep, respectively. Box 4-3 summarizes the principles of divergence and convergence.

The complexity of the neuronal firings and synaptic connections, particularly on the surface of the brain called the cerebral cortex, provides an intricate weaving of impulses into complex spatial and temporal patterns. Sherrington has compared this neuronal activity with the weaving of an enchanted loom. Today, in the age of technology, we tend to compare it with an extremely complex "network." No doubt these ever-changing neuronal designs are the basis for the integrative activity of the nervous system and are the foundations of emotion, thought, language, and action, as well as that most human of behaviors, speaking.

The range of behavior that is assumed to be specifically human, including our rich and complex language system, is sometimes difficult to grasp. Even harder to believe is that this range ultimately can be reduced to

Principles of Divergence and Convergence

Divergence

- Branching of all axons within the human nervous system allows activation of all proximate synapses.
- Creates limitless pathways for potential neuronal activity.
- Allows grouping of neuronal activity: excitation or inhibition.

Convergence

- Individual neurons receive multiple signals simultaneously from many other neurons.
- Signals from multiple neurons can be conflicting (some that excite and some that inhibit).
- Activation or suppression of an individual neuron is based on these incoming signals.

and equated with the mere ebb and flow of minute chemical and electrical changes in tiny, but intricate, synaptic mechanisms. This contemporary interpretation of neuronal function, reductionist as it appears, highlights the vast and mysterious frontier between mind and brain that faces the neuroscientist. Despite this great gulf between mind and matter, the speech-language pathologist should remember that this view of neuronal functioning provides the neurophysiologist with a basis for seeing the workings of the brain as a vast abstract complex of neuronal design on the enchanted loom of Sherrington. Despite the sophistication of studying neuronal function, the specifics of the neuronal patterns for understanding and producing language and speech in the brain remain largely a mystery.

DEGENERATION AND REGENERATION OF NEURONS AND THEIR CONNECTIONS

Degeneration

Primary neuronal loss refers to the immediate necrotic degeneration of neurons directly affected by, for instance, anoxia, physical trauma, or vascular insult such as a cerebrovascular accident (CVA). Secondary neuronal loss, on the other hand, refers to the degeneration of neurons that occurs hours, days, or weeks after the primary insult. The secondary neuronal loss is variable and can have an effect on prognosis.

If the axon of the neuron is damaged or severed, degeneration, but not death, of the neuron may occur. In the case of damage to the nerves of the peripheral nervous system, the damage to the axon may be at a point close to the cell body of origin or to a point far away because they often extend some distance. In the central nervous system, especially with cortical lesions or lesions in the spinal cord, because the cells are so close in proximity, secondary neuronal loss and degeneration of neurons may occur in the region just adjacent to the primary area of infarction. Several variables have an effect on the mechanisms of degeneration. These could include blood flow levels, the integrity of the blood-brain barrier, edema, and inflammation.

Two types of damage may occur in axons. Anterograde degeneration refers to the degradation of axonal structure that spreads *away* from the cell body. Wallerian degeneration is the most common type of anterograde degeneration and is often considered a synonymous term. Wallerian degeneration is the type of deterioration of axons and the myelin sheath resulting from more proximal axonal or neuronal damage. Deterioration consists of a pulling away of the myelin sheath and swelling of the axon with it eventually breaking into segments. The terminals continue to deteriorate, and the distal segment eventually dies. Glial cells then will go through the area and rid it of the debris.

In the PNS, retrograde degeneration, or spread of deterioration *toward* the cell body, may occur and the cell body itself may undergo chromatolysis, or loss of color, from the loss of the Nissl cells. This may eventually lead to cell death.

Regeneration

Axonal regeneration most likely occurs in the PNS when a peripheral nerve is either compressed or crushed but not severed and permanently damaged. The injured axon degenerates distal to the lesion, and the myelin sheath begins to break up. Monocytes from the blood enter and become macrophages to clean up the debris. The macrophages also signal the Schwann cells to secrete trophic substances to feed and guide the growth of new axonal sprouts. The axonal sprouting begins at the site of injury days to weeks after the injury. If regeneration is to be successful, the sprouting axons must make contact with the Schwann cells of the distal stump. The sprouting axons exhibit swellings on their tips. These swellings are called growth cones. The Schwann cells on the distal stump send out processes toward these growth cones. Regeneration usually proceeds at approximately 5 mm/day in the larger nerve trunks, with growth in the finer branches at approximately 2 mm/day.

If the nerve trunk of a peripheral nerve has been completely severed, spontaneous regeneration is not as successful because the axonal sprouts are not as likely to reach the appropriate distal stump targets. If the proximal axon sprouts fail to make contact, a neuroma may form, with whorls of these regenerating axons trapped in scar tissue at the injury site. Surgical repair of a severed nerve trunk is not usually attempted for a few weeks; delay is desired so that connective sheaths can thicken somewhat to be able to hold sutures better.

Central Nervous System Regeneration

If injury occurs to white matter in the CNS, degeneration distal to the point of injury occurs as it does in the PNS. However, clearance of the debris by the microglial cells and monocytes proceeds quite slowly, with debris found months later. Rather than the chromatolysis noted in parent cell bodies of peripheral nerves, the neurons in the CNS that are injured tend to necrose, or die. Surviving neurons in the area may appear wasted and usually do not make many synaptic contacts. This large-scale death of neurons is caused by a process known as orthograde transneuronal atrophy. Neurons of the CNS normally have a trophic effect on each other; that is, they sustain each other. When the main input to a group of neurons is damaged and no longer effective, the whole group is likely to waste away. Sometimes a phenomenon called retrograde transneuronal degeneration occurs in neurons upstream to those initially affected by the lesion.

Astrocytes may initiate the formation of a glial scar, which replaces the neuronal debris in the case of a small lesion. With a large lesion, cystic cavities containing cerebrospinal fluid and blood may be left.

Animal studies in the laboratory have provided hope that CNS neurons have regenerative capacity because they have shown sprouting of axons and invasion of planted peripheral nerves. In the CNS, deterrents to spontaneous regeneration like that seen in the PNS are the glial scar tissue that develops and the growth inhibition caused by breakdown of oligodendrocyte products. Unfortunately, oligodendrocytes of the CNS do not generate growth signals (like the active signaling for growth by the Schwann cells in the PNS). In general the CNS in mammals seems to lack trophic factors required to initiate the significant sprouting of axons. Injured motor and sensory pathways will regenerate only for a few millimeters, and if synapses develop, they are usually on nearby neurons.

At this writing, active areas of research for provision of trophic factors for regeneration in the CNS are the use of embryonic and adult-derived stem cells,[1,5] control of reactive astrogliosis,[8] and injection of the substance secreted by stem cells (secretome).[2] Although medical science has not found a way to regenerate neurons or hasten connections, there is promising research, including clinical trials, giving hope for the future of rehabilitation.

Synopsis of Clinical Information or Applications for the Speech-Language Pathologist

- A neuron is a nerve cell that is the basic anatomic and functional unit of the nervous system.
- Neurons have a cell body that synthesizes proteins.
- The three types of neuronal cells are classified by shape: multipolar, pseudounipolar, and bipolar.
- Each cell contains a nucleus and 1 to 12 projections of varying length that receive stimuli and conduct neural impulses.
- Dendrites receive neural stimuli; shorter ones receive signals from other neurons.
- Axons are longer single fibers that conduct nerve impulses away from the neuron to other parts of the nervous system, glands, and muscles.
- A synapse is the point of contact between the axon of one neuron and another neuron's cell body.
- This action produces neuronal activity or brain activation, thus producing perceptions, thoughts, and voluntary muscle movements.
- Cellular potential is the relative amount of voltage in an electrical field.
- Neurons have two electrical fields—one inside and one outside the cell body.

- Functions of neuron integration (thinking or cognition) depend on electrical properties and how the ions move.
- Resting potential is the ionic difference across the membrane at a steady state in the cell.
- AP is the neural impulse that travels to another cell body, dendrite, or axon.
- APs are brief electrical transients visible when recorded.
- APs occur throughout the body's tissues and regulate secretions of hormones and signal fertilization of the egg by the sperm. In a nervous system, APs integrate neural messages from cell bodies from sense organs.
- Nerve fibers, or axons, are either myelinated or unmyelinated.
- Myelin is a white, fatty, lipid substance that surrounds the axon for protection and transmission.
- Myelin in the CNS is oligodendrocytes.
- Myelin in the PNS is Schwann cells.
- Myelin is white, as opposed to the nonmyelinated cells, which appear gray.
- Myelin develops as the brain develops from the embryonic state.

Continued

Synopsis of Clinical Information or Applications for the Speech-Language Pathologist—cont'd

- Multiple sclerosis is an autoimmune inflammatory response that damages the myelin sheath; it may cause irreversible damage.
- Dysarthria is a speech disorder found in some neurological diseases.
- The synapse is the point at which an electrical nerve impulse in the form of an AP must be transmitted to another neuron, gland, or muscle.
- The presynaptic terminal is at the axon sending the impulse.
- The postsynaptic terminal is the receiving area of the receiving axon.
- The synapse between the presynaptic and postsynaptic space, called the synaptic cleft, is transmitted by chemical reaction.
- Chemical substances known as neurotransmitters are released by the presynaptic terminal; they diffuse across the synaptic cleft and bind with receptors in the postsynaptic terminal.
- Neurotransmitters provide excitatory action from the presynaptic terminal; to ensure completion of the synapse across the cleft, neurotransmitters also provide an inhibitory action from the postsynaptic terminal.
- Neurotransmitters are the fundamental basis for chemical action in the nervous system.
- Neurotransmitter types are named specifically to describe the neurons and axons that are part of the synapse process.
- The neurotransmitter dopamine has cells called dopaminergic neurons; if the cells contain glutamate, they are called glutamatergic cells.
- GABA and glutamate are the most prevalent neurotransmitters.
- Glutamate is a major excitatory neurotransmitter.

- GABA is a major inhibitory neurotransmitter.
- Disorders of neurotransmitter metabolism include Parkinson's disease, which is caused by a decrease in dopamine in the substantia nigra.
- Myasthenia gravis is a condition caused by reduced acetylcholine at the synapse between nerve and muscle.
- Primary neuronal loss is necrotic degeneration of neurons affected by anoxia or CVA.
- Secondary neuronal loss is degeneration of neurons that occurs within hours, days, or weeks after a primary insult; it may include effects on blood flow, integrity of the blood-brain barrier, edema, and inflammation.
- Neurons in the adult brain that are lost to trauma or disease are not replaced.
- In Parkinson's disease and Alzheimer's disease, neurons die in large numbers and leave those areas of the brain nonfunctional for motor function or cognition.
- If axons are simply damaged, then regeneration may be possible.
- Axonal damage is categorized as anterograde or retrograde.
- Anterograde damage is disintegration of the myelin sheath that depends on the Schwann cells or oligodendrocytes.
- Retrograde damage is characterized by swollen cell bodies, an enlarged nucleus, and dissolution of endoplasm.
- Large-scale death of neurons is called orthograde transneuronal atrophy.
- Research on stem cells, astrogliosis, and the secretome is currently being done to investigate neuronal regeneration in the CNS and PNS.

REFERENCES

1. Ali, F., Stott, S. R. W., & Barker, R. A. (2014). Stem cells and the treatment of Parkinson's disease. *Experimental Neurology*, *260*, 3–11.
2. Drago, D., Cossetti, C., Nunzio, I., Gaude, E., Musco, G., Bachi, A., & Pluchino, S. (2013). The stem cell secretome and its role in brain repair. *Biochimie*, *95*, 2271–2285. Retrieved from http://www.ncbi.nlm.nih.gov/pmc/articles/PMC4061727.
3. Fitzgerald, M. J. T., & Folan-Curran, J. (2002). *Clinical neuroanatomy and related neuroscience* (4th ed.). Edinburgh: W. B. Saunders.
4. Haines, D. E. (2006). *Fundamentals of neuroscience* (3rd ed.). St. Louis: Elsevier.
5. Hu, Z., & Ulfendahl, M. (2013). The potential of stem cells for the restoration of auditory function in humans. *Regenerative Medicine*, *8*, 309.
6. Roland, P. E. (1993). *Brain activation*. New York: Wiley.
7. Sherrington, S. C. (1926). *The integrative action of the nervous system*. New Haven, CT: Yale University Press.
8. Sofroniew, M. V., & Vinters, H. V. (2010). Astrocytes: Biology and pathology. *Acta Neuropathologica*, *119*, 7–35.
9. Squire, L. R., Berg, D., Bloom, F. E., du Lac, S., Ghosh, A., & Spitzer, N. C. (2013). *Fundamental neuroscience* (4th ed.). Oxford, England: Academic Press.

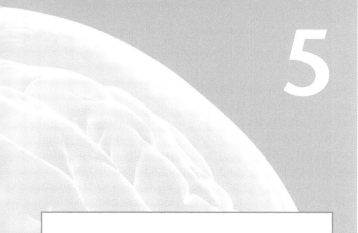

5

Neurosensory Organization

Speech is normally controlled by the ear.
Raymond Carhart, *Hearing and Deafness*, 1947

KEY **TERMS**

agnosia
analgesia
anterior spinothalamic
  tract
astereognosis
atopognosis
audition
auditory agnosia
auditory brainstem
  responses (ABRs)
basilar membrane
cerebellopontine
  angle
cochlea
cochlear duct
dermatome
dorsal column
  pathway
endolymph
exteroceptors
fasciculi
helicotrema
hemianopsia
hyperalgesia
hyperesthesia
hypoalgesia
hypoesthesia
interoceptors

lateral spinothalamic
  tract
mechanicoreceptors
modiolus
nociceptors
optic chiasm
optic disk
organ of Corti
perilymph
peristriate cortex
photoreceptors
proprioceptors
Romberg test
scalae
spinocerebellar
  pathway
spiral ganglion
splenium
stereognosis
stereocilia
striate cortex
tectal (collicular)
  pathway
tectorial membrane
temporal visual cortex
tonotopic
visual agnosia

Classification

During the nineteenth century, neurophysiologists primarily conceived the execution of skilled motor acts as the result of programming in the motor areas of the cerebral cortex, with some additional influences on the descending motor impulses from cerebellar and extrapyramidal mechanisms. This view of the nervous system was modified during the twentieth century to include the concept of sensory feedback control in motor acts. Audition, of course, plays a special and primary feedback role in the control of speech. More recently, specific efforts have been directed at determining the nature of other neurosensory controls exercised in speaking. Before discussion of sensory control in speech, an understanding of the general types of sensation mediated by the nervous system is necessary.

SHERRINGTON'S SCHEME

Charles Sherrington[9] proposed a classification of sensation that has application for the sensory control of speech. He divided the sensory receptors into three broad classes: exteroceptors, proprioceptors, and interoceptors. Exteroceptors mediate sight, sound, smell, and cutaneous sensation. Cutaneous superficial skin sensation includes light touch or pressure, fine touch (also known as two-point or discriminative touch), superficial pain, temperature, itching, and tickling. Proprioceptors mediate deep somatic sensation from receptors beneath the skin, in muscles and joints, and in the inner ear. Proprioception includes the senses of movement, vibration, position, and equilibrium. Interoceptors mediate sensation from the viscera as well as visceral pain and pressure or distention. Pain receptors, either from cellular or tissue injury, are known as nociceptors.

Neurophysiologists have classified the senses as special and general. The term *special senses* reflects the traditional layperson's concept that certain senses are primary. For the neurophysiologist, hearing, vision, taste, smell, and balance are the special senses. The general senses, in this classification scheme, include the remainder of the senses. Further breakdown into visceral and somatic sensations has also been added to the classification schemes. General visceral afferent interoceptors monitor events within the body, including bladder distention and pH changes in the blood. Special visceral afferent receptors are those of taste and smell (olfaction). Special somatic afferent receptors are concerned with vision, audition, and balance or equilibrium.

SENSORY ASSOCIATION CORTICES

In Chapter 2 the functional typology of association cortex was discussed, with unimodal and polymodal association cortices found in the sensory processing areas of the brain. Afferent projections of sensory information initially are processed in unimodal cortex found in the primary sensory cortices, including the visual cortex (area 17 along the calcarine fissure), the auditory cortex (areas 41 and 42 in Heschl's gyrus), and the somatosensory cortex (areas 1, 2, and 3 in the postcentral gyrus). Areas around the primary sensory cortices usually are polymodal association cortex. The visual association cortex includes the entire medial surface of the occipital lobe beyond the primary area, the lateral surface of the occipital lobe (areas 18 and 19), the inferior and middle temporal gyri, and the entire inferior surface of the temporal lobe (areas 20, 21, and 37). The auditory association cortices include the areas around Heschl's gyrus and area 22, a portion of the superior temporal gyrus. Area 22 in the left temporal lobe, however, is considered more of a supramodal association area than simply a polymodal processor because of the language processing capability.

Recognition and identification or classification of a sensory stimulus is a critical function and can preclude or complicate evaluation of communication skills. Perception of a word requires adequate hearing acuity, but the stimulus must also be recognized to be a word. The features must be visually, audibly, or tactilely perceived before an object can be recognized. Sensory disorders resulting in an inability to interpret a sensory stimulus and recognize it are called agnosias.

The term agnosia was introduced to neurology by Sigmund Freud (1856-1939) in 1891. Agnosia is a disorder of recognition caused by cerebral injury. Classic theory places the lesion responsible for the disorder in the sensory association areas of the cerebral cortex, leaving the primary sensory receptor areas intact. To diagnose the classic disorder correctly, certain precautions must be observed. First, the lesion must be determined to be at the level of the cortical association area rather than at the level of the sensory receptor, the sensory pathway, or the primary sensory receptor area in the cortex. Second, unfamiliarity with the test item must be ruled out as a reason for failure to recognize the sensory stimuli. To establish basic knowledge of an item, the patient should match items. If an item can be matched or recognized in other modalities, unfamiliarity can be ruled out as a possible cause for the lack of recognition. The concept of agnosia has been highly criticized in contemporary neurology. Although true agnosias are not common, some patients in clinical practice appear to demonstrate a tactile, visual, or auditory agnosia. Table 5-1 defines the various types of agnosias that may be seen in a clinical practice specializing in neurobehavioral disorders.

The Sense of Hearing

A major aspect of speech and language function depends on audition. **Audition** generally is classified as one of the special senses and as an exteroceptive sense. Knowledge of the neurologic functions of the central auditory pathways is crucial for an understanding of the mechanisms of the communication nervous system.

TABLE 5-1	
Agnosias	
TYPE OF AGNOSIA	CHARACTERISTICS
Agnosia	A disorder of recognition caused by damage to cortical sensory association areas or pathways
Visual agnosia	Inability to recognize objects, colors, and pictures
Auditory agnosia	Inability to comprehend speech or nonspeech sounds (pure forms: auditory nonverbal agnosia and pure word deafness)
Tactile syndrome	Inability to recognize objects by touch; characterized by bilateral parietal lobe lesions
Gerstmann syndrome	Includes finger agnosia, right-left disorientation, acalculia, and agraphia; usually characterized by left parietal lobe lesions

Before discussing the specific levels of the central auditory pathway, a review of how sound is transmitted to the inner ear and the auditory nerve, cranial nerve VIII, is warranted. The physical signal known as sound undergoes a series of complex transformations for it to be heard. These transformations begin when a mechanical disturbance causes molecules in the air to alternately expand and compress (vibrate) and sets up a displacement that is passed along among the molecules. The resulting sound waves are channeled by the external ear structures into the external auditory meatus, or ear canal, the resonating canal that ends at a taut membrane called the eardrum, or tympanic membrane (Fig. 5-1). The eardrum is at the entrance to the middle ear, an air-filled cavity containing the three tiniest bones of the body, the malleus, incus, and stapes, collectively known as the ossicles. This ossicular chain has one end attached to the eardrum and the other to a small opening at the inferior part of the cavity called the oval window. Mechanical transmission of vibration through the ossicular chain helps increase the force that reaches the oval window. The force causes the oval window to move and transmit the movement into the fluid-filled cavity of the inner ear. The inner ear contains the coiled **cochlea** (Fig. 5-2). On the membranes of the cochlea are the sensory hair cells that contain neurotransmitters to be released to stimulate the auditory nerve, cranial nerve VIII. This auditory nerve then carries this signal to the cochlear nucleus in the brainstem and on to its final destination, the auditory cortex.

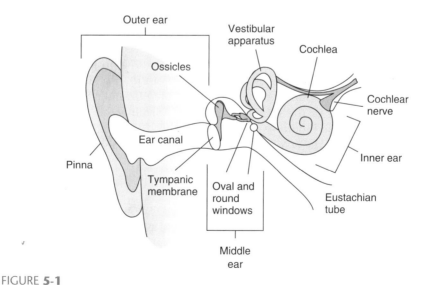

FIGURE **5-1**

Three divisions of the ear. In the outer ear sound waves are directed to the middle ear, where they are converted to oscillations of the ossicles. In the inner ear the oscillations are converted to pressure waves, which in turn are converted to neuronal activity. (From Castro, A., Neafsey, E. J., Merchut, M. P., & Wurster, R. D. [2002]. *Neuroscience: An outline approach.* Philadelphia: Mosby/Elsevier.)

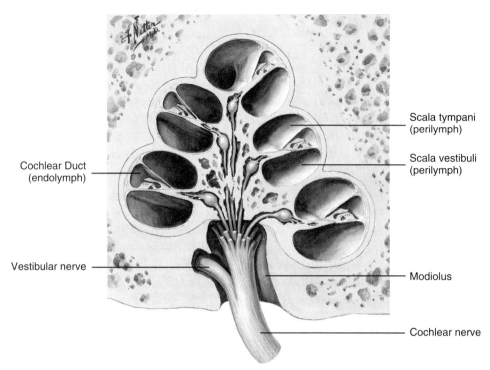

Cochlear Duct
(endolymph)

Vestibular nerve

Scala tympani
(perilymph)

Scala vestibuli
(perilymph)

Modiolus

Cochlear nerve

FIGURE **5-2**
Cross section of the cochlea. (Netter illustrations from www.netterimages.com, © Elsevier, Inc., All Rights Reserved.)

RECEPTOR LEVEL

The cochlea of the inner ear serves as an acoustic transducer, changing fluid vibrations to nerve impulses. The design and function of the cochlea are incredibly complex and intricate. A summary of this fascinating structure for study by the speech-language pathologist is, of necessity, brief. More in-depth information can be found in other texts.[3,10]

Figure 5-2 depicts a cross section of the cochlea. This coiled structure has a central bony, hollow core called the modiolus, which is in the axis of the internal auditory meatus. Running through the modiolus is the cochlear division of cranial nerve VIII, the acoustic-vestibular nerve. The cell bodies of its neurons form the spiral ganglion, and these are the primary or first-order neurons of the auditory pathway.

Forming a coil of two and a half turns around the modiolus are three separate fluid-filled columns called scalae (see Fig. 5-2). The upper compartment is the scala vestibuli, and the lower chamber is the scala tympani. These two chambers communicate at the apex of the modiolus at a site called the helicotrema. Between these two compartments is a third chamber called the scala media, also known as the cochlear duct. The scala vestibuli and the scala tympani are filled with a fluid called perilymph. The cochlear duct is filled with a different fluid, endolymph. These two fluids do not mix because of a tight barrier of epithelium lining the cochlear duct. The vestibular membrane, or Reissner's membrane, separates the cochlear duct and the scala vestibuli and the basilar membrane separates the cochlear duct from the scala tympani.

Membranes of fibrous connective tissue also run between the epithelium and the bones of the cochlea. The spiral lamina projects from the modiolus. Attached to the tip of the spiral lamina is the basilar membrane.

This membrane reaches across the cavity of the cochlea, forming the floor of the cochlear duct, and attaches to the spiral ligament on the outer wall of the cochlea. Figure 5-3 shows a cross section of the cochlear duct, looking at the cochlea in an upright position rather than its usual position on its side.

The basilar membrane is an important structure because it contains the organ of Corti, the sensory epithelium of hearing. When sound occurs, causing vibration of the tympanic membrane and movement of the ossicles of the middle ear, movement of the oval window leading into the scala vestibule occurs. This creates a pressure wave in the perilymph in the scala vestibuli. The pressure waves are transmitted through the vestibular membrane to the basilar membrane. This movement then sets up a neural chain of events in the organ of Corti.

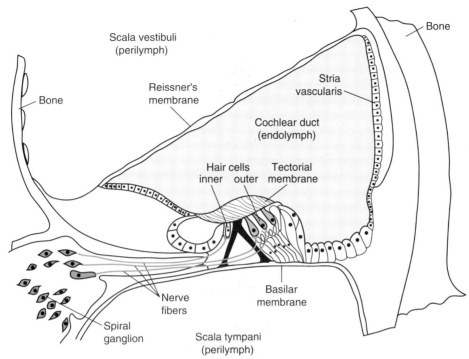

FIGURE 5-3
Cross section of the cochlear duct. (From Nadeau S. et al. [2004]. *Medical neuroscience.*
Philadelphia: Saunders/Elsevier.)

In the organ of Corti are several types of cells, with the two most important being the inner hair cells and the outer hair cells. These cell types are separated by a central tunnel, with the outer hair cells located on the outer side of the tunnel. The hair cells rest on supporting cells; other ancillary cells also are in the structure. On the top of the hair cells are stereocilia, extremely long microvilli extending from the surface. Overlying the hair cells and their stereocilia is a gelatinous structure called the tectorial membrane. The stereocilia of the inner hair cells lie just below the tectorial membrane, whereas those of the outer hair cells are embedded in the tectorial membrane (see Fig. 5-3). The outer hair cells outnumber the inner cells by approximately 3:1, but most of the neurons of the spiral ganglion innervate inner hair cells, with up to 20 large afferent neurons synapsing on each inner hair cell. These myelinated neurons innervating the inner hair cells are called type I cells, and each one responds best to a certain frequency.

The organ of Corti also receives efferent innervation coming from the olivocochlear bundle of the superior olivary complex in the brainstem. Thus some information comes from the brain to the cochlea rather than it all being unidirectional, from cochlea to brain. Some neurons go to the outer hair cells. These well-myelinated efferent neurons (medial olivocochlear bundle) typically cross the midline and exit the brain with the vestibular portion of cranial nerve VIII. They eventually join the cochlear division and travel in the spiral ganglion. They then enter the organ of Corti and synapse on the outer hair cells. Although none of the efferent fiber functions of the auditory system is well understood, these cells are believed to inhibit or reduce the movement of the outer hair cells, effectively reducing the sensitivity of the cochlea at that particular region.

Some efferent neurons also go to the inner hair cells (lateral olivocochlear bundle); these are unmyelinated, usually do not decussate, and follow the same pathway to synapse just under the inner hair cells. These fibers appear to influence the type I spiral ganglion cells by making them more difficult to excite. These efferent pathways of innervation to the cochlea are believed to combine to assist the auditory system in selective listening so that certain auditory input can be attuned to and background noise or other input can be ignored.

CRANIAL NERVE LEVEL

The nerve of hearing, cranial nerve VIII, has two divisions: the cochlear branch, associated with hearing, and the vestibular branch, associated with balance. Central processes of the cochlear nerve (the first-order neurons) proceed from the spiral ganglion through the internal auditory canal. The cochlear nerve is accompanied by cranial nerve VII, the facial nerve, in the auditory canal. The two nerves enter the brainstem at the sulcus between the pons and the medulla, an area known as the **cerebellopontine angle**. The cochlear nuclear complex spans the border between the pons and the medulla.

BRAINSTEM LEVEL

The fibers of the cochlear division of cranial nerve VIII end in the dorsal and ventral cochlear nuclei, which are draped around the inferior cerebellar peduncle. The cochlear nuclei contain the second-order neurons of the auditory pathway. From the cochlear nuclei, most fibers of the auditory pathway proceed to the upper medulla and pons and cross the midline. Other fibers ascend in the brainstem ipsilaterally. Fibers course upward in the ascending central auditory pathway of the brainstem called the lateral lemniscus. The fibers take one of several routes, and synapses in the auditory system may occur at one or more of the following structures: the superior olives, the inferior colliculus, and the nucleus of the lateral lemniscus. The superior olivary nuclei play an important role in localizing sound through neural response to the time and intensity differences arriving from both ears. All of the ascending auditory fibers terminate in the medial geniculate body, a thalamic nucleus.

AUDITORY RADIATIONS AND CORTEX

The fibers arising from the medial geniculate body, coursing to the temporal cortex, are called auditory radiations. They pass through the internal capsule in their route to the bilateral primary auditory areas of the brain in the superior and transverse temporal gyri. These areas are numbered 41 and 42 and are known as Heschl's gyrus.

The nuclei of the auditory pathway—the superior olivary complex, the nucleus of the lateral lemniscus, and the inferior colliculi—serve as relay nuclei as well as reflex centers. The reflex centers make connections with the eyes, head, and trunk, where automatic reflex actions occur in response to sound.

Descending efferent fibers, in addition to the ascending afferent fibers, are present in all parts of the central auditory pathway. They probably serve as feedback loops within the pathways. Figure 5-4 shows a simplified schema of connections along the auditory pathway.

AUDITORY PHYSIOLOGY

Sound is transmitted to the central auditory pathways by a traveling wave set up on the basilar membrane of

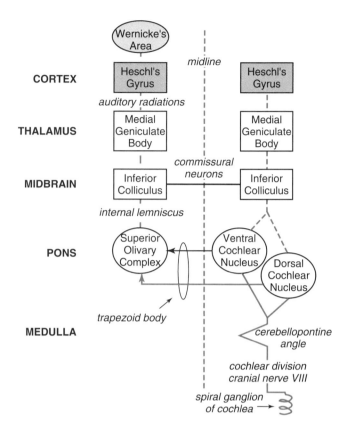

FIGURE **5-4**
The afferent pathways of the central auditory system and the major auditory way stations. The *bold lines* indicate that the majority of fibers in the auditory pathways decussate, although some do travel ipsilaterally *(dotted lines)*. For most of the population, perceptual analysis and comprehension of language occur in Wernicke's area of the left hemisphere, and information coming in to the left ear has to cross to Wernicke's area on the left after reaching Heschl's gyrus in the right hemisphere.

the cochlea. The basilar membrane is narrower at the base of the cochlea than at its apex. The mechanics of the membrane on which the organ of Corti is located vary slightly from base to apex. Traveling pressure waves of a specific frequency cause the basilar membrane to vibrate maximally at a specific point along the length of the membrane. Higher pitched sounds (high-pitched frequency waves) cause the shorter fibers at the basal turn of the cochlea to absorb their energy, whereas lower pitched sounds are absorbed by the longer fibers at the apical turn of the cochlea. Thus the basilar membrane is said to be **tonotopic** in its organization of fibers. This tonotopic organization extends to the inner hair cells as well. These hair cells receive afferent input from the peripheral processes of the spiral ganglion cells. When a local response to a certain frequency occurs in the hair cells, the vibration produces shearing forces, causing depolarization. Electrical charges in the dendrites of the spiral ganglion are set up and, in turn, cause the nerve cells to fire, releasing excitatory neurotransmitters.

Auditory nerve impulses ascend in the pathways of the central auditory nervous system. The organ of Corti serves as an analyzer of sound frequencies. Because of its tonotopic organization, the highest frequencies stimulate hair cells in the most basilar portion of the cochlea, where the basilar membrane is narrowest. The lowest frequencies stimulate the portions of the membrane at the apex. Frequency discrimination is therefore dependent on the frequency of the tone and the spatial response of the basilar membrane. Intensity discrimination depends on the length of the basilar membrane set in motion and the amplitude of the vibration. Displacement of a longer area of the membrane activates more nerve fibers, and a greater amplitude of vibration increases the frequency of the neural discharge.

Localizing the source of a sound depends on a comparison between the arrival time and the intensity of the sound at the two ears. Localization of sound occurs at higher levels in the auditory pathways. Central auditory structures, generally above the level of the inferior colliculus, are capable of making appropriate comparisons for sound localization. Thus in mammals and human beings the temporal auditory cortex is not needed for simple sound recognition, but it is essential for sound localization and recognition of changes in the temporal sequencing of sounds.

Temporal sequencing is a crucial higher auditory function because it is a significant aspect of speech. Sound localization probably requires the inferior colliculus and auditory cortex, whereas temporal sequencing may require the cochlear nuclei, the medial geniculate nuclei, and the auditory cortex. A tonotopic organization is present in all the central auditory nuclei, but the nuclei are used for analysis of several auditory properties of sound other than the recognition of tones or different frequencies.

LESIONS OF THE AUDITORY SYSTEM

The integrity of part of the central auditory system, the auditory brainstem, may be assessed by recording **auditory brainstem responses (ABRs)**. Surface electrodes are placed on the mastoid bone and on the top of the head. Repetitive clicks are presented, evoking responses in a large number of central fibers of cranial nerve VIII. These responses stimulate activity at the cochlear nuclear level, the superior olivary complex, the lateral lemniscus tracts, and the inferior colliculi. The combined potential is enough to be picked up by the skin electrodes. This method may be used to assess hearing objectively in infants and persons who cannot cooperate

in subjective testing. A normal ABR is a strong indication that the middle ear, cochlea, and auditory brainstem are functioning normally. Abnormal ABRs may be caused by a middle ear or cochlear problem or may indicate a pathologic condition at sites in the brainstem such as at the level of the geniculate bodies, the medial colliculus, and the lateral lemniscus. If abnormal ABRs are found, further testing is necessary.

If a lesion occurs unilaterally and involves the auditory nerve in its path from the ear and includes the cochlear nuclei, the person will be deaf in one ear. The results of unilateral cortical damage do not produce complete deafness. Lesions in Heschl's gyrus bilaterally may produce cortical deafness, nonverbal agnosia, or auditory agnosia.

The term *auditory agnosia* usually refers to the inability to identify auditory nonlinguistic stimuli, although many use the term when referring to the inability to recognize nonlinguistic as well as verbal stimuli. Most appropriate is the label *auditory nonverbal agnosia* for a pure deficit in which identification of nonlinguistic stimuli is impaired and the term *pure word deafness* if referring to the disorder in which nonverbal stimuli can be identified but speech cannot be understood. All auditory agnosias occur in the face of normal hearing acuity. The site of lesion for auditory nonverbal agnosia is in dispute but is assumed to be in the auditory association areas of both hemispheres.

Pure word deafness is an uncommon syndrome in which the patient cannot comprehend verbal language but usually reads, speaks, and writes functionally. Errors in speech are often noted and a mild measurable language disorder (aphasia) may be present. Both unilateral and bilateral temporal lobe lesions have been described. Unilateral lesions are deep in the temporal lobe in the fibers projecting to Heschl's gyrus. Bilateral lesions usually have been described as occurring in the midportion of the superior temporal gyri of both hemispheres. Geschwind[4] notes that in pure word deafness with a unilateral lesion, the lesion must be located subcortically in the left temporal lobe so that the auditory radiations as well as the callosal fibers from the opposite auditory region are interrupted, preventing Wernicke's area from receiving auditory stimulation.

In bilateral pure word deafness, the lesions in the temporal lobe spare Heschl's gyrus. The lesions on the left are assumed to cut off connections between the primary auditory receptor cortex and Wernicke's area. A lesion on the right would cut off the origin of the callosal fibers from the right auditory cortex. Auditory nonverbal agnosia, in addition to pure word deafness, may be the basis of the syndrome known as cortical deafness, which is probably associated with bilateral temporal lobe lesions.

5, 6, 7

TABLE 5-2

The Sensory Modalities Represented by the Somatosensory Systems

MODALITY	SUB MODALITY	SUB-SUB MODALITY	SOMATOSENSORY PATHWAY (BODY)
Pain	Sharp cutting pain Dull burning pain Deep aching pain		Lateral spinothalamic Anterior spinothalamic, tectospinal, and reticulospinal tracts Older multisynaptic diffuse tract through RF and periaqueductal gray. Sends fibers to hypothalamus and limbic system; mediates visceral, emotional, and autonomic reactions
Temperature	Warm/hot Cool/cold		Anterior spinothalamic, tectospinal, and reticulospinal tracts Lateral spinothalamic
Touch	Itch/tickle and crude touch Discriminative touch	Touch Pressure Flutter Vibration Muscle tension Joint pressure	Anterior spinothalamic, tectospinal, and reticulospinal tracts Medial lemniscal

The Sense of Touch

SOMATIC SENSATION

The neuroanatomy of the senses is complex. The general somatic sensory pathways—those dealing with bodily sensation—use the spinal cord and spinal nerves. Sensation to the head and vocal mechanism—larynx, pharynx, soft palate, and tongue—use the cranial nerve pathways. When these pathways are assessed for integrity during a routine office examination, the attempt is made to isolate a sensory function, like touch to a particular part of the body. Keep in mind that when you actually touch something and can describe or at least crudely perceive features of it (like weight, temperature, pressure, place on the body that is touching it, etc.), you are using many integrated pathways. In general, most sensory pathways are three-neuron pathways from the periphery to the cerebral cortex, although some variation exists within this three-neuron organization for the sensations of touch, pain, temperature, and proprioception. For most bodily sensations carried to the brain through spinal nerves, the first-order, or prime, neuron is found on the dorsal or posterior spinal root in a mass known as a spinal ganglion. The axons then ascend and synapse on a second-order neuron. A general name for the tract formed by the axon of the second-order neuron is lemniscus. In most systems, fibers of the second-order neuron then cross the midline, and ascend to the third-order neuron in the thalamus. Table 5-2 summarizes the touch pathways for the body, excluding the

pathways for the oral musculature, which is discussed in Chapter 7.

Lateral Spinothalamic Tract

The crossed ascending sensory pathway in the spinal cord, known as the **lateral spinothalamic tract**, transmits the sensations of pain and temperature and perhaps itch (Fig. 5-5). The fibers enter the cord through the spinal root ganglion, travel up or down a few segments in Lissauer's tract, and end in the dorsal root of the gray matter. At this point the first-order neuron synapses with the second-order neuron and promptly crosses to the other side of the spinal cord. There the fibers enter the lateral white column or the lateral spinothalamic tract and ascend to the ventral posterior lateral nucleus in the thalamus. The axons of the lateral spinothalamic tract synapse with a third-order neuron that leaves the thalamus, ascends in the internal capsule, and reaches the postcentral cortical gyri in the parietal lobe (areas 3, 1, and 2).

Anterior Spinothalamic Tract

Approximately 10% of the spinothalamic fibers are sometimes separated in anatomic texts and presented to be fibers of the **anterior spinothalamic tract**. The anterior (or ventral) spinothalamic tract carries sensory information of crude (nondiscriminative) touch, as well as itch and tickle sensations (see Fig. 5-5). These fibers synapse within the dorsal gray horn cells in the spinal cord, cross midline, and ascend in the anterior spinothalamic tract to the brainstem and the posterior

FIGURE **5-5**
Flowchart depicting the lateral spinothalamic tract, which mediates pain and temperature, and the anterior spinothalamic tract, which mediates light or crude touch. *POST. LAT.,* Posterior lateral.

TABLE 5-3	
Human Proprioceptive Pathways	
PATHWAY	DESCRIPTION
Proprioception	Allows temporal and spatial comprehension among body parts
Two-point discrimination	Cognition of adjacent points on dermis
Vibratory sensation	Sensory pathway to detect vibrations by touch
Form perception	Recognition of objects by touch

ventral nucleus of the thalamus. The fibers associated with crude touch particularly branch extensively. The anterior spinothalamic tract also ends in the postcentral gyrus of the parietal lobe.

As the fibers of the spinothalamic tracts ascend, axon collaterals provide for additional neuronal connections, most notable to the reticular nuclei in the brainstem. The reticular nuclei then send projections to the thalamus, hypothalamus, and hippocampus. Descending fibers from these structures provide for mediation of somatic and visceral responses to pain, such as changes in respiration and heartbeat as well as nausea and fainting.

Effect of Damage
Damage to the spinothalamic tracts of pain and temperature usually results in loss to the opposite side of the body. Because of the extensive branching of ascending crude touch fibers, this type of touch is unlikely to be abolished by injury to a specific pathway in the spinal cord.

Proprioception Pathways
Proprioception, two-point discrimination, vibration, and form perception follow different pathways than do those of the spinothalamic tracts. Proprioception is the sense of knowing exactly where body parts are in space and in relation to one another. Two-point discrimination allows two adjacent points on the skin to be distinguished. Two-point sensitivity varies over the brain surface. The lips and fingertips are the most sensitive and the back the least sensitive. Vibratory sensation allows the recognition of vibration from touch. Form perception allows recognition of objects by touch alone. Table 5-3 summarizes the human proprioceptive pathways.

Spinocerebellar Tract
Proprioception is conveyed by fibers from muscle tendons and joints and takes two major routes after entering the spinal cord. One of these major pathways is the spinocerebellar pathway and the other is the dorsal column pathway.

The spinocerebellar pathways are of lesser importance in human neurology because of the poor localizing information available about these tracts. The spinocerebellar pathway has two tracts, dorsal and ventral. These tracts arise from the posterior and medial gray matter of the cord. The dorsal tract ascends ipsilaterally, but the ventral tract crosses in the cord. Both tracts terminate in the cerebellum and allow proprioceptive impulses from all parts of the body to be integrated in the cerebellum. The spinocerebellar pathway has been proposed to function in unconscious perception of already-learned motor patterns.

Dorsal Columns
Conscious proprioception, two-point discrimination, and form perception have been called the sensory modalities of the dorsal, or posterior, columns of the spinal cord. The first-order neuron of the posterior column pathway can be found in the dorsal root ganglion (Fig. 5-6). The axon of the first-order neuron enters the spinal cord and ascends to the medulla aggregately as the dorsal white columns. However, two fiber bundles, or fasciculi, comprise these columns. Axons entering the cord at the sacral and lumbar regions, which mediate proprioception from the leg and lower body, travel in the fasciculus gracilis, which comprises the medial

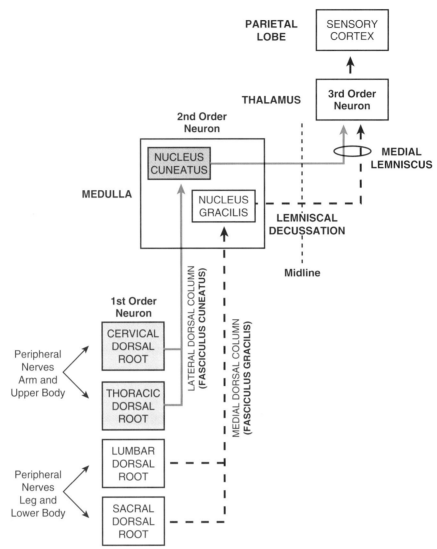

FIGURE **5-6**
Flowchart of pathways mediating proprioception. The pathways are known as the dorsal column modalities.

dorsal column. Axons from the thoracic and cervical regions, generally related to the arm and upper body, travel in the fasciculus cuneatus, comprising the lateral dorsal columns. These first-order neuron axons terminate in the nucleus gracilis and nucleus cuneatus in the medulla. The second-order neuron axons then cross over to the other side of the medulla, where they form a bundle called the medial lemniscus. Fibers of the medial lemniscus ascend to the third-order neuron in the ventral posterior nucleus of the thalamus and then proceed to the somatosensory cortex in the parietal lobe.

Proprioceptive Deficits

Damage to the postcentral gyrus of the parietal lobe, the dorsal columns, or the dorsal root ganglion may produce a loss of proprioception, astereognosis, loss

of vibratory sense, and loss of two-point discrimination in the trunk or extremities. If damage to these dorsal column fibers occurs below the level of the medulla (that is, below the decussation of the fibers), the loss in proprioception is ipsilateral (on the same side) of the injury. Damage above the level of decussation in the medulla produces a loss in proprioception on the opposite side of the body (contralateral to the site of injury).

Sensory Examination

The neurologist uses several traditional and standard procedures for determining sensory loss. These are incorporated into the standard neurologic examination (see Appendix C).

The senses of light touch, pain, and temperature are mediated by the fibers of the dorsal root of the spinal cord, which come from a circumscribed area of the skin known as a dermatome. In peripheral nerve injuries, impairment of touch corresponds to dermatomal zones; however, at the boundary of each segmental dermatome is an overlap area supplied by the adjacent segmental nerves. For instance, if the fifth thoracic nerve (T5) is severed, T3 and T6 will carry many of the pain and temperature sensations supplied by T5. This segmental overlap also is present in the spinal cord. Thus overlap is greater for pain and temperature than for touch.

LIGHT TOUCH

The sense of light touch is tested by determining the patient's ability to perceive light stroking of the skin with a wisp of cotton. Disorders of the sensory pathways from skin to cortex show abnormal sensory reactions. Decreased tactile sensation is called hypoesthesia, and complete loss of sensation is called anesthesia. Abnormally increased tactile sensation is known as hyperesthesia.

Inability to localize touch is called atopognosis. Topagnosis is tested by touching the patient's body. With the eyes closed, the patient is asked to point to the spot where touch occurred. The neurologist compares similar areas on both sides of the body. Atopognosia usually is associated with a lesion of the parietal lobe.

TWO-POINT DISCRIMINATION

Two-point discrimination, or the ability to discriminate the shortest distance between two tactile points on the skin, is sometimes tested with points of a caliper. Right and left sides of the body are compared. Loss of discrimination suggests a parietal lobe lesion.

Double stimulation may also be used to determine a cortical sensory disorder. Two simultaneous tactile stimulations are presented to both sides of the body in similar areas or to different areas. Lateralized sensory loss can then be determined. Sensory pathway or cortical sensory losses frequently accompany lesions that produce cerebral language disorders.

PAIN AND TEMPERATURE

Pain and temperature disturbance are more likely to be sensory pathway disorders, and lesions of the ventral and lateral spinothalamic tracts may be present. Pain perception is lost on the side contralateral to the lesion. Pain is tested by the ability to perceive a pinprick or deep pressure. Increased pain, or tenderness, is called hyperalgesia. A diminished sense of pain is hypoalgesia, and a complete lack of pain sensibility is analgesia.

Temperature disturbances are tested by the ability to distinguish between warm and cold. For this test, the neurologist usually asks the patient to identify a test tube of warm water and one of cold water.

RECOGNITION OF LIMB POSITION

The patient with proprioceptive deficits may not be able to determine, without looking, whether a joint of an arm, hand, or leg is in flexion or extension and may have difficulty identifying the direction of displacement of limbs or digits during movement.

STEREOGNOSIS

Stereognosis is the ability to perceive the weight, form, and other details of a body by touch. Astereognosis is the inability to recognize common objects, such as coins, keys, and small blocks, by touch. The examiner has the patient close his or her eyes and then places various objects in the person's hand, first one and then another, to be identified.

If this recognition disorder is caused by a cortical sensory lesion rather than a dorsal column proprioceptive lesion, it is called tactile agnosia. A lesion in the right somesthetic association area or in the corpus callosum may produce a true tactile agnosia in the right hand. Beauvois et al.[1] have reported a syndrome, which they named bilateral tactile aphasia, in a bilaterally damaged patient. This aphasia is analogous to the auditory and visual agnosia disorders. The patient was unable to name objects by touching them but could give the name when hearing the sound an object made. In this disorder, the lesion is presumed to be in both parietal lobes.

VIBRATORY SENSIBILITY TEST

The sensation evoked when a vibrating tuning fork is applied to the base of a bony prominence is lost with dorsal column problems. The patient cannot differentiate a vibrating tuning fork from a silent one on bony surfaces.

BODY SWAY TEST

This test, called the Romberg test, requires the patient to stand with his or her feet together. The neurologist notes the amount of sway with the patient's eyes open and compares it with the amount of sway with the eyes closed. An abnormal accentuation of swaying with the eyes closed or actual loss of balance is called a positive

Romberg sign. The visual sense can compensate for this loss of proprioception of muscle and joint position if it is caused by a dorsal column disorder, so the patient may correct balance problems by opening his or her eyes. If the lesion is in the cerebellum rather than the dorsal columns, the cerebellar ataxia of balance will not be corrected by visual compensation, as is the case in the sensory ataxia of the dorsal column.

Neuroanatomy of Oral Sensation

The neuroanatomy of oral sensation is different from that of the trunk and extremities in that the cranial and oral sensations are mediated by the cranial nerves, as opposed to mediation by the spinal nerves, as in bodily sensations. The sensory innervation of the speech mechanism is summarized in Table 5-4. Of particular importance to oral sensation is the trigeminal nerve (cranial nerve V). This cranial nerve is the primary somatic sensory nerve for the skin of the face, the anterior portion of the scalp, the anterior two thirds of the tongue, the teeth, and the outer surface of the eardrum. It mediates the sensations of pain, temperature, touch, pressure, and proprioception for the oral and cranial regions.

The glossopharyngeal nerve (cranial nerve IX), which is primarily sensory, also plays a role in mediating general somatic sensation in the cranial and oral regions. It mediates sensation from the posterior third of the tongue, the palatopharyngeal mucosa, and the external ear. Cranial nerve X mediates laryngeal sensation as well as sensation from the lower two thirds of the pharynx. The cranial nerves, their distribution and anatomy, motor innervation, and sensory mediation function are detailed further in Chapter 7.

Oral Sensory Receptors

Sensory receptors in the oral region and respiratory system generally are excited by chemical or mechanical stimulation. Taste, of course, is based on chemical stimulation. **Mechanicoreceptors** respond when stimuli distort them. For instance, the tongue touching the teeth, alveolar ridge, or palate compresses mechanicoreceptors, and the receptors in turn generate electrical impulses to the fibers.

The tongue mucosa and the tongue surface in particular are served by many types of mechanicoreceptors. The endings in these receptors have been divided into diffuse, or free, endings and compact, or organized, endings. Some speech experts believe that free endings provide a general sense of touch in sensory control of speech articulation and that organized endings provide sensitive acuity in speech articulation. Figure 5-7 illustrates the sensory innervation pattern for the tongue. Further discussion of oral sensation and its role in speech and swallowing are discussed in Chapter 7.

The Sense of Vision

RETINA

The visual system processes and decodes a wealth of information, more than any other afferent system in the body. To begin this processing, the eye absorbs the light from an image and passes it through the pupil. The

TABLE 5-4		
Sensory Innervation of the Speech Mechanism		
STRUCTURE	CRANIAL NERVE	FUNCTION
Face	V	Pain, temperature, touch to face
	VII	Proprioception to face
Tongue	V	Touch to anterior two thirds
	IX	Touch to posterior third
Palate	IX	Sensory to soft palate
Pharynx	IX	Sensory to lateral and posterior pharyngeal walls
	X	Sensory to lower two thirds of pharynx (forms pharyngeal plexus with cranial nerve IX)
Larynx	X	Sensory to most of the laryngeal muscles

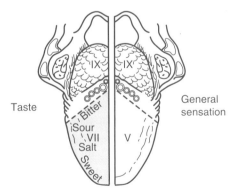

FIGURE **5-7**

Cranial nerve sensory innervation for mediation of taste and general sensation for the tongue.

image is then passed into the lens, where it is reversed and inverted. The lens focuses and projects the light onto the retina, which is a light-sensitive 10-layer formation of nerve cells lining the inside of the eyeball. The retina is composed of two types of **photoreceptors** (rods and cones) and four types of neurons (bipolar cells, ganglion cells, horizontal cells, and amacrine cells). Rods play a special role in peripheral vision and in vision under low light. Cones, on the other hand, function under bright light and are responsible for discriminative vision and color detection. The rods and cones synapse with the first-order neurons, the bipolar cells. These cells in turn synapse with the ganglion cells, which are second-order neurons. The axons of these cells converge to leave the eye within the optic nerve. After leaving the eye the axons acquire myelin sheaths.

This series of transmissions from first- to third-order sensory neurons is modified by horizontal cells and amacrine cells. They essentially sharpen the response of the ganglion cells to certain formations of light.

PATH OF THE OPTIC NERVE

The point of exit for the optic nerve is called the **optic disk**, which can be seen through an ophthalmoscope. Because rods and cones do not overlay the optic disk, it is essentially a small blind spot in each eye. The area on the retina for central fixated vision during good light is

the macula. A small central pit in the macula called the fovea centralis is composed of closely packed cones, and vision here is sharpest and color vision most acute.

The optic nerve conveys visual impulses. It consists of approximately one million nerve fibers, which course through the optic canal of the skull to form the **optic chiasm** (see Fig. 5-4). The fibers from the retina of each eye originate from two different areas on each retina. The retinal fibers can be thought of as exiting either as *temporal fibers*, which come from the lateral half of the retina nearest the temple, or as *nasal fibers*, which originate from the lateral half nearest the nose. As Figure 5-8 shows, at the optic chiasm the nasal fibers from each eye decussate while the temporal fibers continue ipsilaterally. This shift makes stereoscopic three-dimensional vision possible.

Figure 5-8 shows that the optics of the eye are such that the temporal half of one retina and the nasal half of the other retina receive information from the same half of the visual field. In other words, the temporal fibers of the left retina and the nasal fibers of the right retina carry information from the right half of the visual field, and the temporal fibers of the right retina and the nasal fibers of the left retina receive information from the left side of the visual field. Because of the decussation of the nasal fibers at the optic chiasm, all the information from the contralateral side of the visual field travels in one pathway down the optic tract to the visual cortex.

FIGURE **5-8**

Visual pathways with lesion sites and resulting visual field defects. The occipital lobe has been cut away to show the medial aspect and the calcarine sulci.

The visual cortex in the left hemisphere receives information about the contralateral right side of the visual field, whereas the right hemisphere processes information from the left visual field. This information is critical to understanding how a visual field deficit occurs after brain injury.

After passing the point of the optic chiasm, most of the axons forming the optic tract course to the lateral geniculate body, which is a small swelling located under the pulvinar of the thalamus. They then pass through the internal capsule and around the lateral ventricle, curving posteriorly. Some fibers travel far over the temporal horn of the lateral ventricle and form what is called the temporal loop, or Meyer's loop (see Fig. 5-8). These fibers terminate in the visual cortex below the calcarine sulcus. Meyer's loop carries fibers representing the upper part of the central visual field. Other optic fibers travel from the lateral geniculate body to the visual cortex above the calcarine sulcus. These fibers represent the lower part of the central visual field.

Some retinal ganglion cells terminate in the superior colliculus of the midbrain. The superior colliculus also receives synapses from the visual cortex. Fibers from the superior colliculus project to the spinal cord through the tectospinal tracts. These tracts control reflex movements of the head, neck, and eyes in response to visual stimuli.

PRIMARY VISUAL CORTEX

The characteristics of neurons in the visual cortex and the responses of individual cells have been studied in a wide variety of experimental animals. Scientists are interested in how patterns are perceived and recognized by the eye. Hubel and Wiesel,[5] among others, have found many different types of receptive fields in the neurons of the visual cortex. These receptive fields are termed simple, complex, hypercomplex, and higher order hypercomplex. Simple receptive field cells respond to a slit of light of particular width, slant, or orientation and place on the retina. Complex receptive fields respond to slit-shaped stimuli over a large area of the retina rather than a specific place. For hypercomplex fields, the line stimulus must be of a certain length. Cells with higher order hypercomplex fields require more elaborate visual stimuli to respond.

The visual cortex is organized in columns of cells with similar properties. Some columns respond only to one eye and are monocular. Others respond to both eyes and are binocular. Because the eyes are located in different positions on the head, a difference of position exists on the retinas for a stimulus, giving binocular disparity to the columnar cells. This provides information about the depth of objects.

In addition to the primary visual pathways, two other major visual pathways can be distinguished: the tectal, or collicular, pathway and the pretectal nuclei pathway. Thus fibers from the optic tracts do not all go to the lateral geniculate body. Some of them project to the subcortical pretectal nuclei and ascend to the thalamus and out from there to various regions of the cortex. This system seems to be important in the control of certain visual reflexes, such as the pupillary reflex, and certain eye movements.

The tectal, or collicular, pathway projects to the superior colliculi in the brainstem and to the thalamus and out to many regions of the cortex. The superior colliculi also receive input from somatosensory and auditory systems. The tectal pathway seems to be involved in a major way in the ability to orient toward and follow a visual stimulus.

The visual pathways do not operate independently. They are interconnected at every level from retina to cortex, and each receives descending input from the cerebral cortex, providing for the richness of visual perception.

VISUAL ASSOCIATION CORTEX

The area surrounding the striate cortex, the peristriate cortex (Brodmann's areas 18 and 19), is composed of neurons that have firing properties much like those of the primary visual cortex; however, these neurons also tend to show regional specialization for analyzing more complex aspects of visual stimuli such as motion, color, and form. Anatomists have been able to identify at least five regions of this peristriate area, each with a different processing role.

The second major part of the visual association cortex is the temporal visual cortex located within the middle and inferior temporal areas. This association area receives input from the peristriate cortex and has four major cortical output pathways: (1) to the contralateral temporal visual area, (2) to the prefrontal cortical area, (3) to the ipsilateral posterior association cortex of the superior temporal area, and (4) to the paralimbic and limbic areas of the medial temporal lobe. As with other neurons in primary and secondary visual cortex, neurons in the temporal visual association areas are sensitive to properties of the visual stimulus such as wavelength, size, length, and movement. These neurons, however, also seem to trigger in response to specific objects, including faces. Thus this part of the visual system may extract complex features from visual stimuli so that neurons become responsive to individual patterns rather than to isolated stimulus features. This may provide the mechanism for object discrimination. Box 5-1 outlines the two cortices associated with vision.

BOX 5-1

Cortical Output Regions and Pathways for Vision Association

Peristriate Cortex

- Consists of five regions, each having a different role in processing visual stimuli.
- Includes neurons that function as those of the primary visual cortex *and* show regional specialization for analyzing complex stimuli.

Temporal Visual Cortex

Consists of cortical output pathways to the following four areas:

1. Contralateral temporal visual area
2. Prefrontal cortical area
3. Ipsilateral posterior association cortex of the superior temporal area
4. Paralimbic and limbic areas of the medial temporal lobe
   a. Neurons trigger in response to specific objects and individual patterns
   b. May play key role in object discrimination

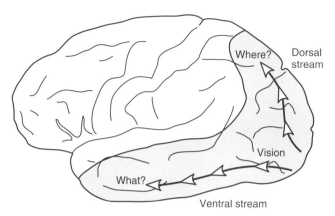

FIGURE **5-9**

Dorsal and ventral parallel processing streams shown emerging from the primary visual cortex in the occipital lobe. The dorsal stream, directed toward the parietal lobe, processes where the stimulus is, its direction of movement, and its speed of movement. The ventral stream, directed toward the temporal lobe, processes stimulus shape, what the stimulus is, and what it is called. (From Castro, A., Neafsey, E. J., Merchut, M. P., & Wurster, R. D. [2002]. *Neuroscience: An outline approach.* Philadelphia: Mosby/Elsevier.)

VISUAL INTEGRATION

As Mesulam[6] points out, object recognition or identification requires interaction between the visual representation in the association areas and other components of mental operation, including integration with past experience. This process requires relay of information from these temporal visual association areas to paralimbic and limbic areas of the brain.

Damage to the association areas in the peristriate cortex or temporal lobes or to their connections to other parts of the brain may have a number of different effects on visual processing. Mesulam lists the following four consequences as possibilities:

1. Impaired specialized visual processing and impaired formation of visual templates.
2. Loss of visual templates previously formed.
3. Disconnection of visual-auditory, visual-motor, visual-somatosensory, and visual-verbal pathways caused by interruption of input from the visual association areas to the frontal and parietal association areas.
4. Interruption of pathways providing input to paralimbic and limbic structures from the visual association area.

Lesions in the peristriate areas have been noted to cause specific disorders, such as difficulty with color vision or movement perception, yet they cause no disturbance to other visual functions. In 1982 Mishkin and Ungerleider,[7] scientists at the National Institutes

of Health, published a study discussing two cortical pathways separating the function of object perception and recognition from location and movement perception. Nadeau et al.[8] referred to these as the "what" and "where" systems in vision. This differentiation of visual processing capabilities begins at the retina, with rod and cone receptors projecting to both pathways. The "where" system allows visually guided hand and eye movements, permitting individuals to direct the eyes at what they want to look at and coordinate the touching or capture of a desired object with a part of the body. The "where" pathway is described as beginning in the occipital cortex and extending dorsally and medially into the parietal cortex (Fig. 5-9).

The "what" system is critical because it allows perception and recognition of objects located anywhere in the visual field; that is, independent of location, the abstract features of an object can be perceived and recognized. The pathway for this system begins in the occipital cortex and extends ventrally along the inferior temporal cortex, progressing into anterior areas of that cortex (see Fig. 5-9). With anterior progression, neurologic responsiveness of the visual receptive fields increases both in the number of neurons responding and the complexity of the stimulus features that generate a response. As Mesulam implies, a point exists at which what is seen is paired with what is already known, and the stimulus can be recognized in many orientations and backgrounds. Lesions in this pathway may result in impairment of object recognition or a visual agnosia.

VISUAL AGNOSIA

Analyzed in disconnection terms, classical visual agnosia is produced when visual associations are lost because of a disconnection of the visual areas from the language area. Also known as associative visual agnosia, the condition results in difficulty in recognizing pictures and objects along with a surprisingly good ability to describe, copy, and match visual stimuli. Patients correctly name the stimulus after tactile or auditory presentation. Bilateral occipital lobe lesions with extension on one side or the other into the medial temporal lobe involving the hippocampus have been found on autopsy. With such lesions both the naming and the memory of objects presented visually are affected.

Visual agnosia may also result from unilateral lesions. With destruction of the left visual cortex in addition to a lesion of the splenium of the corpus callosum, or extensive involvement of the white matter of the association cortex of the left occipital and parietal lobes, a unilateral left visual agnosia may result.

Benson[2] observed that in the few cases of visual agnosia reported, associated findings are common. These may include hemianopsia and prosopagnosia, a visual agnosia for faces. In addition, other associated disorders include constructional impairment, alexia without agraphia, amnesia, and some degree of anomia. A color-naming deficit may also be present; this inability to match seen colors to their spoken names is called color agnosia by Benson[2] and color anomia by Geschwind.[4] Lesions in the calcarine fissure and splenium are usually present. These lesions, according to Geschwind, disconnect the right visual cortex from the left language areas.

Synopsis of Clinical Information and Applications for the Speech-Language Pathologist

- The speech-language pathologist should be quite familiar with the auditory pathways and vigilant in identification of possible hearing loss.
- The central auditory pathway is complex, with the primary auditory receptor in the spiral ganglion of the organ of Corti of the cochlea of the inner ear. The auditory nerve (cranial nerve VIII) enters at the pontomedullary juncture, and damage in this area or to the auditory nerve often results in accompanying damage to cranial nerve VII (the facial nerve) because it also runs through the auditory canal.
- Bilateral damage to Heschl's gyrus or the temporal lobe auditory processing areas produces a spectrum of deficits, including cortical deafness, nonverbal agnosia, and auditory agnosia. Unilateral cortical damage to Heschl's gyrus does not produce total deafness.
- A unilateral lesion along the auditory nerve pathway from the ear and including the cochlear nuclei causes deafness in one ear.
- The lateral and anterior spinothalamic tracts carry sensory impulses of pain and temperature, light touch and pressure, and tactile discrimination from the periphery to the sensory cortex.
- Cerebral lesions marked by language loss may have accompanying sensory loss involving the parietal lobe or subcortical pathways.
- An agnosia is a disorder of recognition of a sensory stimulus. Agnosias result from bilateral damage to the primary cortical receptor areas associated with the particular sensory input affected.
- The oral cavity is rich in sensory receptors and the tactile receptors of the mouth, tongue, pharynx, and teeth; however, the role of sensory feedback in speech production is currently not clear, and no standard clinical method of assessment is widely accepted.
- Interruptions of the visual pathway from the retina to the occipital cortex cause visual field deficits, with the extent and type of deficit depending on the point of interruption in this double-crossed pathway.
- Patients with language disorders caused by posterior lesions are most at risk for visual field deficits that particularly affect reading and writing.

CASE **STUDY**

A 26-year-old male soldier was on duty in Iraq, driving a supply truck. An improvised explosive device detonated on the road near the left side of the truck, causing some damage to the truck and breaking the left window. The soldier had some cuts to his face and arm from the glass and also experienced severe difficulty hearing from both ears after the incident. Fortunately, rupture of the tympanic membranes was ruled out on examination. In approximately 2 weeks, he found that he could hear out of the right ear much better than from the left. He was sent for audiometric testing and consequent radiographs. The radiographs showed a fracture of the left temporal bone.

Questions for Consideration

1. What type of hearing loss would the audiogram show as resulting from a fracture of the temporal bone?
2. What part of the ear would most likely be affected?
3. What cranial nerve would be involved?

REFERENCES

1. Beauvois, M. F., Sailliant, B., Meininger, V., & Lhermitte, F. (1978). Bilateral tactile aphasia: A tacto-verbal dysfunction. *Brain, 101*, 381–402.
2. Benson, D. F. (1979). *Aphasia, alexia and agraphia.* New York: Churchill Livingstone.
3. Cohen, H. (1999). *Neuroscience for rehabilitation.* Philadelphia: Lippincott Williams & Wilkins.
4. Geschwind, N. (1965). Disconnection syndromes in animals and man. *Brain, 88*, 237–294 585–644.
5. Hubel, D. H., & Wiesel, T. N. (1968). Receptive fields and functional architecture of the monkey striate cortex. *Journal of Physiology, 206*, 419–436.
6. Mesulam, M. M. (1985). *Principles of behavioral neurology.* Philadelphia: F. A. Davis.
7. Mishkin, M., & Ungerleider, L. G. (1982). Contribution of striate inputs to the visuospatial functions of the parieto-preoccipital cortex in monkeys. *Behavioral Brain Research, 6*, 57–77.
8. Nadeau, S. E., Ferguson, T. S., Valenstein, E., Vierck, C. J., Petruska, J. C., Streit, W. J., & Ritz, L. A. (2004). *Medical neuroscience.* St. Louis: Elsevier.
9. Sherrington, S. C. (1926). *The integrative action of the nervous system.* New Haven, CT: Yale University Press.
10. Webster, D. B. (1999). *Neuroscience of communication.* San Diego: Singular.

6

Neuromotor Control of Speech

We cannot state exactly the number of muscles that are necessary for speech and that are active during speech. But if we consider that ordinarily the muscles of the thoracic and abdominal walls, the neck and the face, the larynx and pharynx, and the oral cavity are all properly coordinated during the act of speaking, it becomes obvious that over 100 muscles must be controlled centrally.

Eric H. Lenneberg, *Biological Foundations of Language*, 1967

KEY TERMS

action tremor
adiadochokinesia
 (dysdiadochokinesia)
akinesia
alpha motor neuron
 (AMN)
apraxia
areflexia
asynergia
ataxia
ataxic dysarthria
athetosis
atrophy
Babinski sign
bilateral innervation
bilateral symmetry
caudate nucleus (CN)
chorea
clonus
contralateral
 innervation
contralateral motor
 control
corona radiata
corpus striatum
corticonuclear fibers
corticopontine tract
corticospinal tract
decussation
denervation
direct activation
 pathway
dyskinesia
dysmetria
dystonia
extrafusal fibers
extrapyramidal system
feedback
feedforward
flocculi
genu
globus pallidus (GP)
Golgi tendon organs

hemiparalysis
hemiplegia
hyperkinesia
hyperreflexia
hypertonia
hypokinesia
hyporeflexia
hypotonia
indirect activation
 pathway
intention tremor
intrafusal fibers
lateral corticospinal
 tract
lower motor neuron
motor unit
muscle spindle
muscle tone
myoclonus
neocerebellum
nucleus accumbens
nystagmus
paralysis
paresis
peduncles
phasic tone
postural tone
premotor
putamen
pyramidal tract
rest tremor
servomechanism
 control systems
spasticity
striatum
substantia nigra (SN)
subthalamic nucleus
 (STN)
synergy
tardive dyskinesia
tremors
upper motor neurons
volitional

CHAPTER OUTLINE

Speech Production versus Limb and Trunk Movement
The Motor System in Speech Ontogeny
A Hierarchical System
Motor Planning
Trunk and Limb Movement: The Corticospinal Tract
Facial and Oral Movement: The Corticonuclear Tract
Upper and Lower Motor Neurons
Upper Motor Neurons (UMNs)
Lower Motor Neurons
Bilateral Symmetry
Indicators of Upper versus Lower Motor Neuron Damage
Neuromuscular Control
The Influence of Other Systems on Movement
The Basal Ganglia (or Basal Nuclei)
The Cerebellar System
Servomechanism Theory and Speech Motor Control
Feedback
Open and Closed Control Systems

Speech is one of the most complex behaviors performed by human beings. On average, a person utters approximately 14 recognizable speech sounds per second when asked to produce nonsense syllables as rapidly as possible. This unusually brisk rate is maintained even when speaking conversationally or reading aloud. The number of separate neural events supporting this complex coordination of the articulatory muscles is, of course, quite large, and the degree of neural integration in the motor system for routine, everyday talk is truly amazing. The statement that normal speech production requires the finest motor control in the body is no exaggeration.

Speech Production versus Limb and Trunk Movement

The competent speech-language pathologist (SLP) of today must be familiar with how limb, trunk, and speech production muscles work. SLPs work on teams with respiratory, physical, and occupational therapists. It is important that SLPs understand such things as how to reposition a child for the best motor control for feeding or what muscles of the trunk and limbs were affected in a spinal cord injury and how that injury may affect work on speech and language. But, of course, what is most critical to the SLP is understanding of the muscles of speech production. As we reviewed in Chapters 2 and 3, the most obvious difference in these muscles and limb and trunk muscles is that the muscles of speech production receive sensory and motor innervation through the cranial nerves, whereas limb and trunk muscles rely on the spinal nerve innervation. In his excellent discussion of the uniqueness of the speech muscles, Kent[16] provides us with information retrieved from a search of the literature on how the speech muscles are different in their genetic, developmental, functional, and phenotypical properties as well as their innervation. It would be useful for the student of speech-language pathology to read this article, but the main points are summarized in Box 6-1. Review this information before moving on to the discussion of the levels and systems of motor control for both spinal and cranial muscles.

THE MOTOR SYSTEM IN SPEECH ONTOGENY

The student of speech-language pathology about to explore the motor system underlying the production of speech should also keep in mind the structure of the basic unit of speech and how speech is thought to have evolved in humans. Although a great deal of time is spent in early academic classes learning all the phonemes of our language and their distinctive features, it is not the phoneme but the syllable that is the basic unit of speech. The basic or modal syllable frame in English is that of a vowel nucleus alternating with a consonant (usually a CV structure).[19]

This text also adopts the *frame/context* (F/C) theory[17] of the evolution of human speech as a basis for looking at why motor control evolved as it did resulting in the complicated motor pathways and relationships between structures. In formulating the F/C theory, MacNeilage acknowledged the relatively well-accepted theory that before speech output, the content elements (consonants and vowels) are inserted into a syllabic structure or frame. This is based on the fact that when speech errors are made by adults (whether originating from a person with normal brain function or a person with brain damage), the syllable structure does not change;

BOX 6-1

Some Differences in Biomechanical and Functional Properties between Speech Muscles and Limb Muscles

- Muscles of speech production are more complex in nature. The more than 100 muscles involved are composed of several types of muscles that can be grouped into structural and functional classes:
  - Joint-related (for example, masseter and digastric muscles)
  - Sphincteric (for example, orbicularis oris; palatal and pharyngeal constrictors)
  - Muscular hydrostat (for example, intrinsic muscles of the tongue)
  - Specialized for vibration and airway valving (for example, intrinsic laryngeal muscles)
  - Respiratory muscles that inflate and deflate the lungs
- With the exception of the muscles that close the jaw, muscles of speech production are specialized more for speed than for force.
- Speech muscles are capable of more precise coordination of movement sequences.
- The kinematics and force features of speech muscle movements are maintained at normal and fast rates but are different at slow rates.
- Like the skeletal muscles, there is contralateral motor control of the lips, tongue, and jaw with ipsilateral innervation to many of the muscles as well; however, the ipsilateral pathway provides much more assistance in speech muscles, generating bilateral synergistic movements though the contralateral innervation is stronger.

(Data from Kent, R. [2004]. The uniqueness of speech among motor systems. *Clinical Linguistics & Phonetics,* 18, 495-505.)

the consonants and vowels never occupy each other's positions in the syllable.[20] MacNeilage has suggested in his F/C theory that in the evolution of human speech the rhythmic and repetitive opening and closing of the mandible necessary for the intake of food (and thus survival) was combined with vocalization to produce syllables. The open mandible for vowels and the more closed posturing for consonants thus were perpetuated through the evolutionary cycles and never biologically had an opportunity to be substituted for one another. MacNeilage[19] theorizes that there may have been an intermediate stage in evolution of speech where the open/close mandible cycle was combined with other structure movements to produce tongue clicks or lip smacking, for instance; these kind of oral gestures do appear to be used for communication by some primates whose evolution preceded that of humans.

In the study of normal stages of speech development in children, the progression or refinement of the motor movements necessary for increasingly more varied consonant and vowel production can easily be seen. The progress a child makes when going from babbling to reduplicative babbling to variegated babbling to word production to sentence production showcases the advancement of the ability of the motor system to quickly and effortlessly respond to the commands of the language system. It appears miraculous, especially in such a short time, and it is the result of the development and coordination of the nervous system structures we are about to explore.

A Hierarchical System

The motor system for all voluntary and reflexive movement is considered a hierarchical system that becomes progressively less sophisticated as it is descended or more sophisticated as it is ascended. The great neurologist Hughlings Jackson asserted that each level of this hierarchy has a certain autonomy, but the autonomy at the lower levels is partially constrained by the higher levels of the motor system. This is also true for sensation, cognition, and emotion. Speech production requires, as does most motor activity, the action of major mechanisms at every significant motor integration level of the nervous system. The Jacksonian principle that higher centers bring more refinement to neuronal processing while also inhibiting the neural activity of certain lower centers is often demonstrated when disease or injury to the motor system occurs. This loss of refinement and/or effect of disinhibition will become clear when signs and symptoms of the different motor speech disorders are discussed in subsequent chapters. An attempt must first be made to understand the functioning of the motor

system as a whole. Though we are most interested in speech, we will also look at how movement for extremities occurs since the corticospinal pathway is important as well to total patient rehabilitation. As we did when discussing the motor system in Chapters 2 and 3, we begin with the higher levels of control and work our way through subcortical systems and out to the muscle.

MOTOR PLANNING

At the highest level of the motor system hierarchy is the input of cortical areas involved in motor planning to the primary motor area of the cortex. For body movements, this is primarily the premotor and supplementary motor areas (Brodmann's area 6). When considering motor planning for speech production, the supplementary motor area, Broca's area, and the insula must also be discussed.

Premotor and Supplementary Motor Areas

The premotor area (a part of Brodmann's area 6) is usually active bilaterally. It has a major projection to the brainstem nuclei that give origin primarily to the reticulospinal tracts and have minor projections to the major motor tracts. Its primary function appears to be bilateral postural fixation as needed to fixate the shoulders and stabilize the hips. It receives cognitive input from the prefrontal cortex in terms of motor intention and from the parietal lobe in regard to tactile and visual signals. It does get quite active when motor routines are run in response to visual or somatosensory cues (e.g., reaching for an object). The premotor area responds mostly to external cues.

The supplementary motor area (SMA) is involved in motor planning and motor execution. Research on the functional anatomy of the medial wall of the hemispheres found a difference between what has come to be called the pre-SMA area and the SMA proper.[23] For our purposes these two areas can be thought of as being located approximately anterior to (pre-SMA) and posterior to (SMA proper) the anterior commissure in each hemisphere. The SMA proper, in humans and in monkeys, was found to have connections to the primary motor cortex and to the spinal cord. The area designated as the pre-SMA, however, had few projections to the primary motor area but instead had numerous interconnections with the prefrontal cortex and other nonprimary motor areas.

This concept of a pre-SMA and SMA-proper was expanded for the role of the SMA in word production by Alario and colleagues[2] in 2006. Using functional magnetic resonance imaging and intricate research design involving word generation versus reading and repetition, they found the SMA proper to be involved in actual execution of the motor movements for articulation. This functional imaging study also suggested that in word production the pre-SMA area could be further subdivided functionally into an anterior pre-SMA area and a posterior pre-SMA area; word selection during word generation tasks resulted in activation in the anterior pre-SMA. The subsequent "linear encoding" (defined by the authors as the selection, organization, and sequencing of the phonemes to be articulated) resulted in activation of a smaller posterior section of the pre-SMA. This linear encoding is part of what this text calls motor programming for speech.

Thus there is strong evidence to support the existence of a pre-SMA and an SMA proper in Brodmann's area 6 as well as some evidence to support a section of the pre-SMA area being involved in motor encoding for speech and the SMA proper being responsible for providing input into the primary motor cortex for the execution of the associated movements.

Broca's Area

As we said in Chapter 2, Broca's area is found in the motor association cortical area at the foot of the primary motor and the premotor cortices. This area was named after the French neurologist, Pierre Paul Broca, who first described the expressive language disorder we now refer to as Broca's aphasia and described an area on the lateral surface of the brain as the area of damage causing the expressive problem. Described by Broca as the posterior inferior frontal gyrus, roughly the third left frontal convolution, this area in general became known as "Broca's area." The location now considered Broca's area includes the pars opercularis (Brodmann's area 44) and the pars triangularis (Brodmann's area 45) in the posterior inferior frontal gyrus.[12] Review Figure 2-5 to remind yourself of the location on the lateral brain surface of the left hemisphere. The area of the brain designated "Broca's area" is only found in the hemisphere dominant for language (typically the left) and is differentiated from tissue in the frontal operculum of the nondominant hemisphere only by function.

In 1978 Mohr and colleagues[22] found that lesions *confined* to Broca's area caused muteness and difficulty with fluent and accurate articulation; however, with this lesion site, the difficulty with speech production was, in most cases, slight or transient. Only lesions extending outside the subscribed areas 44 and 45 resulted in true difficulty with language or with language and motor speech programming. Thus a diagnosis of "Broca's aphasia," which is a language (not speech) disorder that may occur after damage to the brain, was supported as resulting from lesions that might include Broca's area but must extend outside Broca's area. These two lesion sites, which resulted in different outcomes and

prognoses, came to be termed *baby Broca's* and *big Broca's* lesions.

Price and colleagues[24] used positron emission tomography scanning technology to look at the possible participation of Broca's area as a site of internal models or "higher level representations" of already learned words that enable the speaker to unconsciously predict the auditory output of a spoken word and send these predictions to auditory processing areas in the temporal lobe. This would perhaps allow adjustments to be made in articulation after a mismatch occurs, improving the precision of speech. This predictive/comparative/corrective system seems reasonable and important in such situations as early language acquisition, speech output with a hearing loss, or learning a new language. As the authors note, this theory requires connectivity studies to be done to confirm and clarify the functional pathways.

The Insula

Apraxia is a disorder that impairs performance of voluntary learned motor acts while similar automatic gestures remain intact. It is caused by a lesion in motor association areas and association pathways. Apraxia of speech (AOS) is a disorder of motor planning for speech production. A person with acquired AOS shows difficulty with accurate and rapid movement of the articulators to produce purposeful speech but has little discernable paralysis or weakness of the articulators to account for this. Movement of the oral mechanism for motor activities such as eating, blowing out a match, or licking an ice cream cone, for example, are typically unaffected. AOS in adults with brain damage most often occurs accompanied by a language disorder, and this disorder is often diagnosed as a Broca's aphasia (although the apraxic component is not necessary for a diagnosis of Broca's aphasia to be warranted). The anatomic etiology of apraxia of speech had generally been placed in the traditional Broca's area, although it could not be explained why some patients with a nonfluent aphasia also had an accompanying apraxia of speech whereas others with similar lesions (it appeared from the studies available at the time) did not. A 1996 study of the computed tomography (CT) scans of patients with acquired apraxia of speech by Dronkers[11] persuasively implicated the left superior precentral gyrus of the insula in motor programming for speech production, with follow-up studies continuing to show the involvement of this area in all studied patients who had apraxia of speech.[12] Though the study could clearly suggest that all patients with apraxia of speech had damage to the insula, it and subsequent clinical studies could not strongly support the contention that all patients with damage to the insula had apraxia of speech.[5,10,20]

In 2010, in a masterful review of the literature to that time concerning the role of the insula in speech production, Ackerman and Riecker[1] summarized the research looking at clinical cases and functional imaging studies. The clinical case studies were variable and inconclusive regarding the contribution of the insular cortex. The functional imaging studies as a group, however, did support hemodynamic activity in the insula in conjunction with motor aspects of speech production. The most consistent activity was found in a small area of the rostral insula at the junction with the fronto-opercular cortex. Because the insular cortex is the floor of the lateral sulcus, this area could not be identified on the lateral surface. The small size of the dynamic tissue could explain why it is so difficult to find patients with lesions confined to the insula who demonstrate residual problems with motor speech.

TRUNK AND LIMB MOVEMENT: THE CORTICOSPINAL TRACT

The pyramidal tract is the major voluntary pathway for all movement mediated by the spinal cord (trunk and limbs). Figure 6-1 is a simple illustration of the paths these fibers take. Because this tract passes through and actually makes up the bulk of a certain point in the medulla that looks like a small pyramid, the corticospinal tract is also known as the pyramidal tract. The corticospinal tract controls the skilled movements in the distal muscles of the limbs and digits and is particularly responsible for the precise movements made by the hands and fingers.

The corticospinal tract descends from the cerebral cortex to different levels of the spinal cord; it begins in the motor cortex of the two cerebral hemispheres. As we discuss later in this chapter, the fibers of the corticospinal tract originating from the cerebral cortex are known as *upper motor neurons* until they synapse in nuclei located in the spinal cord. A majority of the corticospinal fibers originate from pyramidal neurons of the primary motor cortex. These motor neurons receive afferent input from the primary sensory cortex and the dorsal column sensory nuclei in the spinal cord. The basal ganglia and the cerebellum also serve as "consultants" to the cortical motor system, influencing timing and coordination of movement. The influence of these inputs occurs before neural firing initiated in the motor cortex and through the corticospinal tract.

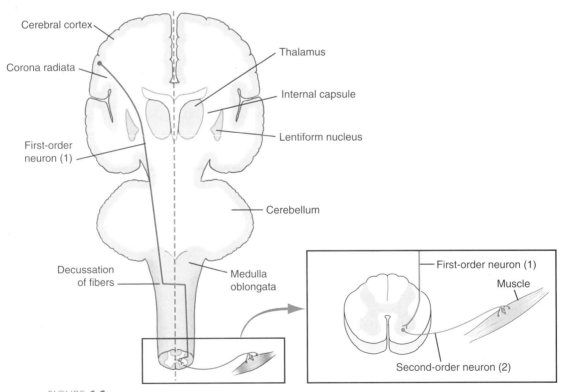

FIGURE **6-1**
Simple illustration of the corticospinal tract descending from the cerebral motor cortex to the skeletal muscle. Note the reference to the neurons involved and the classification of those neurons. (Modified from Snell, R. [2007]. *Clinical neuroanatomy* [7th ed.]. Philadelphia: Lippincott Williams and Wilkins.)

Descending corticospinal fibers also originate from the postcentral gyrus and the parietal lobe. Those fibers are of sensory area origin and terminate on sensory, rather than motor, relay nuclei in the brainstem and in the dorsal horn of the spinal cord; they modulate sensory transmission.

The corticospinal system is actually composed of several tracts that innervate spinal neurons and, eventually, muscles controlled by spinal nerves. The corticospinal tract itself descends from the motor cortex in each hemisphere to subcortical white matter in a fan-shaped distribution of fibers called the corona radiata, or radiating crown. The fibers converge to enter into an L-shaped subcortical structure called the internal capsule. The corticospinal fibers pass through the posterior limb of the internal capsule. As they pass through the internal capsule, they join axons from other areas, such as those projecting to and from other cortical areas, the thalamus, and the brainstem. Damage in the pathway through the internal capsule can result in devastating motor deficits because of the number of fibers going through this narrow point.

From the point of the internal capsule, they descend below the thalamus and lie on the ventral brainstem surface, forming part of the cerebral peduncles of the midbrain. These white matter tracts are found in the ventral portion of the peduncles, a portion called the crus cerebri. Some of the descending fibers may end in or send collaterals to the red nucleus at this point.

Descending to the level of the pons, some cortical axons may begin to intermix with pontine neurons at the base (basis pontis). Many of these axons will synapse on the pontine neurons and become part of the corticopontine tract, which exits through the cerebellar peduncles and out to the cerebellum. This tract allows input from the cortex to be conveyed to the cerebellum. At this point in the pons, some other fibers of the descending cortical axons may synapse in the pontomedullary reticular formation and provide cortical input to the reticulospinal system.

The corticospinal tract neurons that continue to descend collect at the point called the pyramids of the medulla situated at the medullary-cervical juncture. More collaterals are given off by the axons, innervating nuclei of the inferior olivary complex, the posterior column nuclei, and some reticular nuclei of the medulla. At the level of the pyramids, approximately 85% to 90% of the corticospinal fibers cross over (decussate) to the other side of the neuraxis, providing contralateral motor control of the extremities.

Decussation

The crossing of the right and left corticospinal tract is known as decussation, sometimes called the decussation of the pyramids. The few fibers, variable in number, that do not cross are collectively known as the anterior corticospinal tract. The primary crossed corticospinal tract is the lateral corticospinal tract. The decussation means that a lesion interrupting the fibers above the crossing has an effect on the side of the body opposite the site of the lesion. If the corticospinal tract is interrupted in the cerebrum or at any level above the pyramids of the medulla, voluntary movement of the innervated structure is limited on the contralateral side of the body. By contrast, a lesion below the decussation impairs voluntary movement on the same, or ipsilateral, side.

After the corticospinal fibers enter the spinal cord, they synapse in the anterior horn cells of the spinal cord segment dedicated to control of the particular body part associated with that level of the spinal cord (remember cervical, thoracic, lumbar, sacral, and coccygeal segments from Chapter 3). At synapse a new axon is sent out to the muscle fiber controlling or adding to control of a particular muscle or muscle group. At this point, the new fibers resulting from this synapse are now lower motor neuron fibers.

Brainstem Centers for Tone and Posture

When a cross section of the spinal cord is examined, other descending motor tracts besides the lateral and anterior corticospinal tracts can be seen. These additional descending motor tracts found terminating in the spinal cord are the reticulospinal tracts, vestibulospinal tracts, tectospinal tracts, and rubrospinal tracts. These tracts are the major tracts in what is sometimes called the extrapyramidal system, defined as being made up of fibers descending to the spinal cord outside of the corticospinal tracts. Duffy[13] refers to these tracts as the indirect activation pathway. These fiber pathways provide primary input to motor neurons for maintenance of normal tone, body posturing, and reflex responses to sensory stimuli.

According to Duffy,[13] the components of the indirect activation pathway consist of many short pathways and interconnections with structures between the origin of the pathway in the cortex and its termination at the lower motor neuron. The nuclei and tracts considered to be components of the indirect activation system are listed in Table 6-1.

The reticular formation itself is also thought of as part of the subcortical extrapyramidal system. The extrapyramidal system is concerned with coarse stereotyped movements. It has more influence over proximal (midline) than distal (peripheral) muscles. It maintains proper tone and posture. Even with destruction of the pyramidal tract, it can allow a person to eat and walk.

Because muscle tone and body posture are important to the neurologist's examination of the body, this is

TABLE 6-1

Major Components of the Indirect Activation Pathway of the Extrapyramidal System

COMPONENTS (NUCLEI OR TRACTS)	FUNCTIONAL ROLE IN MOTOR CONTROL
Reticular formation or reticulospinal tracts	Excitation or inhibition of flexors and extensors; facilitation or inhibition of reflexes and ascending sensory information
Vestibular nuclei or vestibulospinal tract	Facilitation of reflex activity and spinal mechanisms controlling muscle tone
Red nucleus or rubrospinal tract	Facilitation of flexor and inhibition of extensor neurons

(Modified from Duffy, J. R. [2005]. *Motor speech disorders: Substrates, differential diagnosis and management.* St. Louis: Mosby/Elsevier.)

a good point to discuss those terms as they relate to the neurologic control. Muscle tone is the resistance of the muscle to stretch. The two types of tone are phasic and postural. Phasic tone is a rapid contraction in reaction to a high-intensity stretch (or change in muscle length) and is assessed by testing tendon reflexes. Postural tone is a prolonged contraction in response to a low-intensity stretch. Gravity provides a low-intensity stretch on antigravity muscles, which respond with prolonged contraction and the normal posturing of the head, neck, and extremities that persons without neurologic damage usually maintain.

FACIAL AND ORAL MOVEMENT: THE CORTICONUCLEAR TRACT

Before a recommended terminology change, the corticonuclear fibers were called the *corticobulbar fibers,* a term that is still used in some quarters. Because that name erroneously implies that all fibers terminate in the medulla (the old term for the medulla was the *bulb*), the term *corticonuclear* replaced corticobulbar in the international terminology of neuroanatomic terms in 1998. The corticonuclear fibers of the pyramidal tract innervate the cranial nerves and make up the voluntary pathway for the movements of all speech muscles, except those of respiration. They are the most important motor fibers for the SLP.

Their course is not as direct as that of the corticospinal fibers. Figure 6-2 illustrates the general decussation point of the corticobulbar fibers that do cross. Chapter 7 discusses these neuron pathways individually for the cranial nerves. As the illustration shows, the corticonuclear fibers begin with the corticospinal fibers at the cortex but terminate at the motor nuclei

of the cranial nerves located at various points in the brainstem. Unlike the corticospinal fibers, the corticonuclear fibers have many ipsilateral (terminating in motor nuclei in the brainstem on the *same* side of the brain as the primary site from which the axon began) as well as contralateral fibers (terminating in nuclei on the opposite side from which they began). After the axons of the corticonuclear fibers leave the cortical motor areas, they travel the same path that the corticospinal fibers do through the corona radiata and the internal capsule. The corticonuclear fibers, however, transverse the genu, or bend, of the internal capsule rather than the posterior limb.

The corticospinal and corticonuclear fibers separate at the upper brainstem level. Each of the different cranial nerve axons terminates at its own designated nuclei at some point along the brainstem. Some decussate and others primarily travel ipsilaterally. If they cross, they do so at various levels of the brainstem. The general location of each of the nuclei for the cranial nerves most important to speech is discussed in Chapter 7.

Upper and Lower Motor Neurons

This point in our discussion of the motor system seems like an appropriate place to briefly discuss a useful concept in clinical neurology, the notion of upper motor neurons (UMNs) and *lower motor neurons* (LMNs). This division of designation of the general location in the neural pathway of the axon has been applied in clinical neurologic teaching and practice for a very long time. Knowledge of the different symptoms and signs of damage to each type of neuron pathway will often be useful to SLPs performing motor speech examinations or to the SLP in general trying to understand the basis of the neurologic examination findings in the patients with whom they are working.

UPPER MOTOR NEURONS (UMNs)

All the neurons of the anterior and lateral corticospinal tracts, which send axons from the primary motor area in the cerebral cortex down to the anterior horn cells of the spinal cord, are considered *upper motor neurons.* The neurons of the corticonuclear tracts that send axons from the primary motor area in the cerebral cortex to the nuclei in the brainstem also are *upper motor neurons.* An important concept in trying to learn the difference in upper versus lower motor neurons is this: No axons of upper motor neurons leave the neuraxis. In other words, they are contained within the brain, brainstem, and spinal cord. The pyramidal tract, with its upper motor neuron activation, can be thought of as the direct

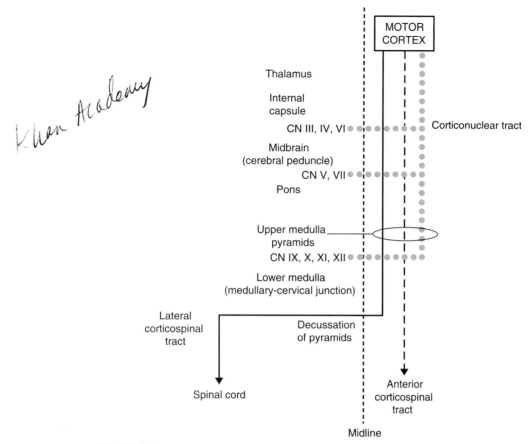

FIGURE **6-2**

Simple outline of the corticonuclear fiber pathways *(bold green circles)*. The corticospinal tract pathway is included for comparison and review.

activation pathway, or direct motor system, because of the direct connection of its upper motor neurons with the lower motor neurons that subsequently send their axons outside the neuraxis.[6] These upper motor neurons in the primary motor area have a major activating influence on their LMN targets.

LOWER MOTOR NEURONS

Lower motor neurons are all the neurons that send motor axons outside the neuraxis into the peripheral nerves: both cranial and spinal nerves. LMNs are designated *second-order* neurons. Sherrington[27] called the lower motor neuron the *final common pathway*. By this he meant that the peripheral nerves, both cranial and spinal, serve as a final route for all the complex motor interactions that occur in the neuraxis above the level of the lower motor neurons. The final muscle contraction is the product of all the interactions that have occurred in the central nervous system.

The concept of the motor unit helps explain the lower motor neuron pathway (Fig. 6-3). A motor unit

FIGURE 6-3

The motor unit and typical lesion sites producing different signs and symptoms of lower motor neuron damage: *1*, Anterior horn cell—motor neuron disease; *2*, nerve axon—denervation, neuropathy; *3*, myoneural juncture—neuromyopathy, myasthenia gravis; *4*, muscle fiber—myopathy or dystrophy.

is a structural and functional entity that can be defined as (1) a single anterior horn cell in the spinal cord or cranial nerve neuron in the brainstem, (2) its peripheral axon and its branches, (3) the myoneural juncture. which is the point where the nerve synapses on the muscle fiber, and (4) each muscle fiber innervated by the branches. Lesions may occur at many points within the motor unit and produce lower motor neuron signs.

BILATERAL SYMMETRY

Because the movements of limbs and digits would not be efficient or effective if the movement of one side mirrored the other, the corticospinal system allows for control of one side of the body to come from only one source (for at least 90% of the fibers), the *opposite* hemisphere's cortical motor areas. In comparison, because the oral musculature movements on one side of the body typically are mirrored by the same movements on the other side, the majority of the midline speech muscles work in bilateral symmetry, making speech more efficient. This is the result of the bilateral innervation to the cranial nerve nuclei that the corticonuclear fibers provide. If a cranial nerve's nuclei are said to receive bilateral innervation, the nuclei on the right side of the brainstem (in this example) receive axons from the primary motor cortices of *both* hemispheres. However, if that cranial nerve were to be one of those only receiving contralateral innervation, the axons providing neural input would come only from the left hemisphere's cortical motor areas. The majority of the paired muscles of the face, palate, vocal folds, and diaphragm work together in synchrony most of the time in wrinkling the forehead, smiling, chewing, swallowing, and talking and thus are bilaterally innervated.

This bilateral input to most of the speech muscles has important implications for the effect of damage to the nervous system on the speech musculature in cases of the motor speech disorders we call the *dysarthria*s (see full discussion in Chapter 8). After damage to the corticonuclear pathway, this bilateral innervation provides a safety feature or compensatory mechanism for speech production. For example, if the left corticonuclear fibers coming from the motor cortex to the nuclei of a cranial nerve are damaged, the motor nuclei of a bilaterally innervated neuron will still receive impulses by way of the intact right corticonuclear tract, and paralysis of the muscle will not be severe. The innervation of the limbs, on the other hand, is primarily contralateral rather than bilateral. Therefore, if the pyramidal tract input from the left side of the brain to the spinal motor nuclei were damaged, there would be little input to those spinal neurons from the opposite side; a severe right limb paralysis would result. Unilateral lesions to corticonuclear fibers typically do not produce a severe weakness because of redundancy provided by the bilateral innervation.

Contralateral and Unilateral Innervation

Even though the cranial nerve nuclei are primarily bilaterally supplied, some of the muscle groups moving the facial and oral musculature have mixed innervation patterns with much variation among the nuclei regarding the amount of unilateral innervation versus contralateral innervation each receives. Areas with a greater ratio of unilateral supply suffer more damage after a unilateral lesion. Because of their primarily contralateral innervation, the muscles of the lower face and the trapezius muscles are most affected by unilateral damage (to the contralateral side). An intermediate paralytic effect, meaning significant weakness but not paralysis, is found in the tongue with a unilateral lesion because the mixture contains a greater ratio of bilateral innervation to the different muscles of the tongue. The diaphragm, ocular muscles, upper face, jaw, pharynx, and muscles of the larynx show little paresis with a unilateral lesion because of primarily bilateral innervation of the muscles controlling movement of these structures.

The nuclei for the facial nerve are complex. The facial nucleus is made up of a ventral and a dorsal component and combines bilateral innervation with contralateral innervation. The muscles of the upper half of the face, supplied by the ventral portion, are far more bilaterally innervated than the muscles of the lower half of the face, which are supplied by the dorsal portion of the motor nucleus and receive more contralateral innervation. In practical terms, among the healthy population most people can wrinkle the forehead or lift both eyebrows together. Only a few people, with more contralateral fibers, are able to lift their eyebrows one at a time. The muscles of the midface receive a more equal combination of bilateral and contralateral innervation. Most, but not all, people can wink one eye at a time because of the increase of contralateral fibers to eyelid muscles compared with forehead muscles.

In the lower face the innervation is primarily contralateral. Most people are able to retract one corner of the mouth alone when asked to do so because of the limited bilateral innervation of the lower face muscles. Table 6-2 summarizes the innervation for the cranial nerves of speech production. Figure 6-4 shows the difference in effect on facial movement of an upper motor neuron lesion compared with a lower motor neuron lesion as a result of this unusual innervation pattern. The principles of bilateral and contralateral innervation are practically applied when a speech cranial nerve examination is performed to determine whether lesions are present affecting the corticonuclear fibers, cranial nerve nuclei, or the cranial nerves themselves.

The concepts of bilateral symmetry and contralateral independence are of crucial clinical utility when analyzing and understanding muscle involvement in

TABLE 6-2

Corticonuclear Innervation in the Cranial Nerves for Speech

Trigeminal (V)	Bilateral innervation
Facial (VII)	Mixed bilateral and contralateral innervation
Glossopharyngeal (IX)	Bilateral innervation (motor innervation of IX is only to a single muscle)
Vagus (X)	Bilateral innervation
Spinal accessory (XI)	Contralateral innervation
Hypoglossal (XII)	Primarily bilateral innervation with contralateral innervation of one muscle (genioglossus)

dysarthria. This is explained further in Chapter 7 in the discussion of testing the cranial nerves involved in speech.

INDICATORS OF UPPER VERSUS LOWER MOTOR NEURON DAMAGE

Once an understanding has been grasped of the anatomy of the pyramidal tract and the final common pathway, the concepts of upper and lower motor neurons, and the concept of bilateral versus contralateral innervation, it is important to understand and be able to identify the signs of upper versus lower motor neuron damage.

Lesions of the upper and lower motor neurons produce fairly different sets of signs and symptoms. Many of the symptoms are easier to identify in the gross

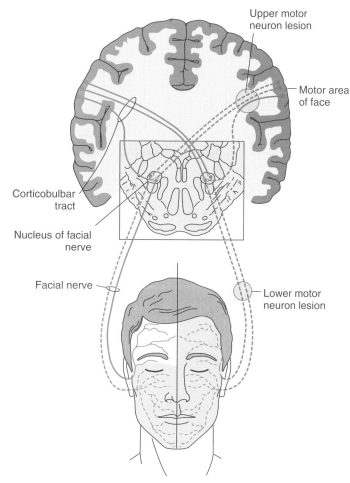

FIGURE **6-4**

Upper versus lower motor neuron facial paralysis. The *shaded areas* of the face show the distribution of the facial muscles paralyzed after an upper motor neuron lesion and a lower motor neuron lesion. (Modified from Gilman, S., & Winans, S. S. [1987]. *Manter and Gatz's essentials of clinical neuroanatomy and neurophysiology* [7th ed.]. Philadelphia: F. A. Davis.)

TABLE 6-3
Signs of Upper and Lower Motor Neuron Disorders

UMN DISORDERS	LMN DISORDERS
Spastic paralysis	Flaccid paralysis
Hypertonia	Hypotonia
Hyperreflexia	Hyporeflexia
Clonus	No clonus
Babinski sign	No Babinski sign
Little or no atrophy	Marked atrophy
No fasciculations	Fasciculations
Diminished abdominal and cremasteric reflexes	Normal abdominal and cremasteric reflexes

muscles of the limbs but it is critical to the SLP that these signs/symptoms are recognized and considered whenever an examination is done on the oral musculature. Table 6-3 presents a contrast of the signs of damage to these two systems. This distinction provides the neurologist with a powerful tool in neurologic examination for deciding where a lesion is located in the nervous system. The most striking sign of a lesion in both upper and lower motor neurons is paralysis. The type of paralysis, however, is quite different depending on the site of the lesion that produces the paralysis. The neurologist would note paresis or paralysis and proceed by assessing muscle tone, muscle strength, and reflexes. Understanding the differences in the type of paralysis, tone, and other confirmatory signs is a large step toward establishing a correct diagnosis of a neurologic disease involving motor disturbance. The differences in strength, tone, and reflexes are much more difficult to assess in the oral musculature than in the larger limb muscles. However, there are differences that can be identified. It is also important that the SLP help confirm these signs, if possible, in the oral musculature to assist in a correct diagnosis of the underlying etiology. It is also important that the SLP recognize these signs in the larger limb muscles so that identification of new problems can be made early or progression could be questioned.

Paralysis, Paresis, and Plegia

A gross limitation of movement is called paralysis, and an incomplete paralysis is known as paresis. A complete or near-complete paralysis of one side of the body is hemiparalysis or, more commonly, hemiplegia. The presence of right-sided hemiplegia or hemiparesis is an extremely important sign for the SLP. Paralysis or paresis

on the right side of the body suggests left hemisphere involvement. As previously noted, the left hemisphere is the primary site of brain mechanisms for language, so right hemiplegia is often associated with language disorders. Lesions of the bilateral motor strip or the corticonuclear tract alone may produce the motor speech disorder of dysarthria.

Upper Motor Neuron Signs and Symptoms

Damage to the corticospinal tract anywhere along its course produces spastic paralysis. Spastic muscles display increased tone, or resistance to movement, a condition called hypertonia. Spastic hypertonicity can be identified by moving a limb through its full range of motion so that the joint is flexed or bent. The neurologic examiner puts an increased stretch on the muscles during range-of-motion testing. He or she thereby elicits a muscle stretch reflex, an increase in tone or tension that resists the flexion of the joint. The examiner can feel this increased resistance to movement. (The muscle stretch reflex controls the degree of contraction in a normal muscle and provides muscles with tonus, or tone.) When an injury occurs to the corticospinal or corticonuclear tract, such as in a vascular stroke, this spasticity may take several days to weeks to develop and stabilize. Temporary flaccid hemiplegia may initially be present, with a more permanent spastic paralysis developing over time. The increasing spasticity of the muscles after a corticospinal injury may be caused by a buildup of collagen in the muscles as well as biochemical changes.[4]

A "clasp knife" reaction occurs in a spastic muscle when the neurologist feels increased tone or resistance to movement in the muscle after the joint has been briskly flexed and then feels the resistance fade. This reaction, which identifies spastic hypertonicity, is analogous to the resistance felt when a knife blade is first opened, followed by the reduction of resistance when the blade is straightened. This reaction occurs more typically in extension rather than in flexion of the elbow. A short span of no tone is usually present, then a rapid buildup of tone and a sudden release as the joint is moved, just as with opening a clasp knife.

Spasticity is also associated with exaggerated muscle stretch reflexes, resulting in hyperreflexia. Reflex action is tested at joints by putting stretch on tendons. This elicits the exaggerated muscle stretch reflex. Spastic paralysis, hypertonia, and hyperreflexia have most often been associated with pyramidal tract damage, particularly lesions of the corticospinal tract. However, the corticonuclear tracts are often also involved when a lesion interrupts the corticospinal tract, and signs of spasticity may be found in the midline speech muscles as well as in the distal limb muscles. Therefore the clinical signs of spasticity, or an upper motor neuron lesion, are of equal interest to the speech-language pathologist and the neurologist. Spastic speech muscles may be weak, slow, and limited in range or movement. Hypertonia may decrease muscle flexibility of the articulators and limit the ability to achieve a full range of motion of the speech muscles.

Other Confirmatory Signs

Several signs, in addition to a clinical demonstration of clasp knife spasticity, hypertonia, and hyperreflexia, are used by the neurologist to help verify the diagnosis of spasticity and localize the lesion to the pyramidal tract.

The Babinski sign, or extensor plantar sign, in particular has been identified as an abnormal reflex sign that develops with corticospinal damage. The lesion causes the release of cortical inhibition. The sign has achieved considerable status in the diagnosis of upper motor neuron lesions because it is a highly reliable abnormal reflex, is new behavior released by the presence of a lesion, and is clearly associated with a relatively specific lesion site—the cortex or the corticospinal tract. The speech-language pathologist is not directly interested in it because it does not involve the midline speech muscles, but its presence as a confirmation of an upper motor neuron lesion of the spastic type is important to all who manage neurologic patients.

The Babinski sign is observed as a reflex toe sign. It is elicited by stimulating the sole of the foot with a strong scratching maneuver. The normal response to stimulation of the sole, or plantar portion of the foot, is a slight withdrawal of the foot and downward turning or curling under of the toes. With a corticospinal lesion, the great toe extends upward and the other toes fan as the foot withdraws slightly. Physicians test this response several times to convince themselves that the upturning great toe sign can be repeatedly and automatically elicited. Automatic repetition of a given response such as this defines it as a reflex. The presence of a repeatable abnormal reflex sharply increases the probability of predicting with accuracy the possible site or sites of a neurologic lesion, though it may not be present if the patient with a vascular lesion is tested early after onset of the insult.

The Babinski sign is more reliable in adults than in infants and children. Normal infants are highly variable in display of the sign. The explanation usually given for this variability is that the immature nervous system and the damaged nervous system often show similar symptoms and signs. Damage to the nervous system often releases early reflex behavior that has become inhibited by development of higher centers, so signs of damage at that point in time are signs of immaturity at an earlier time. Clinical neurologists believe that the extensor plantar sign usually reaches stability by age 2 years.

Other signs, such as a persisting asymmetric tonic neck reflex and the Moro reflex, can be tested to suggest an upper motor neuron lesion in young children (see Chapter 11).

Another confirmatory sign of spasticity is clonus. Hyperactive muscle stretch reflexes associated with spasticity may show a sustained series of rhythmic beats or jerks when a neurologic examiner maintains one tendon of a muscle in extension. To test for clonus, the Achilles tendon in the ankle is often put under extension. If an upper motor neuron lesion is present, the ankle and the calf show sustained jerks. A few clonic jerks, called abortive clonus, are not clinically significant, but if the clonus is sustained over time, it is considered pathologic and an indicator of hyperreflexia. This sign is part of the clinical syndrome resulting from an upper motor neuron lesion.

With *bilateral* upper motor neuron lesions, a characteristic dysarthria may be present. This motor speech disorder, called spastic dysarthria, is discussed in Chapter 8.

Lower Motor Neuron Signs and Symptoms

If a lesion directly damages a cranial or peripheral nerve, or is in the cell bodies of the anterior horn cell in the spinal cord or the nuclei of cranial nerves in the brainstem, neural impulses will not be transmitted to the muscles. This condition is called denervation. The result is that the muscles innervated by the cranial or spinal nerve become soft and flabby from a loss of muscle tone. This is a lower motor neuron paralysis.

The loss of muscle tone is called hypotonia. Hypotonia results in flaccid muscles, thus the term *flaccid paralysis*. Hypotonia may be an acquired condition, with disease or injury affecting the peripheral nervous system pathway, but it may also be a condition found at birth or developing shortly after birth. Infantile hypotonia may result from conditions such as chromosome disorders (e.g., Prader-Willi syndrome), genetic defects, spinal cord disorders, spinal muscular atrophy, muscular dystrophy, metabolic myopathies, or other problems that affect the peripheral pathways.[14] Figure 6-5 shows the posture, the frog-leg position, typically assumed by an infant with hypotonia.

Lower motor neuron paralysis also is sometimes associated with loss of muscle bulk, a condition called atrophy. Muscles undergoing atrophy display some degree of degeneration because they have become denervated. Signs of this degeneration can be observed clinically. Atrophic muscles show fibrillations and fasciculations. These signs are caused by electrical disturbances in muscle fibers resulting from denervation. Fibrillations are fine twitches of single muscle fibers. These generally cannot be seen on clinical examination but must be detected by electro-myographic (EMG) examination. Fasciculations, on the other hand, are contractions of groups of muscle fibers that can be identified, with training, in skeletal muscles through the skin.

When muscle bulk is lost through atrophy in motor neuron disease (e.g., amyotrophic lateral sclerosis), fasciculations are sometimes seen in the muscles of the head and neck as well as other parts of the body. These muscle twitches may be particularly observed in the relatively large muscle mass of the tongue if the bulbar muscles are involved. Fasciculations have no direct effect on speech itself but serve as a sign of lower motor neuron disease.

Interruption of a peripheral nerve by a lower motor neuron lesion also damages the reflex arc involved with that nerve. The result is that normal reflex responses mediated through the sensory and motor limbs of the arc become diminished. Reduced reflex response is called **hyporeflexia**. Complete lack of reflex is known as **areflexia**. Hyporeflexia and areflexia are also associated with lower motor neuron disease.

FIGURE **6-5**
Typical frog-leg position assumed at rest by an infant with hypotonia. The thighs are fully abducted, and the arms lie in a flaccid position next to the head.

Referring back to Figure 6-3 with some explanations of typical disorders can help the reader understand damage caused by more typical types of lower motor neuron disorders. The most obvious example of a disorder is a lesion or cut in the spinal nerve (point 2). This damage paralyzes the muscle innervated by the nerve. In addition, the denervated muscle becomes hypotonic, areflexic, and atrophic. Finally, fasciculations appear. If a cranial nerve is denervated, weakness of speech muscles results from hypotonia and loss of muscle bulk.

A lesion may also occur in the cell body itself and produce paralysis and related lower motor neuron signs (see point 1 of Fig. 6-3). An example is acute bulbar poliomyelitis, which attacks the high cervical anterior horns as well as the cranial nerve nuclei of the bulbar muscles controlling speech. Speech muscles again may become weak and atrophic.

Lesions of the lower motor neuron type may also directly occur in muscles (point 4). An example of this type of disorder is seen in muscular dystrophy. Speech muscles lose strength and show disturbances of muscle bulk. This lower motor neuron disease within a muscle is called a myopathy, as opposed to a disease of the peripheral nerves, which is called a neuropathy. Lesions may also occur at the neuromuscular junction (point 3), as seen in myasthenia gravis. Speech muscles show weakness as well as notable fatigue with use in this myoneural disorder.

A Pause to Review
The study of the levels of control of the motor system and the terms associated with the different levels and different disorders is complicated. Here we will pause and review what has been discussed so far. Basic movement is generated by a neural impulse generated by motor neurons of the primary motor cortex and sent down to either the spinal cord (for movement of the extremities and trunk) or to the cranial nerve nuclei located primarily in brainstem structures. Before the neural firing to muscles of speech production from the motor cortex, there is cortical activity that takes place in the supplementary motor area (pre-SMA portion) and insula (rostral portion), with, perhaps, some participation of part of Broca's area. This cortical activity is concerned with motor planning or motor programming of the movements that need to occur to accomplish the task at hand. If the task is to produce speech, current research suggests that the motor planning takes place primarily in the pre-SMA segment, in the insula, and in a small part of Broca's area.

The corticospinal (pyramidal) tract and the cortico-nuclear (corticobulbar) tract follow similar descending pathways for a short while. They both descend in a fan-shaped manner forming the corona radiata. Both then pass through the narrow space called the internal capsule with the corticospinal fibers traversing the posterior limb and the corticonuclear fibers passing through the genu. From this point the corticobulbar fibers will descend to synapse on their various target nuclei, primarily in the structures of the brainstem. Some of these fibers will decussate and others will continue ipsilaterally. Many of the cranial nerve nuclei receive bilateral innervation, meaning that fibers from both sides of the brain will synapse on the motor nuclei in the brainstem.

There is a different path for the corticospinal fibers from the point of the internal capsule. They descend below the thalamus and form part of the cerebral peduncles of the midbrain, a part called the crus cerebri. They will give off some fibers to nuclei in the pons, and these will become part of the corticopontine fiber pathway taking neural signaling out to the cerebellum. Most fibers will continue descending though some collaterals are given off to the red nucleus, the olivary nuclei, reticular formation nuclei, and posterior column nuclei. Ninety percent of pyramidal tract fibers will decussate at the level of the pyramids of the medulla at the junction of the medulla and the cervical spinal cord. These fibers make up the lateral corticospinal tract. The other 10% will continue into the spinal cord ipsilaterally and make up the anterior corticospinal tract.

There are other descending tracts of fibers that form *indirect activation pathways* and make up the extrapyramidal tracts. These are the reticulospinal tract, the vestibulospinal tract, and the tectospinal tract. They consist of many short pathways with interconnections between the motor cortex and the spinal cord. They are concerned with coarse, stereotyped movements and with maintaining body tone and posture.

Two important concepts of clinical neurology were also discussed: upper motor neurons (UMN) and lower motor neurons (LMN). The neurons and their axons that make up the pathway from the motor cortex down to the nuclei on which they synapse in either the spinal cord (for the corticospinal tract) or the brainstem (for corticobulbar fibers) are known as UMNs. They provide direct input into those targeted nuclei, carrying motor "directives" planned and implemented in the cortex. The second-order neurons found in the nuclei of either the anterior horn cells of the spinal column (for the corticospinal tract) or in the nuclei of the cranial nerves (for corticobulbar fibers) are known as LMNs. The axons of the LMNs take the transmitted information or motor directive out to the peripheral nervous system, exiting the brain or the spinal cord and synapsing on the muscle fibers. The motor unit is a helpful concept in understanding the LMN.

Other terms and concepts included as important to understanding the effect of damage to the pyramidal, corticobulbar, and extrapyramidal tracts were: unilateral and *contralateral innervation, bilateral symmetry, tone (hypertonicity and hypotonicity), Babinski sign, reflexes, paralysis,* and *muscular weakness.* If these terms and concepts are not firm in your mind at this point, please go back and study this section before advancing to the next sections, which will take you to more in-depth information about neural control within muscles and then will introduce other influences on the motor pathways.

NEUROMUSCULAR CONTROL

In the final analysis, motor control of speech muscles, or any other musculature, is brought about by muscle contraction. At one time it was believed that the only route for control of voluntary muscle contraction was by way of the several descending motor pathways in the nervous system that end in nerve cells called alpha motor neurons. In the spinal cord these motor neurons are called anterior horn cells and are in the largest cells in the spinal cord. Homologous motor neurons are the cranial nerve neurons of the brainstem. Along with gamma motor neurons, the alpha motor neurons supply skeletal muscles. They discharge impulses through the spinal nerves to contract muscles of the trunk and limbs in the corticospinal system. Most motor commands for a given articulatory act, other oral-motor acts, or facial movement are transmitted by the alpha motor neuron system through contraction of muscles innervated by cranial nerves.

Alpha Motor Neurons

The alpha motor neuron (AMN) innervates the main fibers that cause muscle contraction. These fibers lie within the muscle and are called extrafusal fibers. Figure 6-6 illustrates the structure of a muscle fiber including the input from the AMN. The axon of each AMN branches to supply the fibers. An axon may supply only a few fibers, as in the case of a small muscle with precisely controlled contraction, or it may control several hundred fibers, as in the case of large muscles with strong, crude movements. This fact is consistent with what you saw on the homunculus illustrated in Figure 2-7. The oral musculature involved in speech and swallowing requires a much larger area on the motor strip because the innervation and control of these muscles requires the involvement of a vastly

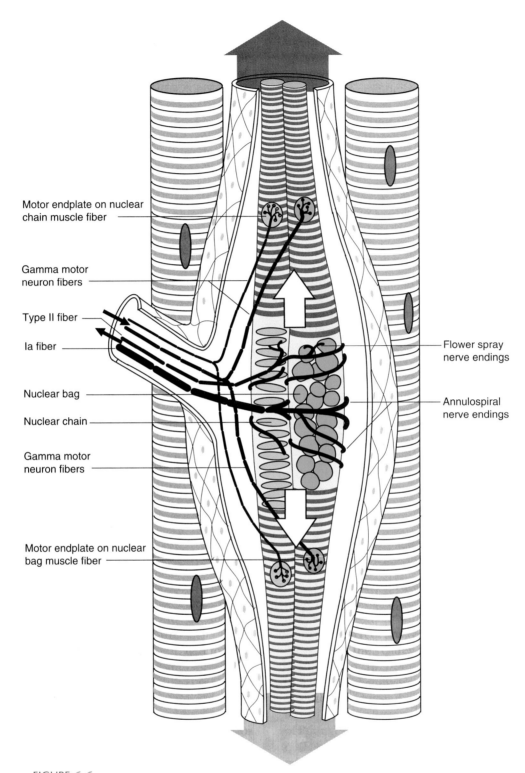

FIGURE **6-6**

A muscle fiber including the alpha motor neuron and gamma motor neuron, extrafusal fibers, and the structures of the muscle spindle.

larger number of neurons to allow fine and precise motor control for these acts.

The alpha motor neuron supplies the trophic, or nutritional, factors, which direct differentiation of muscle fibers and keep the muscle healthy. These substances are called myotrophic factors. The motor neuron also supplies the acetylcholine that stimulates contraction of muscle.

Three types of extrafusal fibers can be differentiated in skeletal muscle. All muscles contain all three types of fibers, but all muscle fibers in one *motor unit* are of the same type. The type is determined by the myotrophic influences of the innervating neuron. The first of the three types of fibers are slow twitch (type I) fibers that contract slowly and are resistant to fatigue. These fibers predominate in sustaining postural activities, including standing. Fast twitch fibers (type IIx in humans) contract faster but fatigue more rapidly. They exert a more powerful force and are primarily found in superficial muscles. An intermediate fiber (Type IIA) has properties between the other two types in terms of speed of contraction and amount of force; it is considered a fast twitch fiber, however.

Muscle Spindles

Another level of neuromuscular control has been identified at the level of the **muscle spindle** (see Fig. 6-6). Muscle spindles serve as sensory, or afferent, receptors within some striated muscles. They provide sensory information on the status of the normal stretch mechanisms in muscle. In muscles that have muscle spindles, the spindle is the mechanism through which, in passive stretch, the muscle contraction is elicited. The spindles receive efferent innervation through gamma (γ) motor neurons (GMN). Because muscle spindles serve as afferent (sensory) receptors yet they themselves receive efferent (motor) innervation, they are considered more complex sensory receptors than those found in the tendons and joints. Muscle spindles are most commonly found in the slow twitch (Type I) fibers and are plentiful in the muscles along the vertebral column, the muscles of the neck, and the intrinsic muscles of the hand. They have been found to be present in large numbers in the muscles that close the jaw as well. The muscle spindle is encapsulated and is *fusiform*, meaning tapered at both ends. It contains a limited number of short fibers that are parallel to other muscle fibers. The extrafusal muscle fibers are outside of the spindle. Fibers of the muscle spindle itself are called **intrafusal fibers**, and they connect to those extrafusal fibers outside the spindle. Intrafusal fibers provide the nervous system with information about the length and the rate of change in length of the muscle. The number of intrafusal fibers within a spindle varies. To accomplish monitoring and

informing the nervous system about length as well as rate of change, there are two types of fibers within the intrafusal fibers: nuclear chain and nuclear bag fibers. There are also two types of sensory endings associated with these fibers: primary endings or annulospiral endings and secondary endings or "flower spray" endings.

Nuclear bag fibers look "chubby" in the middle due to a clustering of nuclei there in this central region. The nuclear chain fibers have nuclei that are arranged in single file and are thinner appearing. These two types of fibers are the sensory receptors within a muscle and need to be associated with a sensory neuron to get the information to the nervous system about the status of stretch on the muscle. This information is conveyed to the central nervous system (CNS) by the primary fibers, the annulospiral endings, and secondary afferent fibers, the flower spray endings. The annulospiral endings are wrapped around the center of both nuclear bag and nuclear chain fibers and are rapidly conducting afferent fibers. The flower spray endings are the more slowly conducting secondary afferents and are found mainly on nuclear chain fibers. These two types of fibers carry information toward the CNS and are thus afferent pathways. Because a majority of the muscle spindles are associated with spinal nerves (as opposed to cranial nerves), most of the body's information regarding muscle stretch enters the spinal cord and goes through the dorsal root ganglion associated with that body part. Muscle spindles associated with cranial nerve innervated muscles will synapse on sensory nuclei associated with that cranial nerve.

When the muscle is stretched, the sensory neurons wrapped around the intrafusal fibers act as length detectors and send information about the stretch into the CNS. The nuclear bag fibers can sense the onset of stretch, and the nuclear chain fibers sense sustained stretch. Both types of fibers will respond immediately, however, to rapid stretch, which is a protective mechanism for the muscle. The rate of firing of these fibers is proportional to the change in length of the muscle. The greater the stretch on the muscle, the more rapid the rate of firing.

Upon the onset of stretch on the muscle, muscle spindles are elongated. Both primary (annulospiral) and secondary (flower spray) afferents are stimulated by the lengthening of the intrafusal fibers within the muscle spindle and the rate of change of their length. This will result in the initiation of action potentials traveling through these afferents to the spinal cord (or the nuclei of the cranial nerve) and synapsing with the AMN, which in turn will fire neural impulses to the extrafusal fibers. It is the efferent signal of the alpha motor neuron to the extrafusal fibers of the muscle that causes the muscle to contract.

Gamma Motor Neurons

Recall that both the alpha and the gamma motor neurons synapse with the sensory afferents coming into the CNS. As with the alpha motor neurons, the GMNs are part of a motor nerve. They are relatively small in size compared with the alpha efferents, but they make up approximately 30% of the motor neurons leaving the spinal cord. Whereas the AMN signals the extrafusal fibers causing muscle contraction, the gamma motor neurons (GMNs) supply efferent innervation to the muscle spindle fibers, the intrafusal fibers.

The central region of an intrafusal fiber does not contract; only the ends have contractile properties. The gamma motor neurons innervate the muscle spindle at each end. At the same time that the sensory afferent synapses in the CNS with the AMN, there is also a synapse with GMNs. The firing of the gamma motor neuron carries an efferent signal back to the ends of the intrafusal fiber causing it to contract. This is an important part of the muscle contraction because when muscle contraction takes place, the muscle spindle's intrafusal fibers tend to go a little slack. Proper functioning of the sensory afferents of the muscle spindle depends heavily on the appropriate amount of tension on the nuclear bag and nuclear chain fibers in the central region of the intrafusal fiber. The coactivation of both the AMN and the GMN allows the contraction of both extrafusal and intrafusal fibers. The GMN activation is at a slightly slower pace than the AMN action. When the ends of the intrafusal fibers contract, the appropriate amount of tension is "reset" within the muscle spindle so that it can be sensitive to any stretch placed on the muscle. This functional contractile process is known as the gamma loop system. Through this system the gamma motor neurons form an important muscle stretch reflex mechanism that acts in conjunction with the alpha motor neurons. This sensitivity to stretch provides fine compensations of muscle length and velocity and helps maintain muscle tone.

The speed with which the spindles convey sensory feedback information to the central nervous system would seem to mark them as likely candidates for the neural mechanisms controlling the fine and rapid movements of speech muscles. Evidence from the speech science laboratory indicates that rapid compensatory motor behavior is necessary for intelligible speech. Motor speech acts are rarely performed exactly the same way twice, but in most cases motor speech production meets the broad specifications of the motor commands in such a way that the listener can recognize an individual speech sound, or phon, as a member of a phoneme class. In the case of density of muscle spindles, the jaw-closing muscles have been found to be rich with muscle spindles.[7] Liss[18] employed cadaver study with particular staining and light microscopy and identified a significant density of spindles in the levator palatini and palatoglossal muscles of the velum. A cadaver study by Cooper in 1953[9] found the presence of muscle spindles in the intrinsic muscles of the tongue, particularly the superior longitudinal muscle at a point proximal and posterior to the tip. Studies by Saigusa et al.[25,26] have found muscle spindles present in the transverse lingual muscles at the base of the tongue and in the genioglossus muscle with the primary distribution being toward the base of the tongue.

Golgi Tendon Organs

Beyond the muscle spindle system are joint receptors and special tendon receptors called **Golgi tendon organs**, which are involved in sensorimotor control of some of the muscles of the body. The Golgi tendon organs are directly attached to the tendons of muscles. They respond when either stretching or contraction places tension on the tendon, or they signal the force of muscle contraction. The Golgi tendon organs temper motor activity and inhibit activity in muscles when high levels of tension are placed on the tendon. Golgi tendon organs dampen oscillation of the limbs, at times producing joint stiffness. If these afferents allow too much freedom (such as in Parkinson's disease), the tendency to oscillate is not inhibited and tremor is seen.

A Pause to Review

In the foregoing section, the neural anatomy concerned with muscle fiber and neural innervation of muscle contraction was discussed. The main fibers within muscles that result in muscle contraction are the extrafusal fibers. These are innervated by large neurons called alpha motor neurons (AMNs). The axon of an AMN will branch out to control more than one muscle fiber depending on the precision of muscle control needed to accomplish that movement. Therefore a large number of fibers may be controlled by only a few AMNs when the movements are cruder, large movements (like the muscles of the quadriceps, for instance); muscles requiring fine, precise movements to accomplish the motor task (like muscles of the finger or tongue, for instance) will require many AMNs because each axon will branch to control only a small number of fibers. The AMNs supply the trophic factors that determine the type of muscle fibers in a motor unit (Type I, Type IIx, or Type IIA most frequently in skeletal muscle in humans). AMNs also supply the primary neurotransmitter, acetylcholine.

Another important level of control at the muscle fiber level is the muscle spindle, which is the sensory mechanism or afferent receptor present in some striated muscles. The muscle spindle contains intrafusal fibers. The muscle spindle provides the AMN information on the status of stretch on a muscle and can elicit muscle contraction. The spindle is a complicated structure with both afferent and efferent mechanisms. Most of the muscles under spinal control contain muscle spindles but research has shown that some of the oral muscles also contain muscle spindles, which is important to the successful use of neuromuscular therapy methodology in treatment of oral-motor deficits.[8]

Other mechanisms or terms in the previous section were *nuclear bag* and *nuclear chain fibers*, *annulospiral* and *flower spray endings*, *gamma motor neurons*, and *Golgi tendon organs*. Please review these if needed before advancing to study other influences on the motor system.

The Influence of Other Systems on Movement

Even if you have only limited experience with patients with neurologic disorders, you likely realize that there are many patients for whom subconscious planning of the movement pattern or grossly implementing movement does not seem to be the main problem. For many patients it is the finer aspects of motor control, the efficiency and coordination of the movements, that appear to be the locus of the disorder. There may be no problem in the direct corticospinal or corticonuclear tracts but, instead (or, sometimes, in addition), there may be damage to pathways associated with the basal nuclei (or basal ganglia as many texts still use) and/or the cerebellum. These structures and their input and output pathways are quite complex, and this text will not attempt to fully explain them. However, it is important for the SLP to be somewhat familiar with their composition and their contribution to movement control so that the effects of damage to these structures can be better understood.

THE BASAL GANGLIA (OR BASAL NUCLEI)

Before beginning the discussion of the basal ganglia, review Figures 2-13 and 2-14 in Chapter 2. The terminology for these structures as a whole has changed through the years with many contemporary texts using *basal nuclei* in place of *basal ganglia*. To acquaint the student with both, the terms are used interchangeably here. These structures include the caudate nucleus, the putamen, the nucleus accumbens, the globus pallidus (both the internal and external segments), the subthalamic nucleus, and the substantia nigra. With the exception of the nucleus accumbens, these deep subcortical nuclei serve to modulate the activity of the motor cortex and brainstem nuclei of the motor system.

The **caudate nucleus (CN)** lies just medial to the anterior limb of the internal capsule and adjacent to the wall of the lateral ventricle, close to the thalamus. The structure is divided into a head, body, and tail by some neuroanatomists, but others divide the caudate into only a head and tail. The entire caudate cannot be illustrated in a coronal section because of its C-shape. Only a part of it (or none at all) will be seen depending on where the sectioning occurs in the anterior-posterior plane. It follows the body of the lateral ventricle with the tail end at about the level of the temporal lobe; it terminates at the amygdaloid nucleus.

The **putamen** is located anterior to the genu of the internal capsule. In humans, the caudate and the putamen are separated structurally by the internal capsule. Functionally, together the caudate and the putamen make up what is known as the **striatum** or, in some texts, the neostriatum. The putamen and caudate are connected by bridges of cells that span across the internal capsule; these strands give the area its striped or striated appearance and, thus, the name *striatum* was given it at some point. Converging excitatory input comes into the striatum from almost the entire cortex, but especially the sensorimotor and frontal areas of the cortex. The thalamus also provides input into the striatum.

The **nucleus accumbens** lies between the caudate and the putamen and is sometimes called the ventral striatum or dorsal striatum. It is part of a mesolimbic circuit involved in dopamine signaling that seems to be involved in establishing associations between rewarding or adversive stimuli and the environment surrounding that experience. It is not involved much at all in control of movement and will not be discussed here further.

The **globus pallidus (GP)** is located medial to the putamen and rostral to the hypothalamus. In primates the GP is separated by a fiber tract (the internal medullary lamina) into two segments, an internal segment (GP_i) and an external one (GP_e). The putamen and globus pallidus (as a whole) together comprise the lentiform nucleus, a thumb-sized structure wedged against the internal capsule. The lentiform nucleus (i.e., the putamen and the globus pallidus), combined with the caudate nucleus, comprises what is known as the **corpus striatum** (Table 6-4).

The other structures of the basal nuclei, the **subthalamic nucleus (STN)** and the **substantia nigra (SN)**, are found near the reticular formation of the midbrain. The STN is located at the junction of the diencephalon and the midbrain, ventral to the thalamus. The SN is located in the ventral part of the midbrain between the red nucleus and the crus cerebri; although it is located in the midbrain, it is functionally a part of the basal ganglia system. There are two segments comprising the substantia nigra: the pars reticulata (SNpr), which is

TABLE 6-4
Nomenclature of the Basal Nuclei

Globus pallidus   Lentiform nucleus
                                              Corpus striatum
Putamen
                          Striatum
Caudate nucleus

Subthalamic nucleus

Substantia nigra

BOX 6-2
Basal Ganglia

Internal Connections
- Caudate and putamen (striatum) = inhibitory (GABA) → GPi, GPe, SNpr, SNpc
- Globus pallidus internal (GPi) = inhibitory (GABA) → subthalamic nucleus
- Globus pallidus external (GPe) = inhibitory → subthalamic nucleus
- Subthalamic nucleus = excitatory (glutamate) → GPi, GPe, and SNpr
- Substantia nigra (SNpc) = mixed (depends on the receptor) dopamine → striatum

composed of few cells, and the pars compacta (SNpc), which is densely packed with cells. The SNpc provides a critical supply of dopamine to the neostriatum.

Excitatory afferent input to the basal nuclei is primarily through the striatum and comes from the entire cerebral cortex and parts of the thalamus. There are projections from frontal, temporal, parietal, and occipital cortical areas stratified throughout the basal ganglia; the head of the caudate receives the largest number of input fibers, those coming from the frontal lobe. The basal ganglia also contain a motor homunculus similar to the one in the primary motor cortex. The projections from the motor cortex to the basal nuclei maintain this somatotopic organization from the source area to the targeted basal ganglia region and could be traced.

Only two structures of the basal ganglia transmit *outside* of this circuitry: the globus pallidus (internal segment, GPi) and the substantia nigra (pars reticulata segment, SNpr). Output transmissions from the basal nuclei project primarily to the thalamus and are relayed back to parts of the cortex. A limited number of fibers also project to the brainstem and some of the SNpr fibers project to the superior colliculus for control of eye movement.

The neurotransmitter secreted by these output basal ganglia structures is gamma-aminobutyric acid (GABA), and the transmission is inhibitory. The strength of the final inhibitory transmission will depend on the pathway taken between the striatum and the output neurons of the GPi or the SNpr. There is more than one pathway, particularly between the striatum and the GPi; there are some excitatory and many inhibitory connections along the various routes. These intervening connections and the neural signaling involved could significantly alter the effectiveness of the final transmission from the output basal ganglia structure (the GPi or the SNpr) and, subsequently, the thalamus.

Students wishing to explore these connections further are referred to Bolam et al.[3]

There is a somatotopic organization of the output of the basal ganglia such that output associated with leg and arm movement is from the GPi and from the face and eyes, the SNpr. The GPi sends approximately 70% of its output to the thalamus and the brainstem. The thalamic nuclei in turn send projections to different parts of the cortex, including the motor, premotor, supplementary motor, and prefrontal areas. Some project back to the striatum for possible feedback loops. Brainstem connections in the midbrain and pons project to reticulospinal neurons. There are some output neurons of the GPi whose eventual connections are not known as of this time.

The other structures of the basal nuclei transmit only within the circuitry. Box 6-2 lists the output targets and the type and target of transmission of the structures. Note that within the basal ganglia circuitry, the SNpc is the source of dopamine to the striatum and that dopamine transmission may result in an eventual transmission that is excitatory or inhibitory. It just depends on what type of receptor (D1 = excitatory; D2 = inhibitory) within the striatum receives the neural signal. Please keep in mind that most connections within this circuitry are inhibitory so that the net effect (strength of inhibition or excitation) of the output transmission of the GPi and the SNpr depends on how many inhibitory versus excitatory connections have been made before the final output. The ramifications of too little or too much inhibition or excitation of the cortical motor areas will be obvious when we review the motor speech disorders associated with damage to the basal ganglia.

The basal ganglia indirectly affect motor function. The input fed into the thalamus and then to the cortex or brainstem can facilitate initiating movement, executing movement or terminating movement. Through this complex circuitry, learned movement patterns can be selectively activated or suppressed so that the intended movement can be accomplished with involvement of appropriate muscle tone, body posturing, and without interference from other unnecessary or disruptive movements.

Damage to the Basal Ganglia

Lesions of the basal ganglia generally produce two major types of movement disorders: poverty of movement (**akinesia**) and excessive involuntary movement (**dyskinesia**).[27] Akinesia is often accompanied by muscular rigidity, as in Parkinson's disease. The basal ganglia particularly influence movements related to posture, automatic movements, and skilled voluntary movements.

Marsden[21] argues that the basal ganglia are responsible for the automatic execution of learned motor plans. This involves subconscious selection, sequencing, and delivery of the motor programs of a learned or practiced motor strategy, such as playing an instrument or writing by hand. When the basal ganglia are damaged, the individual appears to revert to slower, less automatic, and less accurate cortical mechanisms for motor behavior. Civier and colleagues[6] provide an excellent review of studies that support the possibility that the basal ganglia–thalamocortical circuit plays an important role in the pathophysiology of stuttering.

Dyskinesia

Damage to some parts of the basal ganglia produce motor disturbances usually classified as involuntary movement disorders. The most commonly used technical term for them is *dyskinesia* (*dys*, meaning disordered, and *kinesia*, meaning movement). These disorders encompass a full range of bizarre postures and unusual movement patterns. The dyskinesias have long been described by such terms as tremor, writhing, fidgeting, flailing, restlessness, jerking, and flinging. Often the unusual movements that dominate the trunk and limbs of the dyskinetic patient are also reflected in the face and speech mechanism. The result is a serious and typical dysarthria classified under hyperkinetic dysarthria (see Chapter 8). In general, the dysarthria reflects the specific symptoms of each specific type of dyskinesia.

The term *dyskinesia* may be used in a broad sense to include any excess of movement (hyperkinesia) or reduction in movement (akinesia). **Hyperkinesia** has been used to indicate dyskinesias that present too much movement. **Hypokinesia** and akinesia, on the other hand, refer to too little movement and reduced movement, respectively. In actual clinical use, the terms may not always be strictly applied to a person with an identified neurologic lesion. For instance, neurologists may apply hyperkinesia to the well-known twitching or fidgeting of Huntington's chorea as well as the abnormal hyperactivity of children in whom there may not be evidence of an organic lesion in the nervous system, let alone knowledge of a lesion localized to the central nervous system.

Hypokinesia also may be used to describe the reduced activity level of a depressive patient with no suspected neurologic lesion. By tradition, neurologists do not apply the term *hypokinesia* to limitations in movement resulting from lesions of the pyramidal tract or peripheral nerves. In other words, lesions that paralyze voluntary movement are not labeled hypokinetic. Thus hemiplegia, quadriplegia, and paraplegia are not considered hypokinetic disorders.

Dyskinetic Types. The responsibilities of speech-language pathologists do not extend to the identification of lesion sites in the complex circuitry of the motor system, but SLPs should attempt to recognize the standard dyskinesias and determine the effect of the symptoms of specific dyskinesias on the accompanying dysarthria. Undiagnosed cases of movement disorders demand referral to a neurologist. Dyskinesia has several distinct patterns, but not all of them are related to the dysarthrias. Described next are only those motor signs that can produce motor speech symptoms.

Tremors

Tremors are defined as purposeless movements that are rhythmic, oscillatory, involuntary actions. Normal (or physiologic) and abnormal (or pathologic) tremors are usually distinguished. Tremors are pathologic if they occur in a disease and are characteristic of that disease. Normal tremor is called physiologic tremor. Several classifications of tremor are in use today. The speech-language pathologist should be familiar with three types of tremor associated with vocal performance in normal and pathologic conditions.

Rest Tremor. **Rest tremor** designates a tremor that occurs in Parkinson's disease. A tremor of three to seven movements per second occurs in the patient's limbs and hands at rest. The tremor is temporarily suppressed when the limb is moved, and it sometimes can be inhibited by conscious effort. The voice may be affected by the tremor. Tremulous voice has been described in approximately 14% of a large sample of parkinsonian patients. It is a salient vocal deviation that is easily recognized among the other vocal deviations of the hypokinetic dysarthria of parkinsonism.

Physiologic, or Action, Tremor. Healthy people demonstrate a fine tremor of the hands when maintaining posture. The rate may vary with age but usually falls within the range of 4 to 12 cycles per second. This normal tremor is distinguished from pathologic tremors associated with known neurologic diseases such as Parkinson's and cerebellar disorders. An abnormal action tremor may affect the laryngeal muscles and produce a voice disorder known as organic or essential voice tremor.

Intention Tremor. Intention tremor refers to a tremor that occurs during movement and is intensified at the termination of the movement. Intention tremor has been associated with the ataxic dysarthria seen in cerebellar disease. It is often seen in cerebellar disorders but is not exclusive to cerebellar dysfunction.

Chorea

Chorea refers to quick, random, hyperkinetic movements simulating fragments of normal movements. Speech, facial, and respiratory movements, as well as movements of the extremities, are affected by choreic symptoms in this dyskinesia. The movement is close to what is popularly described as fidgets. Chorea is one symptom of a hereditary disorder known as Huntington's disease, or Huntington's chorea, and is seen in other movement disorders as well.

Athetosis

The hyperkinesia of athetosis is a slow, irregular, coarse, writhing, or squirming movement. It usually involves the extremities as well as the face, neck, and trunk. The movements directly interfere with the fine and controlled actions of the larynx, tongue, palate, pharynx, and respiratory mechanism. As with most other involuntary movements, the involuntary movements of athetosis disappear in sleep. In congenital athetosis, the most common type of spastic paralysis may also be observed. Lesion sites in pure athetosis are often in the putamen and the caudate nucleus. Hypoxia, or lack of oxygen at birth, is a common cause, producing death of brain cells before or during birth. Choreoathetotic movements have also been described; they appear to be a dyskinesia that lies somewhere between choreic and athetoid movements in terms of rate and rhythm of movement or that includes both types of movement. In fact, many of the involuntary movement disorders appear to blend one or more of the different clinical dyskinesias, as the term *choreoathetosis* implies.

Dystonia

In dystonia the limbs assume distorted static postures resulting from excess tone in selected parts of the body. The dyskinetic postures are slow, bizarre, and often grotesque, involving writhing, twisting, and turning. Dysarthria and obvious motor involvement of the speech mechanism are common. Often differential motor involvement occurs in the speech muscles, and some dysarthrias have been observed that primarily affect the larynx. Others affect the face, tongue, lips, palate, and jaw. A rare dystonic disorder of childhood is called dystonia musculorum deformans. It may be accompanied by dysarthria in its later stages.

Fragmentary, or focal, dystonias have been described, and some neurologists assert that they contribute to spastic or spasmodic dysphonia, a bizarre voice disorder that mixes aphonia (lack of voice) with a strained, labored whisper. The etiology of spastic dysphonia is unclear. Injections of botulinum are often effective in reducing the dystonia.

Myoclonus

Myoclonus has been used to describe differing motor abnormalities, but basically a myoclonic movement is an abrupt, brief, almost lightning-like contraction of muscle. An example of a normal or physiologic myoclonic reaction occurs when a person is drifting off to sleep but suddenly is awakened by a rapid muscle jerk. This muscle jerk is myoclonus.

Pathologic myoclonus is most common in the limbs and trunk but also may involve the facial muscles, jaws, tongue, and pharynx. Repetitive myoclonus in these muscles, of course, may affect speech. Myoclonic movements in the muscles of speech have been described as having a rate of 10 to 50 per minute, but they can be more rapid. The pathology underlying these movements has been debated, but because they have been associated with degenerative brain disease, the cerebral cortex, brainstem, and cerebellum have all been considered as possible lesion sites.

A special myoclonic syndrome involving speech muscles called palatal myoclonus has been described. It involves rapid movements of the soft palate and pharynx and sometimes includes the larynx, diaphragm, and other muscles. The symptoms most often present in later life and are characteristic of several diseases. This myoclonus has a specific pathology in the central tegmental tract of the brainstem, but the etiology can be varied. The most common cause is a stroke, or cerebrovascular accident, in the brainstem.

Orofacial Dyskinesia (Tardive Dyskinesia)

In orofacial or tardive dyskinesia bizarre movements are limited to the mouth, face, jaw, and tongue. This movement includes grimacing, pursing of the mouth and lips, and writhing of the tongue. These dyskinetic movements often alter articulation of speech. The motor speech signs of orofacial dyskinesia usually develop after the prolonged use of powerful tranquilizing drugs, the most common class of which are phenothiazines. Drug-induced dyskinesias associated with the phenothiazine and related medications may even produce athetoid movements or dystonic movements of the body. Parkinsonian signs and other symptoms associated with movement disorders are also caused by these drugs. Orofacial dyskinesia also occurs in elderly patients without drug use. A rare disorder that includes dyskinesia of the eyelids, face, tongue, and refractory muscles is called Meige syndrome.

Other dyskinesias are included in the spectrum of movement disorders but generally do not include motor involvement of the speech mechanism. These include hemiballismus, which causes forceful, flinging unilateral movements and may involve half of the body. Akathisia refers to motor restlessness or the inability to sit still. Restless leg syndrome is an example of this dyskinesia. Box 6-3 summarizes the dyskinesias.

THE CEREBELLAR SYSTEM

The third major subcomponent of the motor system that affects speech is the cerebellum. Interacting with the other systems of motor control we have been studying, the cerebellum is known to provide significant coordination for motor speech. As previously noted, the cerebellum is located dorsal to the medulla and pons. The occipital lobes of the cerebral hemispheres overlap the top of the cerebellum. The anatomy of the cerebellum is complex, and the speech-language pathologist need only understand it in a gross sense to see the relation of the cerebellum to speech performance.

Anatomy of the Cerebellum

The cerebellum can be divided into three parts. The thin middle portion is called the vermis because of its serpentine, or snakelike, shape. The vermis lies between two large lateral masses of the cerebellum, the cerebellar hemispheres (Fig. 6-7). The vermis connects these two hemispheres. The vermis and hemispheres are divided by fissures and sulci into lobes and also into smaller divisions called lobules. The division into lobes and lobules is helpful in clarifying the physiologic function of the cerebellum. Although the lobes and lobules have been classified differently by different investigators, this text uses a classification system that divides the cerebellum into three lobes.

Three Cerebellar Lobes

The three cerebellar lobes are the anterior lobe, the posterior lobe, and the flocculonodular lobe. The anterior lobe, which is modest in size, is superior to the primary fissure. This part of the cerebellum roughly corresponds to what is known as the paleocerebellum, the second oldest part of the cerebellum in a phylogenetic sense. The anterior lobe receives most of the

---

BOX 6-3

Common Dyskinetic Types

- *Tremors:* Purposeless movements that are rhythmic, oscillatory, involuntary actions. Designated as either normal (physiologic) or abnormal (pathologic).
- Rest tremor: Designated tremor caused by Parkinson's disease. Presenting signs include tremor when affected limb is at rest and may include tremulous voice. Range of three to seven movements per second.
- Action (physiologic) tremor: Fine tremor of hands while maintaining posture. Can affect laryngeal muscles, causing voice tremor. Range of 4 to 12 cycles per second.
- Intention tremor: Tremor intensified at termination of movement. Associated with ataxic dysarthria and other cerebellar disorders.
- *Chorea:* Quick, random, hyperkinetic movements simulating fragments of normal movement. Movements are close to what is commonly described as "fidgets" and present as a symptom of Huntington's disease.
- *Athetosis:* Slow, irregular, coarse, writhing, or squirming movement. Involves extremities and can also directly interfere with fine and controlled actions of the swallowing and respiratory mechanisms.

- *Dystonia:* Limbs assume distorted, static postures resulting in excess tone in selected body parts. Movements include slow, bizarre, and often grotesque writhing, twisting, and turning motions.
- *Myoclonus:* Abrupt, brief, almost lightning-like contraction of muscle. Pathology is still debatable. Has been associated with degenerative brain disease, cerebral cortex, brainstem, and cerebellum. Palatal myoclonus is a special type involving rapid movements of the soft palate and pharynx, commonly caused by stroke or cerebrovascular accident in the brainstem.
- *Orofacial (tardive) dyskinesia:* Bizarre movements limited to mouth, face, jaw, and tongue characterized by grimacing, pursing of mouth and lips, and writhing of the tongue. Shown to develop from prolonged use of tranquilizing drugs, especially phenothiazines. A dyskinesia called Meige syndrome affects the eyelids, face, tongue, and refractory muscles.

Non–Speech-Related Dyskinesias

- Hemiballismus: Forceful, flinging, unilateral movements that may involve the whole body.
- Akathisia: Motor restlessness or the inability to sit still (e.g., restless leg syndrome).

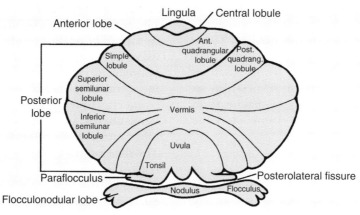

FIGURE **6-7**
A schematic illustration of the cerebellum showing hemispheres, lobes, and lobules. *Ant.,*
Anterior; *Post.,* posterior; *Quadrang.,* quadrangular.

proprioceptive impulses from the spinal cord and regulates posture.

The posterior lobe, the largest part of the cerebellum, is located between the other two lobes. It comprises the major portion of the cerebellar hemispheres. It is the newest part of the cerebellum and is therefore also known as the neocerebellum. The posterior lobe receives the cerebellar connections from the cerebrum and regulates coordination of muscle movement.

The flocculonodular lobe consists of two small wispy appendages, known as flocculi, in the posterior and inferior region of the cerebellum. The flocculi are separated by the nodulus, the inferior part of the vermis. The flocculonodular lobe, the oldest portion of the cerebellum, contains the fastigial nucleus, which is composed of fibers that travel from the nucleus to the four vestibular nuclei in the upper medulla. The cerebellum mediates equilibrium by way of these fibers.

Longitudinal Zones and Deep Nuclei

The cerebellum is also in some texts divided into longitudinal zones that relate to deep nuclei within the cerebellum. The nuclei receive input from the cerebellar cortex and are named (going from medial to lateral placement deep within the cerebellum): the fastigial, the interpositus, and dentate nuclei. The longitudinal zones relate to these nuclei and are called the medial, intermediate, and lateral zones. The fastigial nuclei receive input from the medial zone. This zone receives sensory input from sensory systems such as visual, vestibular and auditory systems. The related fastigial nucleus will output to vestibular, and reticulospinal systems, the thalamus, and the superior colliculus. The interpositus nuclei receive input from the longitudinal division called the intermediate zone. This zone receives information from the spinal cord and also receives input from the motor cortex via the corticopontine fibers.

The interpositus nuclei send output to the red nucleus and to the contralateral thalamus. The third zone, the lateral zone, gets input from widespread areas of the cortex, through the corticopontine fiber tracts. This zone projects to the dentate nucleus, which primarily communicates with the thalamus and the reticular formation.

Synergy and Asynergy

The connections that the cerebellum has with other parts of the central nervous system are important to its function. Through these connections the cerebellum sends and receives afferent and efferent impulses and executes its primary function: a synergistic coordination of muscles and muscle groups. Synergy is defined as the cooperative action of muscles. Ensuring the smooth coordination of muscles is the prime task of the cerebellum. Specifically, the cerebellum, along with other structures of the nervous system, maintains proper posture and balance in walking and in the sequential movements of eating, dressing, and writing. It also guides the production of rapid, alternating, repetitive movements, such as those involved in speaking, and smooth pursuit movements. Voluntary movement, without assistance from the cerebellum, is clumsy, uncoordinated, and disorganized. Motor defect of the cerebellar system has been called asynergia or dyssynergia. Asynergia is a lack of coordination in agonistic and antagonistic muscles and is manifested as deterioration of smooth, complex movements.

Cerebellar Peduncles and Pathways

The cerebellum is connected to the rest of the nervous system by three pairs of peduncles, or feet. The cerebellar peduncles anchor the cerebellum to the brainstem. All afferent and efferent fibers of the cerebellum pass through the three peduncles and the pons to the other levels of the nervous system. The pons, which

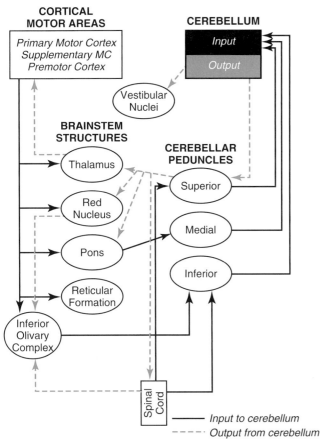

FIGURE **6-8**
Major pathways of the cerebellum. *MC, Motor cortex.*

means bridge, is aptly named; it is literally a bridge from the cerebellum to the rest of the nervous system (Fig. 6-8).

The inferior cerebellar peduncle, or restiform body, carries primary afferent fibers from the structures close to it: the medulla, spinal cord, and cranial nerve VIII. Thus spinocerebellar, medullocerebellar, and vestibular fibers pass through the inferior peduncle.

The middle cerebellar peduncle, or brachium pontis, connects the cerebellum with the cerebral cortex by the pathways that traverse it. The middle peduncle is easily recognized; it is the largest of the three peduncles and also conveys the largest number of fibers from the cerebral cortex and pons. It carries pontocerebellar fibers as well as the majority of the corticopontocerebellar fibers. These fibers convey afferent information from the temporal and frontal lobes of the cerebrum to the posterior lobe of the contralateral cerebellum.

The superior cerebellar peduncle, or brachium conjunctivum, conveys the bulk of efferent fibers that leave the cerebellum. The primary efferent fibers arise from an important nucleus deep in the cerebellum called the dentate nucleus. The rubrospinal and dentatothalamic pathways, along with several other tracts, leave by way of the superior peduncle and terminate in the contralateral red nucleus and ventrolateral nucleus of the thalamus. From here impulses are relayed to the cerebral cortex.

Cerebellar Role in Speech

The major pathways and structures of the cerebellum have been outlined to suggest a rough schematic of the feedback nature of the afferent and efferent connections of the structure. Basic as the presentation is, it still highlights the fact that the cerebellar motor subsystem significantly influences the function of the other motor systems in the production of motor speech. The fact that the cerebellum plays an important part in the synergy of rapid alternating movements and the fine coordination of muscles suggests that it interacts in a crucial way with the corticonuclear fibers to provide the specialized rapid and precise motor control needed for ongoing connected speech.

Auditory, tactile, and visual areas also exist in the cerebellum. These centers in the cerebellum, both cortical and subcortical, project to similar areas in the cerebrum, which in turn project back to corresponding cerebellar areas. The cerebellum therefore is neither completely vestibular, proprioceptive, nor motor in function. Rather, it serves to reinforce or diminish sensory and motor impulses, acting as a critical modulator of neuronal function. There is an abundance of sensory and cortical information conveyed to and from the cerebellum resulting in indirect influence on motor nuclei. There are also many connections with nonmotor areas. Because of this, some have theorized, and it has now been supported through behavioral studies,[28] that the cerebellum's primary role is to evaluate sensory or cortical information during ongoing movement. In this way, the cerebellum is important not only to coordination of learned movements but also in motor learning itself. The cerebellum appears to be primary in comparing the intended movement with the actual movement and, if a mismatch occurs, sending corrective information back to the cortex and brainstem to modify the ongoing program without major disruption of the movement. In the same way that it does for movement of larger muscles and motor systems, the cerebellum assists in coordinating the respiratory, articulatory, and phonatory muscles for speech production.[13]

Clinical Signs of Cerebellar Dysfunction

Cerebellar or cerebellar pathway lesions manifest themselves by affecting coordination of volitional movements and often volitionally maintained postures. Clinical

TABLE 6-5
Cerebellar Dysfunction Signs and Tests

ABNORMALITY	SIGNS AND TESTS
Gait ataxia	Broad-based gait seen on tandem walking test
Arm ataxia	Finger to nose test, hand pronation to supination test results in overshooting of nose and slowed pronation and supination
Overshooting	Rebound noted on arm-pulling test
Hypotonia	Flaccid muscle tone noted on passive movement testing; pendular reflexes elicited on reflex testing; "rag-doll" postures observed
Nystagmus	Pupil oscillation seen when patient attempts to follow finger through field of gaze
Dysarthria	Ataxic dysarthria with disturbance in speech rate and prosody; often associated with left cerebellar hemisphere lesion

signs usually appear on the same side of the body as the cerebellar lesion. Upper motor neuron lesions of pyramidal pathways yield contralateral effects, whereas the cerebellum and its pathways manifest ipsilateral effects. Several classic signs of cerebellar disorders follow and are summarized in Table 6-5, along with tests used to determine the abnormality.

Ataxia

Ataxia is the prime sign of a cerebellar lesion (*taxis* means "ordering in rank and file"). The term *ataxia* is often used in several senses. It may refer to the general incoordination of motor acts seen with cerebellar system lesions. In this sense it often describes a staggering or reeling gait and abnormal posture seen with cerebellar lesions. The patient compensates for the ataxic gait by standing and walking with feet wide apart in what is called a broad-based gait.

Decomposition of Movement

Decomposition of movement is also related to ataxia. The patient breaks a complex motor act into its components and executes the act movement by movement so that the act seems as if it were being performed by a robot. Decomposition of movement is considered an ataxic movement.

Dysmetria

Dysmetria is the inability to gauge the distance, speed, and power of movement. A patient may stop before the movement is performed or may overshoot the motor goal.

Adiadochokinesia or Dysdiadochokinesia

Adiadochokinesia, or dysdiadochokinesia, is the inability to perform rapid alternating muscle movements. Often the rate of alternating movement may be recorded in a neurologic examination. This measure is called an alternate motion rate. Diadochokinetic rate measures of the muscles of the oral mechanism during speech and nonspeech activities have long been used as an assessment task by the clinical SLP. These rates, however, are used as measures of the integrity of the oral muscles in speech pathology and have not specifically been related to cerebellar function.

The neurologist may test alternating movements in many muscle groups in persons suspected of cerebellar disorders. Successive pronation or supination of the hands, rapid tapping of the fingers, and rapid opening and closing of the fists are all diadochokinetic diagnostic tests. During the testing of diadochokinesis or alternate motion rates, awkwardness or clumsiness of alternate movements may be seen.

Rebound

The rebound phenomenon is the inability to check the contraction of the flexors and rapidly contract the extensor. It may account for the lack of smooth diadochokinetic movements.

Hypotonia

Hypotonia (or muscle flaccidity) with a decrease in resistance to passive movement is seen in cerebellar dysfunction. The muscles of the body are flabby and lack normal tone.

Tremor

Tremor is seen as part of cerebellar disease. It is usually an intention or kinetic tremor not present at rest.

Nystagmus

Nystagmus involves oscillatory abnormalities of the pupil of the eye often seen in cerebellar disorders. The rhythmic oscillations may be vertical, horizontal, or rotary.

Muscle Stretch Reflexes

Muscle stretch reflexes are normal or diminished. Pendular reflexes often may be seen in cerebellar disease. When the knee-jerk reflex is elicited, a series of smooth to-and-fro movements of the limb often occur before it comes to rest, as seen with a pendulum. This pendular reflex differs from a normal knee-jerk response.

Dysarthria

Dysarthria associated with damage to the cerebellum is called ataxic dysarthria. Its characteristics are discussed in Chapter 8.

A Pause to Review

In the last section we concentrated on the basal nuclei and the cerebellum and their influence on the coordination, efficiency, and effectiveness of movement initiated at the cortex. The basal nuclei (aka, basal ganglia) structures are the caudate nucleus, the putamen, the globus pallidus, the subthalamic nucleus, and the substantia nigra. The nucleus accumbens is also a part of the basal ganglia but is not involved in movement control. As is typical in neuroanatomy, some structures have been combined and the combination given a different name: the caudate and the putamen together are called the striatum (or neostriatum); the putamen and the globus pallidus together are called the lenticular nucleus; the three structures together make up the corpus striatum. As is also typical in neuroanatomy, some structures have been found to be segmented into different functional parts. The globus pallidus can be segmented into an internal part (GPi) and an external part (GPe) with the internal part sending transmission outside the basal nuclei. The substantia nigra can be separated into the pars reticulata (SNpr) and the pars compacta (SNpc) with the SNpr sending transmission outside of the basal ganglia and the SNpc supplying dopamine to the structures of the basal nuclei. The neurotransmitter of the output of the basal ganglia is GABA and the transmission is inhibitory. The strength of the final transmission depends on the complicated dopamine transmissions within the circuitry, some being excitatory and some inhibitory to the circuit structures. The output transmission of the basal ganglia is primarily to the thalamus, which then relays the transmission to the cortex. There is some transmission to brainstem structures, particularly the superior colliculus, contributing to control of movement of the eyes. Some of the terms and concepts to be learned and associated with basal ganglia function are: *akinesia, dyskinesia, hyperkinesia, hypokinesia, tremor, chorea, dystonia, athetosis,* and *myoclonus.*

The cerebellum contributes significantly to coordination of movement for speech and other motor activities. It is located at the base of the brain and is connected to the brainstem by cerebellar peduncles through which corticopontine fibers traverse. It has three parts, two hemispheres and a middle portion called the vermis. There are also three lobes of the cerebellum, each concerned with a different function including proprioception, motor coordination, and equilibrium. The cerebellum is also made up of different zones and nuclei, which are deep inside the cerebellum. These zones and their nuclei receive input from the cortex, the spinal cord, and sensory systems such as the auditory, vestibular, and visual systems. They then will project output to the thalamus, the reticular formation, or various sensory systems.

The cerebellar system has been found to be critical to synergistic motor control to enable movements to be smooth, well timed, and coordinated. The cerebellum has been supported in research as functioning to compare the actual movement with intended movement. It appears to send corrective information back to the cortex and brainstem about mismatch between the two, enabling "online" nondisruptive modification of the motor program. It is believed that the cerebellum participates in this manner in the coordination of respiration, articulation, and voice for speech production.

Servomechanism Theory and Speech Motor Control

FEEDBACK

Several fruitful engineering concepts have been applied to neuronal transmission problems in the nervous system. These concepts have been particularly useful in explaining the possible control of neural impulses in the speech mechanism. The basic concept, known as the theory of servomechanism control systems, implies the concept of feedback. Feedback describes the functioning principle in self-regulating systems, either mechanical or biologic. Feedback assumes that the output of any self-regulating system, such as a thermostat, is fed back into the system at some point to control or regulate the output of the system. This concept of self-monitoring is most appropriate for understanding the biologic system known as the speech motor control system. For instance, the questions of how a speaker monitors speech and what neuronal feedback mechanisms are available to control speech movements seem likely ones for explanation by servomechanism theory.

OPEN AND CLOSED CONTROL SYSTEMS

Two types of bioengineering control systems have been described as applicable to neuronal transmission in speech production: closed-loop and open-loop control systems. A closed-loop system uses positive feedback in which output is returned as input to control further output. For example, when copying a complex and delicate drawing, the sensory input to the visual system guides the motor output of the hand. Similarly, hearing one's own speech while talking may at times control the motor speech output as one continues to talk more. In these two examples, motor output by hand or speech is assumed to be guided by the sensory input of vision or audition. Furthermore, if the sensory feedback were blocked, the drawing or speech would be assumed to go awry.

In an open-loop system, the output is generally pre-programmed, and the performance of the system is not matched with the system. For instance, if a person has learned a short poem by heart and has practiced it repeatedly, that person may be able to say the phonemes of the words in the poem without error even though his or her ears are stuffed with cotton. In an open-loop system the notion of **feedforward**, rather than feedback, is important. Once a phrase of a well-learned poem has been uttered, it cues the next pre-programmed phrase of speech without the need to hear what was said through auditory feedback. An open-loop system thus typically generates another input by its output system. The term *negative feedback* is also used in control systems of the servomechanism type. That term implies that when errors are fed back into the system, the error information acts to keep a given output activity within certain limits. Correcting an articulation error on hearing it is an example of the use of negative feedback in speech activity.

Much speech research has viewed speech motor control as the product of a closed-loop feedback system with sensory monitoring from hearing, touch, and deep muscle sense guiding the movements of the speech muscles. Circumstantial evidence for this position has come from studies of sensory dysfunction in some speech disorders. Yet evidence exists that much of speech motor control is preprogrammed by the brain and that feedforward control is also critical to speech output. Guenther and colleagues[15] developed a model of feedforward control that works in concert with auditory and somatosensory feedback called the DIVA (Directions into Velocities of Articulators) that can be implemented in computer simulations producing "articulation" and acoustic signals. This model is shown in Figure 6-9 and theorizes the probable feedback and feedforward mechanisms that may be in play in neural processing for speech production. Neurologic control of speech may well involve combinations of both open and closed loops in a multiple-pathway, hierarchical system that provides the necessary flexibility, speed, and precision to program and execute the everyday movements of speech with such complexity and ease.

FIGURE **6-9**

Schematic of the DIVA (Directions into Velocities of Articulators) model of speech acquisition and production. Projections to and from the cerebellum are simplified for clarity. (From Guenther, F. H. [2006]. Cortical interactions underlying the production of speech sounds. *Journal of Communication Disorders, 39,* 350-365.)

Synopsis of Clinical Information and Applications for the Speech-Language Pathologist

- The motor system has a hierarchy. It becomes progressively more sophisticated as the paths ascend and progressively less sophisticated as the paths descend.
- The lower levels of the motor system are partially constrained by the upper levels, but all have a certain autonomy.
- The levels of the motor system can be enumerated as Broca's area and the motor association cortex areas, the corticospinal and corticonuclear tracts, the spinal cord and the brainstem nuclei (lower motor neuron), the basal nuclei, the cerebellum, and the extrapyramidal or indirect activation pathway tracts.
- Motor speech commands are organized in the premotor and SMA (motor association areas) and Broca's area as well as the insula. Apraxia of speech is the disorder associated with damage to the motor speech programming areas.
- The pyramidal system includes the corticospinal tract for motor control of limbs and the cortico-nuclear tract, which provides motor control for muscles of the face, tongue, pharynx, and larynx.
- The corticospinal tract is a primarily contralateral innervation system, with 90% of the fibers decussating at the level of the pyramids of the medulla and terminating in the opposite side of the spinal cord.
- The corticonuclear tract provides primarily bilateral innervation for the majority of the musculature innervated, with the decussation occurring at various levels of the brainstem. Although most of the nuclei receive both unilateral and contralateral fibers, the amount of unilateral versus contralateral innervation varies.
- Upper motor neurons are the first-order neurons in the corticospinal and corticonuclear tracts. The upper motor neurons send axons to the nuclei of the spinal cord or the cranial nerves in the brainstem. They comprise the first fiber pathway of the direct activation pathway that is the pyramidal tract.
- Lower motor neurons are the second-order neurons in the direct activation pathway. They send axons out of the spinal cord or brainstem and become the peripheral nerves. Sherrington called the lower motor neuron the final common pathway because it is the final route for all the complex motor activity occurring above the level of the lower motor neurons.
- The motor unit is a useful concept when studying the lower motor neurons. The motor unit consists

of the cell body, the axon (the nerve itself), the junction of the nerve and muscle fiber (neuromuscular juncture), and the muscle fiber.
- The facial nerve (cranial nerve VII) is unusual in that it has a dorsal and ventral component to its nucleus. The ventral portion, supplying the upper face, is far more bilaterally innervated than the dorsal part, which supplies the lower part of the face. The clinical implication of this is that a unilateral upper motor neuron lesion affecting this nerve results in paresis or paralysis of the opposite side of the lower face, whereas the upper half of the face is relatively unaffected because of its bilateral innervation.
- Lesions of the upper motor neuron tract produce different clinical symptoms than lesions of the lower motor neuron tract. The speech-language pathologist must be able to recognize these signs. Damage to either of the two pathways produces different types of dysarthria as well.
- Alpha motor neurons are the nerve cells that comprise the lower motor neuron. They are found in the anterior horn cells in the spinal cord and in the nuclei of the cranial nerves in the brainstem. They supply skeletal muscles through innervation of the extrafusal fibers of the muscles.
- The muscle spindle is present in many skeletal muscles and provides the sensory feedback to the muscle regarding length. This feedback results in the muscle stretch reflex. With the exception of the jaw-closing muscles, muscle spindles are few and scattered in the muscles concerned with speech and swallowing.
- The extrapyramidal system is composed of the descending indirect activation pathways (vestibulospinal, reticulospinal, rubrospinal, and tectospinal tracts). The reticular formation can also be included.
- The primary structures of the basal ganglia are the caudate nucleus, globus pallidus, and putamen. The substantia nigra and subthalamic nucleus are also included. Four different functional circuits seem to operate in the basal ganglia system: a motor loop, a limbic loop, a cognitive loop, and an oculomotor loop.
- Basal ganglia disease can cause movement disorders and associated dysarthrias. The dysarthria of Parkinson's disease is an example of a hypokinetic dysarthria, and the motor speech disorder associated with Huntington's chorea is an example of hyperkinetic dysarthria. Both result from damage to parts of the basal ganglia.

Continued

Synopsis of Clinical Information and Applications for the Speech-Language Pathologist—cont'd

- The small hemispheres at the base of the brain are the lobes of the cerebellum. The cerebellum, like the basal ganglia, serves as a "consultant" to the motor system and provides coordination needed for smooth, synergistic movement. Signs of cerebellar damage include ataxia, nystagmus, dysmetria, dysdiadochokinesis, and sometimes an ataxic dysarthria.
- Speech motor control seems to be a product of both an open-loop and a closed-loop feedback system according to servomechanism theory. The open-loop system contains feedforward control, with the brain partially preprogramming movements that will be made to accomplish certain productions. The concept of speech motor control as a product of a closed-loop system has been generally accepted as the prime system controlling speech output, meaning that sensory monitoring from hearing, touch, and deep muscle sense guides production. Sufficient evidence exists that feedforward occurs, and both types of systems are probably in operation.

CASE **STUDY**

A 63-year-old man awoke in the early morning with disorientation, inability to speak, and inability to move his right side. He was admitted through the emergency department with a preliminary diagnosis of acute left hemisphere cerebrovascular accident (also known as a stroke). A computed tomography scan was done early to rule out hemorrhage but did not show a lesion site. He was put on blood-thinning medication and began to show some movement of the right lower extremity and some ability to speak, although speech was very hesitant, nonfluent, and difficult to understand. He was able to answer yes/no questions accurately and could read fairly well. Further testing during the next few days revealed difficulty following body movement commands involving facial and oral movements and found him "awkward and slow" in following commands involving movements of the left hand. He was diagnosed with a mild nonfluent aphasia with accompanying apraxia of speech, right hemiparesis, mild right facial weakness affecting the movement of the right side of the lips, and "clumsy hand syndrome" (sympathetic apraxia) on the left side. He was discharged to an acute rehabilitation center, where he participated in occupational therapy, physical therapy, and speech therapy. He did well in treatment. At discharge 3 weeks later, he was walking with a cane, and movement and use of the right arm had improved, providing some gross functional use. Speech was still effortful with simple sentence structure and was distorted though intelligible.

Questions for Consideration

1. Considering the right hemiparesis, mild nonfluent aphasia, apraxia of speech, and sympathetic apraxia, what are the likely structures damaged by this stroke?
2. What is meant by a "sympathetic apraxia"? (You will have to research this outside of this text). How might this complicate the SLP's treatment plan for this patient?

REFERENCES

1. Ackermann, H., & Riecker, A. (2010). The contribution(s) of the insula to speech production: A review of the clinical and functional imaging literature. *Brain Structure and Function, 214,* 419–433.
2. Alario, F. X., Chainay, H., Lehericy, S., & Cohen, L. (2006). The role of the supplementary motor area (SMA) in word production. *Brain Research,* 129–143.
3. Bolam, J. P., Hanley, J. J., Booth, P. A. C., & Bevan, M. D. (2000). Synaptic organisation of the basal ganglia. *Journal of Anatomy, 196,* 527–542.
4. Booth, C. M., Cortina-Borja, M. J., & Theologis, T. N. (2001). Collagen accumulation in muscles of children with cerebral palsy and correlation with severity of spasticity. *Developmental Medicine and Child Neurology, 43,* 314–320.
5. Cereda, C., Ghika, J., Maeder, P., & Bogousslavsky, J. (2002). Strokes restricted to the insular cortex. *Neurology, 59,* 1950–1955.
6. Civier, O., Bullock, D., Ludo, M., & Guenther, F. H. (2013). Computational modeling of stuttering caused by impairments in a basal ganglia thalamo-cortical circuit involved in syllable selection and initiation. *Brain and Language, 126,* 263–278.

7. Clark, H. M. (2003). Neuromuscular treatments for speech and swallowing: A tutorial. *American Journal of Speech-Language Pathology, 12,* 400–415.

8. Clark, H. M. (2005, June). Clinical decision making and oral motor treatments. *The ASHA Leader, 14,* 34–35.

9. Cooper, S. (1953). Muscle spindles in the intrinsic muscles of the human tongue. *Journal of Physiology, 122,* 193–202.

10. Duffau, H., Bauchet, L., Lehéricy, S., & Capelle, L. (2001). Functional compensation of the left dominant insula for language. *Neuroreport, 12,* 2159–2163.

11. Dronkers, N. F. (1996). A new brain region for coordinating speech articulation. *Nature, 384,* 159–161.

12. Dronkers, N. F., Plaisant, O., Iba-Zizen, M. T., & Cabanis, E. A. (2007). Paul Broca's historic cases: High MR imaging of the brains of Leborgne and Lelong. *Brain, 130,* 1432–1441.

13. Duffy, J. R. (2005). *Motor speech disorders: Substrates, differential diagnosis and management* (2nd ed.). St. Louis: Mosby/ Elsevier.

14. Fenichel, G. M. (1993). *Clinical pediatric neurology: A signs and symptoms approach.* Philadelphia: W. B. Saunders.

15. Guenther, F. H. (2006). Cortical interactions underlying the production of speech sounds. *Journal of Communication Disorders, 39,* 350–365.

16. Kent, R. (2004). The uniqueness of speech among motor systems. *Clinical Linguistics and Phonetics, 18,* 495–505.

17. Levelt, W. J. M. (1989). *Speaking: From intention to articulation.* Cambridge MA: MIT Press.

18. Liss, J. M. (1990). Muscle spindles in the human levator veli palatine and palatoglossus muscles. *Journal of Speech and Hearing Research, 33,* 736–746.

19. MacNeilage, P. F. (1998). The frame/content theory of evolution of speech production. *Behavioral and Brain Sciences, 21,* 499–511.

20. MacNeilage, P. F., & Davis, B. L. (2001). Motor mechanisms in speech ontogeny: Phylogenetic, neurobiological and linguistic implications. *Current Opinions in Neurobiology, 11,* 696–700.

21. Marsden, C. D. (1982). The mysterious function of the basal ganglia. *Neurology, 32,* 514–539.

22. Mohr, J. P., Pessin, M. S., Finkelstein, S., Funkenstein, H. H., Duncan, G. W., & Davis, K. R. (1978). Broca's aphasia. *Neurology, 28,* 311–324.

23. Picard, N., & Strick, P. L. (1996). Motor areas of the medial wall: A review of their location and functional activation. *Cerebral Cortex, 6,* 342–353.

24. Price, C. J., Crinion, J. T., & MacSweeney, M. (2011). A generative model of speech production in Broca's and Wernicke's area. *Frontiers in Psychology, 2,* 1–9.

25. Saigusa, H., Niimi, S., Yamashita, K., Gotoh, T., & Kumada, M. (2001). Morphological and histochemical studies of the genioglossus muscle. *The Annals of Otology, Rhinology and Laryngology, 110,* 779–784.

26. Saigusa, H., Yamashita, K., Tanuma, K., Saigusa, M., & Niimi, S. (2004). Morphological studies for retrusive movement of the human adult tongue. *Clinical Anatomy, 17,* 93–98.

27. Sherrington, C. S. (1926). *The integrative action of the nervous system.* New Haven, CT: Yale University Press.

28. Weiner, W. J., & Lang, A. E. (1989). *Movement disorders: A comprehensive survey.* Mount Kisco, NY: Futura.

7

The Cranial Nerves

To those I address, it is unnecessary to go further than to indicate that the nerves treated in these papers are the instruments of expression from the smile of the infant's cheek to the last agony of life.

Charles Bell, 1824

KEY **TERMS**

abducens	hyoglossus
abduction	internuncial
branchial	lacrimal
central pattern	palpate
generator	primary olfactory
chorda tympani	cortex
cranial nerves	ptosis
diplopia	secretomotor
flaccid	solely special sensory
genioglossus	styloglossus
glottal coup	tinnitus

This chapter is intended to help the speech-language pathologist (SLP) understand one of the most important components of the nervous system in regard to the acts of hearing, speaking and swallowing. The cranial nerves comprise a part of the peripheral nervous system that provides crucial sensory and motor information for the oral, pharyngeal, and laryngeal musculature and the auditory and vestibular systems. The speech-language pathologist should be familiar with the names, structure, innervation, testing procedures, and signs of abnormal function of the cranial nerves. This information is especially critical when working with an adult or child with dysarthria and/or dysphagia.

Origin of the Cranial Nerves

NAMES AND NUMBERS

Twelve pairs of cranial nerves leave the brain and pass through the foramina of the skull. They are referred to by their numbers, written in Roman numerals, and by their names. The names sometimes give a clue to the function of the nerves, but the number, name, and concise descriptions of the various functions should all be learned (Table 7-1). Many students use a suggested mnemonic device to help them remember the cranial nerves (e.g., "**O**n **O**ld **O**lympus' **T**owering **T**op **A** **F**inn **A**nd **G**erman **V**end **A**t **H**ops") or create their own, maybe more interesting, mnemonic to aid their memory.

EMBRYOLOGIC ORIGIN

As you will learn in Chapter 11 (or have learned if you were already assigned to read it), the body develops in the embryo from transverse segments as well as from longitudinal tubes. The viscera, including the neuraxis, are developed from the elaboration, or diverticulation, of the hollow longitudinal tubes. The transverse segments are of two types: somites and arches. Somites eventually give rise to muscle, bone, and connective tissue of the body wall. The arches are the branchial or pharyngeal arches and these give rise to structures of the face and neck.

The nuclei of the cranial nerves are of three different types. The motor nuclei are distinguished by the embryologic origin of the muscles they innervate. In the development of the embryo, the branchial (gill) arches are responsible for the structure, muscles, and nerves of the face and neck. Cranial nerves V, VII, IX, X, and XI are thus known as the branchial set. Cranial nerves III, IV, VI, and XII are derived from this somatic segmentation and thus are called the somatomotor, or somitic, set. The elaboration of the longitudinal tubes gives rise to three cranial nerves (I, II, and VIII) known as the solely special sensory set.

TABLE 7-1		
The Cranial Nerves		
NUMBER	NAME	SUMMARY OF FUNCTION
I	Olfactory	Smell
II	Optic	Vision
III	Oculomotor	Innervation of muscles to move eyeball, pupil, and upper lid
IV	Trochlear	Innervation of superior oblique muscle of eye
V	Trigeminal	Chewing and sensation to face, teeth, anterior tongue
VI	Abducens	Abduction of eye
VII	Facial	Movement of facial muscles, taste, salivary glands
VIII	(Vestibular) acoustic	Equilibrium and hearing
IX	Glossopharyngeal	Taste, swallowing, elevation of pharynx and larynx, parotid salivary gland, sensation to posterior tongue, upper pharynx
X	Vagus	Taste, swallowing, elevation of palate, phonation, parasympathetic outflow to visceral organs
XI	Accessory	Turning of head and shrugging of shoulders
XII	Hypoglossal	Movement of tongue

Some branchial and somitic cranial nerves have a visceral component: III, VII, IX, and X. Cranial nerves V, VII, IX, and X also have a general sensory component (i.e., they participate in sensation of pain, pressure touch, vibration, and proprioception).

THE CORTICONUCLEAR TRACT AND THE CRANIAL NERVES

The cranial nerves themselves are part of the peripheral nervous system and consist of efferent motor fibers that arise from nuclei in the brainstem and afferent sensory fibers that originate in the peripheral ganglia. The motor nuclei of the cranial nerves receive impulses from the cerebral cortex through the corticonuclear tracts. The tracts begin in the upper motor neurons found as pyramidal cells in the inferior part of the precentral gyrus and also in the adjacent part of the postcentral gyrus. The tracts then follow the path illustrated in Figure 6-2. They descend through the corona radiata and the genu of the internal capsule and then pass through the midbrain in the cerebral peduncles. They then synapse either with the lower motor neuron directly or indirectly through internuncial neurons, a chain of neurons situated between the primary efferent neuron and the final motor neuron.

The majority of the corticonuclear fibers to the motor cranial nerve nuclei cross the midline, or decussate, before reaching the nuclei. All the cranial nerve motor nuclei have bilateral innervation except for portions of the trigeminal, facial, and hypoglossal fibers, which are discussed later.

The motor fibers of the cranial nerves are formed by axons of nerve cells within the brain, but the sensory, or afferent, fibers of the cranial nerves are formed from processes of nerve cells found outside the brain. These sensory nerve cells are usually found in "clumps" of nerve cells called peripheral ganglia. They are situated on the nerve trunks or in the sensory organ itself (e.g., the nose, ear, or eye). The central processes of these cells enter the brain and terminate by synapsing with cells grouped together to form the nuclei of termination. These cells have axons that cross the midline and ascend and synapse on other sensory nuclei, such as in the thalamus. The axons of the resulting cells then terminate in the cerebral cortex.

Cranial Nerves for Smell and Vision

Cranial nerve I, the olfactory nerve, is a plexus of thin fibers that unite in approximately 20 small bundles called fila olfactoria. The olfactory receptors are situated in the mucous membrane of the nasal cavity. The nerve fibers synapse with other cells in the olfactory bulb and finally end in the olfactory areas of the cerebral cortex, the periamygdaloid and prepiriform areas. Together these are known as the primary olfactory cortex. They also send fibers to many other centers within the brain to establish connections for automatic and emotional responses to olfactory stimulation.

Cranial nerves II, III, IV, and VI are concerned with vision. The optic nerve (II) is the primary nerve of sight. Its nerve fibers are axons that come from the retina, converge on the optic disk, and exit from the eye on both sides. The right nerve joins the left to form the optic chiasma. In the optic chiasma, fibers from the nasal half of the eye cross the midline, and fibers from the temporal half continue to run ipsilaterally. Most of the fibers synapse with nerve cells in the lateral geniculate body of the thalamus and then leave it, forming optic radiations. The optic radiations formed by these fibers terminate in the visual cortex and the visual association cortex.

Cranial nerve III is the oculomotor nerve, the nucleus of which is located at the level of the superior colliculus. Cranial nerve III has a somatomotor component that innervates the extraocular muscles to move the eyeball and a visceral component responsible for pupil constriction. Dysfunction of the third cranial nerve causes ptosis (drooping) of the eyelid. The eye may also be in abduction and turned down. If the visceral component is impaired, the pupillary reflex is lost and the pupil is dilated. Figure 7-1, *A*, illustrates a complete paralysis of the left oculomotor nerve.

Cranial nerve IV is the trochlear nerve, the nucleus of which is at the level of the inferior colliculus. This nerve innervates the superior oblique muscle, which is primarily responsible for intorsion of the eyeball, helping to maintain its position toward the midline of the face. Confirmed lesions cause diplopia (double vision).

Cranial nerve VI, the abducens, has its nucleus on the floor of the fourth ventricle. Dysfunction prevents lateral movements of the eyeball. Figure 7-1, *B*, shows a complete paralysis of the left cranial nerve VI.

The remaining seven cranial nerves are vital for the production of normal speech and thus are given more attention, focusing on the pathway, structures innervated, functional purpose, signs of dysfunction, and testing procedure for each nerve. Learn them one by one. Test yourself on them until you are firmly acquainted with each nerve. Review Figure 3-2 for attachment sites of the cranial nerves to the brainstem.

FIGURE **7-1**
A, Complete left III (oculomotor) nerve paralysis with a fully abducted eye, which is also depressed. The pupil of the eye is nonreactive and fully dilated. The ptosis of the left eye requires the examiner to lift the lid to examine movement. **B**, Complete left VI (abducens) nerve paralysis showing a fully adducted eye resulting from the unopposed pull of the medial rectus. (Reprinted from FitzGerald, M. J. T., & Folan-Curran, J. [2002]. *Clinical neuroanatomy and related neuroscience* [4th ed.]. Philadelphia: Saunders/Elsevier.)

Cranial Nerves for Speech and Hearing

CRANIAL NERVE V: TRIGEMINAL

Anatomy
Both the motor and sensory roots of the trigeminal nerve are attached to the lateral edges of the pons. The motor nuclei are restricted to the pons, but the sensory nuclei extend from the mesencephalon to the spinal cord.

Innervation
The motor part of the trigeminal nerve innervates the following muscles: masseter, temporalis, lateral and medial pterygoids, tensor tympani, tensor veli palatini, mylohyoid, and the anterior belly of the digastric muscle. The sensory fibers have three main branches:
1. The ophthalmic nerve, which is sensory to the forehead, eyes, and nose
2. The maxillary nerve, which is sensory to the upper lip mucosa, maxilla, upper teeth, cheeks, palate, and maxillary sinus
3. The mandibular nerve, which is sensory to the anterior two thirds of the tongue, mandible, lower teeth, lower lip, part of the cheek, and part of the external ear

Figure 7-2 shows a sensory map of the trigeminal nerve supply to the areas of the face and oral structures.

Function
Cranial nerve V is primarily responsible for mastication and for sensation to the face, teeth, gums, and anterior two thirds of the tongue. Innervating the tensor velar palatini, cranial nerve V is partially responsible for flattening and tensing the soft palate and for opening the eustachian tube. Innervating an extrinsic laryngeal muscle (the anterior belly of the digastric), it also assists in the upward and anterior movement of the larynx. Innervating the mylohyoid and part of the digastric,

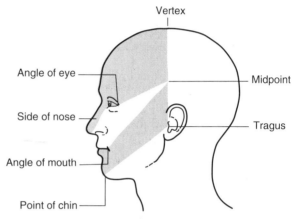

FIGURE **7-2**
Trigeminal nerve sensory map. (Reprinted from FitzGerald, M. J. T., & Folan-Curran, J. [2002]. *Clinical neuroanatomy and related neuroscience* [4th ed.]. Philadelphia: Saunders/Elsevier.)

this nerve contributes to retraction of the tongue. Also innervated by CN V, the tensor tympani in the middle ear works with the stapedius muscle to dampen oscillation of the eardrum in the presence of loud noise.

Testing
The jaw-closing and grinding lateral movements of chewing are the result of the function of the masseter and temporal, medial pterygoid, and lateral pterygoid muscles. The first three contribute to closure of the jaw, but only the masseter can be directly tested. To evaluate the masseter, palpate the area of the muscle (2 cm above and in front of the angle of the mandible) as the patient bites down as hard as possible and then relaxes. As the patient bites, the bulk of the muscle can be felt. Try this to become familiar with the masseter. The muscle body should feel firm and bulky. The temporal muscle cannot be well palpated; however, if it is atrophied (shrunken) from a lower motor neuron lesion, the temple of the face will be sunken.

The strength of jaw closure should also be evaluated. To do so, place your hand on the tip of the patient's mandible as the jaw is held open. Place the other hand on the forehead to prevent neck extension. Ask the patient to bite down hard against the resistance of your hand. The patient should be able to close the jaw against a moderate resistance.

The lateral pterygoids enable the jaw to lateralize in chewing. To evaluate these muscles, ask the patient to open the jaw against resistance of your hand and note how the tip of the mandible lines up with the space between the upper medial incisors. Ask the patient to move the jaw from side to side and observe the facility of movement.

Finally, ask the patient to lateralize the jaw against resistance. Have him or her move the jaw to one side and hold it while you gently try to push it toward the center. Place your other hand against the opposite cheekbone so the patient cannot use the neck muscles to help.

The patient with a unilateral paralysis of cranial nerve V may show a deviation of the jaw to the side of the lesion and an inability to force the jaw to the side opposite the lesion. Atrophy may also be noted after a period. These problems result from lower motor neuron lesions. Upper motor neuron lesions that are unilateral do not affect cranial nerves as much because the nuclei receive so many axons from the other hemisphere. Therefore the paresis is usually transitory or mild unless *bilateral* upper motor neuron lesions are present.

Bilateral upper motor neuron lesions result in an observable limitation of jaw movements. Opening and closing movements of the jaw, though possible, are restricted. Gross chewing movements are seen, but chewing and biting may lack vigor and are performed slowly.

To evaluate the sensory component of the trigeminal nerve, sensation to the face may be tested. The patient is asked to close the eyes, and a cotton swab is used to stroke the face in the three different distribution areas of the nerve. The examiner should stay in the central part of the face because, as shown in Figure 7-2, considerable overlap exists on the periphery. The ophthalmic division may therefore be tested by stroking above the eyebrows; the maxillary division by stroking the upper lip in an upward movement toward the cheekbone; and the mandibular division by stroking between the lower lip and the chin in an upward movement toward the cheekbone. Left and right sides should be done separately and compared. Stroking should be done with firm pressure and kept consistent across all trials.

Sensation to the anterior two thirds of the tongue may also be tested during the examination, especially if chewing and swallowing are of concern. The two sides of the tongue may be compared for sensitivity to the touch of a cotton-tip swab on the anterior as well as medial portion of the tongue.

CRANIAL NERVE VII: FACIAL

Anatomy

The facial nerve is a complex nerve carrying two motor and two sensory components. It involves several different nuclei, all within the pons near the reticular formation.

The special sensory component of the facial nerve involves the taste fibers for the tongue and palate. These fibers have their primary sensory neurons in the geniculate ganglion. They enter the brainstem in the sensory root of the facial nerve, called the nervus intermedius. They run in a bundle, or fasciculus, called the tractus solitarius and are joined in that bundle by the taste fibers from cranial nerves IX and X.

The taste fibers split off from the facial nerve in the middle ear as the **chorda tympani**. This joins the lingual branch of cranial nerve V. The taste fibers then terminate in the nucleus of the tractus solitarius. The fibers are distributed to the taste buds of the anterior two thirds of the tongue. Some fibers also terminate in the taste buds in the hard and soft palates. Ascending fibers from the nucleus solitarius run to the ventroposterior thalamus and then project to the cortical area for taste located at the lower end of the postcentral gyrus in the parietal lobe.

The general sensory component of VII is a small cutaneous component whose nerve cells are found in the geniculate ganglion in the temporal bone. Impulses travel in the nervus intermedius, descending in the spinal tract of the trigeminal nerve and synapsing in the spinal nucleus of the trigeminal nerve located in the upper medulla. This sensory component may supplement the mandibular portion of cranial nerve V, providing sensation from the wall of the acoustic meatus and the surface of the tympanic membrane.

The visceral motor component of cranial nerve VII is composed of cell bodies that are preganglionic autonomic motor neurons. These cell bodies are collectively called the superior salivatory nucleus and the **lacrimal** nucleus. The fibers from the nucleus travel in the nervus intermedius and divide in the facial canal, becoming the greater petrosal nerve and the chorda tympani. The petrosal nerve fibers follow a complicated path and join fibers of the trigeminal to reach the lacrimal and mucosal glands of the nasal and oral cavities, where they stimulate secretion.

The branchial motor component of the facial nerve is of critical importance to the speech-language pathologist. The fibers of the motor nucleus extend to the floor of the ventricle, curve around the nucleus of the abducens (cranial nerve VI), and exit the brainstem near the inferior margin of the pons. These fibers then join those from the nucleus of the tractus solitarius and the autonomic or parasympathetic nuclei and enter the internal auditory meatus as they extend through the facial canal of the petrosal bone. They leave the skull through the stylomastoid foramen. While coursing through the facial canal, the facial nerve travels through the tympanic cavity, innervating the stapedius muscle. The facial nerve can therefore be involved in pathologic conditions related to the ear as well as the oral musculature. Surgeons removing acoustic tumors must be mindful of the location of the facial nerve.

The dorsal motor nucleus of cranial nerve VII innervates the lower part of the face and receives most of its corticonuclear fibers from the opposite hemisphere; thus innervation to these structures is primarily contralateral. The ventral motor nucleus that supplies the upper part of the face receives fibers from both cerebral hemispheres (i.e., receives crossed and uncrossed fibers), and innervation is bilateral.

Innervation

The parasympathetic nuclei are also known as the superior salivatory and the lacrimal nuclei. The superior salivatory nucleus receives afferent information from the hypothalamus and olfactory system as well as taste information from the mouth cavity. It supplies the sublingual salivary glands and the nasal and palatine glands.

The lacrimal nucleus solitarius receives information from afferent fibers from the trigeminal sensory nuclei for reflex response to corneal irritation. The sensory nucleus receives information concerning taste from fibers from the anterior two thirds of the tongue, the floor of the mouth, and the soft and hard palates.

The motor nucleus gives the face expression by innervation of the various facial muscles (i.e., the orbicularis oculi, zygomatic, buccinator, orbicularis oris, and labial muscles). Other muscles innervated are the platysma, stylohyoid, and stapedius and the posterior belly of the digastric.

Function

Most important to the SLP is that the facial nerve is responsible for all movements of facial expression. All facial apertures are guarded by muscles innervated by the facial nerve: the eyes, the nose, the mouth, and the external auditory canal. Cranial nerve VII enables the actions of wrinkling the forehead, closing the eyes tightly, closing the lips tightly, pulling back the corners of the lips, pulling down the corners of the lips and tensing the anterior neck muscles.

Beyond these important movements in speech and swallowing, the facial nerve also helps pull the larynx

up and back (through the belly of the digastric muscle). It provides motor innervation to the sublingual and submaxillary salivary glands, and it guards the middle ear by innervating the stapedius muscle, which, with the tensor tympani muscle, dampens excessive movement of the ossicles in the presence of a loud noise. Finally, the facial nerve also is partially responsible for taste.

Testing

Tests of facial expression are the primary tests in the oral-motor examination for cranial nerve VII. Before any motor testing, however, the patient's face at rest should be visually inspected, especially noting the symmetry. Then begin movement testing at the upper part of the face, focusing first on the forehead, then the eyes, and finally the mouth. Box 7-1 outlines what to observe and note before commencing with speech testing.

BOX 7-1
Facial Assessment

Forehead

Ask the patient to wrinkle the forehead and look up at the ceiling. Note the symmetry of the wrinkling on both sides. Keep in mind that this ability or inability is diagnostic for localization. Because the upper part of the face is innervated bilaterally, only a lower motor neuron lesion would cause complete paralysis of this function. An upper motor neuron lesion causes some weakness on the opposite side, but it will not be nearly as perceptible because of the ipsilateral fiber innervation.

Eyes

Ask the patient to close his or her eyes as tightly as possible. Note the contraction of the orbicularis oculi and the consequent wrinkling around the eyes. Bilateral innervation is also present in this part of the face, although not to the degree that the forehead displays. The lower motor neuron-upper motor neuron difference holds true for dysfunction of this part of the face.

Mouth

Take a close look at mouth movements. First ask the patient to smile or pull back the corners of the lips. It helps to tell the patient to show his or her teeth when doing this, exaggerating the smile somewhat. Again, observe the symmetry of the two sides. Then ask the patient to pucker the lips; observe the symmetry of constriction. Finally, ask him or her to pull down the corners of the lips (as in pouting) or try to wrinkle the skin of the neck. Inspect for symmetry. Also test for the strength of movement against resistance and compare the two sides of the mouth.

The patient with a lower motor neuron lesion of cranial nerve VII has involvement of the entire side of the face on the side of the lesion (ipsilateral). Figure 7-3 is an example of unilateral facial paralysis. Although speech may be distorted, it is usually not significantly hindered by peripheral involvement of cranial nerve VII. The patient with an upper motor neuron lesion shows complete involvement of the contralateral lip and neck muscles, some degree of involvement of the area around the eyes, and little difficulty with the forehead or frontalis muscle. It should be noted that the paralysis occurs on voluntary movement. The patient may have almost normal movement for *emotionally initiated* movements such as a true smile but be unable to lateralize the lips on the affected side when asked to do so voluntarily.

Because the facial nerve innervates the stapedius muscle, it may be paralyzed by a lesion. If this occurs, the patient may report that ordinary sounds seem uncomfortably loud.

The sensory component of the facial nerve may be assessed by testing the patient's sense of taste on the anterior two thirds of the tongue. Sensitivity of the two sides of the tongue should be compared. The patient should be able to identify the four primary tastes (salty, sour, bitter, and sweet) if the sensory pathways are intact.

CRANIAL NERVE VIII: ACOUSTIC-VESTIBULAR OR VESTIBULOCOCHLEAR

The following explanation assumes the reader has studied the anatomy of the ear and is well versed in the structure and function of the cochlea and semicircular canals. A good working knowledge of the anatomy of the ear is imperative; review of the information provided in Chapter 5 on the auditory system is suggested.

Anatomy
As can be ascertained from its name, the acoustic-vestibular, or vestibulocochlear, nerve consists of two distinct parts: the vestibular nerve and the cochlear, or acoustic, nerve. Both take afferent information from the internal ear to the nervous system, but as their names imply, they carry different types of information.

The vestibular nerve consists of nerve cells and their fibers, which are located in Scarpa's ganglion located in the internal acoustic meatus. The fibers enter the brainstem in a groove between the lower border of the pons and the upper medulla oblongata in a sulcus called the cerebellopontine angle. This location is the site of one of the most common brain tumors, a vestibular schwannoma, also known as an acoustic neuroma. A few of the axons terminate in the flocculonodular lobe of the cerebellum. Most

FIGURE **7-3**
Patient with complete facial nerve paralysis on the right side. The patient was asked to show her teeth and look up at the ceiling. Note the inability to raise the eyebrow, drooping of the lower eyelid, inability to retract the mouth, and lack of webbing on the neck (effect on the platysma muscle). This patient also was unable to abduct the eye because of involvement of the abducens. The patient was found to have demyelination affecting the facial nerve and abducens nerve, resulting from multiple sclerosis. (From Parsons, M. [1986]. *Diagnostic picture test in clinical neurology.* London: Wolfe Medical.)

axons enter the vestibular nuclear complex, which consists of a group of nuclei located in the floor of the fourth ventricle.

The cochlear nerve consists of nerve cells and fibers located in the spiral ganglion located around the modiolus of the cochlea. Nerve fibers wrap around each other in the modiolus, with a layering effect. Fibers from the apex, carrying low-frequency information, are found on the innermost part of the core, whereas fibers from the basal part of the cochlea, carrying high-frequency information, are found on the outermost layers. The nerve fibers from these cell bodies enter the brainstem at the lower border of the pons on the lateral side of the facial nerve. They are separated from the facial nerve fibers by the vestibular nerve. Figure 7-4 illustrates the relation of cranial nerve VIII to the inner ear.

When the cochlear fibers enter the pons, they divide into two branches. One branch enters the dorsal cochlear nucleus (high frequencies), and the other enters the ventral cochlear nucleus (low frequencies). Both nuclei are situated adjacent to the inferior cerebral peduncle.

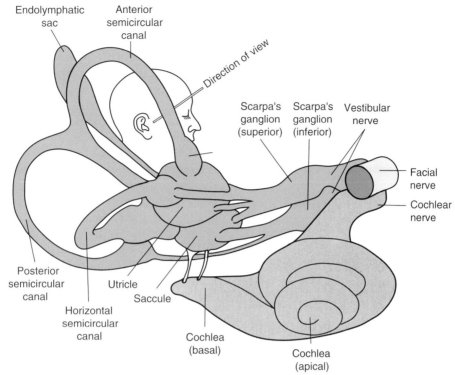

FIGURE **7-4**

Relation of the vestibular, cochlear, and facial nerve to the inner ear. (Reprinted from Nadeau, S. E., Ferguson, T. S., Valenstein, E., Vierck, C. J., Petruska, J. C., Streit, W. J., & Ritz, L. A. [2004]. *Medical neuroscience.* Philadelphia: Saunders/Elsevier.)

From this point the axons take varied and complex paths. The system is largely contralateral. Most fibers decussate after the cochlear nuclei, although there are a few ipsilaterally projected fibers. The fibers form a tract called the lateral lemniscus as they ascend through the posterior portion of the pons and midbrain. All ascending fibers terminate in the medial geniculate body and from there project to the auditory cortex by way of the auditory radiations. Between the cochlear nuclei and the medial geniculate body, the fibers take one of several pathways, including synapses at one or more of the following structures: the superior olives, the trapezoid body, the inferior colliculus, and the nucleus of the lateral lemniscus.

Innervation

Both portions of the vestibulocochlear nerve are primarily sensory in nature. The vestibular nerve receives afferent information from the utricle, saccule, and semicircular canal of the inner ear and from the cerebellum. The vestibular nerve also sends out efferent fibers that pass to the cerebellum through the inferior cerebellar peduncles and also to the spinal cord, forming the vestibulospinal tract. Efferent fibers are also sent to the nuclei of cranial nerves III (oculomotor), IV (trochlear), and VI (abducens) through the medial longitudinal fasciculus. As previously outlined, the cochlear nerve carries afferent fibers from the cochlea to the auditory cortex.

Function

Cranial nerve VIII takes afferent information from the internal ear to the nervous system. It is responsible for sound sensitivity and innervates the utricle and the saccule of the inner ear, which are sensitive to static changes in equilibrium. In addition, innervation of the semicircular canals takes place through this nerve, controlling sensitivity to dynamic changes in equilibrium.

Testing

Although the speech-language pathologist may perform hearing threshold screening or testing that may provide information about the cochlear nerve, the audiologist usually is responsible for thorough assessment of hearing and cochlear function. Neurologists often perform simple tuning fork tests for acuity and sound lateralization, and some prefer to use whispered words.

Testing the vestibular function is also not in the purview of the SLP. Vestibular function usually is investigated with caloric tests that involve raising or lowering the temperature of the internal auditory meatus, thereby inducing current in the semicircular canals and stimulating the vestibular nerve for testing. Neurologists also use maneuvers of changing head position. Dynamic platform posturography is a technique developed in recent years to perform a functional assessment of how senses are used for balance.

The patient reporting reduced hearing acuity, **tinnitus** (ringing in the ears), or dizziness should always be seen by an otologist and receive an audiologic evaluation. The dizzy patient may be referred to a neurologist or a neurotologist, who typically will also refer for extensive audiologic and vestibular testing.

CRANIAL NERVE IX: GLOSSOPHARYNGEAL

Anatomy

The glossopharyngeal nerve carries two motor components and three sensory components. It can be found emerging from the medulla between the olive and the inferior cerebellar peduncle. The main trunk of the nerve exits the skull through the jugular foramen. Three nuclei in the brainstem are concerned with the functions of the glossopharyngeal nerve: the nucleus ambiguus, the inferior salivatory nucleus, and the nucleus solitarius.

Innervation

The nucleus ambiguus receives corticonuclear fibers of cranial nerve IX from both hemispheres and supplies the efferent innervation to the stylopharyngeus muscle, which contributes to the elevation of the pharynx and larynx. The inferior salivatory nucleus receives afferent information concerning taste from the hypothalamus, olfactory system, and mouth cavity. Efferent fibers supply the otic ganglion of the ear and the parotid salivary gland. The nucleus solitarius receives fibers arising from the inferior ganglia. Peripherally these visceral afferent fibers of cranial nerve IX mediate general sensation to the pharynx, soft palate, posterior third of the tongue, fauces, tonsils, ear canal, and tympanic cavity. The fibers decussate and travel upward to the opposite thalamic and some hypothalamic nuclei. From here the axons pass through the internal capsule and carry this sensory information to termination points in the lower postcentral gyrus.

Function

Cranial nerve IX is efferent to one *muscle* only—the stylopharyngeus. This muscle dilates the pharynx laterally and contributes to the elevation of the pharynx and larynx. It thereby serves to help clear the pharynx and larynx for swallowing. **Secretomotor** fibers are efferent fibers provided for the parotid gland's production of saliva. Sensory fibers carry taste information from the posterior third of the tongue. The glossopharyngeal nerve mediates the sensory portion of the palatal and pharyngeal gag. Cranial nerve IX also carries sensory information to the faucial pillars and posterior section of the tongue. This sensory input is responsible for "triggering" the swallow response.

Testing

Most functions of cranial nerve IX cannot be tested separately from those of cranial nerve X because the vagus has predominant control over laryngeal and pharyngeal sensory and motor function. However, testing the sensory portion of the pharyngeal gag does provide information about the integrity of cranial nerve IX. Testing the pharyngeal gag is not easily done in most people because getting so far back in the oral cavity without touching any other structure is difficult. To do the testing, the examiner should use a cotton-tipped applicator with a long wooden end (as used in medical clinics). The examiner carefully puts the cotton tip back against one side of the posterior pharyngeal wall, avoiding any contact with the base of the tongue or the velum. With a gentle poking of the wall, a gag should be elicited. Both sides of the pharynx should be tested.

If stimulation procedure (poking in correct spots) appears to be adequate but pharyngeal gag cannot be elicited, the examiner should ask whether the patient feels the pressure of the touch. If the stimulus is felt and no gag occurs, only the motor portion of the gag (mediated by the vagus) may be impaired. This situation is rare. Because sensation precedes motor activity, the absence of sensation *and* the gag implicates cranial nerve IX and gives the clinician information about the integrity of sensation to the upper pharynx, which can be important information in swallowing assessment.

CRANIAL NERVE X: VAGUS

Anatomy

Like the glossopharyngeal nerve, the vagus nerve also has three associated nuclei: the nucleus ambiguus, the dorsal nucleus, and the nucleus solitarius, also located in the medulla. Axons from vagal cell bodies in the nucleus ambiguus have two major branches: a pharyngeal branch and a laryngeal branch. The laryngeal branch will branch again into the recurrent laryngeal nerve and the superior laryngeal nerve. The superior laryngeal nerve further splits into two branches, the internal laryngeal and the external laryngeal.

The recurrent laryngeal nerve does not divide again. It arises considerably below the larynx and ascends to terminate at the larynx. The right recurrent nerve runs in a loop behind the common carotid and subclavian arteries. The left recurrent nerve is longer, leaving the main laryngeal branch of the vagus at a lower level than does the right. The left recurrent loops under and behind the aortic arch. It then ascends to the larynx in a groove between the trachea and esophagus and enters through the cricothyroid membrane. Damage to the recurrent laryngeal nerve sometimes occurs during surgery, especially heart and thyroid surgery. Following the path of the branching, one can see how this nerve would be vulnerable because of the location within the neck and in the chest cavity.

Innervation

The nucleus ambiguus receives an approximately equal number of corticonuclear fibers of cranial nerve X from both hemispheres; these fibers are efferent to the constrictor muscles of the pharynx and the intrinsic muscles of the larynx. The efferent fibers of the dorsal or parasympathetic nucleus are associated with autonomic functions and innervate the involuntary muscles of the bronchi, esophagus, heart, stomach, small intestine, and a portion of the large intestine. The afferent fibers from the nucleus of the tractus solitarius follow much the same path as those of the glossopharyngeal nerve and terminate in the postcentral gyrus.

Function

Vagus means wanderer, an apt name considering the many functions of the vagus nerve. It is motor to the viscera (heart, respiratory system, and most of the digestive system). It supplies primary efferent innervation to the palatal muscles (except for innervation of the tensor palatini by the trigeminal nerve). The vagus is also the primary efferent for the pharyngeal constrictors. On its own, the vagus innervates all of the intrinsic muscles of the larynx, primarily through the recurrent laryngeal branch. The cricothyroid, however, is innervated by the external laryngeal branch of the superior laryngeal nerve. This can be an important difference to remember during clinical examinations for speech or swallowing.

The vagus has both a visceral and a general sensory component in its afferent pathways. The visceral component carries visceral sensation that is not appreciated at a conscious level. Sensory information from the mucous membranes of the epiglottis, base of the tongue, aryepiglottic folds, and the majority of the larynx is carried in the internal laryngeal branch of the superior laryngeal nerve. Visceral sensation from below the larynx is carried in the recurrent laryngeal nerve.

General sensation (pain, temperature, and touch) from the larynx, pharynx, skin of the external ear, and the external auditory canal is carried in the vagus as well. From the vocal folds and below the larynx, general sensation is carried in the recurrent laryngeal nerve. From above the vocal folds, sensation travels in the internal

laryngeal division of the superior laryngeal nerve. Damage to one or both of these sensory components of these nerves could result in silent aspiration (aspiration with no reflexive cough) because of the decreased sensory input. The sensory information would normally cause the cough reflex to trigger or cause a tickle in the throat or airway, indicating that something foreign is on the membranes and needs to be coughed out.

Testing

Remember that evaluation of palatal function involves testing both cranial nerves IX and X. Palatal function is controlled primarily by cranial nerve X, with the tensor veli palatini innervated by V. Intrinsic laryngeal muscle function is covered solely by cranial nerve X.

Palatal function is tested by first observing the palate at rest as the patient opens the mouth to allow viewing. Look at the palatal arches and observe their symmetry. Note if one arch hangs lower than the other. Next ask the patient to phonate an "ah" and observe. The soft palate should elevate and move posteriorly and symmetrically. If the palate does not elevate, the palatal gag reflex, primarily innervated by cranial nerve IX, should be tested by touching the tongue blade against the palatal arches or against the base of the tongue. The gag is a reflex activity, and it is preserved in an upper motor neuron lesion because the reflex arc is still intact. As in all reflexes, it may be lost acutely after an upper motor neuron lesion; then it may become hyperactive. If both volitional and reflex activities of the palate are diminished, a lower motor neuron lesion is evidenced. Bear in mind that palatal elevation is also reduced by a cleft palate, congenital oral malformations, and soft tissue palatal lesions. Do not overlook these vital facts in vigorously searching for an upper or lower motor neuron lesion.

Laryngeal function evaluation is *adequately* completed only by direct or indirect laryngoscopy in which the vocal cords can be seen. A finer analysis of vocal cord movement patterns can be done by using laryngeal stroboscopy. Damage to the vagus nerve may cause paralysis or paresis of the vocal cord. Innervation is bilateral to the larynx, with the crossed and uncrossed fibers being approximately equal. Therefore complete paralysis of a vocal cord from an upper motor neuron lesion is rare.

Preliminary assessment of laryngeal function is performed by traditional clinical voice evaluation procedures. The patient is asked to phonate and prolong a vowel such as /a/. Maximum phonation time varies for normal adults. If the patient can phonate for a 7- to 8-second duration, laryngeal and respiratory control is presumed acceptable. Perceptual analysis of the voice is done by the clinician during this phonation and during conversation. The patient may be asked to demonstrate laryngeal function and control by raising and lowering the pitch of a prolonged vowel or singing up and down the scale. Remember that the ability to change pitch depends on proper function of the cricothyroid muscle, which is innervated by the superior laryngeal nerve rather than the recurrent nerve. Estimate of the strength of laryngeal closure can be made perceptually by asking the patient to perform the **glottal coup**, which is essentially to make a short, sharp grunting sound. A voluntary (as opposed to reflexive) cough should also be requested. The clinician listens for the sound made at the larynx in these two maneuvers to be strong and sharp. Stress testing of the vocal mechanism is done by asking the patient to count to 300 or to keep talking for a prescribed length of time. More sophisticated analyses of the voice may be performed with instrumentation for acoustic analysis.

In spastic dysarthria cases from an upper motor neuron lesion, a rough, harsh quality is heard on phonation. In bilateral upper motor neuron lesions (pseudobulbar palsy), a characteristic voice quality is heard, characterized by what Darley, Aronson, and Brown[3] describe as *strain-strangle*. This voice is harsh, with a strained, tense quality as if the person is fighting to push the air flow through the larynx and supralaryngeal areas.

A lower motor neuron lesion causes complete paralysis of the ipsilateral vocal cord, resulting in a hoarse, breathy voice. In some lower motor neuron diseases the voice will initially be strong; however, after the patient talks for a while, the voice becomes progressively weaker and more breathy. Hoarseness sometimes results from direct damage to the recurrent laryngeal nerve during carotid artery or thyroid surgery. The hoarseness is transient unless the nerve was severed.

CRANIAL NERVE XI: SPINAL ACCESSORY

Anatomy

The spinal accessory nerve consists of a cranial and a spinal root. The nucleus of the cranial root is found in the nucleus ambiguus of the medulla. It receives corticonuclear fibers from both cerebral hemispheres. These fibers then join the glossopharyngeal, vagus, and spinal accessory nerves.

The spinal root's nucleus is located in the spinal nucleus of the anterior gray column of the spinal cord. The fibers pass through the lateral white column and eventually form a nerve trunk, which joins the cranial root to pass through the foramen magnum. The spinal root then separates from the cranial root, however, to find its way to the sternocleidomastoid and trapezius muscles.

Innervation

The cranial root joins the vagus to innervate the uvula and the levator palatini. As previously mentioned, the spinal root innervates the sternocleidomastoid and trapezius muscles.

Function

The spinal accessory nerve's primary function is as a motor to the muscles (including the sternocleidomastoid) that help turn, tilt, and thrust the head forward or raise the sternum and clavicle if the head is in a fixed position. It provides innervation also to the trapezius muscle, which is responsible for shrugging the shoulders.

Testing

When testing cranial nerve XI, the spinal part is evaluated. The accessory part is accessory to the vagus and cannot be tested alone.

Initially, look at the size and symmetry of the sternocleidomastoid muscles and palpate them. (Do this on yourself and others to become familiar with normal muscle size and firmness.) Ask the patient to turn the head to one side and hold it there while you try to push it back to the middle. Put one hand on the patient's cheek and the other on the shoulder to brace the patient. Gently push against the cheek and observe and palpate the sternocleidomastoid on the opposite side of the neck.

Next have the patient try to thrust the head forward while you gently resist the movement with your hand against the forehead. Again, observe and palpate the sternocleidomastoid muscle.

Finally, ask the patient to shrug his or her shoulders while you press down on the shoulders. You should feel the shoulders elevate against your gentle resistance.

CRANIAL NERVE XII: HYPOGLOSSAL

Anatomy

The hypoglossal nerve runs under the tongue and controls tongue movements. The nucleus, called the hypoglossal nucleus, is located in the medulla beneath the lower part of the fourth ventricle. It receives fibers from both cerebral hemispheres, with one exception. The cells serving the genioglossus muscle receive only contralateral fibers. The nerve fibers pass through the medulla and emerge in the groove between the pyramid and the olive. Other apparent branches of the hypoglossal are not connected with the hypoglossal nuclei but rather are derived from the ansa cervicalis of cervical vertebrae C1, C2, and C3. *Ansa* means "loop," and some branches of these spinal nerves form a loop and join the hypoglossal nerve to help innervate the sternothyroid, sternohyoid, and omohyoid muscles.

Innervation

The hypoglossal nerve innervates the intrinsic muscles of the tongue. It also innervates four extrinsic tongue muscles: the genioglossus, hyoglossus, chondroglossus, and styloglossus.

With the branches from the ansa cervicalis, cranial nerve XII contributes to the innervation of the sternothyroid, sternohyoid, and omohyoid muscles, thus contributing to the elevation and depression of the larynx.

Function

The hypoglossal nerve innervates the muscles responsible for tongue movement. The four intrinsic muscles of the tongue control tongue shortening, concaving (turning the tip and lateral margins upward), narrowing, elongating, and flattening. The extrinsic muscles innervated account for tongue protrusion (genioglossus), drawing the tongue upward and backward (styloglossus), and retraction and depression of the tongue (hyoglossus). The hyoglossus also acts with the chondroglossus to elevate the hyoid bone, thus participating in phonation.

Testing

Ask the patient to open the mouth and let you look at the tongue at rest. Inspect it for signs of atrophy. With a unilateral lower motor neuron lesion, one side of the tongue may look shrunken or atrophied. This atrophy occurs on the same side as the lower motor neuron lesion. A lower motor neuron lesion may cause fasciculations, seen as tiny ripples under the surface of the tongue. Normal tongues may also show some ripples when they are not completely relaxed. Therefore, if fasciculations seem present, ask the patient to move the tongue around and then relax it; again observe the surface for fasciculations. Even in a normal tongue, however, ripples may still be present. Therefore, as DeMyer[4] points out, the clinician does better to rely on atrophy and weakness as signs of lower motor neuron damage. The tongue should also be observed for tremor or random movements at rest.

Next ask the patient to protrude the tongue; evaluate the symmetry of this posture. The tongue tip should be at midline. If the patient has weak lip musculature on one side, that side may be lower, causing the tongue to look as if it deviates to that side. Therefore try to align the tip of the tongue with the midline of the jaw visually. That side of the lip can be pulled back so that it is symmetrical with the other side of the lip; then ask the patient to protrude the tongue. If the cranial nerve is dysfunctional, the genioglossus will not be able to push its side out; the stronger side will overcome the weaker, and the tongue will deviate to the weaker side (Fig. 7-5).

In lower motor neuron damage the weakness is on the same side as the lesion. In upper motor neuron damage, because of the contralateral control, the tongue deviates to the side opposite the lesion. For example, in many stroke patients with left hemisphere damage to the area of the motor strip, the tongue shows a characteristic deviation to the right on protrusion. This is usually less marked than in lower motor neuron tongue weakness.

The patient who has bilateral XII nerve damage has weakness on both sides and is unable to protrude the

FIGURE **7-5**

Unilateral paresis of the tongue. *Left,* The resting tongue shows a smaller weak side (atrophy) with a corrugated surface suggesting fasciculations and the effects of atrophy. These tongue signs suggest denervation. *Right,* The protruded tongue deviates to the weak side. In a lower motor neuron lesion, the deviated tongue points to the side of the lesion. (Modified from Darley, F., Aronson, A., & Brown, J. [1975]. *Motor speech disorders.* Philadelphia: W. B. Saunders.)

tongue beyond the lips. Strength of tongue protrusion may be tested by asking the patient to push against a tongue blade held directly in front of the lips.

Other movements of the tongue must be evaluated to document precisely the range, rate, and strength of the tongue for follow-up in treatment and for diagnostic purposes. Ask the patient to lateralize the tongue (i.e., move it from one corner of the mouth to the other). The tongue should move the full range from corner to corner. Evaluate the strength of lateral movement by asking the patient to push the tongue against the inside of the cheek (i.e., make a "ball" in the cheek) against your fingers placed for resistance on the outside of the cheek. A tongue blade can also be placed along the side of the tongue, with the patient pushing against a light resistance.

The ability to elevate the tongue can be evaluated by having the patient open the mouth to a moderate degree while you hold down the mandible with your finger on it. Ask the patient to try to touch the top lip and also the alveolar ridge with the tongue. This should be done with full range of movement and little effort.

Strength of elevation of the tip, blade, or back of the tongue is difficult to assess with tongue blade resistance. A quick perceptual analysis may be a better informal assessment of strength of elevation. The tip of the tongue should be able to make firm contact to produce /t/, /d/, /tʃ/ (as in chum), and /dʒ/ (as in judge) and to elevate fully for /l/ and /n/. The blade of the tongue should elevate well to produce a distinct /i/ (e as in eat) and /j/ (y as in young). Elevation of the back of the tongue is necessary for production of the velar consonants /k/ and /g/. Careful examination of the production of these consonants and vowels as well as others, in isolation and in context, may provide the most information regarding tongue elevation and strength.

Instrumental Measurement of Strength

If your clinic or practice is fortunate enough, you may have access to instrumentation that could provide you with objective measures of lip and tongue strength. The Iowa Oral Pressure Indicator (IOPI) was introduced to our field through research on dysphagia in 1995 (Robbins, 1995).[9] The IOPI is a small handheld medical device designed to objectively measure lip and tongue strength as well as provide quantitative measurement of tongue fatigability. Since its introduction it has been made available not only to researchers but to practicing clinicians who utilize it for therapy. It has been widely used in research providing validation and normative data for these measures. Obviously, much more accurate assessment and evidence-based treatment can be provided with instrumentation such as this if it is available to you.

Table 7-2 summarizes the five cranial nerves (V, VII, IX, X, and XII) involved in the oral musculature.

Cranial Nerve Cooperation: The Act of Swallowing

The act of swallowing is highly complex and must be studied independently in regard to its cranial nerve innervation. Logemann[7] describes normal deglutition as consisting of four phases: the oral preparatory phase, the oral phase, the pharyngeal phase, and the esophageal phase.

In the oral preparatory phase, the food or liquid stimulates sensory receptors (taste, touch, temperature and pressure). These receptors are activated by saliva. Mastication mixes the food with saliva and forms it into a cohesive bolus. Food and liquid are held by the

TABLE 7-2					
Summary of Cranial Nerve Function for the Oral Musculature					
CRANIAL NERVE	MUSCLES INNERVATED	MOVEMENTS AND SENSATION INNERVATED	TEST PROCEDURE	SIGNS OF LOWER MOTOR NEURON DAMAGE	SIGNS OF UPPER MOTOR NEURON DAMAGE
V: trigeminal	Masseter, tensor tympani, tensor veli palatine, mylohyoid, digastric (anterior belly)	Jaw closing, lateral jaw movement, contribution to laryngeal elevation, sensation to face and anterior tongue	Palpation of masseter, closing and lateralization against resistance, sensation on face and tongue	Weakness, jaw deviation to lesion side, atrophy	Mild, transitory weakness

TABLE 7-2

Summary of Cranial Nerve Function for the Oral Musculature—cont'd

CRANIAL NERVE	MUSCLES INNERVATED	MOVEMENTS AND SENSATION INNERVATED	TEST PROCEDURE	SIGNS OF LOWER MOTOR NEURON DAMAGE	SIGNS OF UPPER MOTOR NEURON DAMAGE
VII: facial	Orbicularis oculi and oris, zygomatic, buccinator, platysma, stylohyoid, stapedius, portion of digastric (posterior belly)	Forehead wrinkling, closing eyes, closing mouth, smiling, pulling down corner of mouth, tensing anterior neck muscles, moving stapedius to dampen ossicles; taste from anterior two thirds of tongue and hard and soft palates	Observation of facial symmetry at rest; have patient wrinkle forehead, close eyes tightly, smile, pucker, and pull down lip corners; identification of tastes	Involvement of entire side of face, weakness, limited range of movement, decreased taste sensation	Complete involvement of lips and neck muscles, less involvement of eye area muscles, little difficulty with forehead muscles; weakness, limited range of movement of affected muscles; decreased taste sensation
IX: glossopharyngeal	Stylopharyngeus, otic ganglion, parotid salivary gland, part of the middle pharyngeal constrictor	Elevation of pharynx and larynx, pharyngeal dilation, salivation; taste from posterior third of tongue; sensation from posterior tongue and upper pharynx	Tested with cranial nerve X for motor; sensory test for pharyngeal gag	—	—
X: vagus	Inferior, middle, and superior pharyngeal constrictors; salpingopharyngeus, glossopalatine, pharyngopalatine, levator veli palatine, uvular, cricothyroid, thyroarytenoid, posterior and lateral cricoarytenoid, interarytenoid, and transverse and oblique interarytenoid muscles; various muscles of the viscera, esophagus, and trachea	Palatal elevation and depression, laryngeal movement, pharyngeal constriction, cricopharyngeal function; visceral and general sensation from base of tongue, epiglottis, larynx, and pharynx	Observation of palatal movement, palatal gag reflex; laryngoscopic evaluation of vocal musculature; ability to change pitch; phonation time; assessment of swallowing	Absence of gag reflex, poor movement of palate or pharyngeal wall, absent or delayed swallow response, aspiration, breathy hoarse voice (may be improved by pushing effort)	Poor palatal or pharyngeal wall movement, harshness or strained-strangled voice quality, delayed or absent swallow reflex, aspiration

Continued

TABLE 7-2
Summary of Cranial Nerve Function for the Oral Musculature—cont'd

CRANIAL NERVE	MUSCLES INNERVATED	MOVEMENTS AND SENSATION INNERVATED	TEST PROCEDURE	SIGNS OF LOWER MOTOR NEURON DAMAGE	SIGNS OF UPPER MOTOR NEURON DAMAGE
XII: hypoglossal	Superior longitudinal, inferior longitudinal, transverse vertical, genioglossus, hyoglossus, and styloglossus	All tongue movements as well as some elevation of the hyoid bone	Observation for atrophy or fasciculations as well as symmetry on protrusion; assessment for lateralization, protrusion, elevation, retraction (to observe range of movement); assessment of movement against resistance for strength testing on lateral, protrusion, and elevation movement; articulation testing	Atrophy, fasciculations, weakness, reduced range of movement, deviation of tongue to side of lesion, decreased tone, consonant imprecision	Weakness, reduced range of movement, deviation of tongue to contralateral side, increased tone, consonant imprecision

tongue against the hard palate prior to swallow initiation though some will also collect in the valleculae and be held there at the base of the tongue. The oral preparatory stage is variable in duration depending on ease of mastication, oral motor efficiency, and individual preference in savoring taste. The sense of smell contributes greatly to the appreciation of taste with the smell carried into the nasal cavity directly through the nares or through chewing action, which results in odors traveling through the posterior nasopharynx.[5] These actions during the oral preparatory stage would actively involve CNs I, V, VII, IX, and XII for smell, taste, salivation, general sensation regarding where food is in the mouth, lip closure, chewing, and movement of the tongue.

The oral stage begins when the lips seal and the back of the tongue begins moving the bolus posteriorly. The tongue forms a central groove that acts as a ramp or chute for the food. This transitions quickly into the pharyngeal phase. At some point during the oral stage (although in much of the literature, it is categorized as the beginning of the pharyngeal stage), the pharyngeal swallow will be initiated (or "triggered"). The swallow may be initiated through sensory receptors on the faucial pillars, tonsils, soft palate, base of the tongue, the posterior pharyngeal wall, and/or the epiglottis.

The sensory input from these receptors is carried mainly by CNs VII, IX, and X and is processed in the nucleus tractus solitarius (NTS) in the medulla. There are several physiologic responses that occur during the swallow with most of them seeming involuntary but with obvious option for placement under voluntary control at times. Groher and Crary[5] indicate that some of these physiologic changes begin during the oral stage with the more pharyngeal changes occurring in the pharyngeal stage. According to these authors, in the oral stage as the tongue begins to move posteriorly there is cessation of respiration, approximation of the arytenoid cartilages, medial approximation of the palatopharyngeal walls, and action of the levator velar palatini to begin elevation of the velum.

The afferent transmission to the NTS appears to be required to be in a specifically organized pattern to lead to initiation of swallowing. This stimulus pattern is conveyed to the reticular formation to make connections with efferent nuclei of CNs V, VII, IX, X, and XII in the nucleus ambiguus (NA) of the medulla. The efferent response that we call the swallow response or the pharyngeal swallow is an orderly configuration of several physiologic actions occurring in the oropharynx simultaneously: velopharyngeal closure; laryngeal elevation; inversion of the epiglottis; closure of all sphincters (aryepiglottic folds, false vocal folds, and true vocal folds); initiation of pharyngeal peristalsis (squeezing); and relaxation of the cricopharyngeal sphincter (or cricopharyngeus) to allow material to pass from pharynx to esophagus. If the swallow is not neutrally triggered, whether this be voluntarily or involuntarily, this physiologic pattern of activity does not occur spontaneously. The bolus may be pushed into the pharynx and come to rest in the valleculae or pyriform sinuses and eventually will spill over into an unprotected airway (i.e., aspirated) unless it is expectorated before this happens. Some of the maneuvers that usually occur "reflexively" or as part of the central pattern of responses when the neural transmission takes place can be put under voluntary control to help provide some protection if the neural triggering is slow or does not occur. This would be primarily the temporary cessation of breathing and the closure of the vocal folds if they are functional. Voluntary maneuvers can be learned that may assist in some of these muscle movements, including elevating the larynx, inverting the epiglottis and opening of the cricopharyngeus, but these only assist and are difficult to pattern and to maintain without the neural swallow initiation.

Finally, in normal swallowing the esophageal phase occurs as the bolus enters the esophagus through the cricopharyngeus. A wave of contractions (peristalsis), innervated by cranial nerve X, is initiated in the esophagus, and the bolus is passed through into the stomach through the lower esophageal sphincter. Normal esophageal transit time is 8 to 20 seconds. Box 7-2 outlines the four phases of deglutition, and Figure 7-6 illustrates the final three stages.

Efficient swallowing demands cooperation and coordination of the cranial nerves also involved in speech production. Figure 7-7 is a simplified summary of the actions that occur in swallowing and the cranial nerves that are responsible. The trigeminal nerve (V) plays an important part because of the efferent control of the muscles of mastication and the afferent control for general sensation to the anterior two thirds of the tongue. Cranial nerve VII, the facial nerve, controls taste for the anterior two thirds of the tongue and controls the lip sphincter and the buccal muscles, allowing food to be held inside the mouth.

The hypoglossal nerve (XII) controls the movement of the tongue. Through research using pharyngeal

---

BOX 7-2

Four Phases of Deglutition

1. **Oral preparatory phase:** Tongue forms the liquid or solid into a cohesive bolus after the solid has been chewed and mixed with saliva. Some of the solid bolus may fall into the valleculae during mastication; the rest of the bolus is held as a cohesive unit against the hard palate.
2. **Oral phase:** Lips seal and tongue moves food to the back of the mouth.
3. **Pharyngeal phase:** Swallow response is triggered, causing several physiologic activities to occur simultaneously and pushing food from the pharynx into the esophagus.
4. **Esophageal phase:** Food passes, by peristaltic action, through the esophagus to the stomach.

---

manometry, it has been found that the tongue is the major force generating the driving pressure that pushes the bolus through the pharynx.[1] This action of the tongue has been compared with that of a plunger and is called the tongue driving force. Pharyngeal constriction, controlled by the vagus nerve, has been found to be much less of a force than originally believed. In the same study, a descending pharyngeal contraction was shown to be applied only to the residual bolus tail.[1] This constriction clears the bolus from the laryngeal vestibule. It is therefore called the pharyngeal clearing force.

The vagus also mediates the action of the cricopharyngeus, which relaxes to allow the bolus to pass from the hypopharynx to the esophagus. The movement of the intrinsic muscles of the larynx to close the entrance to the airway is also innervated by the vagus. The elevation and anterior movement of the larynx are significant mechanical forces contributing to the opening of the cricopharyngeus. Therefore cranial nerves V, VII, IX, X, and XII, all with efferent innervation to one or more extrinsic muscles of the tongue and larynx, are important to this aspect of swallowing. The study also indicated that the opening of the cricopharyngeus creates a negative pressure; thus a suction pump effect significantly increases the rate of bolus flow and contributes to the elimination of the bolus before the larynx reopens.[1]

The hypoglossal, glossopharyngeal, and vagus nerves are all major contributors to clearing the bolus through the pharynx. The tongue driving force and the pharyngeal clearing force, combined with the hypopharyngeal suction pump, produce a rapid transit through the pharynx once the swallow response has been triggered.

FIGURE **7-6**

The initial phase of swallowing, the oral preparatory phase (**A**), involves mastication and mixture of the food with saliva. It is then followed by oral (**B1**), pharyngeal (**B2** and **C1**), and esophageal (**C2**) phases. (Modified from Mahan, K.L., & Escott-Stump, S. [2008]. *Krause's Food & Nutrition Therapy* [12th ed.]. St. Louis: Saunders.)

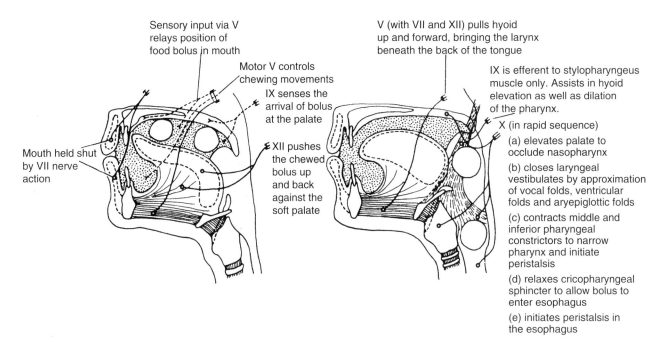

FIGURE **7-7**

The neurology of swallowing. (From Patten, J. [1998]. *Neurologic Differential Diagnosis* [2nd ed.]. London: Springer, Ltd.)

The glossopharyngeal nerve is thought to be the primary afferent of the swallow response, and the vagus is thought to be the secondary afferent. As stated previously, the brainstem center of neural control for swallowing is located in the medulla in the nucleus solitarius (NTS) and in the nucleus ambiguus (NA). Afferent fibers converge on the nucleus solitarius in the medulla. They communicate with neurons in the nucleus ambiguus by way of interneurons, thereby stimulating the motor response. The medullary swallowing center has been referred to as the **central pattern generator**[7] rather than a reflex center for swallowing due to the observation of the timing and sequence of the muscle contractions that follow the onset of the pharyngeal swallow. This physiologic response to a sensory event is obviously more complex than a reflex. As Groher and Crary[5] point out, regulation of swallowing by the nervous system is likely carried out not just by the innervation of CNs and patterns of muscle response but also by involvement of different levels of the central nervous system, including the cerebellum, limbic and other subcortical structures, and areas of the neocortex. We can and do swallow differently for different textures and in different settings or situations. We can talk while eating; we can put swallowing under much greater (although not total) voluntary control in situations such as swallowing a pill; we can eat faster or slower; although rare (as very dangerous), some of us can even control the opening of the esophageal sphincters to "swallow" a sword! These variations in swallowing control support the input of supranuclear structures to swallowing.

If swallowing is inefficient and aspiration occurs, a reflexive cough should occur as one of the respiratory system's defenses against foreign matter. The cough reflex is induced by irritation of the afferent fibers of the pharyngeal distribution of the glossopharyngeal nerve along with the sensory endings of the vagus nerve in the larynx, trachea, and larger bronchi.[2]

ASSESSMENT OF SWALLOWING

The cranial nerve examination is critical to the assessment of swallowing. Careful evaluation of the sensory component of the cranial nerves is probably more important in the swallowing evaluation than when the examination is for a speech disorder alone.

Taste, carried by cranial nerves VII and IX, is not a typical part of the assessment of the sensorimotor control for speech or for swallowing. However, if the etiology and characteristics of a swallowing disorder are particularly difficult to figure out or if treatment is not going as well as planned, taste should be tested with some of the primary tastes (salt, sweet, bitter, and sour). The testing must be done on both sides of the anterior two thirds of the tongue and on both sides of the posterior third of the tongue to include cranial nerves VII and IX. In these cases, smell should probably also be evaluated as the sense of smell is critical to normal taste perception. Smell is carried by CN I. It can be assessed by having the patient identify certain smells that are typically readily identifiable in the patient's culture (e.g., the smell of sulfur ["rotten eggs"], roses, vanilla, peppermint, etc., for Americans). This, of course, would not be relevant for a patient who reports a poor premorbid sense of smell, a laryngectomy patient, or a patient who could not do the task because of cognitive deficits.

General sensation to the tongue, carried by cranial nerves V and IX (posterior third), should be tested with the two sides compared regarding sensitivity to touch. As previously mentioned, testing of the pharyngeal gag can be attempted.

The motor examination for swallowing should consist of the same maneuvers as for the speech examination with additional time for dedicated swallowing assessment. In most settings, if the patient is not so compromised as to be unable to cooperate or to be too at risk for injury, a cursory screening examination of swallowing is performed (often called a "bedside" swallowing evaluation). For this screening, the clinician first does the oral-motor and cognitive testing and then observes the patient's attempt at swallowing a liquid (preferably water), a semisolid (e.g., pudding), and a solid. This swallowing should only be done if the clinician's judgment is that it will be safe to try in the clinic setting. If patient safety is a concern or if the cranial nerve examination has pointed to a likely pharyngeal-stage swallowing disorder, a modified barium swallow or MBS (aka, a videofluoroscopy of swallowing or VFS), or perhaps a fiber optic endoscopic examination of swallowing (aka, FEES) should be requested. These examinations should be performed only by an SLP or other professional with appropriate training and experience in their administration and interpretation. The purpose of the any instrumental examination should be to document problems and evaluate therapeutic alternatives that may improve oral intake.

A VFS is, obviously, a radiographic study that exposes the patient (and clinician) to a small amount of radiation; it does require that barium be mixed with the food consistencies or that a barium solution duplicating normal consistencies be used. The MBS is the gold standard for instrumental evaluation because of the complete view of all stages of the swallow. Figure 7-8 presents a lateral view used during the study and labels the structures.

FEES is another instrumental procedure that may be helpful when a pharyngeal stage disorder is suspected.[5] For this study, a fiber optic endoscope is passed nasally to allow a view superior to the pyriform sinuses and the laryngeal folds. Once the scope is placed, the

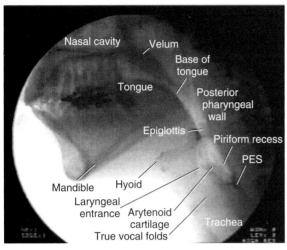

FIGURE **7-8**
Lateral radiographic view of normal swallowing mechanism in an adult. *PES,* Pharyngoesophageal segment. (From Groher, M. E., & Crary, M. A. [2016]. *Dysphagia: Clinical management in adults and children* [2nd ed.]. St. Louis: Mosby.)

FIGURE **7-9**
FEES image of tracheal aspiration. (Modified from Leder, S. B., & Murray, J. T. [2008]. Fiberoptic endoscopic evaluation of swallowing. *Physical Medical & Rehabilitation Clinics of North America*, 19, 787-801.)

patient can be asked to swallow normal liquids, soft solids, or solids with the only addition being perhaps some food coloring. Problems with laryngeal closure in general can also be evaluated during the study with stroboscopy added to the procedure if such technology is available and needed. The major drawback for the use of the FEES study is that the image is blocked at the peak of the swallow when the material being swallowed covers the tip of the scope and this is followed by a brief period of "whiteout" as the vocal folds

close and the larynx rises, blocking any image. It is at this point that aspiration may be missed. Figure 7-9 presents the view during a FEES examination after the "whiteout" but showing residual aspirated material at the entrance to the airway. This residue at the entrance to the vocal folds does not always occur, and the possibility of missing aspiration, especially silent aspiration, is a concern; however, if residue is not coated with barium, the MBS study may miss potential aspiration as well.[8]

Synopsis of Clinical Information and Applications for the Speech-Language Pathologist

- The speech-language pathologist must be knowledgeable regarding the function and assessment of the cranial nerves, which are vital for speech production and swallowing.
- Twelve pairs of cranial nerves can be found exiting the brainstem; seven are concerned with communication and/or swallowing.
- Cranial nerves I (olfactory), II (optic), III (oculomotor), IV (trochlear), and VI (abducens) are concerned with smell and vision as well as movement of the eyes.
- Cranial nerve VIII (vestibuloacoustic) is the auditory nerve carrying the sensation of sound to Heschl's gyrus. The vestibular portion of the nerve controls the sense of equilibrium.
- Cranial nerve XI (spinal accessory) contributes to movement of the uvula and the levator palatini through its cranial root. Testing of the spinal part of the nerve is the only possible test of the nerve's viability.

- The five remaining cranial nerves (V, trigeminal; VII, facial; IX, glossopharyngeal; X, vagus; and XII, hypoglossal) are main motor and sensory nerves for oral-motor and sensory function, enabling speech production, oral feeding, and swallowing.
- Table 7-2 summarizes pertinent clinical information for these five cranial nerves on anatomy, innervation, signs of damage, and testing procedures that can be done during an extended oral-motor examination.
- Beyond a limited "bedside" swallow examination, a fiberoptic endoscopic examination of swallowing (FEES) and/or the modified barium swallow (MBS) would be necessary to adequately evaluate cranial nerve function during swallowing.

CASE **STUDY**

A 34-year-old female welder sought help from her physician for persistent ringing (medically known as *tinnitus*) and "wave crashing" sounds in her right ear. These symptoms were initially attributed to occupational noise exposure. However, a year later she continued to experience the same sounds but with additional symptoms that brought new concern. She now demonstrated a clumsy gait, had pain in her right ear, and reported dizziness. She also thought that her hearing in her right ear had decreased. Her symptoms worsened, and she went to the emergency department. She reported in the emergency department that she had suddenly begun having difficulty seeing clearly out of her right eye, was having some difficulty with swallowing, and had some slurring of speech. Examination showed moderate facial weakness and right-sided weakness of her mouth and tongue. Voice and speech production were notably weak. The physician diagnosed classic signs of a flaccid dysarthria.

Questions for Consideration

1. What, if any, cranial nerves are involved here?
2. Could this patient's symptoms be explained as noise-induced hearing loss with cranial nerve damage?
3. The final diagnosis for this patient was a vestibular schwannoma (or acoustic neuroma). What are some of the characteristics of this tumor? (The answer to this question will involve some research.)

REFERENCES

1. Cerenko, D., McConnel, F. M. S., & Jackson, R. T. (1989). Quantitative assessment of pharyngeal bolus driving forces. *Otolaryngology Head and Neck Surgery, 100,* 57–63.
2. Cherniack, R., Cherniack, L., & Naimark, A. (1972). *Respiration in health and disease* (2nd ed.). Philadelphia: W. B. Saunders.
3. Darley, F., Aronson, A., & Brown, J. (1975). *Motor speech disorders.* Philadelphia: W. B. Saunders.
4. DeMyer, W. (1980). *Technique of the neurologic examination: A programmed text* (3rd ed.). New York: McGraw-Hill.
5. Groher, M. E., & Crary, M. A. (2010). *Dysphagia: Clinical management in adults and children.* Maryland Heights, MO: Mosby.
6. Langmore, S., Schatz, K., & Olsen, N. (1988). Fiberoptic endoscopic examination of swallowing safety: A new procedure. *Dysphagia, 2,* 216–219.
7. Logemann, J. A. (1984). *Evaluation and treatment of swallowing disorders.* San Diego: College Hill Press.
8. Kelly, A. M., Leslie, P., Beale, T., Payten, C., & Drinnan, M. J. (2006). Fibreoptic endoscopic evaluation of swallowing and videofluoroscopy: Does examination type influence perception of pharyngeal severity? *Clinical Otolaryngology, 31,* 425–432.
9. Robbins, J., Levine, R., Wood, J., Roecker, E. B., & Luschei, E. (1995). Age effects on lingual pressure generation as a risk factor for dysphagia. *Journal of Gerontology: Medical Sciences, 50A,* M257–M262.

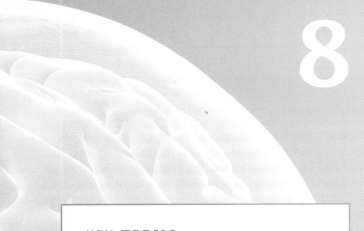

8

Clinical Speech Syndromes of the Motor Systems

Speech is deranged in a variety of ways by disease of the brain. The process of articulation is immediately affected by a mechanism of nerve nuclei situated in the pons and medulla, but these are excited to action by centers in the cerebral cortex. Thus there are higher and lower mechanisms; the former is cerebral, the latter is bulbar.

William R. Gowers, *A Manual of Disease of the Nervous System*, 1888

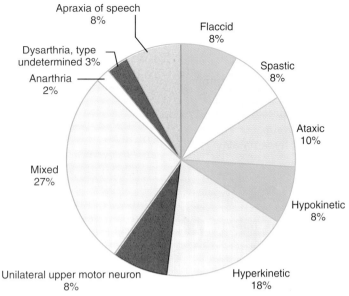

FIGURE **8-1**

Distribution of neurologic communication disorders, Speech pathology, Department of Neurology, Mayo Clinic, 1987–1990 and 1993–2001. (Reprinted from Duffy J. [2005]. *Motor speech disorders: Substrates, differential diagnosis, and management* [2nd ed.]. St. Louis: Mosby.)

Speech-language pathologists (SLPs) must have an understanding of the function of the cranial nerves and the rest of the motor and sensory system for the treatment of motor speech disorders. Data kept at the Mayo Clinic between 1987 and 1990 and from 1993 to 2001 revealed that of the 10,444 people whose primary diagnosis was an acquired communication disorder, 58% were diagnosed with a motor speech disorder.[11]

Figure 8-1 shows the distribution of the different categories of the acquired communication disorders found on evaluation. These data indicate that SLPs whose practice is primarily with adult clients must be well versed in the anatomy and physiology of the motor speech system and familiar with the clinical signs and symptoms of diseases and conditions producing them. This knowledge will be important to the treatment of children with motor speech disorders as well, which is discussed in Chapter 12.

Dysarthrias

In the classic Mayo Clinic study, Darley, Aronson, and Brown[8] defined dysarthria as the speech disorder resulting from paralysis, weakness, or incoordination of the speech musculature that is of neurologic origin. Their definition encompasses any symptoms of motor disturbance of respiration, phonation, resonance, articulation, and prosody.

Damage to the motor system responsible for speech production may occur at any point along the pathway from the cerebrum to the muscle itself. In their classic studies of types of dysarthria resulting from certain sites of damage in the neural system, Darley et al.[8,9] identified six different dysarthrias based on neuroanatomic and acoustic-perceptual judgments of speech. This chapter describes the classic dysarthrias according to neuroanatomic site of dysfunction; associated disease processes; and the effects of these diseases on articulation, resonance, phonation, prosody, and swallowing. The following is not an exhaustive discussion of the diseases or of the types of dysarthrias resulting from neurologic disease. Keep in mind that any disease or trauma that affects the movement, coordination, and timing of the oral musculature may produce a dysarthria.

Upper Motor Neuron Lesions

Upper motor neuron damage may result in a spastic paralysis and hyperactive reflexes. The dysarthria associated with unilateral upper motor neuron lesions is called unilateral upper motor neuron dysarthria. The dysarthria associated with bilateral upper motor neuron lesions is known as spastic dysarthria. An overview of upper motor neuron lesions is found in Box 8-1.

BOX 8-1

Upper Motor Neuron Lesions

Unilateral Upper Motor Neuron Dysarthria

- Primarily caused by stroke but can also result from trauma or tumors
- Imprecise articulation; slow rate and irregular articulatory breakdown may also occur
- Harshness, reduced loudness, and hypernasality common
- Difficulty with oral stage transit

Spastic Dysarthria

- May be caused by stroke, head trauma, tumor, infection, degenerative disease, or inflammatory or toxic-metabolic disease
- Loss of skilled movement, hyporeflexia, positive Babinski sign, muscle weakness, loss of muscle tone
- Usually severe impairment of range of rate of movement of oral musculature
- Harsh voice with strained-strangled quality, low pitch, and monoloudness; often accompanied by hypernasality and imprecise consonant production
- Aspiration common, often with moderate to severe dysphagia

UNILATERAL UPPER MOTOR NEURON DYSARTHRIA

As discussed by Duffy,[12] the dysarthria associated with unilateral upper motor neuron damage has been given scant attention in the literature, probably because the symptoms are usually mild and sometimes transitory. This section on upper motor neuron lesions is primarily devoted to a discussion of spastic dysarthria for the same reasons. However, a brief review of unilateral upper motor neuron dysarthria, as termed by Duffy, is warranted because it is as frequently encountered as the other types discussed in this chapter.

Etiology

The primary etiology of unilateral upper motor neuron dysarthria is stroke. Many other etiologies of upper motor neuron damage cause more diffuse brain injury and result more often in bilateral damage to the pyramidal pathways. Trauma and tumors can result in injury confined to a single hemisphere and can produce a unilateral upper motor neuron dysarthria. Unilateral upper motor neuron dysarthria can result from damage to either hemisphere.

Speech Characteristics

Only a small number of studies have looked at the speech characteristics of unilateral upper motor neuron dysarthria.[12,17] The collective findings of these studies indicate that the most prominent deviant characteristic of speech is imprecise articulation. Slowed rate and irregular articulatory breakdown were also noted in a number of cases. Other characteristics present in some cases were harshness, reduced loudness, and hypernasality. Most characteristics were described as mild to moderate in severity, although some patients had more severe dysarthria. Many patients demonstrated significant recovery during the spontaneous recovery period, but some dysarthrias persisted and required speech therapy for the reduced intelligibility.

Swallowing

Robbins[39] studied patients with left and right hemisphere strokes and showed that the patients differed from healthy individuals in increased oral-stage durations for liquid and semisolid swallows and the occurrence of laryngeal vestibule penetration. This difficulty with oral-stage transit was particularly true for left hemisphere–damaged patients. On further analysis, Robbins also found that patients with right hemisphere cerebrovascular accident (CVA) demonstrated laryngeal penetration and aspiration significantly more often than patients with left-sided CVA. Silent aspiration (i.e., no coughing occurred reflexively) occurred with much greater frequency in patients with right-sided CVA. In addition, more aspiration occurred with anterior lesions than with posterior lesion sites.

Evatt et al.[13] reported on a study of swallowing in 57 acute unilateral stroke patients. They found that aspiration in association with reduced pharyngeal clearance was present in 39% of the right hemisphere–damaged patients and 57% of the left hemisphere–damaged patients. The incidence of aspiration was significantly greater in left hemisphere–damaged patients than in right hemisphere–damaged patients when analysis was performed on individuals older than 65 years. A study by Alberts et al.[1] that used magnetic resonance imaging concluded that stroke patients should be individually evaluated for swallowing dysfunction regardless of the location or site of the lesion because even small-vessel strokes were associated with aspiration in greater than 20% of patients.

SPASTIC DYSARTHRIA

Etiology

Bilateral upper motor neuron damage may result from stroke, head trauma, tumor, infection, degenerative disease, and inflammatory or toxic-metabolic diseases. In most instances of **spastic dysarthria**, bilateral damage occurs to both the direct activation pathway (corticobulbar or corticospinal tract) and the indirect activation pathway (extrapyramidal pathways from cortex to brainstem and spinal cord). This usually occurs because the pathways are in close proximity from cortex to the termination at the cranial nerve or spinal nerve. The resulting oral-motor disorder from bilateral upper motor neuron damage to both systems is sometimes called **pseudobulbar palsy**. This name is derived from the resemblance of the oral-motor and speech characteristics to lower motor neuron damage and flaccid dysarthria (bulbar palsy).

Associated Neurologic Characteristics

Direct activation pathway damage results in the characteristic loss of skilled movement, hyporeflexia, a positive Babinski sign, and muscle weakness and loss of tone.

Damage to the indirect activation pathway causes increased muscle tone (spasticity) and hyperactive stretch reflexes. This hypertonicity and hyperreflexia dominate if both systems are damaged, which is usually the case. Although tone is increased, the muscles are weak, range of movement is limited, and rate of movement is slow because of the direct activation motor system damage.

Oral Musculature

In pseudobulbar palsy, the oral musculature usually shows severe impairment of range and rate of movement. The tongue may extend only to the lips on protrusion. The lips move slowly, and excursion is limited. Palatal movement is severely reduced and sluggish on phonation. The gag reflex may be absent in the acute stages but later returns and may be hyperactive. Chewing and swallowing are both frequently affected, and drooling is present in most cases.

Speech Characteristics

The patient usually demonstrates a classic spastic dysarthria. Speech characteristics are as follows.

Phonation

The voice of the patient with spastic dysarthria is described as harsh, and many have a characteristic strained-strangled quality. An effortful grunt is often heard at the end of vocalizations. Excessively low pitch is frequently found, with pitch breaks in some cases. Little variation in loudness (**monoloudness**) and reduced stress are also noted. Occasionally heard in spastic dysarthria is excess and equal stress (i.e., inappropriate stress on monosyllabic words and the usually unstressed syllables of polysyllabic words).

Resonance

Hypernasality is a frequent component of spastic dysarthria. Nasal emission is uncommon, however.

Articulation

As in most dysarthrias, impreciseness of consonant production is a noticeable part of the speech disorder in spastic dysarthria. Vowel distortion has been noted in some cases. Zeigler and von Cramer's acoustic study[49] of 10 patients with spastic dysarthria revealed a disproportionate impairment of the back of the tongue compared with the blade of the tongue. Impaired acceleration of the moving articulators also accounted for part of the distortion and the increase in production time often noted in these speakers.

Swallowing

Horner et al.[18] studied 70 patients with bilateral hemispheric strokes. By using videofluoroscopy, they found that 49% of the patients aspirated. The following symptoms associated with **dysphagia** are often observed in patients with bilateral upper motor neuron damage: reduced labial, lingual, and mandibular strength and sensation; delayed swallow response; reduced pharyngeal peristalsis; incomplete laryngeal elevation and closure; and cricopharyngeal dysfunction.[6] The dysphagia may be severe, and drooling may be noted. With mild dysphagia, the patient may unconsciously alter the eating pattern to eat more slowly and carefully, denying any difficulty.[13]

Lower Motor Neuron Lesions

FLACCID DYSARTHRIA

Damage to the lower motor neuron system affects the final common pathway for muscle contraction. The muscles become hypotonic or **flaccid**. Thus every type of movement is involved (voluntary, automatic, and reflexive movement are all impaired), and **flaccid dysarthria** may be seen.

Etiology

Any disease that affects part of the motor unit—the cell body, its axon, the myoneural junction, or the muscle fibers themselves—may yield lower motor neuron symptoms. Thus viral infections, tumors, trauma to the nerve itself, or a brainstem stroke with involvement of the nerve fibers may be the cause of the dysarthria. Myasthenia gravis results from impairment of transmission across the myoneural junction or the synapse between the nerve and muscle. Bulbar palsy results from damage to the motor units of the cranial nerves. Möbius syndrome (congenital facial **diplegia**) involves bilateral sixth (abducens) and seventh (facial) nerve palsies of congenital origin rather than generalized bulbar palsy. Most patients with these palsies speak acceptably except for slurring. Direct muscle involvement is found in diseases such as muscular dystrophy, myotonia, and myositis.

Associated Neurologic Characteristics

Damage to the lower motor neuron system causes flaccid paralysis. Reflexes are reduced (i.e., hyporeflexia is present). The affected muscles usually become shrunken or atrophied over time. Many times the involved muscles, especially the tongue muscles, show **fasciculations**— tiny spontaneous muscle contractions of the motor unit or muscle fibers innervated by an axon. The fasciculations appear as spontaneous dimpling of the tongue, which may look as though tiny worms are moving just beneath its surface.

Oral Musculature

Because the cranial nerve nuclei are dispersed throughout the brainstem rather than being clustered together, the oral structures may be selectively impaired and should be carefully evaluated.

Muscle tone in lower motor neuron damage is flaccid or hypotonic. Muscles are weak. The affected side of the lips sags, and in some cases drooling may be present. In bilateral weakness the whole mouth may sag, and the lower lip may be so weak that habitual open-mouth posture results. The patient may have difficulty puckering the lips or pulling up the corners of the lips to smile.

Weakness of the mandibular muscles may not be readily evident in unilateral involvement. Careful observation reveals that the jaw deviates to the side of weakness. With bilateral damage the jaw obviously sags. With damage to any component of the motor unit supplying the tongue, the muscles become atrophied and shrunken over time, and the tongue is atonic or flabby. This tends to affect protrusion, lateralization, and elevation, particularly of the posterior portion of the tongue. Fasciculations are often observed after a period.

Palatal weakness or immobility may also be present, and the gag reflex is reduced or absent. Pharyngeal involvement may occur, causing swallowing difficulty and possibly nasal regurgitation of fluids.

Speech Characteristics

Speech-language pathologists are most likely to be consulted concerning patients with a bulbar palsy resulting from vascular disease, head trauma, or diseases such as amyotrophic lateral sclerosis (ALS). These patients may exhibit a flaccid dysarthria and show some of the following characteristics on speech testing.

Phonation

Unilateral vocal fold paralysis is relatively unusual in disease processes affecting the brainstem nuclei. If unilateral damage is present, the quality of phonation depends on the position of the vocal fold. If it is paralyzed in an adducted position, the voice is harsh, and loudness is reduced. If it is in the abducted position, more breathiness is heard with reduced loudness.

More likely is bilateral vocal cord involvement. The characteristics of this are a breathy voice, inspiratory stridor (or audible inhalation), and abnormally short phrases. Monotony of pitch and loudness is distinctive in many patients as well.

Resonance

Hypernasality is noted as an outstanding characteristic of the patients with flaccid dysarthria whose disease or injury affected velopharyngeal function. Nasal emission of air is also found in a high percentage of those patients.

Articulation

Imprecise consonant production may be present to a mild to severe (unintelligible speech) degree. The consonants requiring firm contact from tongue tip elevation are particularly vulnerable. Plosives such as /p/, /t/, and /k/ and fricatives such as /f/ and /s/ are frequently distorted because of the lack of intraoral pressure that results from palatal dysfunction.

Swallowing

A brainstem CVA can cause flaccid dysarthria with lesions affecting the motor nuclei. A study of over 500 stroke patients admitted to a rehabilitation unit found that 15% were admitted with brainstem strokes.[46] Robbins et al[39] studied 10 patients with brainstem CVAs and found that these patients aspirated more frequently than did the patients with left or right cortical CVAs. Aspiration usually occurred during the swallow because of reduced airway protection or after the swallow because of large amounts of stasis in the pharyngeal recesses, particularly in the piriform sinuses. Incomplete as well as delayed relaxation of the cricopharyngeal sphincter was also noted in these patients.

Myasthenia Gravis

Myasthenia gravis is a chronic autoimmune disease resulting from a reduction in available acetylcholine receptors at the neuromuscular junction due to the disease process, which produces acetylcholine (ACH) antibodies. It may be associated with other autoimmune diseases, such as rheumatoid arthritis, and with a thymoma in the chest. Symptoms may include changes in the eyes such as drooping of the eyelid, known as ptosis (Fig. 8-2). Double vision may also occur. There are

FIGURE **8-2**
A, Ptosis of the left eyelid. **B,** Left eyelid elevates during the Tensilon test.

patients who present with dysphonia as their primary and only symptom initially.[30] The muscles may be weak, with the jaw sagging accompanied by weak chewing. Swallowing difficulty, or dysphagia, is not uncommon, and myasthenia especially should be considered with a history of difficulty with swallowing that worsens in use and improves with rest.[23]

Voice symptoms can exist without other signs of dysarthria. The flaccid dysphonia of myasthenia should be suspected when, despite normal laryngoscopic findings, the voice nevertheless becomes progressively more breathy and reduced in intensity as the client speaks. Respiratory weakness, in addition to extremity weakness, may be present, and myasthenia can occur with no oral motor involvement. Administration of an anticholinesterase agent, known as the *Tensilon test*, is a diagnostic procedure used to confirm a diagnosis of myasthenia. Figure 8-2 shows improvement in eyelid elevation during the Tensilon test. For speech, the client would be asked to continue to speak until the dysarthric symptoms are noted in articulation, resonance, or voice. The Tensilon would then be injected a little at a time, and if myasthenia is the correct diagnosis, dramatic improvement in speech would result in a short period of time as the client continues to speak. Treatment includes drugs such as cholinesterase inhibitors, corticosteroids and immunosuppressants, plasma exchange, immunoglobulin infusion (IVIg), and thymectomy.[43] Box 8-2 summarizes the lower motor lesions.

Mixed Upper and Lower Motor Neuron Lesions

AMYOTROPHIC LATERAL SCLEROSIS

A common finding in clinical practice is a lesion or disease process that has not confined itself to one motor system but instead has affected both upper and lower

---

BOX 8-2

Lower Motor Neuron Lesions

Flaccid Dysarthria

- May be caused by any disease that affects part of the motor unit (viral infections, tumors, nerve trauma, brainstem stroke)
- Selective impairment of a muscle or muscle group can occur, resulting in a flaccid paralysis, brainstem CVA, or bulbar palsy
- Damage resulting in flaccid paralysis, hyporeflexia, and shrunken or atrophied muscle
- Hypernasality and nasal emission common; selective consonants, plosives, and fricatives often affected
- Frequent aspiration
- Myasthenia gravis, a chronic autoimmune disease caused by reduced acetylcholine receptors at neuromuscular junctions, results in a unique symptomatology
  - Ptosis, double vision, muscle weakness, and dysphagia common
  - Flaccid dysphonia, progressive breathiness, and reduced voice intensity common

---

motor neuron systems. The most frequently encountered example of this damage is amyotrophic lateral sclerosis (ALS, also known as Lou Gehrig's disease).

Etiology

ALS causes progressive degeneration of the neurons of the upper and lower motor neuron systems and is of unknown etiology. Onset is typically in the fifth decade, although it may be earlier or later, and early symptoms depend on which motor neurons initially are affected. If brainstem nuclei are the first to be affected, the initial signs may be slurring of speech or difficulty swallowing. Often only a slight change in voice quality is the first sign. The bulbar or brainstem symptoms are particularly devastating, and verbal communication and oral feedings usually become impossible over time. The patient with this type of ALS has a variable life expectancy but typically may survive only 1 to 3 years after onset. Pneumonia is frequently the cause of death. ALS has no known effective treatment or cure, although many palliative treatments are available, including physical therapy, drugs for reduction of muscle pain, and speech therapy in some cases. The primary involvement of the SLP is to help the patient understand the possible effect on speech and swallowing and to prepare for eventual need for safe swallowing strategies and for dependence on augmentative and alternative communication systems.

Associated Neurologic Characteristics

Signs may be present from damage to both upper and lower motor neuron systems. Muscles are weak but reflexes are hyperactive. Spasticity is usually present unless the lower motor neuron damage is well advanced.

Oral Musculature

Oral peripheral examination yields indications of a pervasive weakness in lips, tongue, and palate. Range of movement is reduced, and sometimes one side is slightly more affected than the other. The tongue may show fasciculations and, in more advanced cases, atrophy. The patient may report and demonstrate difficulty swallowing, especially liquids, and, with progression, difficulty handling oral secretions.

Speech Characteristics

Signs of involvement of both upper and lower motor neuron systems are again present. It is unpredictable as to which signs will predominate in a given case and what changes may occur through the course of the disease. A Mayo Clinic study involved 30 patients with ALS. The characteristics of the speech of this group were as follows.[11]

Phonation

Some patients showed symptoms similar to those shown by patients with pseudobulbar palsy, with much harshness and a strain-strangle quality associated with low pitch. The harshness associated with ALS may often have a wet, gurgly quality. Other patients showed signs more like those of the bulbar group, with poor vocal fold **adduction** resulting in breathiness and short phrases. Audible inspiration was also noted. Monotony of pitch and loudness as well as reduction of stress was present in most patients.

Resonance

Hypernasality was frequent in these cases. Nasal emission, although noted, was not prominent.

BOX 8-3

Amyotrophic Lateral Sclerosis

- Most common example of mixed upper and lower motor neuron lesions; also known as Lou Gehrig's disease
- Causes progressive motor neuron degeneration; usually appears in fifth decade; etiology unknown
- Weak muscles, hyperactive reflexes, and spasticity common
- Weakness in lips, tongue, and palate with reduced range of movement and/or atrophy
- Mixed upper and lower motor neuron symptoms, frequent hypernasality, and imprecise consonant production
- Degree of dysphagia variable; usually follows or parallels degree of dysarthria

---

Articulation

Imprecise consonant production was a principal characteristic. Vowels were often distorted, as were consonants. The slow rate and reduced range of movement of the articulators greatly affected sound production. Hypernasality also contributed to phoneme distortion, and precision of articulation was often so poor as to render speech unintelligible.

Swallowing

The degree of dysphagia in patients with ALS varies greatly depending on the extent of involvement of the oral musculature and the type of motor system involvement predominating. Evidence of poor lingual control is frequently found, with lingual stasis and aspiration before the swallow. A delayed swallow response may also be present, causing aspiration before the swallow. Poor tongue propulsion, weak pharyngeal contractions, and/or cricopharyngeal dysfunction may also result in pharyngeal stasis and aspiration after the swallow. Airway protection may be significantly better in patients with predominantly spastic (upper motor neuron) symptoms than in those with primarily lower motor neuron symptoms. The amount of aspiration may thus be reduced in these patients despite a severe dysarthria.

Dysphagia usually parallels or follows the loss of speech. Managing secretions and maintaining appropriate amounts of fluid intake often are huge challenges for ALS patients.

Box 8-3 presents an overview of ALS, the most common example of mixed upper and motor neuron lesions.

Basal Ganglia Lesions: Dyskinetic Dysarthrias

The basal ganglia control circuit contributes to complex movements by integrating and controlling the component parts of the movements and also helps inhibit unplanned movement. Lesions produce dyskinetic movements and may yield two types of dysarthria, hypokinetic and hyperkinetic, as summarized in Box 8-4.

HYPOKINETIC DYSARTHRIA: PARKINSONISM

The most common disease associated with hypokinetic dysarthria is Parkinson's disease. This disorder is characterized by degenerative changes in the substantia nigra, which cause a deficiency in the chemical neurotransmitter dopamine in the caudate nucleus and putamen.

Etiology

Parkinson's disease (PD) usually is idiopathic (i.e., spontaneous, not caused by another disease), but parkinsonism (or Parkinson-like symptoms) can be caused by carbon monoxide poisoning, arteriosclerosis, manganese poisoning, and some tranquilizing drugs (e.g., prochlorperazine [Compazine], trifluoperazine [Stelazine], and haloperidol [Haldol]).

Associated Neurologic Characteristics

The three cardinal features of parkinsonism are tremor, rigidity, and bradykinesia.[20] A tremor may be present at rest that tends to subside on movement and is absent during sleep. It is often called a pill-rolling tremor because of the pattern of movement of the fingers, as if rolling a small pill between the thumb and the fingers. Rigidity is a common characteristic and is elicited by passive movement of the limb, which induces involuntary contractions in the muscle being stretched. The rigidity

---

BOX 8-4

Basal Ganglia Lesions

Hypokinetic Dysarthria: Parkinsonism

- Parkinson's disease: most common disease associated with hypokinetic dysarthria; usually idiopathic
- Three cardinal features: tremor, rigidity, and bradykinesia
- Slow rate of movement of tongue, lips, and palate
- Speech varies considerably with pathology, but hypophonia and accelerated speech rate are key features in most patients
- Dysphagic symptoms in all four stages of swallow

Hyperkinetic Dysarthria

Essential Tremor
- Encountered as organic voice tremor when larynx involved; may be pure with no other tremor present
- Regular alteration of pitch and loudness noted in mild cases; in severe cases, voice stoppage

Chorea
- Two major types: Sydenham's chorea (childhood disease) and Huntington's chorea (progressive and fatal genetic disease)
- Huntington's characterized by dementia and involuntary movements
- Variable presence of hypotonia and involuntary movement

- Harsh, strained-strangled voice quality common, along with transient breathiness, excessive loudness, and problems with pitch; often imprecise consonants and distorted vowels
- Dysphagia common in Huntington's; oral swallowing stages significantly affected

Dystonia and Athetosis
- Classified as the slow hyperkinesias; no well-established etiologies
- Dystonic (with excessive tone) trunk, neck, and proximal limb parts; athetotic (writhing) movements of arms, face, and trunk
- Dystonia: harsh, strained-strangled voice, imprecise consonants, vowel distortion, hypernasality, and velar control
- Athetosis: excessively loud or breathy; problems with jaw, tongue, and lip movement
- Limited information on dysphagia

Tardive Dyskinesia
- Caused by long-term use of phenothiazines and similar classes of drugs
- Choreiform, myoclonic, peculiar rhythmic movements and abnormal oral movement
- Usually mild speech disorders
- Possible poor coordination in any stage of swallow

may be smooth or intermittent (referred to as cogwheel rigidity). Bradykinesia is defined as reduced speed of movement of a muscle through its range. Hypokinesia, or reduced amplitude of movement, is a prime characteristic as well. Figure 8-3 depicts characteristic posturing and tremor of Parkinson's disease.

Dementia is a correlate of Parkinson's disease, with an incidence between 15% and 40%.[4] Language characteristics of this dementia include impaired receptive vocabulary, difficulty in comprehending the meanings of ambiguous sentences, impaired ability to describe objects verbally, and impaired ability to identify a speaker's intention. Discourse comprehension is certainly at risk.[32]

Tremor

Masklike facies

Arms flexed
at elbows
and wrists

Tremor

Stooped
posture

Rigidity

Hips and
knees
slightly
flexed

Short,
shuffling
steps

FIGURE **8-3**
Parkinson's disease. (From Monahan, F. D., Drake, T., Neighbors, M. [1994]. *Nursing Care of Adults*. Philadelphia: WB Saunders.)

Other features of parkinsonism are referred to as minor, but at least one of these "minor" findings should be present for the diagnosis to be made. These features include micrographia, which is the tendency for the height of the handwritten letters to get smaller as the person writes. Excessive salivation and a dysphonia, described later in this chapter, may be present. The parkinsonian facies is described as a masked facies, with little movement used in facial expression. The parkinsonian posture is stooped and leaning slightly forward. A characteristic gait, called a festinating gait, may also be present that involves short, slow, shuffling steps.

Treatment for parkinsonism usually involves prescription of a dopamine agonist drug and may include speech therapy, physical therapy, and, in some cases, surgery.[42] Until recently, most drugs contained a chemical called L-dopa such as carbidopa/levodopa (Sinemet) or bromocriptine (Parlodel). Other dopamine agonists and other drugs that potentiate the effect of levodopa are now available. A surgical procedure called *deep brain stimulation* (DBS) has been used successfully to treat associated tremor, rigidity, slowness, and problems with walking in PD. It has also been used to treat symptoms of essential tremor and dystonia.[35] In DBS a surgically implanted battery-operated medical device called an implantable pulse generator is placed in the brain. In Parkinson's disease the target area is most often the subthalamic nucleus, although implantation in the GPi is not uncommon. The mechanism through which stimulation affects neurotransmission in different brain regions has not been determined. It appears that the postsynaptic effect of the cortical stimulation results from activation of the efferent axons themselves rather than activation of the cell body and that abnormal signaling to the sensorimotor cortex is blocked.[34,35] The best candidates for DBS are patients who show improvement on L-dopa or similar medications. DBS does not cure the disease and does not slow neurodegeneration, but it can provide substantial relief for some. Physical therapy and speech therapy are also often prescribed for persons with Parkinson's disease, with techniques such as the methodology called Lee Silverman Voice Therapy (LSVT) having shown much promise for improving speech and voice production in selected patients.[38]

Oral Musculature

Frequently the standard oral examination yields only slow rate of movement of the lips and tongue as the major finding, with some reduced range of movement. Palatal movement may be sluggish.

Diadochokinetic rate testing may yield the most interesting information. When a patient is asked to execute the syllable repetition for the diadochokinetic testing, reduction of range of movement becomes more evident. The patient also tends to show an accelerated or rapid rate of speaking. As repetition continues, constriction for consonant production may lessen, and syllables may seem to run together. Some patients may use so little movement that, combined with a rapid rate, no differentiation can be made between syllables and more of a humming or whirring sound is heard.

Speech Characteristics

The speech of patients with Parkinson's disease varies tremendously depending on the stage of the disease and the effectiveness of medication. A study of the vocal tract characteristics of 200 patients with Parkinson's disease helped quantify and describe certain features of this disorder.[26] Only 11%, or 22 of the patients, were found to have no vocal tract problems.

Phonation

Laryngeal disorders were found to be present in 89% of the patients in the study by Logemann et al.[26] Hoarseness was the major perceived characteristic, occurring in 45% of the patients. Roughness, breathiness, and tremulousness also occurred. All patients, except one who had articulation problems, also showed laryngeal dysfunction.

Duffy[11] notes that, even when not pervasive, a strained, whispered aphonia occasionally is noted in the midst of a breathy, harsh vocal quality; it occurs toward the end of a vowel-prolongation task and persists for several seconds. Dysphonia may, in fact, be the presenting and most debilitating speech feature in persons with hypokinetic dysarthria. Monopitch and monoloudness are also frequent characteristics of the vocal production of these patients. Maintaining adequate intensity is quite difficult for most patients.

Articulation

A detailed analysis of the articulatory errors of the 200 Parkinson's patients in the study by Logemann et al.[26] showed that changes in the manner of articulation predominated over changes in the place of articulation.[25] Stop plosives, affricates, and fricatives were most affected, as well as the features of continuance and stridency. Inadequate narrowing or constricting of the vocal tract as a result of inadequate tongue elevation appeared to be the reason for these changes. Netsell et al.[34] have called the result of this phenomena articulatory undershoot.

Resonance

Ten percent of the patients in the study by Logemann et al.[26] showed hypernasality. No regular pattern of hypernasality occurred with articulation or laryngeal disorders.

Prosody

Approximately 20% of the patients in the study by Logemann et al.[26] showed what the authors called a rate disorder. Furthermore, 10% of the patients were judged as using syllables that were too short, whereas 6% used syllables that were too long. Abnormally long pauses

occurred in 2% of those tested. In other descriptions of rate and prosody, variable rate, short rushes of speech, and inappropriate silences have been noted as characteristic. Patients with hypokinetic dysarthria are often described as showing prosodic insufficiency.

Compulsive repetition of phonemes and syllables, noted as dysfluency, has been frequently observed in patients with Parkinson's disease. The presence of palilalia has also been noted with Parkinson's disease. Palilalia is characterized by repetitions that usually involve words, phrases, or sentences and is usually associated with bilateral subcortical damage.

In summary, the typical patient with Parkinson's is expected to have a phonatory disorder characterized by monopitch, monoloudness, and decreased intensity.

Speech rate is likely accelerated, especially during alternate motion rate testing and within segments of conversational speech. Repeated phonemes as well as inappropriate silences are noted.

Swallowing

Dysphagic symptoms have been identified in all four stages of the swallow in patients with Parkinson's disease. The exact nature of the disorder is still not well understood.[24] The oral stage of the swallow may show a rocking pattern, with the anterior tongue repetitively moving the bolus upward and backward while the posterior tongue remains elevated against the palate, preventing the bolus from entering the pharynx and preventing initiation of the swallow response. Although this may last for several seconds and significantly lengthen the oral stages, many patients are unaware of the abnormality. Incoordination and tremulousness, with difficulty initiating tongue movement, are often a part of the oral stages in patients who do not demonstrate the rocking pattern.

Delay of the swallow response, causing aspiration before the swallow, often is noted in these patients. Other disorders include problems with soft palate function, poor laryngeal closure, and reduced pharyngeal peristalsis. Esophageal hypomotility or dysmotility may also be present.

Logemann[24] notes that it is not unusual to find patients with Parkinson's disease who have chronic aspiration, as demonstrated by videofluoroscopy study but few indications of aspiration in their history or other examinations. These patients tend to aspirate silently, without cough or other external signs, and self-report is often not consistent with objective findings. Pneumonia is the most common cause of death in Parkinson's disease, and in a large study of PD patients in nursing homes, the presence of aspiration pneumonia was found to present the highest mortality risk ratio of all the comorbidities.[14] Much variability exists among individuals regarding onset and degree of dysphagia, but progression of the disease results in a greater tendency toward development or worsening of dysphagic symptoms. Medication can have a positive effect, and consideration should be given to timing its administration with meals. Overmedication can cause increased problems, however. The effect of medication should be considered as a part of the diagnostic workup.[40]

HYPERKINETIC DYSARTHRIAS

Hypokinetic dysarthria and hypokinesia are related to reduction of movement from extrapyramidal system damage, but hyperkinetic dysarthria is related to increase in movement. The involuntary movement disorders of tremor, chorea, athetosis, and dystonia also result from extrapyramidal damage. The specific localization of the damage in these disorders is not well understood.

PATHOLOGIC TREMOR

Tremor can be classified as either normal or abnormal (i.e., pathologic) depending on whether it is associated with a disease state. Both normal and **pathologic tremor** may occur at rest, in static postures, or with movement.

Essential tremor (also called action, senile, or heredofamilial tremor) is the tremor most often encountered in speech-language pathology practice. Essential tremor of the voice is known in speech pathology as organic voice tremor. In this condition the extrinsic and intrinsic muscles of the larynx may show tremor either independently or along with tremor of other parts of the body, such as the hands, jaw, or head.

Speech Characteristics

In a pure organic voice tremor, articulatory and resonance characteristics are normal and only phonation is affected. On prolongation of a vowel, the mildly affected patient's voice has a regular tremor of altering pitch and loudness. With more severe disease the voice may simply stop, resembling the disorder known as spastic dysphonia. However, significant differences have been found between the two disorders in terms of regularity of voice arrest and accompanying characteristics. Patients with organic voice tremor also demonstrate excessively low pitch and monopitch, intermittent or constant strained-strangled harshness, and pitch breaks.

CHOREA

Although there are other inherited or noninherited causes of chorea, there are two major diseases in the disorder group that are frequently cited. These are **Sydenham's chorea** and **Huntington's chorea**. Huntington's chorea is autosomal dominantly inherited, and a child of an affected individual has a 50% chance of developing the disease. Onset is typically in the fifth decade, although a so-called juvenile variant and senile variant also occur. The cause is unknown, and the disease is progressive and fatal. Pathologic changes documented usually include loss of neurons from the caudate nucleus, pallidum, and cerebral cortex, with less-constant changes in other areas.

Sydenham's chorea (called "Saint Vitus's dance" in ancient terminology) is a noninherited infection/immune-related childhood disease that may follow such conditions as strep throat, rheumatic fever, or scarlet fever. The symptoms usually clear up within 6 months.

Associated Neurologic Characteristics

Huntington's chorea or Huntington's disease is characterized by rapid, involuntary nonstereotypical, usually purposeless movements. They occur unpredictably and may involve any group of muscles but are more likely to involve distal rather than proximal muscles. Voluntary and automatic movements may be interrupted so that coordinated breathing and speech may be quite difficult. The limbs are hypotonic. Postures cannot be maintained. Cognitive changes accompany the progression of the disease eventually resulting in an associated dementia, and some psychiatric symptoms are also associated, with depression being the most common.

Oral Musculature

The presence of hypotonia and involuntary movement of the oral musculature is variable in chorea. A common characteristic of Huntington's disease is the inability to keep the tongue protruded for more than a few seconds. Sydenham's chorea often involves involuntary movements of the mouth and larynx. Even if little involuntary movement of oral musculature is present, speech will probably be affected by the movements of other parts of the body.

Speech Characteristics

In the Mayo Clinic study of 30 adults with chorea, the following problems were noted.[11]

Phonation

A harsh voice quality and/or a strained-strangled sound were found in many patients. Transient breathiness also occurred. Excess loudness variations were prominent as a result of the poor control of ancillary movement. Lower-than-average pitch levels, voice stoppages, and pitch breaks were other characteristics noted in various patients. Sudden forced inspiration or expiration was observed in some patients.

Resonance

Forty-three percent of the patients in the study by Darley et al.[10] demonstrated hypernasality. The interference with resonance also contributed to articulatory problems, including imprecise consonants and short phrases.

Articulation

The difficulty of muscular adjustment yielded imprecise consonant production and, in 23 patients in the study by Darley et al.,[10] distorted vowels. Misdirection of movement resulted in a feature called irregular articulatory breakdown. Reduced stress and short phrases were also displayed by many of the chorea patients. Prolonged intervals and variable rates were quite prominent and contributed to the perception of prosodic deviations.

Swallowing

Dysphagia is noted to be a frequent symptom in Huntington's disease.[21] Severity of dysphagia varies from patient to patient primarily because of the constantly changing postures and interpatient variability inherent in the clinical population. The oral stages of the swallow are significantly affected by the irregular and uncoordinated tongue movements and changes in facial tone. Aspiration before the swallow may occur because these random movements prematurely push the bolus over the base of the tongue.

Irregular and uncoordinated movements of the vocal folds and the respiratory musculature as well as neck hyperextension may compromise airway protection. Pharyngeal peristalsis may be weak, and esophageal dysmotility has been reported.

DYSTONIA AND ATHETOSIS

Dystonia and athetosis are movement disorders classified as the slow hyperkinesias. Movements are characteristically unstable and sustained, suggesting possible conflicts between flexion and extension of the muscles.

Etiology

Most of these disorders do not have well-established etiologies or focal lesion sites. Encephalitis, vascular lesions, birth trauma, and degenerative neuronal disease are often precipitating diseases. Most hyperkinesias show localized damage to the confines of the basal ganglia. Involuntary movement disorders are sometimes caused by the effects of drugs such as phenothiazines and related compounds, especially the more powerful tranquilizers.

Athetosis is a rare disorder usually seen as a form of congenital cerebral palsy. It is also seen as a rare progressive disease of adolescence, the cause of which is unknown, and as an accompanying residual deficit with hemiplegia after cerebral infarction. Localization of the lesion is difficult, but the putamen seems to be almost always involved.

Associated Neurologic Characteristics

Dystonia implies excess tone in selected parts of the body. Dystonia mainly affects the trunk, neck, and proximal parts of the limbs. The slow movements are usually sustained for a prolonged period. The movements usually build up to a peak, are sustained, and then recede, although they occasionally begin with a jerk.

Athetotic movements are slow and writhing and are predominantly of the arms, face, and tongue. The movements tend to be exaggerated by attempts at voluntary activity, which make voluntary movements clumsy and inaccurate.

Speech Characteristics

Phonation

The dystonic patient usually has a harsh or strained-strangled voice quality. Some patients, although fewer in number, may demonstrate intermittent breathiness and audible inspiration. Monopitch and monoloudness are also seen in these patients. Because of the involuntary movements, dystonic patients often have voice stoppages and periods of inappropriate silence. Excess loudness variations accompany the excessive movement. Voice tremor is also found among dystonic patients.

Phonation in athetosis is often significantly affected. The patient often has poor respiratory reserve and respiratory patterns. Both dilator and constrictor spasms have been noted in laryngeal functioning. Voicing is often excessively loud or excessively breathy, and it is unpredictable and frequently poorly coordinated with articulation.

Spasmodic dysphonia (SD) is a chronic, task-specific focal dystonia of unknown etiology.[33] Aronson and Hartman[2] discussed differential diagnoses for patients with essential tremor who had SD. The signs of SD also occur in cases that appear to be psychogenic or idiopathic. No single cause has been identified.

At one time this disorder was known in the literature as *spastic dysphonia* but has come to be more accurately referred to as *spasmodic* dysphonia in more current literature. This change helps clarify the fact that there are three forms of this disorder and that the physiologic basis for the disorders described here is not true spasticity. Thus the word *spasmodic* allows the perception that spasm or dystonia is involved but does not suggest only spasticity. The three forms of spasmodic dysphonia are adductor, abductor, and mixed. Adductor is the most common by far, but the other two forms are certainly seen, and differential diagnosis is important to treatment.

Adductor SD is characterized by a strained voice quality with voice arrests caused by laryngeal adductor spasm. It is frequently associated with pain in the laryngeal area. The interruptions to phonatory airflow are assumed to be caused by hyperadduction of the vocal folds, but indirect laryngoscopy usually reveals normal vocal fold movements.

Abductor SD is caused by laryngospasms during abduction of the vocal cords resulting in intermittent breathiness or aphonia. Both intermittent strained quality and breathy quality are perceived when there is a mixture of adductor and abductor spasms; the mixed form occurs in a smaller percentage of patients.

Rosenfield[41] postulated years ago that voice production in SD could be viewed as a primary problem resulting from abnormal movements in the speech motor system and could also be considered as resulting from an attempt to cope with the underlying movement disturbance. The etiology of any type of SD is unknown at this point, but the studies of the pathogenesis of this disorder are supporting a neurologic basis and quantifying the contribution of extrinsic and intrinsic factors. Childs and colleagues[7] found evidence to suggest that extensive voice use under stress may be related to adductor SD. It is evident in the literature that further studies on the pathology and the psychological factors related to SD are needed.[7,45]

Treatment of SD is controversial, and although various treatments have been shown to be successful, no single treatment has been discovered. The injection of the neurotoxin botulinum (BTX) into the affected muscle(s) of the vocal cord has been used successfully in the treatment of SD for more than 30 years now.[29] Initially the treatment was used only for adductor SD, but it has now also been used successfully in the treatment of the abductor type.[33]

Selective adductor denervation surgery (SLAD-R)[16] involves removing some of the thin muscle fibers that make up the thyroarytenoid muscle of the vocal folds. This reduces the closing force and alleviates the tight spasm involved in adductor SD. It is not used frequently now but is considered a good option if BTX injections fail or wear off.[33]

Articulation

As might be predicted, the articulation of patients with these involuntary movement disorders is highly variable, with a range of severity from slight distortion to unintelligible. The dystonic patients of the Mayo Clinic study demonstrated prominent articulation imprecision of consonant production.[9] Results also showed vowel distortion and irregular breakdown of articulation. Short phrases were noted with prolonged intervals. Prolongation of phonemes and variability of rate were also frequently observed. Reduction of stress was a relatively prominent characteristic of speech production.

Kent and Netsell[19] and Platt et al.[36] have investigated the articulation of athetoid adults by using cinefluorographic and intelligibility measures. The studies found that athetoid speech is frequently reduced in intelligibility as a result of articulation problems. Kent and Netsell[19] found large ranges of jaw movement, inappropriate tongue positioning, prolonged transition time, and retruding of the lower lip. Platt et al.[36] found particular difficulty with accuracy of anterior tongue placement, reduced precision of fricatives and affricatives, and inability to achieve extreme positions in vowel formation. They found place and voicing errors to be predominant, particularly in final consonants.

Resonance

Of the 30 dystonic patients studied by the Mayo Clinic, 11 were found to show hypernasality.[9] In the Kent and Netsell[19] cinefluorographic study of athetoid adults, all subjects had trouble achieving velopharyngeal closure. The most severe problem, however, was velar control. Instability of velar position was frequently noted. The velum sometimes moved inappropriately, causing a loss of closure, or in some cases the velum showed repetitive movements that were not related to respiration.

Swallowing

Dysphagia in dystonic patients has been described on a limited basis in the literature. Bosma et al.[3] describe difficulty with lip control and lingual coordination in a patient with drug-induced bulbar and cervical dystonia. The patient had difficulty holding food in the mouth and controlling it to prevent premature entrance into the pharynx. The pharyngeal stage was normal in this group's patients.

Pharyngeal stage efficiency may depend on the posturing of the head and neck. A pulling of the neck to the side or a hyperextension often occurs, which may cause stasis and perhaps aspiration if the airway cannot be protected during the prolonged posturing.

TARDIVE DYSKINESIA

Another movement disorder resulting from extrapyramidal damage is tardive dyskinesia, which is attributable to the long-term use of phenothiazines and similar drugs. Symptoms include choreiform, myoclonic, and peculiar rhythmic movements, with a high incidence of abnormal movements in the oral region. Constant random movements of the lips and tongue may be found, with a frequent "fly catcher's" movement of the tongue in which the tongue involuntarily moves in and out of the mouth. Velar movement may also be involved. Intelligibility is variably affected, with some patients becoming unintelligible because of the random movements. Most patients, however, have only a mild speech disorder.

The random movements may result in poor coordination in any of the four stages of swallowing. Pocketing of food; pharyngeal stasis; and aspiration before, during, and after the swallow may be found on study of the dysphagia. Reflux of food may be a result of esophageal discoordination. Decreased sensation may also result in lack of reflexive cough or silent aspiration.

The Cerebellum and Cerebellar Pathway Lesions

ATAXIC DYSARTHRIA

As noted, the cerebellum serves as an important center for the integration or coordination of sensory and motor activities. It receives fibers from the motor and sensory cortex either directly or through intervening nuclei. Damage to the cerebellum and/or its pathways causes a disorder called ataxia, and the motor speech symptoms yield an **ataxic dysarthria**.

Etiology

Ataxic dysarthria is caused by damage at some point in the cerebellar control circuit. Damage may occur localized to the cerebellum alone or may be part of more generalized damage affecting several systems. Causes include degenerative diseases (Friedreich's ataxia, olivopontocerebellar atrophy, and multiple sclerosis), stroke, trauma, tumors, alcohol toxicity, drug-induced neurotoxicity (from such drugs as phenytoin [Dilantin], carbamazepine [Tegretol], lithium, or diazepam [Valium]), encephalitis, lung cancer, and severe hypothyroidism.

Associated Neurologic Characteristics

Ataxia is a disruption in the smooth coordination of movement with failure to coordinate sensory data with motor performance. The hand may overshoot its target when reaching for an object. If the outstretched arm is pushed aside, it swings past its former position and overcorrects. Abnormalities such as these are shown when the patient is asked to touch his or her nose or run the heel down the shin. Rapid alternating movements may be affected. Equilibrium is affected and gait may be impaired. Because alcohol affects cerebellar function, law enforcement officers will often use tests of some of these skills in sobriety tests (e.g., walking on a narrow line, alternating hands touching finger to nose). With ataxia, movement is slow to be initiated and slow through the range. Repetitive movements may be irregular and poorly timed, a condition called dysdiadochokinesia. Muscle tone is hypotonic. Intention or kinetic tremor (tremor during purposeful movement) is also present.

Speech Characteristics

Dysarthria with localized damage to the cerebellum has the following characteristics.

Phonation

The voice may be approximately normal or occasionally may show excessive loudness variations. Harshness similar to a coarse voice tremor may also be noted.

Resonance

Velopharyngeal functioning is usually intact, with normal resonance characteristics. Hypernasal resonance occasionally is found. Nasal emission is less frequently demonstrated.

Articulation

Imprecise consonant production, vowel distortion, and irregular articulatory breakdown mark the speech of ataxic dysarthria. Rate is usually slow, although some patients use normal rate.

Prosody

Prosodic changes are usually readily observable in ataxic dysarthria. A speech prosody characteristic termed **excess and equal stress** by Darley et al.[8] is a predominant feature, although it is not found in all speakers with ataxic dysarthria. This description refers to the tendency to put excessive vocal emphasis on typically unstressed syllables and words using a slow, metered pattern. Duffy[11] postulates that in some patients the irregular articulatory breakdown may predominate, giving the speech an intoxicated, irregular character that overrides the measured aspect of excess and equal stress patterns.

Also contributing to the prosodic changes is the prolongation of phonemes and normal intervals in speech. The term **scanning speech** often is used in connection with ataxic dysarthria. This term was originated by Charcot[5] to describe the speech of a patient with multiple sclerosis. Charcot described the speech as being very slow, with a pause after each syllable as if the words were being measured or scanned. This seems to be almost equivalent to what Darley et al.[8] describe as excess and equal stress. Others have used the term *scanning speech* to describe a different set of characteristics; therefore the term has not been found useful and is not recommended.

The term **explosive speech** also has been used to describe ataxic production. The Mayo Clinic study noted excess loudness variations with excessive effort in 10 of 30 ataxic speakers.[8] This forceful effort and increase in intensity, especially noted after pauses, give the impression of explosiveness.

Damage to the cerebellum resulting in ataxic dysarthria is summarized in Box 8-5.

Ataxic Dysarthria

- Caused by damage to the cerebellum and/or its pathways (e.g., degenerative diseases, stroke, trauma, tumors, alcohol toxicity, drug toxicity, encephalitis, lung cancer, hypothyroidism)
- Failure to coordinate sensory data with motor performance, hypotonic muscle, and kinetic tremor
- Irregular articulatory breakdown, slow rate, and readily observable prosodic changes; harshness, excessive loudness, and voice tremor possible

Other Mixed Dysarthrias with Diverse Lesions

MULTIPLE SCLEROSIS

The National Institute of Neurological Diseases and Stroke (NINDS) characterizes multiple sclerosis (MS) as a neuroinflammatory disease that affects myelin; researchers have also found more recently that the disease process attacks the nerve cell body and the axons of cells in the brain, spinal cord, and optic nerve.[37] On magnetic resonance imaging (MRI), areas of scar tissue (sclerosis) of varying size are seen in the white matter of brains of persons diagnosed with MS. It is an autoimmune disease in which the immune cells that are normally actively surveying for infectious or unhealthy cells in our body suddenly attack healthy cells. In the case of MS, these healthy cells are cells that make up myelin in the central nervous system. MS usually begins between ages 20 and 40 and, as with most autoimmune diseases, it occurs more frequently in women.

Etiology

MS is a complex disease, and its etiology has not been discovered. The favored explanation has been that (for unknown reasons) the immune system mistakenly identifies normal nervous system cells as foreign, but there is some research suggesting that the immune system may be fighting an infectious agent, like a virus, that is guilty of "molecular mimicry," mimicking brain cells and that the immune system may actually be attacking brain cells that are unhealthy. There is active research into this and other autoimmune disease processes but no answers at this time. The NINDS reports that there appears to be genetic vulnerability as well as environmental factors involved in MS causing demyelination in various tracts of mainly white matter. Figure 8-4 shows a magnetic resonance image of a patient with MS. With MS, the lesions involve the entire central nervous

FIGURE **8-4**
Multiple demyelinated plaques *(arrows)* are seen in this magnetic resonance image of a patient with MS. (Reprinted from Nadeau, S. E., Ferguson, T. S., Valenstein, E., Vierck, C. J., Petruska, J. C., Streit, W. J., & Ritz, L. A. [2004]. *Medical neuroscience.* Philadelphia: Saunders.)

system, but the peripheral nervous system is seldom involved.

Associated Neurologic Characteristics

Early signs are often mild or unnoticed. They may include transient paresthesias of the extremities, transient diplopia or blurring of vision, mild weakness or clumsiness, and mild vertigo. More severe signs of MS include marked difficulty with gait, dysarthria, significant weakness, visual disturbances, nystagmus, bladder disturbance, and personality change caused by frontal lobe involvement. Van den Burg et al.[47] also noted impairments in perceptual motor functioning and mild deficiencies in intelligence, specifically in memory, in a group of 40 mildly disabled MS patients.

MS may take different forms. Some patients have a relapsing-remitting type of MS in which they have attacks (or exacerbations) from which they recover completely, especially in the early stages of the disease. In the later stages these patients may accumulate disabilities with each new attack. Other patients may have the primary progressive form that follows a chronic progressive course, which usually involves progressive spinal cord dysfunction. This form may evolve from the relapsing form or be present from the onset of the disease.[48]

Speech Characteristics

Duffy[11] cautions that a mixed spastic-ataxic dysarthria may be the most common type of dysarthria associated with MS but should not be considered the only type found in MS. Because of the variable sites of damage in the disease, many different dysarthrias are possible. Spastic, ataxic, or a mixture of these dysarthrias occurs more frequently.

In a Mayo Clinic study of 168 patients diagnosed with MS, 59% were judged as having normal overall speech performance.[10] Twenty-eight percent showed minimal impairment, and 13% had more severe impairment. Darley et al.[10] labeled the dysarthria they most often found as a mixed spastic-ataxic dysarthria.

Phonation

The most frequently encountered deviation was impairment of loudness control. Harsh voice quality also was frequently seen. Breathiness was noted in 37 patients. Pitch control and inappropriate pitch levels were also found.

Articulation

Approximately half of the patients were judged to have defective articulation. Although the cerebellar system is frequently involved in MS, only 9% of patients showed the irregular articulatory breakdowns characteristic of ataxic dysarthria.

Resonance

One quarter of MS patients demonstrated some degree of hypernasality.

Prosody

A characteristic called impaired emphasis ranked high in the speech of these subjects. Impaired features included judgments of rate, appropriateness of phrasing, pitch and loudness variation for emphasis, and increased stress on typically unstressed words and syllables. Only 14% of patients demonstrated the ataxic characteristic called excess and equal stress.

Swallowing

If corticobulbar tracts or lower brainstem nuclei are involved, dysphagia may result in patients with MS. Merson and Rolnick[31] report that dysphagia is common in MS. Because the types, severity, and rate of deterioration in MS are so variable, characterizing common symptoms is difficult. Careful examination is critical. Sensory changes, including abnormal taste, have been reported for some patients.[6]

SHY-DRAGER SYNDROME

Etiology

This syndrome was first described by Shy and Drager in 1960.[44] It usually appears after the fourth decade of life and affects men more often than women by a ratio of 3:2. It is a degenerative disease of the autonomic nervous system that may also affect several components of the central nervous system. Prognosis is usually poor, although progression is slow.

Associated Neurologic Characteristics

With this disease, involvement may include the pyramidal, extrapyramidal, or cerebellar system or some combination of the three systems. Early signs usually involve autonomic nervous system disorders, including bowel and bladder incontinence, impotence, reduction of perspiration, and difficulty maintaining blood pressure when standing (known as orthostatic hypotension). Later symptoms include a gait disturbance, weakness, tremor of the limbs, and dysphagia and dysarthria.

Speech Characteristics

A study by Ludlow and Bassich[28] comparing acoustic and perceptual analyses of Parkinson's disease and Shy-Drager syndrome documented the following characteristics for the speech of seven patients diagnosed as having Shy-Drager syndrome.

Phonation

Strained-strangled voice quality and breathiness were noted in the voice quality of these patients. A wet hoarseness was also identified in many cases. The voice was often judged too soft and mean intensity level was below normal.

Resonance

Hypernasality may occur if the involvement of the pyramidal system produces elements of a spastic dysarthria.

Articulation

Imprecise consonants are a predominant part of this dysarthria. A variable rate was also ranked high in the deficiency ratings.

Prosody

Although patients with Shy-Drager syndrome were shown to have poorer-than-normal ability to change fundamental frequency, their ability was better than that of patients with Parkinson's disease. Acoustic analysis showed, however, that the patients with Shy-Drager use their retained ability to change pitch quite poorly. The results are acoustically perceived as monopitch and reduced stress.

The dysarthrias associated with MS and with Shy-Drager are summarized in Box 8-6.

Apraxias

Praxis comes from the Greek word *prassein* meaning "to do." Hence, praxis means performance of an action. Performing an action that is not reflexive or automatic

BOX 8-6

Other Mixed Dysarthrias with Diverse Lesions

Multiple Sclerosis

- Unknown etiology, although studies suggest a viral agent may be responsible
- Early signs mild; severe signs include gait difficulty, dysarthria, visual disturbances, nystagmus, bladder disturbances, and personality changes
- Mixed spastic-ataxic dysarthria most common; frequent problems with volume and pitch control
- Possible dysphagia with corticobulbar or lower brainstem involvement

Shy-Drager Syndrome

- Degenerative disease of the autonomic nervous system
- Early signs: bowel and bladder incontinence, impotence, reduction of perspiration, difficulty maintaining blood pressure while standing
- Later signs: gait disturbance, weakness, limb tremor, dysphagia, dysarthria
- Strained-strangled voice quality, wet hoarseness, hypernasality, imprecise consonants, and a poor ability to change pitch all possible

TABLE 8-1

Apraxias

TYPE	DESCRIPTION
Apraxia	A disorder in performing voluntary learned motor acts caused by a lesion in motor association areas and association pathways, in which similar automatic gestures are intact
Ideomotor apraxia	A disorder in which motor plans are intact, but individual motor gestures are disturbed
Ideational apraxia	A disorder in performing the steps of complex motor plans
Apraxia of speech (AOS)	A disorder of motor programming of speech
Oral apraxia (buccofacial apraxia)	A disorder of nonspeech movements of the oral muscles
Childhood apraxia of speech (CAS)	A disorder in which motor speech programming is disturbed in childhood

requires planning, timing, and sequencing. Recall that the motor association cortex of the brain has areas devoted to performing the action of muscle movement to produce speech, and we called these motor planning or motor programming areas.

Apraxia (also called dyspraxia) is a disorder of learned movement in which the difficulty with movement is not caused by paralysis, weakness, or incoordination of the muscles and cannot be accounted for by sensory loss, comprehension deficits, or inattention to commands.[15] It has also been defined as a disorder of motor planning. Apraxia is a high-level motor disturbance of the integration of the motor components necessary to carry out a complex motor act. Review the section on motor planning in Chapter 6 while studying the description of the disorders of motor programming described here.

Apraxias are important to the speech-language pathologist because certain types of apraxia may directly affect the motor programs of the speech muscles. Other forms of apraxia often accompany the aphasias and other cerebral language deficits associated with the cortical motor association areas and the association pathways of the brain. The major apraxias are defined in Table 8-1.

Hugo Liepmann (1863-1925) is credited with elucidating the concept of apraxia around 1900, although

John Hughlings Jackson described an apraxic disturbance of the tongue as early as 1866. Liepmann used early disconnection theory to explain apraxia and demonstrated lesion sites to support the variety of apraxias described.[22] Because this text is concerned with clinical speech and language syndromes, the apraxias that affect movements of other parts of the body are not discussed. Remember, however, that a limb or an ideomotor apraxia may also be present in patients with apraxia of speech. Features associated with oral apraxia and apraxia of speech are summarized in Box 8-7.

Oral Apraxia

Speech-language pathologists recognize a nonspeech disorder of the oral muscles called oral apraxia, the inability to perform nonspeech movements with the muscles of the larynx, pharynx, tongue, and cheeks, although automatic and sometimes imitative movements of the same muscles may be preserved. This disorder is not the result of paralysis, weakness, or incoordination of the oral musculature, and it may be isolated or coexist with an apraxia of speech. Oral apraxia is usually called buccofacial apraxia by neurologists.

Oral praxic disturbance must be differentiated from disorders of the motor pathways involved in

---

BOX 8-7

Apraxias

Oral Apraxia

- Inability to perform nonspeech movements with muscles of the larynx, pharynx, tongue, and cheeks
- Paralysis, significant weakness, or incoordination of oral musculature not noted on examination
- Affects voluntary and sometimes imitative movements; reflexive preserved

Apraxia of Speech

- Impaired ability to execute speech movements voluntarily in the absence of paralysis, weakness, or incoordination of speech musculature
- May appear independent or in conjunction with oral apraxia
- Most often associated with Broca's aphasia
- Speech impaired by inconsistent initiation, selection, and sequencing of articulatory movements; no consistent disturbances of phonation, respiration, and resonance; no related neurologic impairments of oral musculature

---

upper motor neuron and lower motor neuron systems. A careful cranial nerve examination usually indicates whether the disturbance is on the higher level of motor planning of praxis as opposed to being a lower level motor deficit associated with either supranuclear lesions or cranial nerve lesions. In lower level motor deficits of the central and peripheral nervous systems, motor involvement generally affects both voluntary and reflexive oral acts. Voluntary oral motor acts are limited by paralysis, weakness, and incoordination, and the more reflexive acts of mastication and deglutition are affected as well. Supranuclear lesions are associated with typical tongue deviation, hypertonic oral muscles, palatal paresis, hyperactive gag reflex, and lower facial paresis. Lower motor neuron lesions are associated with tongue deviation and atrophy, hypotonic oral muscles, palatal paresis, and a hyporeflexive gag reflex. Facial paresis is hypotonic. Extrapyramidal lesions produce involuntary movements of oral muscles, and ataxic movements of oral muscles are found in cerebellar disorders. Disorders of praxis will present different signs on oral and speech examination than these.[10]

Oral apraxia testing is completed on a spontaneous level to verbal command and on an imitative level. Commands requiring oral-facial movements such as "lick your lips" or "clear your throat" may be used. Failure to perform appropriately on a number of similar commands suggests a diagnosis of oral apraxia in

brain-injured adults. Love and Webb[27] used a 20-item informal test for assessing oral apraxia. Published tests of apraxia of speech usually include tasks for assessing nonverbal oral apraxia.

Apraxia of Speech

Apraxia of speech is an impaired ability to execute voluntarily the appropriate movements for articulation of speech in the absence of paralysis, weakness, or incoordination of the speech musculature. In 1900 Liepmann[22] discussed a form of apraxia that could be localized to the speech muscles; some 40 years earlier, Broca described elements of this disorder as part of aphemia. Aphemia, the defect in speech and language that Broca believed resulted from damage to the third left frontal convolution of the brain, has become known as Broca's aphasia. The disorder is marked by effortful groping for articulatory movements produced in an apparently trial-and-error manner. Articulation on repeated utterances is inconsistent. Speech is dysprosodic, often characterized by great difficulty in initiating utterances. A developmental form of verbal apraxia is known as **childhood apraxia of speech** (see Chapter 12). The current discussion concerns acquired apraxia of speech in adults.

Oral apraxia and speech apraxia may appear independently or coexist. Oral apraxia may be the basis of a speech apraxia. Speech apraxia may appear in a pure form but is most often accompanied by a language disorder, as seen in classic Broca's aphasia. Some neurologists and speech-language pathologists deny that what is called apraxia of speech is a pure disorder of praxis. They view the apraxic elements in Broca's aphasia as more of a linguistic problem than a motor problem. Evidence is not yet available to resolve the issue.

If the speech-language pathologist is presented with a case that appears to be a pure speech apraxia, it must be differentiated from dysarthria. In speech apraxia, articulation is impaired by *inconsistent* initiation, selection, and sequencing of articulatory movements; in dysarthria, articulatory movements are more consistent, with distortion errors predominating. Speech apraxias do not display consistent disturbances of phonation, respiration, and resonance, whereas persons with dysarthrias almost always display consistent phonatory, resonance, and respiratory disorders. With dysarthria there is impairment of nonspeech musculature, including paralysis, weakness, involuntary movement, and/or ataxia. Persons affected by apraxia of speech do not have these neurologic impairments of the oral musculature or if they are present, the apraxia is not the cause of these deficits.

Synopsis of Clinical Information and Applications for the Speech-Language Pathologist

- Of the acquired neurogenic communication disorders seen in large speech-language pathology practices, the majority are likely to be motor speech disorders.
- Dysarthria and apraxia of speech are the two primary classifications of motor speech disorders.
- Dysarthria implies true organically based paralysis, weakness, or incoordination of the oral musculature that results in distortion of speech and/or difficulty with feeding or swallowing.
- Apraxia of speech is a sensorimotor disorder of motor programming of the speech musculature for the production of speech. The primary symptoms are not the result of weakness, paralysis, or incoordination of the oral musculature.
- The evaluation of a patient with suspected motor speech disorder should include assessment of hearing and language (to rule out other causes of the communication problem or to define accompanying

problems), an oral-motor examination, speech-production tasks, and a screening or full assessment of feeding and swallowing.

- The Mayo Clinic classification system categorized the dysarthrias into six major classes: spastic, flaccid, hypokinetic, hyperkinetic, ataxic, and mixed. Unilateral upper motor neuron dysarthria has been added more recently as a separate type. Each of these dysarthrias is associated with disorders or diseases affecting certain parts of the motor system. Each has associated classic perceptual features that the student should learn.
- Apraxia of speech also is associated with damage to the motor speech planning areas of the motor cortex and also has certain perceptual features that should be learned.
- Other diseases and disorders produce dysarthrias but were not included in the discussion of the more common disorders. These can be found in Table 8-2.

TABLE 8-2

Other Neurologic Diseases Associated with Dysarthria

NAME	ETIOLOGY	SPEECH SYMPTOMS
Bell's palsy	Inflammation or lesion of cranial nerve VII	Slurring caused by unilateral weakness of labial muscles
Polyneuritis	Follows infections or may be caused by diabetes or alcohol abuse	Flaccid dysarthria
Hemiballismus	Lesions of subthalamic nucleus	Hyperkinetic dysarthria
Palatopharyngolaryngeal myoclonus	Brainstem lesions producing rhythmic myoclonic movements of the palate, pharynx, and/or larynx	Hyperkinetic dysarthria, which is sometimes only noted on vowel prolongation
Gilles de la Tourette's syndrome	No known etiology	Hyperkinetic dysarthria with spontaneous, uncontrolled vocalizations such as barking, grunting, throat clearing, snorting; echolalia and coprolalia (obscene language without provocation) may be present
Olivopontocerebellar atrophy	Degeneration of olivary, pontine, and cerebellar nuclei	Mixed dysarthria of hypokinetic, spastic, and ataxic types
Progressive supranuclear palsy	Neuronal atrophy in brainstem and cerebellar structures	Mixed dysarthria, which may include hypokinetic, spastic, and ataxic types

CASE **STUDY**

A 48-year-old accountant reported excess stress in his life. He often made presentations to various companies looking to hire his accounting firm. For the past several months, he reported to his physician that he had been having difficulty speaking and swallowing. He described his speech as "sounding like I am speaking through my nose." He also admitted to noticing mild tremors of his eyebrows and mouth. An oral peripheral mechanism examination revealed bilateral facial weakness, reduced tongue strength, and a hyperactive gag reflex, which was a new finding for him. After an extensive diagnostic workup, the physician diagnosed this patient with ALS.

Questions for Consideration

1. What type of dysarthria is usually present for patients with ALS?
2. What parts of the motor system are impaired with this type of dysarthria?

REFERENCES

1. Alberts, M. J., Horner, J., Gray, I., & Brazer, S. R. (1992). Aspiration after stroke: Lesion analysis by brain MRI. *Dysphagia, 7,* 170–173.
2. Aronson, A. E., & Hartman, D. E. (1981). Adductor spastic dysphonia as a sign of essential (voice) tremor. *Journal of Speech and Hearing Disorders, 46,* 52–58.
3. Bosma, J., Geoffrey, V., Thach, B., Weiffenbach, J., Kavanagh, I., & Orr, W. (1982). A pattern of medication induced persistent bulbar and cervical dystonia. *International Journal of Orofacial Myology, 8,* 5–19.
4. Brown, R. G., & Marsden, C. D. (1984). How common is dementia in Parkinson's disease? *Lancet, 2,* 1261–1265.
5. Charcot, J. M. (1877). *Lectures on the diseases of the nervous system.* (Vol. 1). London: The New Sydenham Society.
6. Cherney, L. R. (1994). *Clinical management of dysphagia in adults and children.* Gaithersburg, MD: Aspen.
7. Childs, L., & Rickert, S. (2011). Patient perceptions of factors leading to spasmodic dysphonia: A combined clinical experience of 350. *Laryngoscope, 121,* 2195–2198.
8. Darley, F., Aronson, A., & Brown, J. (1969). Differential diagnostic patterns of dysarthria. *Journal of Speech and Hearing Research, 12,* 246–269.
9. Darley, F., Aronson, A., & Brown, J. (1969). Clusters of deviant speech dimensions in the dysarthrias. *Journal of Speech and Hearing Research, 12,* 462–496.
10. Darley, E., Aronson, A., & Brown, J. (1975). *Motor speech disorders.* Philadelphia: W. B. Saunders.
11. Duffy, J. R. (2005). *Motor speech disorders: Substrates, differential diagnosis, and management* (2nd ed.). St. Louis: Mosby.
12. Duffy, J. R., & Folger, W. N. (1986). *Dysarthria in unilateral nervous system lesions.* Detroit, MI: Presented at the annual convention of the American Speech-Language-Hearing Association.
13. Evatt, M. L., Reus, C. M., Brazer, S. R., Massey, E. W., & Horner, J. (1993). Dysphagia following unilateral ischemic stroke [Abstract]. *Neurology, 43*(Suppl), A159.
14. Fernandez, H. H., & Lapane, K. L. (2002). Predictors of mortality among nursing home residents with a diagnosis of Parkinson's disease. *Medical Science Monitor, 8,* CR241–6.
15. Geschwind, N. (1975). The apraxias: Neural mechanisms of disorders of learned movements. *American Scientist, 63,* 188–195.
16. Green, D. C., & Berke, G. (1990). An in vivo canine model for testing treatment effects in laryngeal hyperadduction disorders. *Laryngoscope, 100,* 1229–1235.
17. Hartman, D. E., & Abbs, J. H. (1992). Dysarthria associated with focal unilateral upper motor neuron lesions. *European Journal of Disorders of Communication, 27,* 187.
18. Horner, J., Massey, E. W., & Brazer, S. R. (1993). Aspiration in bilateral stroke patients: A validation study. *Neurology, 43,* 430–433.
19. Kent, R., & Netsell, R. (1978). Articulatory abnormalities in athetoid cerebral palsy. *Journal of Speech and Hearing Disorders, 43,* 353–374.
20. Kirshner, H. S. (2002). *Behavioral neurology: Practical science of mind and brain* (2nd ed.). Boston: Butterworth-Heinemann.
21. Leopold, N. A., & Kagel, M. C. (1985). Dysphagia in Huntington's disease. *Archives of Neurology, 42,* 57–60.
22. Liepmann, H. (1900). Das Krankheitsbild der Apraxie ("motorischen asymbolie"). *Monatsschrift fur Psychiatrie und Neurologie, 8,* 15–44, 102–132 182-197.
23. Logemann, J. A. (1983). *Evaluation and treatment of swallowing disorders.* San Diego: College Hill Press.
24. Logemann, J. A. (1988). Dysphagia in movement disorders. In J. Janokovic, & E. Tolosa (Eds.), *Advances in neurology: Vol. 49. Facial dyskinesias.* New York: Raven Press.
25. Logemann, J. A., & Fisher, H. B. (1981). Vocal tract control in Parkinson's disease: Phonetic feature analysis of misarticulations. *Journal of Speech and Hearing Disorders, 46,* 348–352.
26. Logemann, J. A., Fisher, H. B., Boshes, B., & Blonsky, E. R. (1978). Frequency and co-occurrence of vocal tract dysfunction in the speech of a large sample of Parkinson patients. *Journal of Speech and Hearing Disorders, 43,* 47–57.
27. Love, R. R., & Webb, W. G. (1977). The efficacy of cueing techniques in Broca's aphasia. *Journal of Speech and Hearing Disorders, 42,* 170–178.
28. Ludlow, C., & Bassich, C. J. (1983). The results of acoustic and perceptual assessment of two types of dysarthria. In W. R. Berry (Ed.), *Clinical dysarthria.* San Diego: College Hill Press.

29. Ludlow, C. L., Naunton, R. F., Fulita, M., & Sedory, S. E. (1990). Spasmodic dysphonia: Botulinum toxin injection after recurrent nerve surgery. *Otolaryngology Head and Neck Surgery, 102*, 122–131.

30. Mao, V. H., & Abaza, M. (2001). Laryngeal myasthenia gravis: Report of 40 cases. *Journal of Voice, 15*, 122–130.

31. Merson, R. M., & Rolnick, M. I. (1998). Speech-language pathology and dysphagia in multiple sclerosis. *Physical Medicine & Rehabilitation Clinics of North America, 9*, 631–641.

32. Murray, L. L., & Stout, J. C. (1999). Discourse comprehension in Huntington's and Parkinson's diseases. *American Journal of Speech-Language Pathology, 8*, 137–148.

33. Murray, T. (2014). Spasmodic dysphonia: Let's look at that again. *Journal of Voice, 28*, 694–699.

34. Netsell, R., Daniel, G., & Celesia, G. G. (1975). Acceleration and weakness in parkinsonian dysarthria. *Journal of Speech and Hearing Disorders, 40*, 467–480.

35. Perlmutter, J. S., & Mink, J. W. (2006). Deep brain stimulation. *Annual Review of Neuroscience, 29*, 229–257.

36. Platt, L. J., Andrews, G., & Howie, P. M. (1980). Dysarthria of adult cerebral palsy: II. Phonemic analysis of articulation errors. *Journal of Speech and Hearing Disorders, 23*, 41–55.

37. National Institute of Neurologic Diseases and Stroke. (n.d.). Multiple sclerosis. Retrieved from http://www.ninds.nih.gov/disorders/multiple_sclerosis/detail.

38. Ramig, L. O., & Dromey, C. (1996). Aerodynamic mechanisms underlying treatment-related changes in vocal intensity in patients with Parkinson's disease. *Journal of Speech and Hearing Research, 30*, 798–807.

39. Robbins, J. (1989). *Swallowing and brain imagery in asymptomatic normals and stroke patients.* Evanston, IL: Presented at Swallowing and Swallowing Disorders: From Clinic to Laboratory, Northwestern University.

40. Robbins, J., Webb, W. G., & Kirshner, H. S. (1984). *Effects of Sinemet on speech and swallowing in parkinsonism.* San Francisco, CA: Presented at American Speech-Language-Hearing Association Convention.

41. Rosenfield, D. B. (1988). Spasmodic dysphonia. In J. Jankovic, & E. Tolosa (Eds.), *Advances in neurology: Vol. 49. Facial dyskinesias.* New York: Raven Press.

42. Schultz, G. M., & Grant, M. K. (2000). Effects of speech therapy and pharmacologic and surgical treatments on voice and speech in Parkinson's disease: A review of the literature. *Journal of Communication Disorders, 33*, 59–88.

43. Schwendimann, R. N., Burton, E., & Minagar, A. (2005). Management of myasthenia gravis. *American Journal of Therapeutics, 12*, 262–268.

44. Shy, G., & Drager, G. (1960). A neurological syndrome associated with orthostatic hypotension: A clinical pathologic study. *Archives of Neurology, 2*, 511–527.

45. Tanner, K. (2012). Epidemiologic advances in spasmodic dysphonia. *Perspectives on Voice and Voice Disorders, 22*, 104–111.

46. Tessell, R., Foley, N., & Doherty, T. (2002). Clinical characteristics of patients with brainstem strokes admitted to a rehab unit. *Archives of Physical Medicine and Rehabilitation, 83*, 1013–1016.

47. van den Burg, W., van Zomeren, A. H., Minderhoud, J. M., Prange, A. J. A., & Meifer, N. S. A. (1987). Cognitive impairment in patients with MS and mild physical disability. *Archives of Neurology, 44*, 494–501.

48. Weiner, H. L., & Levitt, L. P. (1994). *House officer series: Neurology* (5th ed.). Baltimore: Williams & Wilkins.

49. Zeigler, W., & von Cramer, D. (1986). Spastic dysarthria after acquired brain injury: An acoustic study. *British Journal of Communication Disorders, 21*, 173–187.

9

Central Language Mechanism and Learning

Nothing defines the function of a neuron better than its connections.

Marcel Mesulam, 2006

KEY TERMS

cingulate cortex
cognition
constraint-induced therapy (CIT)
declarative memory
executive functions
graceful degradation
hippocampus
input fibers
intrinsic neurons (interneurons)
left fusiform area
long-term memory
metacognition
motor association areas
neocortex (archicortex)
neurogenesis
neuroplasticity
perisylvian cortex
phoneme
prefrontal cortex (PFC)
presynaptic inhibition
procedural memory
projection neurons
reasoning
reticular formation
selective engagement
short-term memory
spatial summation
summation
temporal summation
thalamic reticular nucleus
thalamocortical circuit
thalamus
transcranial magnetic stimulation (TMS)

In the preceding chapters, a foundation has been laid for you to be able to identify where a brain structure is and its primary and associated function(s). Neuronal function as well as the primary motor and sensory systems have been introduced and discussed. If your instructor is following the textbook organization as written, we then began our journey into the clinical world of speech language pathology, beginning with the motor system and speech and swallowing disorders in adults. We do the same for speech disorders in children in the pediatric section at the end of the text. We now take a simplified, but expanded, look at the cortical mechanisms underlying the extraordinary capacity of human beings to use and understand language and to learn and create new ideas. These abilities begin to form a foundation from birth and, barring injury or disease, continue throughout life. This chapter introduces current thinking regarding how neurons work together to accomplish this task. Also highlighted are the anatomic structures involved in language processing, as well as some of the historically popular models of language underlying explanations of language disorders acquired from brain damage. The more common acquired adult language disorders and cognitive-linguistic disorders are discussed in Chapter 10. Language and learning disorders of children are covered in Chapter 13.

Neocortex

The highest level of cortex in terms of cytoarchitecture is **neocortex** (or **archicortex**), covering approximately 90% of the brain. This vast brain structure is believed to give humans their unique cognitive abilities, including language. The total area of cortex is approximately 2500 cm^2, with a range of 2 to 4 mm in thickness; sensory cortex is thinner than motor and association areas. The thickness is determined by the aggregation of neuronal cell bodies. Until recently the commonly accepted estimated count of neurons was around 100 billion with an 8- to 10-fold greater number of neuroglial cells in the cortex. Using a method called *isotropic fractionating*, a group of Brazilian researchers[4] found an estimated 86.1 billion (± 8.1 billion) neurons and 84.6 (± 9.1 billion) neural glial cells in the adult male brains studied, which called into question the assumption of the massive number of nonneuron cells in the human cortex. This finding suggested that the ratio of neural to nonneural cells in the human brain is equivalent to that found in other primates. This chapter primarily is concerned with the work of the neurons.

NEURAL NETWORKS

Early neuroanatomists were acutely aware of and frustrated by the limitations of their knowledge of the brain, being unable to provide much detail about this exceedingly complex and fragile organ. Early advances were made using staining techniques that eventually allowed tracing of some fibers and the identification of association pathways. Clinicopathologic studies added to the knowledge by studying brain structure of patients with disorders and looking for relationships between the structures and pathways lesioned and the resulting behavioral changes. All investigation and theorizing in these very early days of neuroscience was constrained by the lack of knowledge about how neurons worked and how neural signals transmitted any information between them. Whole brain integration could not be understood without this knowledge though most neuroanatomists knew that there existed circuitry and neural networks that communicated in some fashion. Not until 1986 was any complete mapping of a cellular connection network done, this one on the nematode *Caenorhabditis elegans*. Still there was a lack of ability to record much about physiologic properties of the cells and their synapses. The cellular mapping breakthrough with *C. elegans* did not contribute much to the ongoing early efforts to map mammalian networks.

In the 1980s researchers began to create computational models based on both anatomy and knowledge of physiology, attempting to explain and potentially predict neural interactions. Also, in the late 1980s and early 1990s, anatomic and physiologic studies of the visual cortex of the monkey produced early connectional matrices and promoted the idea that cortical areas were unique in terms of specific input and output fiber connections and could be distinguished by these patterns.

In 1998, the concept of *small world networks* was introduced in a letter in the publication *Nature*.[59] The authors suggested a mathematical method in which dynamic systems or network models could be computationally "rewired" to explain the middle ground between network connections organized in regular patterns and those seemingly organized in completely random connections. They noted that the regular or random patterns could not explain many biologic, technical, or social networks. They postulated that dynamic systems organized in a "small world" networks have the distinction of more local connections (or cliques) within the nodes of the network than a random network would and shorter path lengths between the nodes than a regular network would. This high clustering with shortened path connections was dubbed "small world" with an analogy to the "six degrees of separation" phenomena.[59] Examples were given of how this could explain or predict the operation, efficiency, and power of such varied systems as social networks, the spread of an infectious disease, power grids, and the neural network of the *C. elegans* nematode. Since that time this concept of small world networks as a critical component of neuronal organization in the neocortex has been accepted as a viable model for neural connection, allowing for both specialized processing in local circuits as well as distributed or integrated processing over the entire network.[1,50]

A breakthrough in mapping large cortical networks came with the development of new techniques of diffusion imaging. These noninvasive imaging techniques and associated computational methods were being constantly refined, providing neuroanatomists opportunities for cortical mapping that had not been available before this development. A review article published in 2005 introduced the term *connectome* and defined it as "a comprehensive structural description of the network of elements and connections forming the human brain."[50] In 2010 the U.S. National Institutes of Health began The Human Connectome Project to map this network as accurately as possible. In this two-phase project, 36 investigators from 11 institutions delineated methods for collection and analysis of data; the project then began collecting data on a pool of 1200 adults, primarily from three of those institutions. The information collected is made freely available to the scientific community on a user-friendly informatics platform.[39] The general public may see breathtaking images of some of the brain's pathways in their website gallery.[26]

The study of brain connectivity involves looking at either the anatomic connectivity, statistical dependencies (functional connectivity), or causal interactions (effective connectivity).[48] Although these studies have generated much excitement and our knowledge is increasing almost daily, the study of connectivity is not without its limitations and challenges.[24,49] At the rate of new discoveries in methodologies and computational models, these limitations eventually will be overcome. New imaging methods are constantly refined and new computational models are being used extensively by researchers in a number of fields (e.g., neuroanatomy, physiology, psychology, neurology, speech-language pathology). These efforts are aimed at contributing to the data on neural connectivity, understanding normal brain function, attempting to correlate it with behavior, and understanding what happens when there is abnormal development or injury to the brain that changes behavior. The student should know, however, that these studies are complex and challenging. The limitations of the methodology, the design, and the findings should always be acknowledged and discussed by the researcher.

BRAIN CONNECTIVITY

Cortical neurons, like all neurons, transmit and process neural information through synapses and fiber pathways. Synaptic organization is concerned with the way neurons form connections, circuits, and units in the nervous system that mediate the function of different regions of the brain.

What abilities do the neurons have in connection building? Obviously they are transmitters, sending millions of signals throughout the brain. They are also transducers, for example, converting sound waves into neuronal impulses. Neurons are switches, turning on and off or causing another neuron to switch on or off in response to a neurotransmitter release. They have the capability to encode information; they then express that code providing information about such things as spatial location, timing, or even higher level information such as color. Neurons are thought to be minute storage vessels as well; connections at strong synapses are thought to temporarily store memory traces. And, finally, another important property of neurons is oscillation. As a neural spike travels down the axon, neurons move back and forth, creating complex waveforms. This signaling can spread from one cellular array to another, resulting in areas or regions of the cortex that are busy sending and resending signals. These oscillations are the signals identified on electrophysiologic studies of the brain.

Connections between neurons result in pathways that run between them. Connections are made locally as well as outside the particular region, perhaps a relatively long distance away. Essentially three types of neural elements make the connections possible. **Input fibers** synapse onto the cell body and/or dendrites or dendritic spines found on the dendrites. **Projection neurons** (also called principal or relay neurons) send out a long axon fiber that carries information signals to other regions. The third type is composed of cells concerned only with local processing within a certain region, the **intrinsic neurons**, or **interneurons**. Sometimes a projection neuron takes action locally and behaves as an interneuron; the distinction between the two is not rigid. Inhibitory interneurons have been shown to synchronize the firing of excitatory neurons, enhancing the probability of activation of the target neuron downstream. The relations among these three elements of synaptic organization vary in the different regions of the brain and determine the function of that region.

SPATIAL ORGANIZATION

Given the density of tissue in the cortex with the estimated trillions of connections, as many as 1 billion synapses may be present per cubic millimeter of cortical tissue.[45] These connections form circuits, although they are not of a simple input and output nature. The nervous system is organized in a complex manner

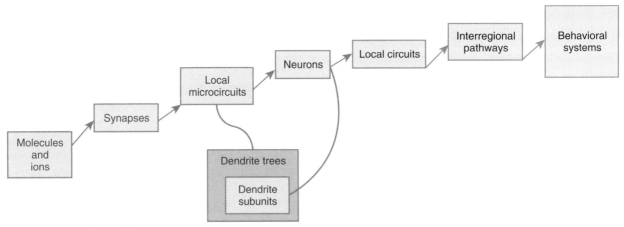

FIGURE **9-1**

Levels of hierarchical organization in the nervous system. *Arrows* should be read as
"organize into." *Curved line connection* indicates that local microcircuits are grouped to
form dendritic subunits within the dendritic trees, which are part of the individual neurons.

from the molecular level to complex behavioral systems. This organization can be viewed in terms of levels of scale.[48] At the microscale level, microcircuits are formed from small bunches of synapses between individual neurons. At the mesoscale level, networks or local circuits are formed in arrangements of columns or mini-columns that connect those neuronal populations. Interregional fiber pathways that connect brain regions make up the macroscale level and result in systems of behavior. Figure 9-1 breaks this organization down further. Microcircuits form dendritic connections and subunits within the connections between dendrites of individual neurons. These neurons with their connections interact, forming local circuits ("small worlds") and performing the operations of a particular region of the brain. These regions are organized with interregional pathways, columns, and laminae. Neural impulses traveling by the interregional connections between these multiple local circuits provide for integration of this varying neural information resulting in behaviors.

LAMINAR ORGANIZATION

Not only is there columnar organization of the cortex, there is also a horizontal laminar organization. You may remember from Chapter 2 that the fully developed neocortex is composed of six layers, with the sixth layer being the innermost. How the laminae develop is discussed in Chapter 11. These cortical laminae are often broken down into subareas within the layer for the more finite study of their composition and physiology, but for our purposes we look only at their broad composition. Table 9-1 summarizes the name and some information about the composition of each layer.

PATTERNS OF SYNAPTIC CONNECTION

There is both specificity and variability of the anatomic connections at all three levels of scale.[48] You find specificity in the connections between distinct neuronal types, in the branching pattern of the axon collaterals, and in the connections made over long distances between certain cell nuclei and particular brain regions. On the other hand, much variability exists in the shape of neurons and their processes, as well as in size, place, and connection pattern of different brain structures. Across species there is variability in the same brain structure. Across time in the same individual, variability will be found due to development, plasticity, and, perhaps, repair. As Sporn[48] notes, anatomic variability is most likely the main source of the functional variability we see in behavior.

The neural microcircuits are the most localized synaptic patterns that can be studied. Chapter 4 presented two basic patterns of connectivity—divergence and convergence. These are important to remember when thinking about how information processing occurs within these circuits. Microcircuits are built of three types of elements: divergence, convergence, and a variation of convergence called presynaptic control.

To refresh your memory, synaptic *divergence* means that an action potential can trigger multiple excitatory postsynaptic potentials simultaneously, affecting many dendritic terminals at once. This amplifies the activity of a single axon. This kind of divergent synaptic action is found, for example, in the cerebellum, which demonstrates great divergence, and in the sensory afferents of the thalamus. Another method of achieving divergence is also found in the nervous system. Axons branch into collaterals and give rise to multiple terminals, thus resulting in numerous synaptic contacts. This kind of divergence is common in the cortical cells.

TABLE 9-1

Summary Description of the Laminar Organization of the Neocortex

LAYER NUMBER	LAYER NAME	DESCRIPTION	SPECIAL FEATURES
I	Molecular	Contains mostly horizontal axons and a few neuronal bodies	
II	Outer granular	Contains a mixture of small neurons (granule cells) and slightly larger neurons (pyramidal cells); apical dendrites extend up to layer I and axons descend into and through deeper layers	
III	Outer pyramidal	Contains primarily medium and large pyramidal cells; apical dendrites extend up to layer I and axons descend into and through deeper layers	
IV	Inner granule	Contains stellate (starlike) neurons, smooth and spiny; no pyramidal cells	Primary target layer for ascending sensory information from the thalamus
V	Inner pyramidal	Contains medium and large pyramidal cells; apical dendrites of medium size extend up one or two layers; large cells project to layer I	Large pyramidal = major source of cortical efferent fibers that send axons to corpus striatum, brainstem, and spinal cord; some corticocortical connections
VI	Multiform	Contains an assortment of neuron types	Axons project to subcortical structures such as thalamus; also make corticocortical connections

Synaptic *convergence*, on the other hand, occurs when multiple synapses occur on one postsynaptic dendrite. When this occurs, two kinds of **summation**, or additive effects, may take place. **Temporal summation** may occur in which the effect of the neurotransmitters may be enhanced, for example, if all synapses are excitatory. The convergence may also summate with the excitatory and inhibitory potentials canceling each other out, resulting in the resting potential being maintained. The integration of the excitatory and inhibitory synapses usually functions, however, to *modulate* the action; thus there is a change in potential, but it is not as strong as it would have been without the convergence. Another kind of summation is **spatial summation**, in which the varied sites of synapse along the dendritic surface of the neuron cause responses to rise in the different parts of the neuron. This may increase the possibility of more local mechanisms during activation from the site on one dendritic tree to another.

A third type of action that is similar to convergence is **presynaptic inhibition**, in which two sequential axonic synapses occur. One axon terminates on another with inhibitory action. When the second axon is then presynaptic to a third axon, there is an inhibitory effect on the synapse that will occur on the postsynaptic membrane of the third axon. Box 9-1 summarizes the three kinds of connectivity patterns.

DENDRITES AND NEURONS

The complexity of neuronal processing is exemplified by the extensive variety of patterns of dendritic branching unique to different types of neurons. The different branching patterns are said to impose geometric constraints on activity. These patterns, combined with the different sites of input and the passive and active electronic properties of the membrane of the dendrites, account for the complex nature of the activity of dendrites and consequently the neurons. This text does not go in depth into this complex organization of the dendritic input to the neuron. However, the fact that the dendritic tree is responsible for the variety of actions the neuron may undertake is important to understand.

Of note, the smallest functional unit within the dendritic tree is the dendritic spine, which is, as it sounds, a thornlike protuberance on the dendrite. Being quite numerous in the nervous system, they account for most postsynaptic sites in the brain, especially within the cerebellum, basal ganglia, and cortex. Within the cortex most excitatory synapses are made onto spines, and an estimated one third of the inhibitory synapses occur there. Approximately 15% of all dendritic spines carry potential for both kinds. Aside from the obvious function of increasing the surface

Synaptic Connectivity Patterns

Synaptic Divergence

- Occurs when action potential triggers multiple excitatory postsynaptic potentials, affecting many dendrites; can also occur when axons branch into collaterals, creating multiple terminals and synaptic contacts
- Acts to increase amplification of a single axon
- Commonly found in the cerebellum, the sensory afferents of the thalamus, and in cortical cells

Synaptic Convergence

- Occurs when multiple synapses fire on one postsynaptic dendrite, adding activity from multiple axons to one dendrite
- Two kinds of summation can occur at a synaptic convergence:
- Temporal summation—effect of neurotransmitter may be enhanced if all synapses are excited or if resulting excitatory and inhibitory potentials create a resting potential
- Spatial summation—various sites along synapse cause responses in different parts of neuron

Presynaptic Inhibition

- Occurs when two axonic synapses are in sequence and an inhibitory effect occurs on the postsynaptic membrane of the third of three axons

FIGURE **9-2**
The use of event-related potentials (ERPs) is a popular noninvasive technique to track brain activity in subjects of all ages. (From Haith, M.M., & Benson, J.B. [2008]. *Encyclopedia of Infant and Early Childhood Development*. Amsterdam: Elsevier, Ltd.)

dendritic spines on both parts and different excitatory and inhibitory synapses occurring at different levels of the parts of the dendritic tree. It also, of course, has an axon that in most instances gives off collateral axons that synapse within the local circuit as well as at sites some distance from that region.

BRAIN WAVES

We have discussed mapping brain activity through functional magnetic resonance imaging (fMRI), but there is another way of trying to "observe" brain activity, which is to map the oscillatory activity through an electroencephalograph (EEG). Advanced computers have made it possible to separate and analyze the complex waveforms that make up the neural signals. The frequency bands are somewhat arbitrary but have come into common use and are now believed to represent distinct processes coordinated by the brain.

Raw data from an EEG reflect activity of billions of neurons and are difficult to interpret when reading from the scalp even though waveforms can be identified. However, if the EEG signals are averaged over many trials and locked to a specific point in time, the waveforms become more regularized and can yield much more information. This study is called event-related potentials (ERPs). Because it is noninvasive and the equipment is more accessible now, this technique is becoming more and more common in research in SLP (Fig. 9-2).

Learning

As you use your brain to study your brain, there are a tremendous number of neural events occurring

area available for connective integration, spines are theorized to have significance for rapid signal processing.[45] The foundational study of neuronal functioning in Chapter 4 discussed the basics of impulse initiation and synaptic connection, with the impulse being generated at the axon hillock and traveling down the axon to synapse with another neuron. Also discussed was the graded potential set up in the cell itself. To take this further, evidence exists that to various degrees electronic back-spread of this propagated current occurs back into the soma and the dendrites. This may be sufficient to activate dendrite-to-dendrite (dendrodendritic) synapses, further facilitating or inhibiting action within that neuron's local circuit.

Basic Circuits

The basic cortical neuron (usually a pyramidal cell type) is structured well for the integrative actions beginning to emerge. The typical cortical neuron has dendritic trees that are divided into apical and basal parts, with

with new connections made and old connections enhanced or weakened. What is learning in terms of neural functioning? Learning is simply (well, it's really not simple at all!) the brain increasing the efficiency of synaptic connections. Increasing the efficiency means enabling faster flow of neural signals from one neuron to another. Two of the ways our brains may accomplish this are by growing more synapses between the neurons or by enhancing the neurochemical supply of glutamate, the excitatory neurotransmitter, in the neural circuit to increase the speed of transmission.

When neurons begin to form connections in microcircuits and then in local areas and the connections are strengthened by repeated stimulation and neural firing, these connections and the pattern formed between them in a circuit become stronger. By *stronger*, we mean that they are more likely to fire when appropriate stimulation is present and they are more likely to fire together. In turn, when neurons fire together in synchrony, the connections between them are even further strengthened. What has come to be known as the Hebbian learning principle proposed by Donald Hebb in 1949[25] puts forth that assemblies of spiking cells learn an input pattern by strengthening the connections between cells that fire at the same time. This resulted in the old saying, "Neurons that fire together, wire together." Hebbian learning principle relies on the theory that synaptic connections are the physical foundation for learning and memory. There is now much evidence gathered from modern techniques of neuroscience that this principle is solid.

The synchronous firing in a neural circuit may result in a representation that we experience as a percept such as a word, a recognizable sound, a familiar shape or visual object, or a combination of facial features that we recognize as a certain person, for example. If the pattern of firing does result in a representation that is familiar or meaningful to you, it means that the particular neural input has been transformed across its input into an output pattern that the brain recognizes. A simple example is the transformation of auditory phonologic representations into articulatory phonologic representations. This involves a number of systems (sensory, cortical association, motor) with repeated neural signaling across those systems strengthening the connection weights (or likelihood of firing together) in a particular pattern. All of the primary and association cortices in the brain are thought to be essentially collections of pattern associator networks, quite often working in parallel. This is where the term *parallel distributed processing* (PDP) came from that is used in explaining computing. It is a simple construct for describing the operation of the brain because the brain is thought to be much more advanced a system than any computer yet built. PDP has been seen as useful, however, in trying to explain some of the aspects of neural networks.

What Parts of the Brain Participate Most Actively in Learning?

There are, as you know, different kinds of learning. Some learning appears to be undemanding and accomplished simply by making ourselves conscious of it—paying attention. Our brains are best at those tasks because we have evolved to interact with the things we come into contact with, problem solve in those situations, and, basically, survive. We can learn how to do things such as develop motor skills by repetitive practice of the proper movements with the proper timing and force until a *motor memory* is established. The type of learning that students have to do, however, requiring recall of facts and consolidation of those facts into concepts and principles is different, and our brains have to work even harder! The parts of the brain that are involved may be the same, but they are taxed by the mental effort required to build the more diffuse synaptic circuits that will support consolidation and long-term retention of information.

We will take the task you are attempting to do now, to learn parts of the brain active in learning and use it to figure out the answer. First of all, to commit anything to memory (learning is a process of acquiring lasting brain representations that we call memories), we must attend to whatever it is, obviously requiring that you be conscious and awake. Thus that deep core of the brainstem, the **reticular formation**, must be actively channeling sensory information through the **thalamocortical circuit** resulting in a state of awakeness. In learning, we are concerned with voluntary attention, not automatic attention (e.g., directing attention to the sound of a siren). Voluntary attention implies selecting stimuli and responses depending on the goals set; it is a "top-down" process.[11] With the exception of the neurons out in the sensory periphery, selective attention involves activity of neural circuitry at all levels of the sensory system involved. Learning often involves visual, auditory, and tactile senses, and it is usually considered optimal to involve more than one sensory system. Once the sensory information is relayed through the **thalamus** and on to the targeted primary sensory area, executive control systems in subcortical and cortical areas, particularly the cingulate cortex, the parietal cortex, and the **prefrontal cortex (PFC)** enable the brain to selectively attend to the stimulus. It has been suggested in some models that dopaminergic (DA) neurons in the midbrain may act to provide gating signals that instruct the PFC to *maintain* that neural activity, supporting the ability to sustain attention once the object of attention has been selected.[51]

Once attentional control has been established, the features of the thing to be learned must be analyzed, and a percept must be established with which a memory can be associated. When learning through reading, an accomplished reader already has the established input-output circuitry in the neocortex to make sense of the shapes the visual cortex forwarded. The brain of a skillful reader has *automatized* the steps necessary to read with understanding: recognition of the letters, the letter combinations into words, the associations between the words and their meaning, and the association of meaning with the particular combination of words in each sentence. In neural terms, strong neural circuits have been established that will easily carry out the reading task without that reader having to switch to *controlled* processing unless the reader happens upon an unfamiliar word.

For example, before this class, unless you had another class in which it was introduced, you likely had no association for the word *dysarthria*. You may try to sound out the word using phonologic representations stored in the temporal lobe and transformed into articulatory movements in the **motor association areas** of the frontal cortex. Even if you pronounce it correctly (and if you have no experience with the word, you are not sure), you find that there are no memory traces stored for that word. In that case, you may choose to read on, hoping there will be a definition provided in the context or you may go to the glossary or a dictionary. Those strategies are due to cognitive processes we call executive functions—ruled by your *prefrontal cortex*. Your brain has learned over time what options are available to you to solve this problem and you employ metacognition, an executive function, to discern what usually works best for you as a learner.

Once you find how to pronounce this word and what it means, your brain can begin to learn it—that is, establish a memory trace associated with both the visual form of the word, the phonologic representation of the word, and the meaning(s) associated with it. Recent research on new word learning indicates that the brain may store written words as "pictures" in an orthographic lexicon in the **left fusiform area**, which the researchers referred to as the visual word form area.[20] This research indicates that the neural firing associated with recognition of the written word is to the word form as a whole, not to the individual phonemes and letters.

The associations that you learn for a word and commit in the brain as memory traces form what SLPs call a semantic field around it. For *dysarthria* maybe such things as motor system, movement, speech disorder, a particular disease, a particular patient, or a particular teacher are associated. Episodic memories associated with the meaning, for example, in whose class you first heard the term, are likely consolidated in the **hippocampus** in the medial temporal lobe. The semantic associations, the word and the meaning itself are likely consolidated in the *temporal lobe* and the *neocortex*. Many things that we learn have both episodic and semantic memories associated with them. Over time as you have more experience with the word and concept of "dysarthria," associated memories will be stored over a wide area of different brain regions as part of cortical network circuits. The larger the number and type of associations, the more likely you are to remember the meaning.

This system of memory storage in the brain in which the associated information is distributed across many cortical connections helps explain why a breakdown in processing rarely results in a total loss of a percept or concept. The loss of one component of this distributed processing network results in a reduced level of performance, but not a complete inability to process. For example, in word retrieval failures, patients often know something about the word. They have not completely lost all information about it. This reduction in performance of the system is called **graceful degradation** in engineering terms and has been a useful concept in neural processing. SLPs often use it to great advantage in treatment.

As you read and process the information, you are establishing concepts you wish to commit to memory. The sentences have been encoded in the temporal lobe and neocortex. In memory consolidation, meaning is begun to be established through association with previous learning, previous experience, and recent learning. This may involve sensory memories as well as episodic and semantic memories. The medial temporal lobe and the temporal lobe will begin to resonate with the neocortex to begin establishing the memory. This involves synaptic changes. You may read the text again, you may take notes, you may read aloud to yourself; again, your metacognitive skills are put to work figuring out what typically works best for you. Your professor may go over the same material in class. All of these will help consolidate the meaning of what you have read because the synaptic changes that take place in the MTL, temporal lobe, and neocortex will be strengthened by the repetitive firing in that circuit. The connections also may be adapted and enhanced by new connections to the circuit as you learn more about it or it makes more sense to you. Repetition and an increased number of associations may eventually result in learning—establishing the concept in long-term memory. This requires protein synthesis. For more permanent memories or representations of knowledge to be established there must be changes at the synapses such as growth of dendritic spikes and increased excitatory (and perhaps inhibitory) connections that need to become efficient and more permanent.

The consolidation of memories and learning takes place most efficiently while we are sleeping. A period of non–rapid eye movement (NREM) sleep called *slow-wave sleep* or *delta sleep* may be the most important period for consolidating explicit or declarative memories. Rapid eye movement (REM) sleep may be the more important period for consolidating procedural memories. However, some studies on humans suggest that both periods are important as a two-step process in consolidation of memory for learning.[51]

The Power of Connection

The brain is the ultimate information processor. No computer built to date can process information, learn new information, and create from imagination with the efficiency and productivity of the human brain. Because of (1) the properties of the neurons and their links across association cortices; (2) the input from sensory mechanisms, limbic structures, basal ganglia, cerebellum, and so forth; and (3) output back to some of these areas, processing in this supreme network is a two-way function. Processing is both from the bottom up and from the top down. From peripheral sensory input comes a forward press of converging neural information, traveling through the intermediate subcortical pathways to early sensory association cortical processing areas (unimodal and polymodal association cortex) to higher and higher cortical association areas (supramodal or heteromodal cortex). At each local circuit station are also back-projections occurring at the synapses onto the neuron, with this output from the circuits occurring in a mostly divergent rather than convergent manner.

This convergent/divergent action within neuronal circuits enhances or changes the strength of connections within the circuit and thus output to other regions. This allows changes in behavior. These neuronal operations allow translation of what is thought into what is said, written, or signed—in other words, to communicate thoughts.

LANGUAGE

The contribution of French neurologist Pierre Paul Broca's study of the brain of two patients with language loss was acknowledged earlier in this text. We credit Broca as well as a German neurologist, Carl Wernicke, with the first descriptions of the acquired language disorder we call *aphasia*. The discovery of specific speech-language areas in the left hemisphere of the brain had dramatic consequences for neurology. It prompted European neurologists to formulate numerous hypothetical models of the central language mechanism. Several of these models were highly speculative and based on limited evidence of the correlation between behavioral deficits and brain lesions. Even today the central mechanism

for language is not completely understood, and it remains risky to attempt to formulate a model for normal and abnormal communication. However a model formulated by Carl Wernicke is generally conceded to be a powerful and still clinically relevant model of the central language mechanism. The model was later elaborated by Dr. Norman Geschwind (1926-1984)[18] and Geschwind and his colleagues in Boston did numerous research studies on patients with acquired language disorders finding this model to help explain some of the clinical findings. The Geschwind model is a connectionist conception of the higher mental functions of speech and language and as such it gives importance to the classic language and speech centers and highlights the significance of the interconnection of the association fibers between major centers. Figure 9-3 highlights the important perisylvian areas for language function from the Broca/Wernicke/Geschwind research. The model has been of significant use to clinical neurologists because it allows a high degree of predictability of symptoms associated with specific lesion sites. In addition, the model also predicted possible aphasic syndromes that were not yet described by postulating possible lesion sites for those syndromes. In general the model has been confirmed by clinical studies. The classic language centers postulated by Wernicke and Broca continue to be confirmed as critical to language and comprehension through computerized tomography and other current objective neurodiagnostic procedures.

Geschwind,[18] however, pointed out that some conditions exist under which the model has not always fulfilled its promise. First, the model does not readily explain certain features of aphasic syndromes. Second, aphasic cases occasionally occur whose existence is not predicted by the model. Third, in a few cases the expected symptoms do not appear when an adequate lesion exists. As we will see, research has continued the work of Geschwind with advanced tools that have begun to help clarify the language processing areas of the brain.

Research in acquired communication disorders began to feel the influence of the field of cognitive neuropsychology as experimental psychologists developed information-processing models of cognition and language in individuals with brain damage. Much of the initial work was done in the United Kingdom, mainly with investigations of reading (Colheart, Patterson, and Marshall, 1980).[10] These models were testimony to the belief in cognitive neuropsychology that investigations of individual patients from a particular theoretical stance are preferable to comparisons of groups of patients categorized by the classic syndrome models.[9]

These information-processing models required that a task be fractionated into its different components. Individuals were then studied in such a manner as

FIGURE **9-3**

Important perisylvian cortical regions of the central language mechanism. (From Brookshire, R. [2007]. *Introduction to neurogenic communication disorders* [7th ed.]. St. Louis: Mosby.)

to identify where during the process the breakdown may occur, resulting in inaccurate or inefficient performance. The models usually represented the brain as a specialized computer that has domain-specific modules associated with defined neural structures, with input and output routes mapped as the model becomes more specific to function. The modules were usually represented as boxes with the input and output routes as arrows. These models appealed to clinicians because techniques for assessment and treatment can be adapted from them. As the use of advanced imaging techniques and electrophysiologic studies have begun to proliferate in literature relevant to speech language pathology, these models are also appealing because of potential relevance to neural circuitry and connectivity.

As imaging and electrophysiologic studies become more common and innovative, we are closer to combining the information gained from them and computational modeling for information processing. For example, see Figure 9-4, which is from a 2002 study on auditory sentence processing.

Neurologic Substrates of Language Processing and Production

PERISYLVIAN ZONE

The major neurologic components of language are situated in the area of the dominant hemisphere known as the perisylvian cortex. Table 9-2 summarizes the components of the language model as hypothesized by Geschwind and colleagues from the initial work of Wernicke. This zone contains Broca's area, Wernicke's area,

the supramarginal gyrus, and the angular gyrus as well as the major long association tracts that connect the many language centers. These areas are composed of primarily supramodal association cortex. We begin by briefly discussing the areas considered as "classic" in any model of language. We then take a look at some recent research that is expanding the notion of what brain structures may be involved in language and how they are involved. They do not detract from this original work by Geschwind and colleagues, but they certainly enhance our understanding of brain function, although confirming the complexity of this skill we humans have and, most often, take for granted.

Before describing these classic areas, describing the basics of language processing within them may be helpful. Nadeau et al.[36] provide a simplified description of the processing in these areas. As previously mentioned, the smallest unit of language is the phoneme, many of which can be written as letters and all of which a speech-language pathologist can write in phonetic symbols. It is thought that the cortex of the perisylvian area contains a distributed representation of phonemes and that this representation is in all the various forms in which they are used. There are motor, auditory, visual, and tactile representations. Depending on the communication system (e.g., verbal vs. signing), the representation of one type may be stronger than others because of the strengthening of the connections through use. These representations are supported by their links or connections with appropriate cortical processing areas within the perisylvian cortex. These links allow abstract representations of phonemes to be translated into reality. The translation allows a sound to be spoken, a letter representation to be written or signed, and a spoken

Working Memory

Online Processes

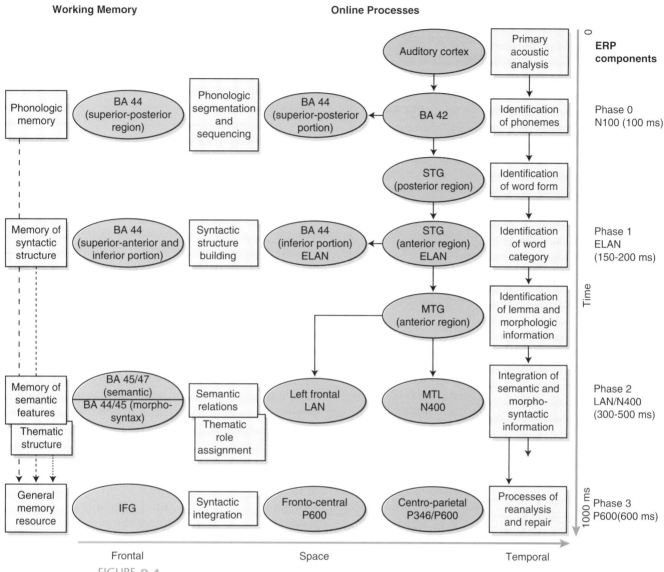

FIGURE **9-4**

Neurocognitive model of auditory sentence processing. The boxes represent the functional processes, and the ellipses represent the underlying neural correlate identified by functional magnetic resonance imaging (fMRI), positron emission tomography (PET), or event-related potentials. The neuroanatomic specification (indicated by text in parentheses) is based on either fMRI or PET data. (From Friederici, A. D. [2002]. Towards a neural basis of auditory sentence processing. *Trends Cogn Sci 6(2)*: 78-84.)

representation of that phoneme to be correctly understood as that particular phoneme as opposed to other ones. Another functional aspect of the perisylvian cortex is to sequence these individual phonemes into combinations found in a particular language, the phoneme blends, syllables, and words that make up a language. This is the first step, but without a consequent linking to a particular neural pattern that corresponds to meaning, these combinations would have no value. Research is supporting the notion that "meaning corresponds to the particular pattern of neural activity distributed across association cortices throughout the brain that actually represents a particular concept" (p. 544).[36] This is the fundamental concept underlying the neural association and function of the areas now discussed.

BROCA'S AND WERNICKE'S AREAS

The location and limits of Broca's area in the frontal lobe are well defined by research from several sources (see Chapter 2). Research with transcranial magnetic stimulation suggested a functional division in this area.[21]

TABLE 9-2

Major Components of the Central Language Mechanism Model

STRUCTURE	FUNCTION
Broca's area	Motor programming for articulation
Motor strip	Activation of muscles for articulation
Arcuate fasciculus	Transmission of linguistic information to anterior areas from posterior areas
Wernicke's area	Comprehension of oral language
Angular gyrus	Integrates visual, auditory, and tactile information and carries out symbolic integration for reading
Supramarginal gyrus	Symbolic integration for writing
Corpus callosum	Transmission of information between hemispheres

These experiments found that the anterior (pars triangularis) and ventral (pars orbitalis) parts seemed to be involved in semantic processing, whereas the posterior portion (pars opercularis) was engaged with syntactic and phonologic processing as well as motor control of speech.

Wernicke's area, found in the temporal lobe, rivals Broca's area as a major component in a model of neurologic language functioning. The function of the center is well agreed on, although its borders are sometimes disputed. In contrast to Broca's area, which serves the expressive aspects of motor speech, Wernicke's area is devoted to another major aspect of language—reception of speech. Neural structures in Wernicke's area are assumed to allow for comprehension of oral language and underlie the formulation of internal linguistic concepts.

ARCUATE FASCICULUS

Wernicke[60] must be given credit for developing a language model that highlights the connective association pathways between the frontal and temporal speech-language areas. The major fiber connection between Broca's area and Wernicke's area is now generally agreed on to be the arcuate fasciculus (AF). The fibers, as described in Chapter 2, leave the auditory association area in the temporal lobe, arch around and under the supramarginal gyrus, and pass through the parietal operculum. They travel forward as part of the long association tract known as the superior longitudinal fasciculus (SLF), finally ending in Broca's area.

ANGULAR GYRUS

Included as a significant component of the language model is the angular gyrus (AG) in the left parietal lobe. Joseph J. Dejerine (1849-1917) suggested that this area was one of two sites associated with the reading disorder alexia.

SUPRAMARGINAL GYRUS

Anterior to the angular gyrus is the supramarginal gyrus (SMG), curving around the posterior end of the sylvian fissure. Together with the AG, it is known as the inferior parietal lobule. Sensory information is analyzed and integrated in this area, which is thought to play an important role in perception. Lesions of the SMG in the dominant hemisphere have been associated with agraphia, or writing disorders.

NEW UNDERSTANDING OF THE STRUCTURES INVOLVED WITH LANGUAGE

We know from fMRI studies that mature brains are organized into functional networks that work together to support cognitive and linguistic functions. Fair[16] and colleagues studied the functional network organization in subjects across an age span of 7 to 31 years of age. They found that like mature brains, the developing brain in children is also organized into this kind of network but that the "small world" network in the younger brains was organized primarily by anatomic proximity. As the brain matures, the proximal networks become less segregated and become more integrated into regional connections. That is, we develop from more locally organized neural networks to the more distributed networks discussed earlier.

When we look at the neural circuitry for language in the mature brain, we are quite aware of the regional connections forming the perisylvian zone. Friederici and Gierhan[17] provide an excellent summary of the macrocircuits for language that have been suggested by fMRI studies. These circuits include the structures highlighted by Geschwind's model but also include other regional connections not discussed in earlier literature as supporting language. Figure 9-5 shows the regions for distributed networks supporting language.

This model provides substantiation for Wernicke's model from more than 100 years ago, which asserted that neural circuitry supporting language must connect brain regions in the inferior frontal cortex with regions in the superior temporal cortex. The studies reviewed by Friederici and Gierhan summate to support the

FIGURE **9-5**
Language-relevant brain regions and fiber tracts (schematic and condensed view of the left hemisphere). The dorsal pathway connecting dorsal premotor (dPMC) with posterior temporal cortex (pMTG/STG) involves the SLF III and/or the SLF II and the SLF-tp (discussed in detail later); the dorsal pathway connecting Brodmann's area (BA) 44 with the posterior STG involves the AF. The ventral pathway connecting the frontal cortex (FC), that is, BA 45 and others, with the temporal (TC), the parietal (PC), and the occipital (OC) cortices, involves the inferior-frontal-occipital fasciculus (also called the extreme capsule fiber system); the ventral pathway connecting the anterior inferior FC (aIFC), that is, BA 47 and others, and the FOP, with the anterior TC (aTC), involves the UF. (Modified from Friederici, A. D., & Gierhan, S. M. E. [2013]. The language network. *Current Opinion in Neurobiology, 23,* 250-254.)

existence of two dorsal and two ventral pathways each serving different functions in language.

Dorsal Pathways

These two fiber pathways identified have been discussed by Geschwind: the arcuate fasciculus (AF) and part of the superior longitudinal fasciculus (SLF). They are not easily distinguished and sometimes are placed together in discussion. The AF connects the posterior portion of Broca's area, the pars opercularis (Brodmann's area 44), with the posterior and middle superior temporal gyrus (STG). Functional imaging studies using the area 44 as a *region of interest* (ROI) for processing of complex syntactic sequences found direct fiber connections to the STG via the AF. This higher order function of processing syntax was found for the AF in both artificial grammar paradigms and natural language and is supported by lesion studies as well.

The SLF was not mentioned as a critical structure in Geschwind's model of language and the perisylvian zone. In the traditional model, the AF was an important

structure and was considered critical for auditory to motor connection for sentence repetition. More recent literature has begun to contradict this and to discuss the SLF's role in sentence repetition. The bundle of fibers we call the SLF has been found in macaque monkeys as actually consisting of three separate parallel components, called SLF I, II, and III. This has been proposed as true for humans as well,[55] documenting fiber bundles deemed SLF-tp, SLF-II, and SLF-III. The SLF-tp connects the temporal cortex to the inferior parietal cortex. The SLF-II connects the angular gyrus with the frontal cortex and, the SLF-III connects the supramarginal gyrus to the inferior frontal cortex. Studies of white matter damage in humans support the involvement of these fiber pathways when deficits in sentence repetition are present.

Ventral Pathways

According to the fMRI data reviewed by Friederici and Gierhan, there are at least two ventral fiber connection pathways between the frontal cortex and the temporal cortex. These two pathways are the unci-nated fasciculus (UF) and the inferior-frontal-occipital fasciculus (IFOF). The IFOF is sometimes referred to as the extreme capsule fiber system (ECFS). The UF connects the anterior frontal cortex with the anterior temporal cortex. The IFOF provides the connection between the frontal cortex and the three posterior cortical areas, the temporal, parietal, and occipital cortices. With these pathways, areas in the anterior frontal cortex that are activated during semantic and syntactic processes such as semantic judgment, categorization, lexical-semantic access, and sentence plausibility are linked with the posterior areas in the temporal, parietal, and occipital cortices involved with lexical or sentence semantic processing. In addition to participating in semantic processing, the UF connections between the frontal operculum and the temporal cortex have been found to support syntactic processing for local phrase structure and for sentences that are syntactically simple. The connections of the ventral pathway also support the framework proposed by Hargoort,[23] which included the left inferior frontal gyrus as an important area for language.

SUBCORTICAL LANGUAGE MECHANISMS

The strictly cortical model of language mechanisms has been questioned numerous times because patients with what appeared to be only subcortical lesions were found to have language problems. Wilder G. Penfield and Lamar Roberts were among the first investigators to present evidence for possible subcortical mechanisms for language and speech.[41] They suggested that the pulvinar and ventrolateral nuclei of the thalamus serve as relay stations between Broca's and Wernicke's areas. They demonstrated massive fiber tracts to and from the thalamus and the major cortical speech and language areas. In addition, direct electrical stimulation of the left pulvinar and ventrolateral nuclei has produced naming problems.

Subcortical aphasias have been reported since the nineteenth century, but their existence has remained controversial. Although the language disturbance observed after thalamic infarct or damage to other subcortical mechanisms (caudate, globus pallidus, internal capsule) was originally believed to be a direct result of damage to a structure that must be somehow responsible for language, better imaging capability has shown that to be incorrect. New explanations have recently been put forth that describe the complicated nature of subcortical-cortical connections and their influence on language processing and production when those connections are interrupted by damage to certain subcortical structures.

THALAMIC LESIONS

Wallesch and Papagno[58] suggested that subcortical structures involved in a cortical-subcortical loop serve to monitor and select lexical input, which is then sent forward to the anterior language cortex in a modular fashion. The lexical alternatives from which the loop selects information originate in the posterior language cortex of the left hemisphere. In 1992 Crosson[12] proposed that cortical-striatal-pallidal-thalamic-cortical loops are involved in language. He suggested that the loop triggers the release of language segments at the appropriate time after semantic monitoring, thus serving more of a regulatory than an information-processing function. Crosson also theorized that the thalamus arouses the anterior language cortex and transmits semantic segments from the anterior to the posterior cortex for monitoring. These theories were early indictments of the assumption that the language deficits found in patients with thalamic stroke or hemorrhage were directly related to the damage to the thalamus itself. This premise of language disorder being caused directly by dysfunction of the thalamus alone has been shown to be essentially incorrect. Rather, the language disorder (aphasia) appears to result from the disruption of *cortical* function caused by the thalamic damage. It is an indirect cause resulting in a neural system disruption. Nadeau and Crosson[35] present an extensive analysis and discussion of the mechanisms summarized here.

Chapters 2 and 5 discuss the primary relay functions of the thalamic nuclei. A vast number of relays are synapsing in the thalamus, going from peripheral sensory nerve organs to the cortex. Also mentioned are extensive relays from the cortex to the thalamus. Most of the connections of thalamic nuclei and cortical areas are two-way, with numerous projections back to the thalamus from the cortex, as well as the more typically discussed projections from the thalamus to the cortex. In relation to language function, the two most interesting thalamocortical loops relay from the dorsomedial nucleus and the pulvinar-lateral posterior nucleus of the thalamus. The dorsomedial nucleus relays information originating from prefrontal cortex areas involved in executive functioning as well as some subcortical areas. This neural information originates from these areas and is relayed back to them after processing in the thalamus. For the pulvinar-lateral posterior nucleus, projections are from the frontal, temporal, and parietal cortices and back.

The specific function of the thalamus in language and cognition is now thought to be not a simple relay mechanism in the neural pathway but a regulated or gated relay mechanism. A cogent and lengthy discussion of these mechanisms, their purported function, and relevance to treatment can be found in Nadeau and Rothi.[37] To summarize their points, deeper discussion of the structure of the thalamus is required. PDP, as discussed earlier in this chapter, also plays an important role.

Most of the thalamus has a layer of cells enveloping it that forms what is called the thalamic reticular nucleus. These cells do not send their axons out but rather send them back into the thalamus and synapse on either relay neurons or on inhibitory interneurons. The reticular neurons themselves employ gamma-aminobutyric acid (GABA) and are inhibitory. Thus the action of these neurons can be to facilitate transmission to the cortex (through inhibition of the inhibitory action of the interneurons) or to block transmission to the cortex (by inhibiting the relay neurons).

These reticular neurons are under the control of (or regulated by) a number of brain systems, with two important ones being the reticular formation of the midbrain and projections from the cerebral cortex. Global and nonselective are said to describe the effect of the midbrain on thalamic transmission. With high levels of arousal comes a strong excitation of the thalamic cells, causing inhibition of the interneurons and consequently allowing ready transmission through the thalamus in an unregulated fashion. During low arousal (with sleep and coma being the most common examples), little can quell the action of the inhibitory interneurons, and most transmission through the thalamus is blocked. Compared with the global and nonselective effect of the midbrain is the effect of the cortical-thalamic-cortical projections, which are thought to be local and selective. Thalamic transmissions from specific nuclei are believed to be selectively gated to the cortex. Nadeau and Rothi,[37] acknowledging that errors do occur in localization of stroke damage, indicate that lesion data support that patients found to have aphasia after thalamic lesions show primary involvement of structures related to this gating mechanism of the thalamus. Thus it is proposed that rather than damage to the thalamus per se causing the dysfunction, the deleterious effect on cortical language mechanisms upstream results in the symptoms seen in these patients with thalamic lesions.

In the proposal developed by Nadeau and Rothi,[37] the thalamus is involved in normal language functioning by regulating the engagement of certain neural networks in different association cortices to participate in lexical semantic access. They theorize that the cortical-thalamic disruption that occurs in the presence of damage to certain parts of the thalamus impairs the cortical network that supports declarative memory (knowledge of facts and events). The language function most dependent on declarative knowledge and memory is naming, which is, in neurolinguistic terms, lexical-semantic access. The patients with subcortical damage affecting the thalamus show the most difficulty with naming, whereas most of the other aspects (grammar, comprehension, articulation, and repetition) are maintained.

NONTHALAMIC SUBCORTICAL LESIONS

In addition to thalamic lesions causing aphasia, lesions in the internal capsule, striatum, and globus pallidus also have been documented as seeming to give rise to language disturbances. These descriptions are discussed in Chapter 10. Again, the language disturbance documented in these patients is most likely caused by cortical dysfunction that is an indirect result of the subcortical damage. Metter et al. (1988)[31] found that a subcortical lesion is accompanied by remote hypometabolism, indirectly affecting the left perisylvian area. This was found to be related to language functioning in the patients studied. In their study of patients with striatocapsular lesions (head of the caudate nucleus, anterior half of the putamen, and anterior limb of the internal capsule in these cases), Nadeau and Crosson[35] found that the infarct was caused by the spread of the thrombus or the movement of the embolus into the portion of the middle cerebral artery that serves the lenticulostriate arteries, which perfuse these structures, naturally resulting in their cellular death. However, beyond this effect, a reduced flow of blood to the middle cerebral artery branches serving the overlying cortex was also discovered. If the collateral circulation mechanisms through the anterior cerebral and posterior cerebral arteries are viable, the cortex will be minimally affected in function. With poor collateral structure and operation, however, a much larger stroke will occur. Despite this, the damage to the cortical region that takes place through the secondary mechanism of infarct initially is not visible on imaging studies, though cortical atrophy can be imaged later.[58] Because the mechanism of damage to cortical areas is much the same as in direct cortical damage, the resulting language disorders will predictably be of many types depending on the site of cortical hypoperfusion.

RIGHT HEMISPHERE

The role of the right hemisphere in communication had been trivialized until relatively recently. It had been referred to as the silent, or minor, hemisphere, while much of the research on the central language mechanism in the left hemisphere was being done through studies of aphasia. The right hemisphere was acknowledged as having a major role in visual perception and as having a special (perhaps minor) role in visuospatial processing. In the 1960s the technique of commissur-otomy (disconnecting the two hemispheres by severing part of the corpus callosum) was found to be successful in controlling seizures if the corpus callosum was almost completely severed and the two hemispheres almost completely disconnected. This resulted in the research on split-brain patients (see Chapter 2) and heralded a new interest in right brain function. Evidence from hemispherectomies and callosal sections suggests that the right hemisphere can assume some language func-tion, although the extent of recovery may be limited. In adult patients with hemispherectomy with no cortical tissue remaining, language behavior is similar to that in a person with extensive infarction of the perisylvian area and a global aphasia. What language remains appears to be completely the product of the right hemisphere.

Research began later on right hemisphere function in non–brain-damaged patients. These studies have indicated that the right hemisphere differs from the left in discrete functions and in its role in communication and cognition. Myers[34] reports that research began to show that the right hemisphere was important in visual processing as well as holistic, nonlinear, and parallel processing. Important to information synthesis, the right hemisphere seemed to be superior in seeing the "big picture" or the gestalt and in incorporating and dealing with novel stimuli. The current concept of right hemisphere functions shows it to be superior for the following:

- Visuospatial processing and visual perception
- Integration of different types of incoming stimuli
- Comprehending and producing emotion in the face and voice
- Maintaining a normal state of arousal and alertness
- Attending to the left side of space
- Attention in general, selecting what to attend to and maintaining attention or shifting attention

At approximately the same time that this interest in right hemisphere processes was burgeoning, the con-cept of communication began to change and expand beyond the traditional informational processing input-output model. Communication style, nonverbal aspects of communication, as well as language use or the pragmatic aspects of language, were now of interest to clinicians and researchers. SLPs, linguists, and neuropsy-chologists began to look at discourse versus just words, phrases, and sentences and to put much more emphasis on meaning (both literal and implied). As in research with patients with left hemisphere damage, the com-munication abilities of patients with right hemisphere damage were studied and analyzed. As Myers discusses throughout her book, when studying patients with right hemisphere damage who have trouble communicating normally (not all patients have difficulty), the problems

clearly are not language-based in the traditional sense; the patients have problems with communication in the broader context. The problems may be complex and are just beginning to be understood. Communication problems of the patient with right hemisphere damage are discussed in Chapter 10.

The right hemisphere is known to become more active in language processing after left hemisphere damage to language areas. Some treatment methods, such as melodic intonation therapy, have tried to capi-talize on this neural effort by homologous areas in the nondominant hemisphere. Some evidence from **tran-scranial magnetic stimulation (TMS)** studies shows that this activity in the right hemisphere can be actually interfering with language recovery in the left hemi-sphere.[38] Improvement in naming in a person with chronic, global aphasia was noted and maintained over time after TMS treatment was targeted to inhibit function of the pars triangularis area in the right hemi-sphere. A negative effect occurred, however, when the inhibitory stimulation was applied to the posterior por-tion (pars opercularis) of the homologous Broca's area in the right hemisphere. Stimulation to other areas in the right hemisphere did not improve speech or lan-guage performance. TMS was hypothesized to suppress overactivity in the right hemisphere area of the pars triangularis and consequently improved interhemi-spheric modulation of semantic processing for nam-ing pictures. Much interesting research remains to be done on the role of the right hemisphere in normal communication and recovery of language after brain insult.

ROLE OF COGNITION IN COMMUNICATION

As Chapey[8] notes in her discussion of cognitive inter-vention in aphasia, the definition of cognition varies greatly across the speech-language literature as well as that of other professions. An acceptable generic defini-tion often used is that **cognition** is the act or process of knowing, perceiving, or remembering.[32] Examin-ing cognition at work is examining "functional mental events" that take place during behavior. These events are such things as perception, recognition, reasoning, judgment, concept formation, and problem solving. In laying the groundwork for cognitive communica-tive evaluation and intervention with traumatic brain-injured patients, Gillis[19] discusses four key aspects of cognition as critical for the clinician to understand: (1) attention and information processing, (2) memory, (3) reasoning and problem solving, and (4) metacognition and executive functions. The following sections briefly describe these functions and their neurologic bases.

Attention and Information Processing

The word *attention* has many definitions. This text accepts attention as being the capacity to focus on particular stimuli over time and to manipulate flexibly the information.[47] This definition implies that an active response occurs rather than simply reflexive behavior. For attention to occur as a process, the organism must be in a general physiologic state of readiness, called arousal. Arousal, or as some have termed it, alertness, is the initial stage of attention. Arousal is mediated by the reticular activating system and is subject to internal and external influences. For attention to take place, perception must also occur. Perception is the recognition of sensory input. Gillis points out that it is often difficult to separate and distinguish perception from other aspects of cognition.

When studying attention, the organism's attentional capacity or information processing capacity and the capability for attentional control must be considered. Attentional capacity is the amount of information that can be attended to at any one time. Attentional control is the process of guiding or directing this attentional capacity where it is needed. This control may be automatic in process, such as when overlearned tasks are performed, or it may be controlled processing, which is used for novel or complex stimuli. The latter is conscious processing.

Some simply characterize attention as either intentional or reactive. However, some researchers and clinicians divide attention into different subcomponents because attentional mechanisms are seemingly not damaged in an all-or-none manner in brain injury. Solberg and Mateer break attention down into five component areas: focused attention, sustained attention, selective attention, alternating attention, and divided attention.

Nadeau et al.[36] present attention as a part of the more general neural process they call **selective engagement**. They describe this process in engineering terms as bringing certain neural networks (depending on the task) "online" while taking others "offline" because they are not needed for that task. This is part of the self-organizing system of the brain. Two systems are said to be critical for many of the higher level tasks that require selective engagement. These are corticocortical systems and corticothalamocortical systems. The latter was previously discussed in the section on subcortical language mechanisms. This gated relay function of the thalamus is thought to be part of the mechanism that allows the cortex to engage one neural network selectively over another.

The corticocortical system actively participating in selective engagement (a large part of which is manifest in attention) is thought to reside in the dorsolateral prefrontal cortex. This part of the cortex is the supramodal cortex involved in planning and other executive functions. It also is critical to the orienting response, allowing movement of the eyes, head, and perhaps whole body to attend to something. The neural basis of attention is strongly related to the neural basis of the orienting response. This area of the cortex seems to process the significance of neural activity communicated from posterior association areas. Studies of lesioned monkeys also indicate that this prefrontal area allows the engagement to be maintained neurally and thus process information in working memory. The next chapter discusses the attention and memory problems of patients with closed-head injury. These patients have frequently had damage impairing function of the prefrontal cortex.

Memory

Dudai[13] defines learning as an experience-dependent (including changes related to maturation, injury, and fatigue) generation of enduring internal representations or modification in these representations. Memory is the retention of these experience-dependent changes over time. Separating memory from attention or from the other aspects of cognition is difficult. Memory is not a unitary construct. Varying temporal domains exist, such as short-term and long-term memory, and different stages of information processing are necessary before a memory is constructed. The first step in information processing leading to memory is a sensory store, with visual and auditory information storage being the most familiar. Some refer to the sensory storage as a sensory register because it is extremely brief in duration. Some perceptual analysis may take place at this stage, or it may simply be a brief holding tank for information that will need attention.

Sensory registration or storage initially occurs in the process of encoding or information processing for memory. Some level of meaning is extracted during encoding. A person's associations, experiences, and perceptions influence this extraction. These are unique to each individual, although everyone shares some associations. During encoding, the information is organized, and the level of analysis and organization is important to its storage and later retrieval. Two main types of storage exist in many theories of memory processing: short-term memory and long-term memory. **Short-term memory** is temporary in nature, and the brain has limited capacity for this storage. Information in short-term memory must be continually acted on (rehearsed, imaged, etc.) or the memory will decay in a brief time. The decay time posed by the research literature varies from 30 seconds to a few minutes.[19] Short-term memory and working memory are considered synonymous terms by some; others consider short-term memory as the storage site and working memory as the active processing to hold the information. **Long-term memory** is the permanent storage of information with unlimited capacity. The two primary types of knowledge store in memory are referred to as **procedural memory** (also known as implicit memory) and **declarative memory** (also known as explicit memory or propositional memory). Information thought to be stored in procedural memory is an integral part of rule-based skills and behaviors, and this type of memory can be accessed only through performance of learned behaviors. This primarily involves motor behaviors, but acquisition of some mental behaviors is also included. Nadeau and Rothi[37] proposed the concept that grammatical function depends on procedural rather than declarative memory and therefore may require a different approach in treatment than other deficits, such as semantic access problems. Declarative memory, both semantic and episodic types, is directly accessible through recognition and recall tasks. These memories may be brought to mind verbally or visually.

Rahmann and Rahmann[42] point out that information processing and storage are immensely complex processes and that many factors still stand in the way of research aimed at localizing memory. Some of the factors listed are (1) the exceedingly complex organization of the brain with its several hundred trillion synapses, (2) the total length of all neuronal fibers in the brain (similar in length to the distance from the earth to the moon and back), and (3) the enormous number of neurons activated during each memory event. According to these authors, "memory is ultimately stored in the form of molecular changes in the synapses of the neuronal structures involved in perception, analysis, and further processing of acquired (learned) information" (p. 264). This storage is in the brain and spinal cord, not in the sensory or neuronal pathways. Research on the visual system has suggested that memory storage events may occur through reciprocal feedback mechanisms between neuronal representations in the cortex and neuronal assemblies in subcortical regions. The formation of a memory is likely caused by an alteration in the strength of neural connection. The connections are enhanced when the neurons are simultaneously active.

The two subcortical regions that participate in memory formation are thought to be the hippocampus and the amygdala. A system in the basal forebrain depends on acetylcholine transmission (a cholinergic system) to assign a certain value to the pattern of neural activity being accessed. This is a crucial task of the limbic system and the hippocampus in particular. The limbic system "judges" the neural activity regarding import and communicates this to the rostral cholinergic system that, in turn, supplies cholinergic input to the targeted cortical area. The message to the cortical area from the limbic system is that this information is important and worth learning. Chemical changes can then be facilitated in the targeted cortical area and the hippocampus that produce permanent changes in neural connectivity and establish that representation in memory. The amygdala may partially be responsible for feelings or emotions that accompany the processing of certain sensory input or certain memories.

Reasoning and Problem Solving

Reasoning is the process of evaluating information to come to a conclusion.[19] Two types of reasoning are discussed and evaluated clinically. In *deductive reasoning*, a number of premises, facts, and opinions are considered, and a conclusion is made about one thing (person, fact, circumstance, etc.). In *inductive reasoning* generalization from one fact or instance is turned into a broad interpretation. In most cases problem solving and reasoning are simultaneous mental activities performed while trying to reach a conclusion needed to solve a problem. Guilford and Hoepfner[22] think of problem solving as having five steps: preparation, analysis, production, verification, and reapplication. These steps obviously point to problem solving (and reasoning) as being a multifaceted process. Impairments in problem solving and reasoning are often associated with lesions in prefrontal regions of the brain, although subcortical damage also can cause difficulties.[56] A study using rats with lesioned orbitofrontal cortex demonstrated that this area appears to be important for decision making.[44] When faced with a problem to solve when a previously learned strategy did not work and a new way was needed, the neural firing rate in the orbitofrontal cortex of the lesioned animals was slow and sluggish. Consequently, they were not able to change behavior efficiently to accomplish a task under new demands. The researchers hypothesized that the orbitofrontal cortex seems to process visual and other informational cues that help make decisions in the presence of new information. Damage to this area of the brain may cause persons to have difficulty adapting their behavior to new situations despite being able to learn new information in a fairly normal way. A recent study of social problem-solving skills of a large group of persons with focal brain damage suggested that social problem solving, psychometric intelligence, and emotional intelligence are supported by a shared network of frontal, temporal, and parietal regions with white matter tracts that connected and bound them into this shared network.[5]

Metacognition and Executive Functions

Metacognition and executive functioning were not routinely discussed by SLPs until recently, when work with patients with cognitive communicative disorders became more widespread. **Metacognition** is knowledge about all cognitive processes and involves the monitoring of these processes.[19] Metacognition, then, refers to the seemingly subconscious ability to know how and when to attend, remember, and organize information and recognize and solve certain problems with certain strategies.

Executive functions refer to the skills human beings use to carry out nonroutine processes. Executive functions are thought to be mediated by the prefrontal cortex in the frontal lobes. These functions include anticipation, goal direction, planning, monitoring of internal and external events, and interpretation and use of feedback. The fact that most nonroutine processes are carried out in a deliberate, coordinated manner and that human beings are typically self-regulating and able to inhibit inappropriate behaviors are testament to the executive system of the frontal lobes. The prefrontal cortex of the frontal lobes is composed of

a heteromodal cortex that integrates information from both unimodal and other heteromodal areas. The frontal lobes have multiple direct and indirect connections to all other areas of the brain. They are well positioned and equipped to perform this important central executive officer job. Box 9-2 summarizes the four key concepts that the clinician should consider when performing a cognitive assessment.

Changing the Brain

Any neurology text that is written is behind in its acknowledgment and explanations of new discoveries and research the day it is surrendered for publication. In the past two decades the research findings and the technology enabling this science to proceed has exploded. Although still slow, the transmission of these findings to others is much more rapid than was once possible. Many more journals are being published, some online,

---

BOX 9-2

Cognitive Factors in Communication

Attention and Information Processing

- Attention requires a certain level of arousal (alertness) as well as perception of sensory input
- Attentional capacity refers to the amount of information one can hold; it is directed by attentional control mechanisms
- Concept of attention can be considered as reactive in nature or as part of general neural processes described as selective engagement
- Thought to reside in dorsolateral prefrontal cortex, which also is involved in planning and other executive functions, the orienting response, and additional executive functioning

Memory

- Retention and recall of internal representations of experience-dependent changes over time
- Visual and auditory sensory storage that can be broken into two types of information processing:
  - Short-term memory—temporary storage that begins to decay in 30 seconds to a few minutes
  - Long-term memory—permanent storage of unlimited capacity
- Two kinds of information stored in memory:
  - Procedural (implicit) memory—recalled from performance of repetitive, learned motor behaviors over time

- Declarative (explicit) memory—recalled through verbal or visual sensory recognition and recall cues

Reasoning and Problem Solving

- Two types of reasoning:
  - Deductive reasoning—evaluation based on a number of facts to create a conclusion about one thing (person, fact, event, etc.)
  - Inductive reasoning—evaluation based on generalization of one fact to create a broad interpretation and conclusion
- Problem solving involves evaluation based on reasoning and application to produce a conclusion
- Lesions to the prefrontal and subcortical areas have been shown to impair both reasoning and problem-solving processes

Metacognition and Executive Functioning

- Metacognition refers to the ability to recognize how and when to use reasoning and problem-solving skills to solve specific problems with the most effective cognitive strategies
- Executive functions include anticipation, goal direction, planning, monitoring of internal and external events, and feedback interpretation
- Frontal lobes carry out metacognitive and executive functioning processes

and many more conferences and other interactions are taking place. This engages other scientists and advances even more discovery.

A text such as this, with the task of teaching students the names, locations, and primary purpose and physiologic mechanisms of parts of the brain most important to a certain function (in this case, communication), is of necessity simplistic in nature. It tends to present the brain as developing over time into an essentially hardwired structure. This is not the impression that students should take away. The mature brain is actually a somewhat flexible organ, capable of more change and development than previously accepted by scientists and medical practitioners.

NEUROPLASTICITY AND NEUROGENESIS

Neuroplasticity

Just how much neuroplasticity the brain is capable of demonstrating has been surprising. Studies of congenitally blind persons who use Braille have demonstrated that the visual cortex, along with the somatosensory cortex, is activated when Braille is being read.[43] An early study[40] showed the same kind of reorganization in the brains of adults deaf since birth or early childhood when evoked potentials were measured in response to a flash of light. The response of persons who were deaf to the flash was stronger than that of normal-hearing subjects and was registered from the auditory cortex rather than the visual cortex. This indicated that the brain's auditory region, denied of its normal input, had somehow begun picking up signals from the retinas. Visual cortex activity has been found in blind adult subjects when verbal processing tasks are studied.[3] When the visual cortex was inhibited in these subjects, performance deteriorated, confirming the primary participation of the visual cortex.[2] This may help explain why blind children are often found to be delayed in language development.

Many studies wait to be done based on the belief and increasingly documented evidence that brain development can be enhanced through structured experiences. Ways to be more effective in the educational system, train new skills in adults, and maintain optimal cognitive function into advanced age must be found. Further research in neuroscience will pave the way for this progress.

Neurogenesis

Through studies duplicating earlier findings in animals, scientists now accept that there is **neurogenesis** (birth of new neurons) in some parts of the adult brain[7,45,57]. In most mammals there is well-documented neurogenesis for neurons in the olfactory bulb. However, humans are unique in this aspect because there are few if any new neurons in the olfactory area in the postnatal period. The evolutionary decrease in dependence on smell and increased dependence on cognitive and social brain areas for human survival is likely related to the finding of no neurogenesis in the olfactory bulb of human brains.

Neurogenesis has been documented for two areas of the adult human brain: the hippocampus[14] and the striatum.[15] The neurons are able to generate because the brain has a reserve of neural stem cells that can differentiate themselves into neurons or other cells of the nervous system. In humans these stem cells or neuroblasts are born in the hippocampus for neurogenesis there. For striatal neurons, they appear to be derived from the subventricular zone (see Chapter 11) and migrate to the striatum. These new neurons can make new connections and establish themselves into functional circuits that already exist, enhancing the structure as well as the function. Thus even the adult brain is now believed to demonstrate neuroplasticity, although certainly not to as great an extent as that of a young child.

Neurogenesis in the hippocampus appears to be a continuous process[7] with the newborn neurons having specialized electrophysiologic properties for about a month. After this period of time, they cannot be distinguished from older neurons.[33] Bergmann and Frisén[7] discuss that these new neurons participate in a process called *pattern separation*. The neural process of pattern separation allows the brain to discriminate similar experiences and organize them for storage as distinct memories. They use the example of humans being able not only to remember parking a car in a parking lot but remembering where it was parked this time. This process, as you can see from that example, is critical for human adaptation to our increasingly complex environment.

To date, the functional purpose of neurogenesis in the striatum of the mature brain has not been established.[15] The striatum plays an important role in planning and modulating movement, in cognitive flexibility, and in reward/motivation cycles.[15] The adult neurogenesis may help account for individual functionality in these areas with neural integration of these cells. The rate of neurogenesis in the striatum is low under homeostatic conditions for the body and brain. However, the rate increases in response to pathologic conditions, adding small numbers of neurons to the striatum over a long period of time. Investigation of how these new striatal neurons could be used to promote renewal of function in diseases that attack striatal neurons such as Huntington's chorea or in disorders such as schizophrenia or addiction, which alter striatal response to reward could be important to finding treatment modalities for these illnesses.

RECOVERY IN THE DAMAGED BRAIN

Although not discussed in this chapter, there is evidence for generation of new cells in the mature brain outside of neurons: new neuroglial cells. Oligodendrocytes account for most of the new glial cells produced in the adult brain. The normal function of many nerve fibers depends on myelination of those fibers, as you will remember. As new connections and new fibers appear in the brain, new oligodendrocytes are necessary for new production of myelin to wrap around these fibers enhancing signal transmission. Myelin can be regenerated by these cells to restore some neurologic function. Disease processes may cause incomplete regeneration, resulting in the death of these fibers that have lost myelin. You see this process in action in such diseases as advanced multiple sclerosis.

Astrocytes are another type of glial cell for which there is evidence for limited new generation in the mature nervous system.[7] However, after local injury there is commonly a large increase of astrocytes generated by neural stem cells or by duplication of existing astrocytes. This generation of astrocytes in the damaged brain may not be a positive factor, however. The cells will combine with connective tissue cells and form scar tissue. This scar tissue may then prevent the regrowth of axons, for example, after stroke.[46]

SLPs must believe that the brain can change and reorganize. If they did not, no one would show up to work every day to treat clients attempting to improve their communication skills. Research in neuroscience supports the belief that a permanent change in behavior does involve a change in brain organization. This does not mean change only in the strength of connections in the neural networks involved in the behavior, as takes place when memories are formed. It also may mean a change in where in the brain these connections are made or in which pathways are used—a type of "rezoning" or reassignment of the duties of cells in a certain part of the brain. With better technology and more elegant research design, perhaps we will one day be able to know exactly what changes are taking place in the brain during successful (or, in some cases, unsuccessful) treatment for a communication disorder.

One new treatment method that has resulted from the curiosity of a neuroscientist about brain reorganization and its usefulness in rehabilitation is **constraint-induced therapy (CIT)**, introduced by Taub et al.[53] for improving the use of the paralyzed arm after a stroke. In CIT the functional arm is restrained in a sling, with the hand covered to prevent use. In the initial study, the patients who were 1 year or more poststroke received intensive treatment for 10 days and performed all tasks for most of their waking hours with the paralyzed limb as best they could. At the end of the 10-day period, clients had regained considerable functional use of the formerly paralyzed limb, whereas control subjects who did not receive treatment showed no change. Taub hypothesized a "use-dependent cortical reorganization." Investigation using TMS to map the cortical activity before and after CIT proved Taub's hypothesis.[27] Treatment resulted in improved motor functioning and caused the area of the motor cortex controlling the hand to enlarge with recruitment of more neurons in the motor cortex, particularly those adjacent to the area that originally controlled the arm. With more extensive damage to the motor cortex, neurons in the premotor cortex or even in the opposite hemisphere are hypothesized to participate in the network supporting the improved function.

The strong evidence for success with CIT for paralyzed limbs of stroke patients[54] led to interest in CIT for improvement of communication in persons with aphasia. Several studies were initially performed in Europe, showing that constraint-induced aphasia therapy involving the principles of prevention of compensatory communication and massed practice produced significant and stable improvement. Changes in performance on standardized testing as well as in communication as measured by patient and family report and communicative effectiveness ratings were all significantly greater than for patients who participated in the same amount of therapy with more traditional treatment methods allowing compensatory communication use.[30] A pilot study from the Houston Veterans Administration Hospital also demonstrated more consistent improvement of patients receiving constraint-induced language therapy compared with more traditional treatment, although both groups had positive outcomes.[29] Since that time several studies have been published with varying methodology and outcomes. A controlled randomized trial of CILT versus no therapy on a group of 24 patients with chronic aphasia was reported in 2014 with the CILT being provided over 10 daily 4-hour sessions.[52] With this intensity and length of therapy, no significant differences on various language measures were found between the groups at the end of the study.

Students interested in more in-depth study of the brain's capacity for change are encouraged to begin by reading a notable published book by the science columnist for the *Wall Street Journal*, Sharon Begley.[6] At first glance, the book's title, *Train Your Mind, Change Your Brain*, seems to suggest that this is one of the pseudoscience self-help texts that are stacked high in bookstores. However, the book documents the collaboration between leading scientists, many of whom are referenced in this text, and the Dali Lama, which resulted in a landmark study at the University of Wisconsin on brain reorganization and differences in monks who are highly advanced in meditation.[28] It also provides a highly readable summary of the history of neuroscientific study of brain–behavior relations and how the brain is transformed by the environment, experience, and thought.

This chapter ends on a positive note for the clinician because of the work of neuroscientists to prove that the brain can be changed by chemical and surgical intervention as well as by behavioral treatments that replace or supplement other treatments. Chapter 10 describes some of the acquired disorders of communication that adults may experience when damage occurs to language processing areas of the brain. It is hoped that clinicians will not only learn from the literature of neuroscience but will continue to contribute findings that support enhancement of brain function even after the brain has been damaged.

Synopsis of Clinical Information and Applications for the Speech-Language Pathologist

- Six layers comprise the neocortex, consisting primarily of pyramidal cells with axons and dendrites ascending and descending from one layer to another.
- Studies using isotropic fractionating have suggested that the ratio of neurons to nonneurons in the brain may be more equal in number than originally thought.
- Synaptic organization is concerned with the way input neurons, projection neurons, and interneurons organize themselves and connect through synapses, becoming neural circuits.
- Dendritic connections and subunits within microcircuits form local circuits in regions of the brain. The connections between these regions and their circuits account for behaviors.
- These connections form "small world communities" at the microlevel. At the macrolevel, the neuronal processes expand out for long-range connections.
- The brain's vast circuitry is made possible by convergence and divergence of synapses in the nervous system.
- Most postsynaptic sites in the cerebellum, basal ganglia, and cortex are on dendritic spines, increasing the surface area and probably enabling rapid signal processing and long-term potentiation.
- A pattern-associator network allows the input patterns to be transformed into output patterns (e.g., sequences of letters transformed into spoken words read aloud).
- All the primary association areas are thought to be collections of pattern-associator networks in which neural representations (percepts, concepts, etc.) are formed.
- The first mapping of cellular connection was done on a nematode in 1986.

- Human brain connectivity is being traced through advanced diffusion tensor imaging methods through a U.S. government–funded multicenter study called the Human Connectome.
- The pattern of neural connections strengthened into a representation is difficult to lose completely. Rather, some components of the representation may be activated, although others are not, degrading the representation. This is called *graceful degradation*. This often allows people to deal successfully with ambiguous or partial information.
- Learning is the brain increasing the efficiency of synaptic connections.
- Synaptic connections within networks are strengthened by synchronous firing.
- Synaptic connections in neural networks are the physical foundation of learning and memory and account for Hebbian learning.
- Learning requires active participation by multiple brain areas, including the reticular network, sensory and/or motor association areas, thalamocortical circuitry, fusiform area, hippocampus and other medial temporal lobe structures, lateral and superior temporal lobe, cerebellar and striatum circuitry, and diffuse areas of the neocortex.
- Geschwind's model of language, based in large part on the work of Wernicke, is a traditional localization or connectionism model but has held up over time and is not negated by neural network theory or by evidence from neuroimaging.
- Geschwind's model emphasizes Broca's area, Wernicke's area, the arcuate fasciculus, and parietal areas of the angular and supramarginal gyrus. These areas comprise the perisylvian language zone. Recent research has identified other connections laid out in a ventral and dorsal stream within the perisylvian zone.
- Language disorders may appear to result from damage to subcortical structures, especially the thalamus

and parts of the basal ganglia. However, research into the etiology of the language difficulty has demonstrated that the language disorders result from the indirect effects on cortical language areas.

- Hypoperfusion of the cortex follows basal ganglia and capsular damage because of reduced flow through the lenticulostriate arteries. The language symptoms depend on what area of the perisylvian zone is affected.
- The right hemisphere is dominant for visuospatial processing, integration of different kinds of stimuli, attention, intention, and holistic processing. Right hemisphere damage affects communication in a broader sense with discourse and communication style as well as processing of more intangible input (e.g., humor, sarcasm).
- Cognition is the process of knowing, perceiving or remembering. It is the examination of mental events, such as perception, reasoning, problem solving, and concept formation.
- Four key aspects of cognition important to the treatment of patients with cognitive-linguistic disorders are (1) attention and information processing, (2) memory, (3) reasoning and problem solving, and (4) metacognition and executive functioning. The study of these cognitive functions involves the dorsolateral cortex, the hippocampus and amygdala, orbitofrontal cortex, and the greater association area in the frontal lobes.
- New neuroimaging techniques and interest in neurogenesis (the birth of new neurons) and neuroplasticity of the brain have spawned exciting research into enhanced learning and recovery after brain damage.

CASE **STUDY**

A 64-year-old former van driver experienced sudden onset of confusion, slurred speech, and left-sided paralysis of the arm and leg. He was admitted to the hospital stroke unit and begun on blood thinners after computed tomography ruled out hemorrhage. He was admitted to the acute rehabilitation unit in 2 days. Testing showed mild unilateral upper motor neuron dysarthria with fair intelligibility, poor pragmatics (poor eye contact, inattention to speaker if on his left, poor topic maintenance, apathy during communication), mild to moderate neglect of left side of space, mild anomia on confrontation naming and questioning, and constructional deficits in drawing and copying. After a 3-week stay, he was ambulatory with a leg brace, had little functional use of his left upper extremity, had improved intelligibility, and was learning to compensate for his left side neglect.

Questions for Consideration

1. What part(s) of the brain was (were) affected by this stroke?
2. Why is neglect more prominent with this location of damage to the brain?
3. What could be the cause of the perception of apathy in the patient's communication interactions?

REFERENCES

1. Achard, S. S., Salvador, R., Whitcher, B., Suckling, J., & Bullmore, E. (2006). A resilient, small-world human brain functional network with highly connected association cortical hubs. *The Journal of Neuroscience, 26*, 63–72.
2. Amedi, A., Floel, A., Knecht, S., Zohary, E., & Cohen, L. G. (2004). Transcranial magnetic stimulation of the occipital pole interferes with verbal processing in blind subjects. *Nature Neuroscience, 7*, 1266–1270.
3. Amedi, A., Raz, N., Pianka, R., Malach, R., & Zohary, E. (2003). Early visual cortex activation correlates with superior verbal memory performance in the blind. *Nature Neuroscience, 6*, 758–766.
4. Azevedo, F. A., Carvalho, L. R., Grinberg, L. T., Farfel, J. M., Ferretti, R. E., Leite, R. E., et al. (2009). Equal numbers of neuronal and non-neuronal cells make the human brain an isometrically scaled-up primate brain. *The Journal of Comparative Neurology, 513*, 532–541.
5. Barbey, A. C., Colm, R., Paul, E. J., Chau, A., Solomon, J., & Grafman, J. H. (2014). Lesion mapping of social problem solving. *Brain, 137*, 2823–2833.
6. Begley, S. (2007). *Train your mind, change your brain.* New York: Ballantine Books.
7. Bergmann, O. A., & Frisén, J. (2013). Why adults need new brain cells. *Science, 340*, 695–696.

8. Chapey, R. (2001). Cognitive intervention: Stimulation of cognition, memory, convergent thinking, divergent thinking and evaluative thinking. In R. Chapey (Ed.), *Language intervention strategies in adult aphasia* (4th ed.). Baltimore: Williams & Wilkins.

9. Code, C. (Ed.). (1990). *The characteristics of aphasia (Brain, Behaviour and Cognition series)*. New York: Taylor and Francis.

10. Coltheart, M., Patterson, K., & Marshall, J. C. (Eds.). (1980). *Deep dyslexia*. London: Routledge and Kegan Paul.

11. Corbetta, M. K., Kincade, J. M., & Shulman, G. L. (2002). Neural systems for visual orienting and their relationships to spatial working memory. *Journal of Cognitive Neuroscience, 14*, 508–523.

12. Crosson, B. (1992). *Subcortical functions in language and memory*. New York: Guilford Press.

13. Dudai, Y. (1989). *The neurobiology of memory: Concepts, findings, trends*. New York: Oxford University Press.

14. Eriksson, P. S., Perfilieva, E., Björk-Eriksson, T., Alborn, A. M., Nordborg, C., Peterson, D. A., & Gage, F. H. (1998). Neurogenesis in the adult human hippocampus. *Nature Medicine, 4*, 1313–1317.

15. Ernst, A., & Frisén, J. (2015). Adult neurogenesis in humans—common and unique traits in mammals. *PLoS Biology, 13*(1), 1–12.

16. Fair, D. C., Cohen, A. L., Power, J. D., Dosenback, N. U., Church, J. A., Miezin, F. M., et al. (2009). Functional brain networks develop from a "local to distributed" organization. *PLoS Computational Biology, 5*, 1–14.

17. Friederici, A. A., & Gierhan, S. E. (2013). The language network. *Current Opinion in Neurobiology, 23*, 250–254.

18. Geschwind, N. (1969). Problems in the anatomical understanding of aphasia. In A. L. Benton (Ed.), *Contributions to clinical neuropsychology*. Chicago: Aldine.

19. Gillis, R. J. (1996). *Traumatic brain injury: Rehabilitation for speech-language pathologists*. Boston: Butterworth-Heinemann.

20. Glezer, L. K. (2015). Adding words to the brain's visual dictionary: Novel word learning selectively sharpens orthographic representations. *The Journal of Neuroscience, 35*, 4965–4972.

21. Gough, P. M., Nobre, A. C., & Devlin, J. T. (2005). Dissociating linguistic processes in the left inferior frontal cortex with transcranial magnetic stimulation. *Journal of Neuroscience, 25*, 8010–8016.

22. Guilford, J. P., & Hoepfner, R. V. (1971). *The analysis of intelligence*. New York: McGraw-Hill.

23. Hagoort, P. (2005). On Broca, brain and binding: A new framework. *Trends in Cognitive Neuroscience, 9*, 416–423.

24. Harris, K. A., & Shepherd, G. M. (2015). The neocortical circuit: Themes and variations. *Nature Neuroscience, 18*, 170–181.

25. Hebb, D. (1949). *The organization of behavior*. New York: John Wiley and Sons.

26. Laboratory of Neuro Imaging and Martinos Center for Biomedical Imaging at Massachusetts General Hospital. (n.d.). *Human Connectome Project Gallery*. Retrieved from Human Connectome Project: http://www.humanconnectomeproject.org/gallery.

27. Liepert, J., Bauder, H., Wolfgang, H. R., Miltner, W. H., Taub, E., & Weiller, C. (2000). Treatment-induced cortical reorganization after stroke in humans. *Stroke, 6*, 1210–1216.

28. Lutz, A., Greischar, L. L., Rawlings, N. B., Richard, M., & Davidson, R. J. (2004). Long-term meditators self-induce high-amplitude gamma synchrony during mental practice. *Proceedings of the National Academy of Sciences, 101* 16369–16373.

29. Maher, L. M., Kendall, D., Swearengin, J. A., Rodriguez, A., Leon, S. A., Pingel, K., et al. (2006). A pilot study of use-dependent learning in the context of constraint-induced language therapy. *Journal of the International Neuropsychological Society, 12*, 843–852.

30. Meinzer, M., Djundja, D., Barthel, G., Elbert, T., & Rockstroh, B. (2005). Long-term stability of improved language functions in chronic aphasia after constraint-induced aphasia therapy. *Stroke, 36*, 1462–1466.

31. Metter, E. I., Riege, W. H., Hanson, W. R., Jackson, C. A., Kempler, D., & van Lancker, D. (1988). Subcortical structures in aphasia: an analysis based on (F-18)-fluorodeoxyglucose, positron emission tomography, and computed tomography. *Archives of Neurology, 45*, 1229–1234.

32. *Miller-Keane encyclopedia and dictionary of medicine, nursing, and allied health* (7th ed.) (2003). St. Louis: Saunders.

33. Ming, G. L., & Song, H. (2011). Adult neurogenesis in the mammalian brain: Significant answers and significant questions. *Neuron, 70*, 687–702.

34. Myers, P. S. (1994). Communication disorders associated with right-hemisphere brain damage. In R. Chapey (Ed.), *Language intervention strategies in adult aphasia* (3rd ed.). Baltimore: Williams & Wilkins.

35. Nadeau, S. E., & Crosson, B. (1997). Subcortical aphasia. *Brain and Language, 58*, 355–402 436–458.

36. Nadeau, S. E., Ferguson, T. S., Valenstein, E., Vierck, C. J., Petruska, J. C., Streit, W. J., & Ritz, L. A. (2004). *Medical neuroscience*. St. Louis: Saunders Elsevier.

37. Nadeau, S., & Rothi, L. G. (2001). Rehabilitation of subcortical aphasia. In R. Chapey (Ed.), *Language intervention strategies in adult aphasia* (4th ed.). Baltimore: Williams & Wilkins.

38. Naeser, M. E., Martin, P. I., Nichols, M., Baker, E. H., Seekins, H., Helm-Estabrooks, N., et al. (2005). Improved naming after TMS treatments in a chronic, global aphasia patient—case report. *Neurocase, 11*, 182–193.

39. National Institutes of Health. (2015, July 24). *Human Connectome Project* Retrieved from NIH Blueprint: The Human Connectome Project: . http://www.humanconnectome.org/about/project.

40. Neville, H. J., Schmidt, A., & Kutas, M. (1983). Altered visual-evoked potentials in congenitally deaf adults. *Brain Research, 266,* 127–132.

41. Penfield, W. G., & Roberts, L. (1959). *Speech and brain mechanisms.* Princeton, NJ: Princeton University Press.

42. Rahmann, H., & Rahmann, M. (1992). *The neurobiological basis of memory and behavior.* New York: Springer-Verlag.

43. Sadato, N., Pascual-Leone, A., Grafman, J., Ibañez, V., Deiber, M. P., Dold, G., & Hallett, M. (1996). Activation of the primary visual cortex by Braille reading in blind subjects. *Nature, 380,* 526–528.

44. Saddoris, M. P., Gallagher, M., & Schoenbaum, G. (2005). Rapid associative encoding in basolateral amygdala depends on connections with orbitofrontal cortex. *Neuron, 46,* 321–331.

45. Santarelli, L., Saxe, M., Gross, A., Surget, A., Battaglia, F., Dulawa, S., & Weisstaub, N. (2003). Requirement for hippocampal neurogenesis for behavioral effects of antidepressants. *Science, 301,* 805–809.

46. Shepherd, G. M., & Koch, C. (1998). Introduction to synaptic circuits. In G. M. Shepherd (Ed.), *The synaptic organization of the brain* (4th ed.). New York: Oxford University Press.

47. Silver, J., & Miller, J. H. (2004, February). Regeneration beyond the glial scar. *Nature Reviews Neuroscience, 5,* 146–156.

48. Solberg, M. M., & Mateer, C. A. (1987). Effectiveness of an attention-training program. *Journal of Clinical and Experimental Neuropsychology, 9,* 117–130.

49. Sporns, O. (2007). Brain connectivity. *Scholarpedia, 2*(10) Retrieved from http://www.scholarpedia.org/article/Brain_connectivity.

50. Sporns, O. (2013). The human connectome: Origins and challenges. *Neuroimage, 80,* 53–61.

51. Sporns, O. T., Tononi, G., & Kötter, R. (2005). The human connectome: A structural description of the human brain. *PLoS Computational Biology, 1,* 245–251.

52. Squire, L. B., Berg, D., Bloom, F. E., du Lac, S., Ghosh, A., & Spitzer, N. C. (2013). *Fundamental neuroscience* (4th ed.). Waltham, MA: Academic Press/Elsevier.

53. Szaflarski, J. A., Allendorfer, J., Ball, A., Banks, C., Dietz, A., Hart, K., et al. (2014, April). Randomized controlled trial of constraint-induced aphasia therapy in patients with chronic stroke. *Neurology, 82*(Suppl. S21.001).

54. Taub, E., Miller, N. E., Novack, T. A., Cook, E. W., III, Fleming, W. C., Nepomuceno, J. S., & Crago, J. E. (1993). Technique to improve chronic motor deficit after stroke. *Archives of Physical Medicine and Rehabilitation, 74,* 347–354.

55. Taub, E., Uswatte, G., King, D. K., Morris, D., Crago, J. E., & Chatterjee, A. (2006). A placebo-controlled trial of constraint-induced movement therapy for upper extremity after stroke. *Stroke, 37,* 1045–1049.

56. Thiebaut de Schotten, M., Dell'Acqua, F., Valabregue, R., & Catani, M. (2012). Monkey to human comparative anatomy of the frontal lobe association tracts. *Cortex, 48,* 82–96.

57. Tompkins, C. A. (1995). *Right hemisphere communication disorders: Theory and management.* San Diego: Singular Publishing Group.

58. Van Praag, H., Christie, B. R., Sejnowski, T. J., & Gage, F. H. (2002). Functional neurogenesis in the adult hippocampus. *Nature, 415,* 1030–1034.

59. Wallesch, C. W., & Papagno, C. (1988). Subcortical aphasia. In F. C. Rose, R. Whurr, & M. A. Wyke (Eds.), *Aphasia.* London: Whurr.

60. Watts, D. A., & Strogatz, S. H. (1998). Collective dynamics of "small world" networks. *Nature, 393,* 440–442.

61. Wernicke, K. (1874). *Der aphasische symptomkomplex.* Breslau: Kohn and Neigert.

10

Adult Disorders of Language

Let the young know they will never find a more interesting, more instructive book than the patient himself.

Giorgio Baglivi

KEY **TERMS**

acceleration-deceleration injury
agraphia
alexia
alexia with agraphia
alexia without agraphia
Alzheimer's disease
amyloid plaques
aneurysm
anomic aphasia
aphasia
aphasic alexia
aprosodia
arteriosclerosis
arteriovenous malformation (AVM)
atherosclerosis
border zone
Broca's aphasia
capsular
central (parietal-temporal) alexia
cerebrovascular accident (CVA)
circumlocution
cognitive-communicative (cognitive-linguistic) disorders
conduction aphasia
confabulation
chronic traumatic encephalopathy (CTE)
deep dyslexia
dementia

dementia of the Alzheimer's type (DAT)
denial
diffuse axonal injury (DAI)
dyslexias
dysprosody
encephalopathy
extinction
focal lesions
frontotemporal dementias (FTD)
glioma
global aphasia
infarction
ischemia
molecular commotion
neoplasm
neurofibrillary tangles
paraphasia
phonologic alexia
posterior (occipital) alexia
primary progressive aphasia (PPA)
prosopagnosia
subcortical aphasia
surface dyslexia
thromboembolic
thrombus
transcortical aphasias
transient ischemic attack (TIA)
traumatic brain injury (TBI)
unilateral inattention
Wernicke's aphasia

CHAPTER **OUTLINE**

The speech-language pathologist (SLP) who chooses a career path working with adults quite often works with patients with acquired neurogenic language disorders. This chapter discusses language disorders that have focal brain damage as the etiology—aphasia, alexia, and agraphia—as well as disorders of communication referred to as cognitive-communicative (or cognitive-linguistic) disorders. Although communication disorders of patients with right hemisphere lesions and dementia are not treated as intensively by the SLP as are the aphasias and the problems resulting from traumatic brain injury, the SLP should understand the underlying pathology, the communication deficits, and the contribution the SLP can make to the quality of life for these patients.

Aphasia

Persons with brain damage that is focal in nature and affects the functioning of the cortical and/or subcortical language mechanisms of the dominant hemisphere (i.e., in most people, the left hemisphere) may experience some form of aphasia. Aphasia is defined by Rosenbek et al.[52] as "an impairment, due to brain damage, of the ability to comprehend and formulate language. Aphasia may affect function in one or more modalities of language: auditory comprehension, reading, oral-expressive language, and/or writing. The language impairment may be worsened by physiologic inefficiency or impaired cognition, but it cannot be explained by dementia, sensory loss or motor dysfunction."

ETIOLOGY AND NEUROPATHOLOGY OF APHASIA

As stated previously, aphasia results from focal damage to areas of the brain primarily responsible for the understanding and production of language. A focal lesion is different from diffuse damage to several parts of the brain. Focal lesions are caused by interruption in the blood flow to the area of the brain supplied by the particular arterial distribution. The blood supply to the brain is discussed in Chapter 3 and should be reviewed to understand the discussion of etiology of aphasia. Figure 10-1 elaborates slightly on what is presented in Chapter 3, showing the branches of the middle cerebral artery, also known as the *artery of aphasia*. It clearly demonstrates that the

FIGURE **10-1**

Lateral view of the cerebral arteries detailing the branches of the anterior and middle cerebral arteries. (From Swaiman, K., Ashwal, K., Ferriero, D., et al. [2012] *Swaiman's Pediatric Neurology* [5th ed.]. Philadelphia: Saunders.)

middle cerebral artery perfuses most of the perisylvian language areas.

Reduction of blood flow to an area is called **ischemia**. Blood carries oxygen to the brain, which is the biggest user of oxygen, consuming approximately 20% of the body's supply at any given time. Without an ongoing flow of oxygenated blood, the brain cannot function for long. If the brain is deprived of blood for approximately 10 to 12 seconds, the average person will lose consciousness; after 3 to 5 minutes irreparable brain damage or death may result. Exceptions exist, such as interruption to blood flow in the presence of hypothermia. The reduction in body temperature seems to have a protective effect on the brain, reducing the consequences of reduction of flow. When an area of the brain is damaged because of a lack of blood, cell death or **infarction** has occurred. If an area of the brain is infarcted, necrotic tissue then remains in that area. Eventually the infarcted area softens and liquefies, with this waste removed, probably by astroglial action (gliosis). This usually leaves a cavity that has the appearance of a crater in the brain with a rim of scar tissue around it formed by the astrocytes.

Several medical conditions may interrupt the vital oxygenated blood supply to the brain. These include cerebrovascular accident (CVA), traumatic brain injury (TBI), brain infections leading to focal abscess, vasculitis (or arteritis), and neoplasm. Trauma is discussed later in this chapter. Throughout these discussions, keep the fact in mind that TBI can result in *both* focal and diffuse brain damage. The following discussion of common causes of interruption to blood flow concentrates on CVA and neoplasms.

Cerebrovascular Accident

The most frequent cause of interrupted blood flow is **cerebrovascular accident (CVA),** also known as stroke (or "a brain attack"). Stroke, although decreasing in incidence in the United States, is the third leading cause of death in persons older than 55 years, but it is increasing in younger adults and children. American Heart Association[43] statistics show that each year approximately 795,000 people in the United States experience new or recurrent strokes (ischemic or hemorrhagic in origin). On average, every 40 seconds someone in the United States has a stroke, and there is a stroke-related death every 4 minutes. CVA can result from two mechanisms of interruption: occlusion or hemorrhage.

Occlusive Mechanisms

In a stroke of occlusive origin, the opening of an arterial vessel has been occluded, reducing or stopping the flow of blood through that artery. The most common cause of arterial occlusion is a disease process known as **arteriosclerosis**, which is characterized by a thickening or hardening of the arterial wall with consequent reduction of elasticity of the vessel. The diagnosis of **atherosclerosis** is frequently made before or after CVA and indicates a form of arteriosclerosis in which blood vessel walls thicken. This thickening is caused by a proliferation of cells, particularly blood platelets, along the wall. Also found are abnormal fatty deposits in the artery with deterioration of the inner coating of the wall, again resulting in loss of elasticity, or fibrosis, of the vessel wall. The thickening plaques on the wall continue to enlarge and hinder diffusion of nutrients from blood to deeper tissue of the wall. This results in fraying and ulceration of the wall. Eventually a protrusion into the vessel begins to build up. If this accumulation is formed exclusively of blood platelets, it is known as a **thrombus**. As the deterioration of the wall begins to build in the vessel, the wall increases in rigidity, leading to a rise in hypertension (high blood pressure), which puts the person at an even higher risk for CVA.

Current thinking is that most CVAs are embolic in origin, meaning that this extraneous material in the vessel has occluded a cerebral vessel *distal* to its point of origin. This embolus has broken away from the vessel wall, traveled through the vessel and become lodged in some part of the brain, stopping or disrupting the flow through that vessel's distribution (Fig. 10-2). If a thrombus has built up on a vessel wall and completely occluded the vessel at that point, the CVA would be considered thrombotic in origin, but that diagnostic precision is often not possible and the diagnosis may be **thromboembolic** stroke. It may take

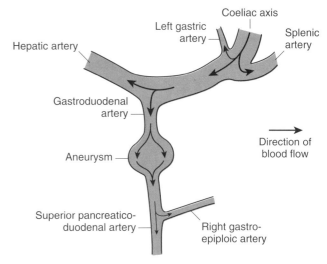

FIGURE **10-2**
Illustration of an aneurysm (of the gastroduodenal artery). (From Kessel, D., Robertson, I. [2011]. *Interventional Radiology* [3rd ed.]. A Survival Guide: Churchill Livingstone: Edinburgh.)

minutes or weeks to clog an artery fully. The resulting dysfunction may seem to arise suddenly and increase in severity over minutes, hours, or even days. When the symptoms seem to increase, it is referred to as "stroke in evolution" and it may proceed in a stepwise fashion. The maximal deficit is referred to as a completed stroke.

The most common source of emboli is the heart. Other extraneous material building up in the vessel may be tumor cells, a clump of bacteria, air, or plaque from the fatty deterioration. Emboli may also be a secondary effect of trauma. With an embolus that suddenly reaches a point at which it cannot continue flowing with the blood through the artery, often at a branching point in the artery, the time for occlusion is quicker or more abrupt than in the case of a thrombus and the time to maximal deficit may be seconds or minutes.

Another term heard when working with patients with compromised vascular systems is transient ischemic attack (TIA). A TIA is often referred to by the layperson as a "mini stroke," which is acceptable because the symptoms often mimic the effects of a completed stroke. However, with a TIA the disruption of blood flow is temporary and the neurologic signs are transient, usually lasting less than 1 hour and completed within 24 hours. The occurrence of a TIA usually indicates that platelet formation is underway, generally in the internal carotid artery distribution. There is a 20% chance of suffering a stroke during the first year after the TIA and a 30% to 60% chance within 5 years. A TIA is a warning and should be taken seriously. Research on persons who experienced either a TIA or a nondisabling stroke suggested that the use of a CT scan to identify acute ischemia (newly damaged tissue as a result of the oxygen deprivation) and other indicators of cerebrovascular disease can be most useful for stroke prevention.[62] The researchers found that the patients who showed acute ischemia on the CT were 2.6 times more likely to have another stroke. If the scan showed acute ischemia plus small vessel damage (microangiopathy), the likelihood increased to 4.6; with acute plus chronic ischemia found, it increased to 5.3; and with all three factors seen on CT, the likelihood increased to 8.4 times more likely. Thus a relatively inexpensive and common procedure could help determine how critical the need for more intensive intervention to decrease the risk of a debilitating CVA.

Hemorrhage

The rupture of a vessel in the brain causes a cerebral hemorrhage. Trauma to the brain often results in hemorrhage into the subarachnoid area and can cause hemorrhaging into other areas. The two most common causes of hemorrhage of a cerebral artery without

trauma occurring are rupture of an aneurysm and arteriovenous malformation.

Cerebral Aneurysm. An aneurysm is a dilated blood vessel, usually an artery, that involves a stretching of all layers of the wall, weakening the vessel. Often the weak part of the wall can be seen extending from the vessel surface (see Fig. 10-2). Approximately 85% of aneurysms are found on branches of the internal carotid artery system, with 10% to 15% in the vertebrobasilar distribution.[30]

Points at which cerebral vessels branch off or make a sharp turn are the most vulnerable for aneurysm development. Many of the aneurysms are congenital in nature. Hemorrhage into the subarachnoid space is referred to as a subarachnoid hemorrhage and in the brain proper as an intracerebral hemorrhage. Small aneurysms may never rupture and remain silent throughout life. Large aneurysms may cause symptoms before rupture because they compress adjacent structures, such as cranial nerve roots.

Arteriovenous Malformation. Arteriovenous malformation (AVM) occurs when the capillary network between arteries and veins is absent and vessels are twisted and tangled (see Fig. 10-2). This is presumably a congenital condition and may not be detected until a seizure or a hemorrhage occurs. An aneurysm can grow and change in configuration and may damage adjacent structures. With deterioration of the walls in these abnormal vessels, a hemorrhage can occur into the subarachnoid space, brain tissue, ventricles, or brainstem, depending on where the AVM is located.

Neoplasms in the Brain

A neoplasm is an abnormal mass of tissue, better known as a tumor. Benign tumors do not spread and are not recurrent. Malignant tumors expand and are resistant to treatment, though new treatments are being developed daily. As a brain tumor spreads, it presses on adjacent structures and may invade and destroy the tissue, obstructing circulation. If the damage is directly to the language areas or indirectly affects normal function of the language mechanisms, an aphasia may result. With a slow-growing tumor, the surrounding tissue may accommodate it for a time with few symptoms noted.

Tumors are classified according to their origin, with the most common source in the brain being the neuroglia; the term glioma is the general name for a tumor arising from these supportive tissues of the brain. Of the gliomas, astrocytomas, ependymomas, oligodendrogliomas, and tumors with mixtures of two or more cell types (fibrillary astrocytomas) are the most common primary brain tumors in adults. In the medical workup the tumor is graded, indicating its tendency to spread.

Tumors with distinct borders are classified as grade I because they usually are benign, do not grow, or grow slowly. Grade IV indicates a fast-growing, destructive tumor.

As previously stated, any condition or disease process that can damage a blood vessel carrying blood to the brain, and thus oxygen, can result in a focal lesion affecting function of the language areas of the brain.

APHASIA CLASSIFICATION

The aphasia literature is characterized by a proliferation of clinical classification schemes. The history of aphasia is peopled by students of the disorder who either communicated poorly to each other about the disorder or were in clear disagreement about the nature of the syndromes. Syndromes were often named or classified in terms of personal bias. This situation has resulted in a number of confusing classification systems. Similar names in two classification systems may be used to describe radically different language syndromes, each with strikingly different lesion sites.

SLPs who have devised classification systems have generally disregarded the site of the lesion in their systems, basing their classifications on patterns of performance on standardized language tests. Tests that use classification systems based on performance alone, rather than extensive neurologic data, are Schuell's Minnesota Test for Differential Diagnosis of Aphasia[54] and the Porch Index of Communicative Ability.[48] The approach to classification based on language performance alone has further complicated the issue of classification.

Dichotomous Classification

Patients commonly are broadly classified into one of two categories on the basis of the general locus of the presumed lesion before specific syndromes are identified. The dichotomous classification of receptive and expressive aphasia, introduced in 1935 by the neurologist Theodore Weisenburg and the psychologist Katherine McBride, has been one of the most widely used modern divisions. Expressive aphasia generally is associated with anterior lesions and receptive aphasia with posterior lesions.

The motor and sensory division of aphasia introduced by Wernicke has been widely used. Motor aphasia usually implies an anterior cortical pathology, usually located in the frontal lobe. Sensory aphasia implies a posterior lesion in the temporal lobe. Some experts have done away with the classic terms *motor* and *sensory* and directly classify the aphasias as anterior and posterior, referring to lesion site.

A widely used dichotomy for spontaneous language in aphasia is fluent versus nonfluent. All persons with aphasia show some degree of expressive involvement in conversational language, and, for most, their expressive language can be appropriately described as fluent or nonfluent. In general, the person with a fluent aphasia has expressive output that is perceived by the listener (even a listener unfamiliar with the language) as smooth and effortless, although some speakers show a hyperfluency in which the output is constant and fairly unrelenting. A person with a nonfluent aphasia, on the other hand, is perceived by the listener as having difficulty with getting words out, with notable hesitancies, revisions, inappropriate silences, and perhaps even visible struggle. This dichotomy is often considered to be better than classification as expressive versus receptive because it recognizes that practically all persons with aphasia demonstrate some expressive difficulty.

Much of the supposed confusion in classification is artificial. In general, more agreement exists on the critical features that distinguish various aphasia syndromes than on the names applied to them. The syndromes of the language area, or perisylvian zone, are the most widely accepted of the aphasic syndromes. These include Broca's, Wernicke's, and global aphasia, generally considered the most common aphasic syndromes. Conduction aphasia is a less common perisylvian syndrome. The transcortical aphasias and various alexic or agraphic syndromes have their lesion sites outside the perisylvian zone, and they are even less common. These syndromes became popular as the primary classification system for aphasias that could be grouped by pattern of performance. The research and development supporting two assessment instruments still in use today, the *Western Aphasia Battery*[33] and the *Boston Diagnostic Aphasia Exam,*[26] resulted in the widespread use of this classification system known as the Boston Classification System.

Classifications under the Boston System

Broca's Aphasia. **Broca's aphasia** is marked by nonfluent conversation, decreased verbal output, increased effort in speaking, shortened sentence length, **dysprosody**, and agrammatism (reduction of syntactic filler words with retention of nouns, verbs, and adjectives). Motor speech disorders often are present, such as apraxia of speech and dysarthria. Some neurologists believe that what are referred to as speech apraxic symptoms by SLPs are merely a form of transient nonfluent aphasia. Lesions limited to Broca's area alone produce speech apraxia or this form of transient aphasia. More widespread lesions produce a chronic and classic clinical picture.

Comprehension of spoken language is always qualitatively better in Broca's aphasia than is production of language. Language production varies widely from near normal to clearly abnormal. Persons with Broca's aphasia often have difficulty in understanding syntactic relations and show deficits in comprehending syntactic items they have difficulty expressing. Repetition is always abnormal, and confrontation naming (naming objects and pictures) is poor. Oral reading and reading comprehension usually are poor, although some patients do relatively well. Writing is poor, marked by misspellings and letter omission. In addition, the patient usually has a right hemiparesis and uses the left hand for writing. Some patients cannot write at all because of paresis. Figure 10-3 shows a computed tomographic scan of a patient with a left hemisphere CVA resulting in Broca's aphasia.

Wernicke's Aphasia. **Wernicke's aphasia** is a fluent aphasia characterized by difficulty in understanding language as well as difficulty in repetition of language. The speech is fluent but paraphasic. **Paraphasia** includes the omission of parts of words, incorrect use of correct words, use of neologisms ("new words"), and substitution of incorrect phonemes for correct ones. Verbal or semantic paraphasia is the incorrect use of words; literal paraphasia is the substitution of incorrect phonemes for correct phonemes.

The fluent verbal output may be excessive, a condition called logorrhea. Phrase length is normal, and in most cases syntactic structure is acceptable. Articulation and prosody are usually not abnormal. The speech often lacks meaningful and substantive words and clinically is described as empty speech. Use of jargon is common. Sometimes neologistic jargon is documented, implying that meaning is incomprehensible because output primarily consists of excessive jargon and neologistic terms (neologistic jargon aphasia).

With Wernicke's aphasia, comprehension of language is poor, especially early after onset, and some patients appear to understand no spoken language at all. Others understand only some words, and certain patients have distinct problems in discriminating phonemes. Patients with Wernicke's aphasia characteristically demonstrate poor awareness of their comprehension or expression difficulty. Repetition of spoken language is poor, and failure and paraphasic

FIGURE **10-3**
Computed tomography scans of four horizontal slices from a patient with Broca's aphasia and a right hemiparesis. Note the darkened area in the left hemisphere, which defines the infarction. (Courtesy of Howard S. Kirshner, MD, Department of Neurology, Vanderbilt University School of Medicine, Nashville, TN.)

errors characterize confrontation naming tasks. Reading is generally disturbed, often paralleling the disturbance in comprehension of spoken language.

The damage in Wernicke's aphasia is to the posterior portion of the superior temporal gyrus of the dominant hemisphere, the auditory association area, or to Wernicke's area in the sylvian fissure.[16] Extension into the area of the supramarginal gyrus and angular gyrus has also been found to be present in patients with persisting Wernicke's aphasia.[34] Because the damage is to posterior portions of the brain, the motor areas in the frontal lobe and those pathways usually are spared. Therefore the patient with Wernicke's aphasia will only infrequently show any motor weakness in the limbs or the face. A visual field deficit should be ruled out because of this posterior lesion site.

Conduction Aphasia. One form of fluent aphasia is characterized by intact comprehension and fluent, melodic speech. Despite the good comprehension, repetition is poor in contrast to the fluency in spontaneous speech. Phoneme substitutions are frequent because of the inability to match acoustic information with motor plans for the output of phonemes; word retrieval deficits are present. Wernicke postulated a disconnection theory, proposing the cause to be a lesion in the arcuate fasciculus, the connection between Broca's and Wernicke's areas. **Conduction aphasia** is less well accepted as a diagnosis than Broca's or Wernicke's aphasia because of questions about the site of the lesion. The lesion is not always in the arcuate fasciculus as Wernicke postulated, and conduction aphasia is almost never seen in diseases that interrupt white matter tracts and may involve the arcuate fasciculus (such as multiple sclerosis). However, the language syndrome has been repeatedly described and can be diagnosed from symptoms alone without neuropathologic evidence. Two distinct locations of pathology have been demonstrated in conduction aphasia. One involves the arcuate fasciculus in the dominant hemisphere, usually deep in the supramarginal gyrus. Some experts argue that the supramarginal cortex or the inferior parietal cortex rather than deep white matter is the critical site. The other major site is said to be in the left temporal lobe in the auditory association area.

Conversational speech is fluent and often paraphasic, but generally the speech quantity is reduced compared with that of Wernicke's aphasia. Reactive pauses and hesitations from awareness of incidents of word-finding difficulties are common, so the melodic line may be interrupted; however, the fluency is much better than in Broca's or global aphasia. Literal paraphasia is often present. Articulation is good. Comprehension of spoken language is also adequate in most cases. If

comprehension is disturbed, the diagnosis of conduction aphasia should be questioned.

Repetition of language presents a serious problem to the person with conduction aphasia, and the dramatic difference between comprehension and repetition is a clue to correct diagnosis. Repetition is much poorer than the ability to produce words in conversational speech, and paraphasic substitutions of words often are present in repetition attempts. Errors also are present in confrontation naming. Reading comprehension usually is intact, but reading aloud often results in increased paraphasia. Writing disturbance or dysgraphia is present. Spelling is poor, with omissions, reversals, and substitutions of letters. Words in sentences may be reversed, omitted, or misplaced.

Associated characteristics vary. Some patients show a right hemiparesis and/or hemisensory loss. Patients may also show a visual field deficit. Some patients may also demonstrate an ideomotor apraxia.

Global Aphasia. **Global aphasia** is marked by severe impairment of both understanding and expression of language. The person usually is mute or uses repetitive vocalization. This aphasia is usually associated with a large lesion in the perisylvian area. The lesion does not serve as a localizing one for the neurologist except when in the left perisylvian area.

Expressive language always is limited, although true mutism rarely appears other than initially. The patient can often use inflected phonation and sometimes simple words, such as expletives, repetitively. Comprehension is often reported to be better than production with global aphasia; patients may also become adept at interpreting nonverbal communication through gestures and facial and body language. This nonverbal comprehension may be mistaken for comprehension of the spoken word.

The person with global aphasia does not repeat. If a patient who appears to have global aphasia repeats adequately, the SLP and neurologist should suspect that one of the transcortical aphasic syndromes, described later in the chapter, is present instead of a true global aphasia. Confrontation naming is severely or completely impaired, and reading and writing are also severely or totally impaired. Many of the language dysfunctions are not reversible with treatment.

Transcortical Aphasias. These language disturbances are a set of aphasic syndromes whose lesions fall outside the perisylvian area. They have been given various names, but Lichtheim[36] identified them as **transcortical aphasias,** and they are probably identified most commonly by this name. Benson[6] called them **border zone** aphasic syndromes because the lesions usually are found in the association cortex in a vascular border zone (also known as a watershed area) between the field of the middle cerebral artery and the area supplied by the anterior or posterior cerebral arteries. A hallmark of the transcortical aphasias is the retention of the ability to repeat with good accuracy. In contrast, the aphasias of the perisylvian area all present a repetition defect.

Three transcortical aphasias are generally recognized: transcortical motor aphasia, transcortical sensory aphasia, and mixed transcortical aphasia. This last type also has been called a syndrome of isolation of the speech area.

Transcortical motor aphasia is a nonfluent aphasia marked by more dysfluency and effort in conversation than usually is seen in Broca's aphasia. Serial speech, repetition, and comprehension appear surprisingly adequate. The lesion is anterior or superior to Broca's area in the dominant hemisphere.

Transcortical sensory aphasia is fluent and marked by paraphasia with semantic and neologistic substitutions. Comprehension is poor, in sharp contrast to repetition, which is surprisingly good. Reading, writing, and naming are poor. The site of the lesion is controversial. It is usually found deep to and posterior to Wernicke's area in either the temporal or the parietal border zone, or it may be located in both of these sites.

Mixed transcortical aphasia is rare. The most striking feature is severely disordered language except in one area—repetition. Patients do not speak unless they are spoken to and answer only in repetition. The most striking feature is echolalia, the repetition of heard phrases.

Examples of echolalia may be incorporated into the patient's speech. The articulation of phonemes is good, but the expressive language as a whole is nonfluent. Comprehension is defective, with little or no demonstrable understanding of spoken language. Visual field defects and other neurologic signs are common. The pathology is mixed but generally appears to involve the vascular border zones of the left hemisphere.

Anomic Aphasia. Word-finding difficulty, known as anomia, is common in many types of aphasia as well as in nonaphasic medical conditions. In fact, many neurologists believe a diagnosis of aphasia should not be considered without evidence of some anomia. Further, anomia occurs in most types of dementia and is a clear diagnostic feature of Alzheimer's syndrome, a major dementia. Anomia often is the only major language residual after recovery from aphasia of any clinical type and may remain a long-lasting problem in the recovered aphasic.

Clearly anomia is not a good localizing symptom for the neurologist. Rather, it is a common symptom in what is called nonfocal brain disease. In those neurologic conditions in which the whole brain is generally affected, anomia is a common language symptom. It occurs in many brain conditions, including encephalitis, increased intracranial pressure, subarachnoid hemorrhage, concussion, and toxic-metabolic **encephalopathy**.

When anomia is the most prominent symptom in the aphasic syndrome, the condition is known as **anomic aphasia**. The clinical picture generally includes only limited receptive or expressive difficulty, but on occasion a disorder of confrontation naming may take an extreme form in these patients, and given patients may be unable to produce virtually any appropriate names. Spontaneous speech usually is fluent but interrupted by word-finding difficulties. Nonspecific words may be substituted for precise lexical items. These verbal para phasias are usually semantic rather than phonemic errors. Usually the patient exhibits good expressive syntax except for pauses for word recall. **Circumlocution**, the utterance of circuitous and wordy descriptions for unrecalled words, is common in anomic aphasia. Comprehension is normal or near normal and repetition generally is intact. Reading and writing are more variable, and word-finding difficulties are obvious in written language.

Anomic aphasia may appear as an isolated syndrome or be the final stage of recovery from other syndromes, such as Wernicke's, conduction, and transcortical aphasias. Some controversy exists regarding whether a recovered aphasic who becomes anomic at the end point of recovery should be classified as an anomic aphasic or according to the primary syndrome at the onset of the aphasia.

The site of the lesion causing anomic aphasia varies as does the presence of associated neurologic defects. However, anomic symptoms, in and of themselves, are less variable than in other classic aphasic syndromes. In severe and isolated anomia, a possible focal lesion may be found in the left hemisphere. A prominent site for a lesion is in the left angular gyrus. Anomia is a common early sign in the syndrome called primary progressive aphasia.

Subcortical Aphasia. With the continued advancement of imaging technology, a new category of aphasia based on lesion site emerged and is known as **subcortical aphasia**. Although many aphasia experts have hypothesized the existence of subcortical speech and language disturbance over the years, not until the lesions were documented did the brain-behavior relation became an interest of study. The reports of several investigators suggested that basal ganglia and thalamic lesions are primarily responsible for subcortical aphasia. Subcortical aphasia associated with thalamic hemorrhage without involvement of the cerebral cortex established the disorder, and then the availability of better imaging techniques used in cases of ischemic infarction of the thalamus allowed more precise localization than had been attempted earlier. Bogousslavsky et al.[7] looked at the

FIGURE **10-4**

Magnetic resonance imaging scan showing a lesion in the head of the caudate, anterior putamen, and anterior limb of the internal capsule (*black arrowhead*) resulting in a mild subcortical aphasia characterized by hesitant speech and anomia. The patient showed good recovery after a period of speech therapy. (Courtesy of Howard S. Kirshner, MD, Department of Neurology, Vanderbilt University School of Medicine, Nashville, TN.)

presence of aphasia with infarction of four separate vascular territories. They found aphasia characterized by hypophonia, verbal paraphasia, impaired comprehension, and intact repetition to be present after infarction affecting the vascular supply to the anterior thalamus, including the ventral anterior and part of the ventral lateral nuclei.

Radanovic and Scaff[49] studied patients with left and right thalamic lesions. Their findings showed primarily deficits in naming and some difficulty in individual patients with auditory comprehension. These problems were thought to be possibly related to verbal memory and attention deficits rather than true language deficit. The aphasias reported after thalamic lesions do not match any of the classic cortical aphasia syndromes, and research indicates primary difficulty with naming in these patients, although some difficulty with comprehension is noted in the worst cases. As discussed in Chapter 9, the etiology of the lexical-semantic access deficits is most likely related to the indirect effect on cortical function that results from the thalamic gating mechanism damage. Nadeau and Rothi[45] propose that treatment be directed to remediation of the declarative memory deficits.

Subcortical aphasias associated with basal ganglia lesions have sometimes been classified by anatomic sites. Each site is said to be associated with a different cluster of speech and language symptoms. Several speech and language syndromes affecting the basal ganglia have been described. The syndromes vary widely, and no general clinical descriptions are associated with basal ganglia lesions. Kirshner[34] identified the head of the caudate nucleus, anterior limb of the internal capsule, and anterior putamen as the most commonly reported lesion sites causing an aphasia (Fig. 10-4). These lesions result in the anterior subcortical aphasia syndrome, which is characterized by dysarthria and decreased fluency but with a longer phrase length than in Broca's aphasia. Paraphasia is also noted.

Alexander and Naeser[2] suggested that four distinct syndromes affecting language and/or speech exist. Each is associated with a different subcortical anatomic site or combination of sites. These sites include (1) striatal lesions (basal ganglia alone), (2) internal capsule lesions, (3) striatal and internal capsular lesions, and (4) insular and capsule lesions. Figure 10-5 lists the signs and symptoms of each of the subcortical speech or language disorders that they identified. Other findings have been described in the literature as well. For example, disproportionate impairment of writing has been reported with subcortical lesions.[60]

Subcortical Aphasia

Striatal Lesions
No aphasia
Dysarthria possible
Hypophonia

Striatal and Internal Capsule Lesions
No definite aphasia
Dysarthria possible

Internal Capsule Lesions
No aphasia
Left dysarthria possible
Right affective dysprosody

Insular and External Capsule lesions
Fluent aphasia
Anomia
Paraphasias in repetition oral reading spontaneous speech
No dysarthria

FIGURE 10-5

The signs and symptoms of language and speech disorders associated with subcortical lesions. (Modified from Alexander, M. P., & Naeser, M. A. [1988]. Cortical-subcortical differences in aphasia. In F. Plum [Ed.], *Language, communication and the brain.* New York: Raven Press.)

BOX 10-1

Localization of the Aphasias in the Central Language Mechanism

Aphasias of the Perisylvian Zone

Broca's aphasia
Wernicke's aphasia
Global aphasia
Conduction aphasia

Transcortical Aphasias of the Border Zone

Transcortical motor aphasia
Transcortical sensory aphasia
Mixed transcortical aphasia

Aphasias of the Subcortical Areas

Thalamic aphasia
Striatal disorders
Internal capsule disorders
Striatal or capsular disorders
Insular or capsular disorders

(Data from Alexander, M. P., & Naeser, M. A. [1988]. Cortical-subcortical differences in aphasia. In F. Plum [Ed.], *Language, communication and the brain.* New York: Raven Press.)

A simplified localization scheme based on current knowledge for all major aphasia syndromes is provided in Box 10-1. As described in Chapter 9, the aphasic deficits seen with subcortical lesions are most likely related to the indirect effect on perfusion of cortical language and speech areas from the blockage of flow through lenticulostriate areas and poor collateral filling. These deficits probably should be treated as a cortical aphasia of the same nature.[45]

TESTING AND INTERVENTION FOR APHASIA

Aphasia testing has had a long history in neurology and speech-language pathology. Broca reportedly tested his patients with conversational questions in addition to testing tongue movements, writing, and arithmetic. He also described their gestures. In 1926 the British neurologist Henry Head (1861-1940) published the first systematic aphasia examination in English. The test was not standardized and contained some items that were even difficult for healthy people to perform. Today clinical neurologists usually assess language and aphasia disturbances as part of the mental status examination of higher cerebral functions, which is part of the traditional neurologic examination. The mental status examination assesses major functions of the total nervous system and lateralizes and localizes dysfunction when it is present.

The language functions tested by the neurologist are found in Table 10-1. An example of a bedside examination of speech and language designed for the clinical neurologist is found in Appendix C.

SLPs and psychologists have been more concerned about developing aphasia tests that precisely measure language behavior under standardized conditions than about providing tests that predict and confirm possible lesions or verify the validity of classic models of neurologic language mechanisms. Testing is performed to assist in discharge and treatment planning. Direct intervention for the language deficits may be provided on an individual or group basis, and literature is growing on treatment techniques.

ROLE OF THE SPEECH-LANGUAGE PATHOLOGIST

The SLP is perhaps the most critical member of the rehabilitation team for the person with a significantly limiting aphasia. Numerous books, articles, websites, and treatment programs are devoted to language therapy with patients with aphasia. An attempt to describe treatment methods would not do justice to this vast amount of literature and is not the purpose of this text. Research on innovative treatments involving constraint-induced aphasia therapy,[3,12] transcranial magnetic stimulation[4] or transcranial direct current stimulation,[22] and group communication therapy[56] is helping clinicians combine or replace more traditional evidence-based treatment methods with these newer methodologies to enhance recovery of language skills. The SLP should be well

TABLE 10-1

Language Functions of Major Classic Aphasias

	SPONTANEOUS SPEECH	COMPREHENSION	REPETITION	READING	WRITING
Broca's	Nonfluent	+	−	±	−
Wernicke's	Fluent	−	−	−	Paragraphic
Conduction	Fluent	+	−	+	−
Global	Mute	−	−	−	−
Anomic	Disorder of word recall	+	+	+	+
Transcortical motor	Nonfluent	+	+	+	−
Transcortical sensory	Fluent	−	+	+	−
Mixed transcortical (isolation of speech area)	Nonfluent	−	+	−	Paragraphic

+, Relatively intact; −, impaired; ±, variable.
Developed by Howard S. Kirshner, MD, Department of Neurology, Vanderbilt University School of Medicine, Nashville, TN.

versed and dedicated to evidence-based medical and behavioral treatments and, as a member of the rehabilitation team, know something about pharmacologic intervention as well.

PHARMACOLOGY IN APHASIA

The use of medication to aid the language-impaired patient has been attempted for many years. The internationally known Russian neurologist Alexander Luria was one of the first to use a powerful anticholinesterase agent, galantamine, to improve speech and gnostic and praxic functions in brain-injured individuals.[37] In recent years intensive study of the actions of neurotransmitter systems has increased the use of drugs in aphasia rehabilitation, though the number of studies reported in the literature remains limited. de Boissezon et al.[19] reviewed the PubMed database for studies on the use of drugs to improve communication in persons with aphasia. This review found 24 studies published between 1970 and 2005. These included trials of bromocriptine (a dopaminergic agent), amphetamines, cholinergics, GABAergics, and serotoninergic agents. The review and summary indicated that two pharmacologic agents, piracetam (a gamma-aminobutyric acid derivative "cognitive enhancer") and amphetamines, showed limited efficiency in enhancing and maintaining the communication of persons with the type of aphasia studied for those reports. All studies the authors reviewed reported that drug therapy was more efficacious if it was combined with language therapy.

In brief, biochemical intervention appears to be a useful adjunct to the more traditional methods of behavioral therapy used with persons with aphasia. Drug therapy certainly will not supersede traditional methods of therapy, but the future appears brighter for more effective drug therapies combined with other approaches for the rehabilitation of aphasia.[19]

PRIMARY PROGRESSIVE APHASIA

Historically, the diagnosis of the presence of aphasia implied that the language disorder was static, at least after the evolution of the stroke or the damage to the brain from an injury, and only improvement was expected after this period (given no other insult). The identification of a slowly progressive aphasia without generalized dementia changed that, and a new classification was born. This syndrome, now called primary progressive aphasia (PPA), is defined as an adult-onset, degenerative language disorder syndrome that selectively affects the language areas of the dominant hemisphere, with preservation of other mental functions as well as the ability to perform normal activities of daily living for at least 2 years. PPA was first described in contemporary neurology and then further elaborated by Mesulam.[40,41] Anomia is often an early sign, but poor auditory comprehension, stuttering, deteriorating verbal memory, and reading and spelling difficulties have been reported. As stated in the definition, other intellectual functions remain intact for at least 2 years with psychometric testing revealing overall intelligence quotients within the normal range. It is difficult during the first 2 years particularly to classify it under dementia, and this is why it is placed here in our discussion. It is often the case, however, that symptoms of cognitive impairments outside of the language modality will begin to appear at some point though there certainly are patients in whom the deficit remained only in speech and language. Other neurologic conditions

FIGURE **10-6**
Coronal magnetic resonance imaging scan of a patient with progressive, nonfluent aphasia. Note the marked atrophy of the left temporal lobe, which is easiest to see in a coronal
projection. The temporal lobe atrophy and his symptoms of slow speech and anomia,
which were progressive in nature, are consistent with the descriptions of the logopenic
variant of primary progressive aphasia. (Reprinted from Bradley W. G., Daroff, R. B., Fenichel, G. M., & Marsden, C. D. [Eds.]. [2000]. *Neurology in clinical practice* [Vol. I, 3rd ed.].
Boston: Butterworth-Heinemann.)

as well as behavioral or social problems may develop
over time. The patient may become mute and unable
to understand written or spoken language. A diagnosis
of PPA should always be made carefully and with full
disclosure to the patient of probable progression of the
language disorder and possible progression into other
impairments.

As more cases of PPA began to be identified and discussed in the literature, observations of subtypes of the
disorder were documented.[28] A study of 31 patients
with PPA with detailed speech and language evaluations
identified three clinical variants: nonfluent progressive
aphasia (NFPA), semantic dementia (SD), and logopenic progressive aphasia (LPA). Although early magnetic
resonance imaging (MRI) studies classified all patients
as having focal degeneration in the left frontal or anterior temporal lobe, further investigation found distinctive
patterns. Figure 10-6 depicts a coronal MRI scan of a
patient who was diagnosed with PPA, with the finding of
atrophy in the left temporal lobe and the description of
nonfluent speech and anomia.

Because of the difficulty of clinical classification and
the variety of classification descriptions of patients with
PPA found in the literature, an international group of
researchers and clinicians met for a conference in 2011 to
discuss the clinical and imaging findings that could lead to
a consensus regarding criteria for classification of patients
into one of the three variants of PPA. This led to the publication of the results of that consensus conference.[27]
The clinical findings that were agreed upon for each of
the variants are listed in Table 10-2. Because it is not the
task of the SLP to correlate the language symptoms with
the MRI or other medical findings, the consensus recommendations concerning the findings on imaging are not
included. Most SLPs will be greatly interested and want to
try to do such correlation, and thus the original article and
follow-up articles should be read (as well as, of course, any
research done since the time of this writing). Given with
the clinical markers in the article are imaging findings that
suggest pathology that are used as imaged-supported diagnosis for each variant. Medical finding of either "Histologic evidence of a specific neurodegenerative pathology"

(e.g., Alzheimer's disease or frontotemporal lobar degeneration) or "Presence of a known pathogenic mutation" plus a clinical diagnosis of one the variants was listed as *definitive* for classification in all three variants.[28]

Despite, or perhaps because of, the detailed description of features that needed to be present for the three variants, diagnosticians continued to be challenged in classifying some patients. In 2014 Wicklund and colleagues[63] reported on this difficulty finding that only 69% of the 84 patients studied with PPA could be classified using the clinical criteria. Responding to this, Mesulam and Weintraub[42] made suggested revisions to the criteria. These suggested revisions are also listed in Table 10-2. Perhaps by the time this text is published, these or other criteria will be adopted or other classifications emerge.

At this time there is no evidence-based treatment protocol for PPA. There are likely drug trials ongoing and the clinical literature contains some small case studies. The use of transcranial direct current stimulation in one study of eight patients found some positive and lasting (12 weeks) changes on measurements of sentence productivity, grammatical comprehension, and naming.[25]

Associated Central Disturbances

While testing the language system, the SLP or the neurologist often finds or suspects that other disturbances are present that are not a part of the aphasia but accompany the true aphasia. The examiner may also find one of these disturbances with no true aphasia present.

TABLE 10-2

Clinical Diagnostic Criteria for Variants of Primary Progressive Aphasia

VARIANT	CORE FEATURES	OTHER FEATURES	SUGGESTED REVISIONS
Agrammatic	At least one of these must be present: Agrammatism in language production Effortful, halting speech with inconsistent errors and distortions (apraxia of speech)	At least two of these must be present: Impaired comprehension of syntactically complex sentences Spared single word comprehension Spared object knowledge	
Semantic	Both of these must be present: Impaired confrontation naming Impaired single word comprehension	At least three of these must be present: Impaired object knowledge, especially low-frequency or low familiarity items Surface dyslexia or dysgraphia Spared repetition Spared speech production (grammar and motor speech)	
Logopenic	Both of these must be present: Impaired single word retrieval in spontaneous speech and in naming Impaired repetition of sentences and phrases	At least three of these must be present: Phonologic errors in spontaneous speech and in naming Spared single word comprehension and object knowledge Spared motor speech Absence of frank agrammatism	Make absence of definite grammar and comprehension impairment a core criterion Reclassify impaired repetition as an Other rather than Core impairment
Unclassifiable by the 2011 criteria			Consider a fourth variant to include patients with a combination of agrammatism and semantic impairment, often referred to as "mixed PPA"

From 2011 Consensus Conference[29] with Suggested Revisions[31] to Enhance Classification Inclusiveness.

These disorders are referred to as associated central disturbances because the site of the lesion is within the areas described under central language mechanism, but these are not properly classified as aphasic disturbances in most cases. Accompanying central disturbances may be agnosia, apraxia, alexia, and agraphia. Apraxia is discussed in Chapter 6 because it is a motor speech disorder; agnosia is discussed in Chapter 5 as part of the discussion on the various sensory systems. Alexia and agraphia are briefly reviewed here.

ALEXIA

Alexia is an inability to comprehend the written or printed word as the result of a cerebral lesion. Terms relating to alexia and agraphia (the inability to produce written language normally) are found in Table 10-3. In current usage, alexia is an acquired reading disorder, in contrast to dyslexia, an innate or constitutional inability to learn to read. The childhood disorder is often called developmental dyslexia. Although this distinction in

TABLE 10-3	
Alexia and Agraphia	
ASSOCIATED CENTRAL DISTURBANCE	DESCRIPTION OF DISTURBANCE
Agraphia	A disorder of writing caused by cerebral injury; lesion in the left frontal or parietal lobe or in the complex pathways necessary for writing
Alexia	A disorder of reading caused by cerebral injury
TYPES OF ALEXIA	LOCALIZATION
Alexia with agraphia	Lesion usually in the dominant parietal lobe in the angular gyrus area
Alexia without agraphia	Lesion site is controversial; often two lesions, one in the dominant occipital lobe and the other in the splenium of the corpus callosum (according to Dejerine)
Frontal alexia	Lesion in the dominant frontal lobe in Broca's area and adjacent deep structures; associated with a nonfluent aphasia
Aphasic alexia	Lesions are the same as in the major aphasias

terms is not universal, it is becoming popular. The classic term *word blindness* is rarely used in neurology or speech pathology. When used, it implies difficulty in reading words although letter recognition is more intact. Literal alexia means the inability to recognize letters; verbal alexia indicates that letters are recognized but words are not. Pure alexia is a reading disorder without a writing disorder (agraphia). A variety of terms and types of alexia have been reported, but a limited number of alexic syndromes are widely accepted. The modern understanding of alexia is attributed to Joseph Dejerine (1849-1917), who in 1891 and 1892 described two classic syndromes, **alexia without agraphia** and **alexia with agraphia**.

Alexia without Agraphia

Alexia without agraphia is also known as **posterior alexia** or **occipital alexia**. The cardinal feature of this uncommon syndrome is loss of the ability to read printed material but retained ability to write both to dictation and spontaneously. Other language functions generally are intact. This alexia occurs suddenly as the result of a left posterior cerebral artery occlusion in a right-handed person. A striking clinical feature is the patient's ability to write lengthy meaningful messages, with a contrasting inability to read his or her own writing and, generally, to understand words spelled aloud. Initially patients with pure alexia may show difficulty with letters and words, but letters are easier. Patients usually are able to regain some reading ability, but reading usually remains quite an effort. The writing seen in the syndrome is not entirely normal, but retained writing capacity is impressive compared with the minimal reading ability. Often the patient writes better to dictation or spontaneously than when copying. Right homonymous hemianopsia usually is present.

Dejerine[20] found a cerebral infarct in the left occipital lobe and involvement in the splenium of the corpus callosum in a patient with alexia without agraphia. Because the left visual cortex was damaged, all visual information entered the right hemisphere. The right visual cortex perceived the written material but could not transfer it to the left hemisphere because of the callosal lesion. The inferior parietal lobe in the dominant hemisphere, known as the angular gyrus, combined the visual and auditory information necessary in both reading and writing; however, the inferior parietal lobule was disconnected from all visual input. Because the lobule and its connections with the language area were intact, the patient was able to write normally.

Alexia with Agraphia

Also known as **central alexia** or **parietal-temporal alexia**, alexia with agraphia was classically described as an almost total reading disorder, with limited writing ability, only minimal aphasia, and acalculia (acquired difficulty with calculations). In clinical practice the language symptoms vary more widely than in alexia without agraphia. Some authors separate alexia with agraphia into two types: the classic syndrome described and the reading and writing disorder discussed in this chapter as aphasic alexia. Most accounts of the syndrome relate some aphasia, which is always a fluent aphasia. Gerstmann syndrome is sometimes present. This syndrome is defined when agnosia for the fingers, acalculia, right-left disorientation, agraphia, and alexia are all present. A right homonymous visual field defect frequently is reported but not consistently present.

Writing disturbance varies in severity but is not severe enough to preclude writing of letters. Patients often cannot copy letters, unlike patients with alexia without agraphia, who copy laboriously and slowly. Also unlike in pure alexia, these patients do not comprehend words spelled aloud.

Dejerine localized the neuropathology in alexia with agraphia to the angular gyrus of the dominant parietal lobe, and this localization has been universally confirmed since 1891. Dejerine surmised that the angular gyrus in the inferior parietal lobule was essential for the recall of written letters and that its destruction results in disturbances in reading and writing in adults.[25]

Aphasic Alexia

The most common type of alexia is the reading disturbance that accompanies the major clinical types of aphasia. In **aphasic alexia**, significant aphasic symptoms produce so much disturbance of language that reading is secondarily involved. In aphasiology alexic symptoms in aphasia generally are recognized as belonging in a classification of aphasia, not in an outline of alexia. Reading disturbances in each of the major aphasic syndromes have been previously described.

PSYCHOLINGUISTIC CLASSIFICATIONS

In the 1970s British psychologists became interested in reading disorders; literature began to include references to new classifications of reading disorders. The British refer to these disorders as **dyslexias**, even though they are acquired, not developmental, disorders.[13,38] Three types of reading disorder classifications have resulted from psycholinguistic models of patient performance on tasks primarily requiring reading aloud of single words. These disorders are known as deep dyslexia, surface dyslexia, and phonologic alexia. These classifications have become fairly well accepted and the symptoms often are identified in patients.

Deep dyslexia is identified by the presence of semantic errors in reading aloud. Reading errors, such as saying "child" for "girl" or "quiet" for "listen" are common. Derivational errors such as reading "invitation" for "inviting" are present, as are visual confusions. Deep dyslexia implies that the dyslexic reader goes directly to the semantic value of a word from its printed form without appreciating the sound of the word. Deep dyslexia has also been called phonemic, syntactic, or semantic dyslexia.

Surface dyslexia is distinguished by poor ability to use grapheme-to-phoneme conversion rules, although the reader relies heavily on these rules. The errors are phonologically similar to the target, and great sensitivity is paid to spelling regularity. Therefore, although many nonsense words can be pronounced, irregularly spelled words (e.g., yacht) are impossible for the patient to pronounce correctly. There is little sensitivity to meaning; the patient may not recognize that the word does not fit with the context.

Phonologic alexia is characterized by an inability to read nonsense words, with some difficulty noted with low-frequency words.[5] Errors often are visual errors. These patients are assumed to be impaired in the ability to use letter-to-sound conversion rules of the language.

AGRAPHIA

Writing is a complex learned motor act that involves a conversion of oral language symbols into written symbols. The language symbols to be written are assumed to originate in the posterior language areas in the dominant hemisphere of the brain. These oral symbols are translated into visual symbols in the inferior parietal lobe. The linguistic message is then sent forward to the frontal lobe for motor processing. Lesions in any of these language areas or pathways may produce the writing disorder called **agraphia**. The most common type of agraphia is secondary to aphasia and known as aphasic agraphia. Agraphia also may be seen in the absence of aphasia.

Cognitive-Communicative Disorders

The information presented in Chapter 9 regarding cognition was brief and simplistic in nature. It was intended to give the student an introduction to the topic and to the relatively little we know about the neurologic basis of cognition as well as an appreciation for the rapid expansion of knowledge that occurred at the end of the last century. After digesting this information, compare it with Wernicke's model of the central language mechanism. This should highlight how brain injuries or diseases that involve the right hemisphere or that are more diffuse and involve bilateral cortical and subcortical areas or neural networks could produce a different type of language disorder than that seen with focal left hemisphere damage.

This understanding became critical when SLPs began to be employed more widely in various medical settings, eventually resulting in involvement with a more diverse population of neurologically based communication disorders. This included patients with right hemisphere lesions, traumatic brain injury, and dementia. As previously noted in the discussion of right hemisphere function, the communication disorders that these patients experienced were not truly language based. Rather, all these disorders may lead to neurobehavioral consequences that result in cognitive and communicative problems. This sometimes affects the aspects of language on which aphasia focuses—semantics, syntax, morphology, and phonology—but to a much lesser extent. These disorders more often result in communication problems that affect the accuracy, efficiency, and effectiveness of communication in ways that differ greatly from focal, left hemisphere damage. These are referred to as **cognitive-communicative disorders** or **cognitive-linguistic disorders**. All or some of the four key aspects of cognition tend to be affected by these disorders, and the resulting communication disorder is clinically quite different from the aphasias previously described. They each have a different neuroanatomic basis and require different approaches to assessment and intervention.

COMMUNICATION DISORDERS RELATED TO RIGHT HEMISPHERE DAMAGE

At the beginning of this chapter, under the section on aphasia, the etiology of brain damage resulting in focal lesions in the language area of the dominant hemisphere was discussed. While learning about deficits seen in patients with right hemisphere (typically nondominant) damage, remember that the right hemisphere is equally vulnerable to these causative factors of reduced blood flow. Thus the same conditions—CVA, focal trauma, neoplasms—are the common causes of focal damage to parts of the right hemisphere.

With right hemisphere lesions in patients who are left hemisphere dominant, a broad spectrum of deficits are seen. These depend on the site of damage and the expanse of the lesion. The most dramatic deficits are neglect, inattention, denial, visual and spatial perceptual disorders, and constructional disturbances. These may be thought of as nonlinguistic deficits, but as Myers[44] and Tompkins[61] point out, they often have notable influence on communication and result in what Myers terms extralinguistic deficits. These fall in the category of cognitive-communicative deficits rather than aphasia.

If the clinician tests patients with nondominant right hemisphere damage, mild linguistic deficits may be found. Problems that may be noted are difficulty with confrontation naming, word fluency, body part naming, oral sentence reading, writing (especially letter substitutions and omissions), and deficits in auditory comprehension when the input is complex. Although these problems may appropriately be classified as linguistic in nature, a strong argument exists that most of the communication deficits are in reality caused by the nonlinguistic and extralinguistic problems resulting from the brain damage. Attentional problems seem to have a major effect on communication function in patients with damaged right hemispheres.

Box 10-2 lists some of those nonlinguistic and extralinguistic deficits that may be discovered in a careful diagnostic examination of a patient with a right hemisphere lesion, and they are briefly discussed next. As you review these deficits, keep in mind that great variability exists in the incidence and severity of all these symptoms in the population of persons with right hemisphere damage.

Neglect, Inattention, and Denial
Neglect is a syndrome in which a patient fails to recognize one side of the body and the environmental space

---

BOX 10-2

Signs and Symptoms of Nonlinguistic and Extralinguistic Deficits

Nonlinguistic Deficits

Difficulty in recognizing and using significant contextual cues

Difficulty integrating these significant cues into an overall pattern

Extralinguistic Deficits

Distinguishing significant from irrelevant information

Integration and interpretation of contextual information

Inhibiting impulsive responses

Grasping figurative and implied meaning

Topic maintenance and efficiency of expression

Appreciation of the communicative situation and listener needs

Recognizing and/or producing emotional responses

(Modified from Myers, P. S. [1999]. Right hemisphere damage. San Diego: Singular Publishing Group.)

surrounding that side. Patients may use only half of their bodies, even using only one sleeve in their shirts, even though the neglected side of the body is free of paralysis. Neglect of half of the environmental space is not the result of a visual field defect.

The exact neurologic locus of the neglect syndrome with right hemisphere lesions is not exactly known. Chronic parietal lobe damage shows a high correlation with the syndrome. **Unilateral inattention** may be considered a subtle form of the neglect syndrome. Neurologists test for unilateral inattention through a procedure called double simultaneous stimulation, in which all sensory modalities, tactile, auditory, and visual, are tested. Visual testing involves having the patient fixate on a point on the neurologic examiner's face. The examiner moves his or her fingers into both the right and left peripheral visual fields, and the patient reports where the fingers are seen. **Extinction** is present when the patient suppresses stimuli from one side. Extinction may occur in all modalities or in a single modality. When extinction is elicited, the degree of inattention can be assessed by increasing the strength of the stimulus on the inattentive side.

Many patients develop a dramatic **denial** of their neurologic illness; the denial may range from mild to severe and is usually associated with signs neglect as well. An example of severe denial is the patient's lack of recognition of a hemiplegia. The condition was documented by the Russian neurologist Joseph Babinski (1857-1932), who had a patient with a left-sided hemiplegia and left-sided sensory loss who appeared completely unaware of his neurologic deficit. If the patient's hemiplegic arm was placed on the bed along his left side and the neurologist placed his own arm across the patient's waist, the patient would lift the physician's arm aloft. If he were asked to grasp his left arm with his nonparalyzed right arm, he would grasp the physician's arm. Asked to move his paralyzed arm even though his arm was completely hemiplegic, the patient would emphatically say that he could move his arm. Babinski used the term *anosognosia* to describe this unawareness. Anosognosia is sometimes used to describe symptoms of denial other than the ones described here, but it probably is best to limit it to the specific denial impairment Babinski described. Denial is common in right-hemispheric lesions but much less common in left-hemispheric lesions. Anosognosia does not appear to be based on a psychological mechanism but, rather, a more fundamental neurologic mechanism of gnostic loss.

Prosopagnosia

Prosopagnosia refers to the inability to recognize familiar faces and their expressions. The patient recognizes individuals by voice rather than visual perception.

Bilateral lesions usually are found in the occipital-temporal areas in this disorder. The lesion in the right hemisphere is usually in the right temporal-occipital region. A specific type of color agnosia often accompanies prosopagnosia. The lesions that cause the facial recognition deficit also cause the color agnosia.

Visual-Perceptual Deficits

Right hemisphere lesions are associated with deficits in meaningful interpretation and recall of complex visual structures. Deficits in the perception and recall of letters, words, and numbers may produce problems in reading.

Spatial Organizational Deficits

As previously noted, constructional disturbances are present with right or left parietal lobe lesions. In most instances right hemisphere lesions tend to cause more frequent and severe constructional deficits, but constructional deficits can also indicate a left hemisphere lesion.

Prosodic Deficits

A common defect in the right hemisphere syndrome is known as **aprosodia**. Prosody, among other things, conveys appropriate emotional affect. Prosody also carries pragmatic information, allowing a listener to discriminate among questions, statements, and explanations. When normal stress or emphasis is disturbed in a sentence, conveying new information becomes difficult.

Ross[53] has reported widely on patients with deficits of both prosodic production and comprehension. Patients often are unable to provide variations in their voices and have a flat emotional tone. Comprehension defects are called affective aprosodia and may include several distinct components. However, these individuals report being able to feel emotions and hear emotions in the voices of others. Ross has developed a set of eight aprosodias and proposed that motor aprosodia is associated with right frontal damage. He has also suggested that sensory aprosodia is associated with right posterior damage. A motor aprosodia on the right is analogous to a motor aphasia in Broca's area, and a sensory aprosodia on the right is analogous to a Wernicke's aphasia on the left.

Many other neurologists have confirmed the presence of prosodic defects in comprehension and expression, but lesion localization for these and other symptoms in Ross's scheme have not been consistently found in the literature. Various lesion sites of left and right hemisphere aprosodia have been associated with lesions in the basal ganglia of the right or left hemispheres and in the anterior temporal lobe.

Careful and thoughtful consideration of the list of nonlinguistic and extralinguistic deficits in Box 10-2 in the context of discourse and other complex tasks of even routine communication reveals why some patients may have communication disorders that are subtle in nature but devastating to effective, efficient communication interaction. Joanette et al.[32] suggest that these deficits may make it difficult for the person to understand fully the context in which communication is taking place; the person thus appears to demonstrate a change in attitude when facing a communication situation and is often ineffective because of these factors.

DEMENTIA

Cummings and Benson[15] adopted the following operational definition of **dementia**: "an acquired persistent impairment of intellectual function with compromise in at least three of the following spheres of mental activity: language, memory, visuospatial skills, emotion or personality, and cognition (abstraction, judgment, executive function, and so forth)" (pp. 1-2). The definition emphasizes that dementia is acquired, is persistent, and does not affect all aspects of intelligence equally. The neurologist and SLP specializing in neurogenic communication disorders should recognize the early features of this syndrome so that the patient and family, if they want, can be proactive to prevent the serious social, economic, and vocational consequences of unrecognized intellectual deterioration.

The incidence and prevalence of dementia are difficult to determine because studies differ vastly depending on how dementia is defined and what particular population is studied. All agree that the incidence of dementia is rising rapidly, with an increasing percentage of the population being affected. This is especially true because most forms of dementia are found in persons older than 65 years, and the number of elderly people in the population is greater than ever before and is expected to rise. The frequency of dementia diagnosis is estimated to be approximately 2% in persons aged 65 to 69 years, 5% in persons aged 75 to 79 years, and 20% for persons between the ages of 85 and 89 years. After age 90, the frequency increases to approximately 30%. The cost of caring for patients with dementia in the United States has been estimated to exceed $30 billion annually.

The causes of dementia are many, and determination of the cause is critical because some dementias can be reversed. Before a diagnosis of dementia of the Alzheimer's type or Pick's disease can be supported, other diseases or disorders that could result in cognitive decline must be ruled out. These are conditions such as ischemic episodes resulting in multiple infarctions, extrapyramidal syndromes (including Huntington's and Parkinson's disease), hydrocephalus, metabolic disorders, toxic disorders, trauma, neoplasms, central nervous system infections, and demyelinating diseases. Even depression can result in cognitive decline and memory loss that mimic the beginning of a dementia such as Alzheimer's. These diseases or conditions, however, have other signs and symptoms of a disease process or a disorder, whereas in the diseases discussed in this section, such as **Alzheimer's disease**, the dementia is the primary symptom.

Classification of Dementias

Cummings and Benson[15] classify the dementias into two basic patterns of neuropsychologic impairment with identified neuroanatomic correlates: cortical and subcortical dementia. A third category of mixed is also noted.

Cortical Dementias

Dementia of the Alzheimer's Type. Alzheimer's disease, or **dementia of the Alzheimer's type (DAT)**, afflicts a high percentage of patients with cortical dementia. Cummings and Benson[15] report that the clinical course of DAT can be divided into three stages, the characteristics of which are fairly agreed on by most experts. These stages and their characteristics are summarized in Table 10-4.

Focal Cortical Dementias. In 1892 Dr. Arnold Pick described atrophy of the frontal lobe with an accompanying dementia in which the patients first presented with psychiatric symptoms and then later developed memory loss, fluent aphasia, and finally a dementia that continued to progress. This syndrome eventually was named after him and is known as Pick's disease. It is quite rare when strict diagnostic criteria are enforced in identification. It has, however, been designated by the National Institute of Neurological Diseases and Stroke as a part of a syndrome complex known as **frontotemporal dementias (FTD)**. The hallmark of FTD is a gradual progressive decline in behavior and/or language. Onset is at a relatively young age (average age of onset is 55-60 years). The clear difference between FTD and DAT is that these patients with FTD retain important features of memory, keep track of day-to-day events, and are fairly well oriented in time and space, unlike patients with DAT. Grouped with Pick's disease under the designation of focal cortical dementias is a complex of disorders of which the SLP should be aware. These disorders are categorized under primary progressive aphasia.

Neuropathology of the Cortical Dementias. The neuropathology of Alzheimer's disease shows the presence of **neurofibrillary tangles** and **amyloid plaques** in the cytoplasm of nerve cells. These plaques, which begin in the walls of small blood vessels, are thought to result from defective enzymes that cause abnormal production of beta-amyloid protein. The tangles are associated

TABLE 10-4
Clinical Features of the Stages of Dementia of the Alzheimer's Type

STAGE	CHARACTERISTICS
Stage I: Mild	Memory for new learning is defective, and remote recall is mildly impaired. Language shows word retrieval problems and some difficulty understanding humor, analogies, and complex implications. The patient may be vague and may not initiate conversation when appropriate. The patient may also show indifference, anxiety, and irritability.
Stage II: Middle	Memory for recent and remote events is more severely affected, and language shows vocabulary diminishment. The patient repeats ideas, forgets topics, has difficulty thinking of words in a category, loses sensitivity to conversational partners, and rarely corrects mistakes. Comprehension is reduced, and language may rely on jargon and paraphasias. The patient becomes increasingly indifferent, irritable, and restless.
Stage III: Late	Memory is severely impaired, as are all intellectual functions. Language is rarely used meaningfully, and some patients are mute or echolalic. Motor function is compromised by limb rigidity and flexion posture.

with an abnormal tau protein production and are made up of clumps of these microtubules. These tangles are pronounced in certain granular layers of the inferior temporal lobe, which has connections with the hippocampus.[18] Tangles also tend to accumulate in the amygdala and in the posterior association regions of the cortex. In an individual the two hemispheres may show differences in the density of the tangles. Eventually the tangles are replaced by amyloid. Cortical dementia shows extensive loss of pyramidal neurons in all parts of the brain and a loss of up to 50% of cholinergic neurons from the production areas in the basal nucleus of Meynert and from the septal area. Microscopic examination of the brain tissue of persons with DAT also shows neuritic plaques, which are remains of degenerated nerve fibers.

Subcortical and Mixed Dementias
Subcortical dementias may accompany extrapyramidal syndromes (as in Parkinson's disease and

Huntington's chorea), depression, some white matter diseases (such as multiple sclerosis and AIDS-related encephalopathy), and some vascular diseases causing lacunar states. With subcortical dementias, cognition slowly and progressively deteriorates. Forgetfulness and alterations of affect are noted. Retrieval in memory is often aided by cues and structure. In mood, the person may appear depressed or apathetic with decreased motivation. The cognitive impairment has been described as one of dilapidation. Patients seem to be unable to synthesize and manipulate information to produce sequential steps to solve a complex problem, although they may correctly perform individual steps. The neurologic examination of these patients is abnormal, with motor, posture, tone, and speech problems noted.

The mixed cortical-subcortical dementias result from such entities as multiple infarcts, toxic and metabolic encephalopathy, trauma, neoplasms, and anoxia. The mixture of characteristics depends on the parts of the brain affected by the disease, trauma, or dementing process.

Role of the Speech-Language Pathologist in Dementia
The SLP usually is called on to help identify subtle language disorders that may signal intellectual deterioration because language is highly sensitive to even mild changes in brain function. The purpose of the assessment by the SLP may be to assist in making the differential diagnosis by trying to determine whether true aphasia, apraxia, or amnesia is present without language involvement. In Alzheimer's disease, the clinician may be asked to assess the effect of the intellectual deterioration on functional communication and suggest ways that family and other caregivers might improve communication with the patient. In some cases, the SLP may provide a short period of treatment oriented toward training family and other caregivers on how to facilitate and maintain communication with the individual with dementia for as long as possible. In cases of PPA, especially before evidence of much cognitive decline, the SLP works closely with the patient and the family to give them strategies to cope with the changing ability to communicate. Specific treatment targeted at providing alternative communication methods to patients with PPA has been found to show promise if the patients do not have concomitant cognitive deficits.[47]

ACUTE CONFUSIONAL STATES

Several conditions produce confusion, which is characterized by rapid onset over a period of hours or days.

The causes of confusion include metabolic imbalance, adverse drug reactions, and alcohol and drug withdrawal reactions. Patients generally are inattentive, incoherent, and irrelevant; they demonstrate fluctuating levels of consciousness. Agitation and hallucinations, usually visual, often are present. Acute confusional states generally respond to primary medical treatment. Confusional states usually are not the result of focal brain lesions; widespread cortical and subcortical neuronal dysfunction generally is present. Confusional symptoms also are seen during the period of posttraumatic amnesia in traumatic head injury.

Symptomatic language impairment is seen in confusional states. The language disturbance may be viewed as a secondary symptom of the confusional state. Halpern et al.[31] reported on the language symptoms of patients with confused language in contrast to other language impairments of cerebral involvement. Lesions in these patients were either bilateral or multifocal. Vocabulary and syntax generally were normal. The most striking feature of the language of these confused patients was its irrelevancy and confabulatory nature. Other investigators also have found irrelevant language response and confabulation in dementia, so it is not a pathognomic feature of confused states.

Confabulation is the verbal or written expression of fictitious experiences, generally filling a gap in memory. It is less marked in the presence of aphasia because it is a response in which the language areas must be relatively intact. Confabulation is more often associated with generalized cerebral deficit or dysfunction rather than focal lesions. Some instances in which focal lesions are associated with confabulation are in the Wernicke-Korsakoff amnestic syndrome and in ruptured aneurysms of the anterior communicating artery.

TRAUMATIC BRAIN INJURY

Traumatic brain injury (TBI) is defined by the Brain Injury Association as "an alteration in brain function, or other evidence of brain pathology, caused by an external force."[8] The total combined rate of TBI-related emergency department visits, hospitalizations, and deaths sharply rose between 2008 and 2010 with the rate in 2010 being 823.7 per 100,000.[11] This increase was driven largely by an increase in the number of TBI-related ED visits; the rate of hospitalization remained relatively stable (91.7 per 100,000 in 2010) while the death rate decreased slightly (17.1 per 100,000 in 2010).[11] The primary causes of TBI for nonmilitary situations are falls, motor vehicle accidents or related incidents, and assaults. For military

personnel in war zones, blasts are the leading cause of TBI. Risk is higher for men than for women and for persons between the ages of 0 to 4 years and 15 to 19 years.[35] The direct medical costs and the indirect costs in loss of productivity are estimated to be in the billions.

Knowledge about the deficits resulting from TBI has greatly increased over the past 10 years, as have the number of rehabilitation programs and treatment methods devoted to TBI. Patients usually display the language of confusion but often present a more serious and pervasive language deficit, now termed a *cognitive-communicative disorder* or a *cognitive-linguistic disorder.*

Neuropathology of Injury

The predominant type of injury, outside of a combat situation, is an acceleration-deceleration injury, in which the head accelerates and then suddenly stops, such as in a motor vehicle accident. Because of the laws of physics, the hard object (the skull) will move faster than the softer object (the brain tissue encased within). With the speed differentiation, the brain will still be moving as the skull stops abruptly upon hitting the windshield or the ground. The brain tissue then will hit the skull. Discrete focal lesions may result from this direct impact force (known as *coup* damage). Contusions may be found at the point of direct impact, and evidence of brain damage may be present at the site opposite the point of direct impact. Damage sustained at the site opposite the point of impact is called *contrecoup* damage. When there is focal damage, frontal (frontopolar and orbitofrontal) and temporal (anterior temporal, but not necessarily medial temporal) lobes are the most likely sites.[1]

Pioneering research in 1941[21] showed that a blow to a moving head produced devastating damage while a blow to a rigidly fixed head produced very little brain damage. Although not always the case, there is commonly an expectation, when considering the cause of the trauma, that a person who, for example, was hit with a baseball bat in an assault would sustain less total damage to the brain than the person who sustained a head injury in a motorcycle accident. Frequently with acceleration-deceleration injuries, no evidence exists of *focal* lesions, but *diffuse* brain injury is present as a result of several factors, one of those being molecular commotion. The molecular structure of the brain is disrupted as the impact force causes acceleration, rotation, compression, and expansion of the brain within the skull. Another factor causing devastating diffuse injury occurs as the brain tissues are compressed, torn apart, and sheared on the bony prominences of the skull, resulting in diffuse axonal injury (DAI). These forces placed on the axon trigger processes within the tissue such as breakage of the microtubules and destabilization of the cytoskeleton; this damage impairs rapid axonal transport. Fluid may collect in the axon at the various points of disruption causing swelling at those points, giving it a beaded appearance.[59] Sufficient localized swelling may, over time, cause the axon to rupture, a process called secondary axotomy.[59] DAI can result in permanent microscopic alterations of white and gray matter.

DAI, even severe DAI, may occur without skull fracture or cortical contusion. This accounts for the fact that CT scans in the emergency department may show no abnormality. In nonhuman primate models, DAI has been produced just on rapid acceleration of the head with no impact as well as in cases of mild brain injury in which the nonhuman primate had only transitory alterations in the level of consciousness (e.g., in sports such as football and in blast-related TBI).

DAI and focal lesions are primary mechanisms of injury in traumatic brain insult. Secondary mechanisms that occur as a result of the initial direct forces also cause further brain damage. These secondary mechanisms of injury include ischemia, hypoxia, edema, hemorrhage, brain shift, and raised intracranial pressure (ICP). They all may produce further deleterious effects on brain function, and medical/surgical efforts in the emergency department are often targeted at treating or preventing secondary injury to improve the prognosis. Such procedures may include a blood transfusion, placing the patient in a drug-induced coma, performing a craniotomy or removing a part of the skull, or administering hormone therapy.

Neurobehavioral Effects

The neurobehavioral sequelae of moderate to severe TBI are usually divided into two classes: focal deficits and diffuse deficits. Focal deficits may be manifested as a specific language deficit (aphasia, alexia, agraphia, etc.) or as a paralysis of specific muscles or muscle groups. Disorders such as mutism, dysarthria, palilalia, voice disorder, hearing loss, and visual or auditory perceptual dysfunction may be considered focal deficits. If present they are complicating factors in rehabilitation efforts and their specific treatment may be enormously complicated by the presence of diffuse deficits.

Diffuse deficits are more common and are most often manifested as cognitive disorganization. Ylvisaker and Szekeres[64] note that the cognitive processes of attention, perception, memory, learning, organization, reasoning, problem solving, and judgment are affected. These aspects of cognition and the possible effects of their disruption on behavior and language are outlined in Table 10-5.

Assessment and Treatment

Although standard aphasia batteries are used in assessing the language impairment in TBI, testing must extend beyond these batteries in most cases. As examination of Table 10-5 reveals, the cognitive and communicative deficits of TBI can be quite different from the aphasia of a patient with a vascular lesion. The SLP must attempt to determine which, and to what degree, cognitive processes underlying language performance are disrupted and must also determine whether the language impairment has a true aphasic component. Informal or formal testing and observation with assessment scales such as the Rancho Los Amigos Levels of Cognitive Recovery[29] can help the team members identify the patient's best level of cognitive functioning throughout the course of rehabilitation. Parrish and colleagues[46] established a protocol they were testing to help identify the cognitive communication problems of returning combat veterans with mild TBI. This protocol consisted of a rating scale, selected portions of the Woodcock-Johnson III, the Functional Assessment of Verbal Reasoning and Executive Strategies (FAVRES), and the Attention Process Training Test as well as informal measures of conversation collected while the patients were in a group situation.

MILD TRAUMATIC BRAIN INJURY

Earlier we noted that the number of TBI-related emergency department visits has increased sharply in the past several years. Of those persons receiving urgent care, approximately 80% were probably treated for a mild TBI based on symptoms at the time they were injured. These symptoms are typically described as feeling dazed or confused, "seeing stars," or as experiencing a brief loss of consciousness or a brief amnesia period.[59] The following is a definition of mild traumatic brain injury (mTBI) established in 2004 through collaboration of the World Health Organization and the Centers for Disease Control and Prevention (CDC):[10] "MTBI is an acute brain injury resulting from mechanical energy to the head from external physical forces. Operational criteria for clinical identification include: (1) one or more of the following: confusion or disorientation, loss of consciousness for 30 min or less, post-traumatic amnesia for less than 24 h, and/or other transient neurologic abnormalities such as focal signs, seizure, and intracranial lesion not requiring surgery; and (2) Glasgow Coma Scale score of 13–15 after 30 min postinjury or later upon presentation for healthcare. (3) These manifestations of MTBI must not be due to drugs, alcohol, medications, caused by other injuries or treatment for other injuries (e.g., systemic injuries, facial injuries or intubation), caused by other

TABLE 10-5

Cognitive Impairment after Traumatic Brain Injury: Effect on Behavior and Language

ASPECT OF COGNITION	EFFECT ON BEHAVIOR	EFFECT ON LANGUAGE
Attention Holding objects, events, words, or thoughts in consciousness	Short attention span; distractible, weak concentration	Decreased auditory comprehension, confused or inappropriate language, poor reading comprehension, poor topic maintenance
Perception Recognizing features and relations among features	Weak perception of relevant features; possible specific deficits (including field neglect); poor judgment based on visual or auditory cues; stimulus bound (i.e., focus on part of the whole); spatial disorganization	Difficulty in reading and writing, poor comprehension of facial and intonation cues
Memory and Learning Encoding: recognizing, interpreting, and formulating information, including language, into an internal code (knowledge base, personal interests, and goals affect what is coded) Storage: retaining information over time Retrieval: transferring information from long-term memory to consciousness	Memory problems, inability or inefficiency in learning new material	Difficulty following multistep directions, word-finding problems, difficulty with reading comprehension and spelling, poor integration of new and old information; language may be fragmented, lacking logic, order, specificity, and precision; difficulty with math also seen
Organizing Processes Analyzing, classifying, integrating, sequencing, and identifying relevant features of objects and events; comparing for similarities or differences; integrating into organized descriptions, higher level categories, and sequenced events	Poor organization of tasks and time; difficulty setting and maintaining goals; poor problem solving, self-direction, self-confidence, and social judgment	Disorganized language (verbal and written), difficulty discerning main ideas and integrating them into broader themes, poor conversational skills (may get lost in details), difficulty outlining material for study, difficulty with math
Reasoning Considering evidence and drawing inferences or conclusions; involves flexible exploration of possibilities (divergent thinking) and use of past experience	Concrete, impulsive, and reactionary; may be easily swayed; vulnerable to propaganda; difficulty discerning cause and effect and consequences of behavior; poor social judgment	Difficulty understanding and expressing abstract concepts; socially inappropriate, lack of tact; difficulty using language to persuade, understand humor, learn academic subjects, and follow complex conversations
Problem Solving and Judgment Problem solving: ideally involves identifying goals, considering relevant information, exploring possible solutions, and selecting the best solutions Judgment: deciding to act or not to act based on consideration of relevant factors, including prediction of consequences	Impulsive, uses trial-and-error approach, difficulty predicting consequences of behavior, shallow reasoning; poor safety and social judgment, inflexible thinking, poor self-direction, poor use of compensatory strategies	Difficulty understanding and expressing steps in problem solving to get a particular outcome; difficulty in math and higher academic tasks, socially inappropriate behavior, lack of tact, difficulty in understanding explanations for behavior

Modified from Szekeres, S. F., Ylvisaker, M., & Holland, A. L. (1985). Cognitive rehabilitation therapy: A framework for intervention. In M. Ylvisaker (Ed.), *Traumatic brain injury rehabilitation: Children and adolescents.* ed. 2, Boston, 1998, Butterworth-Heinemann.

problems (e.g., psychological trauma, language barrier or coexisting medical conditions) or caused by penetrating craniocerebral injury " (p. 115).

The terms *mild TBI* and *concussion* are mostly used interchangeably, although some believe that concussion is a subtype of mTBI. In the TBI literature, a type of injury called *subconcussive* may be diagnosed. This refers to a traumatic impact to the head that does not result in any immediately appreciable clinical symptoms. It is believed that many people who experience a mild TBI, even with some symptoms experienced, do not seek medical care; because of this, the estimate by the CDC is that the true incidence of mTBI may be close to 3.8 million annually. Although prognosis is fairly good, given appropriate rest and education about mTBI, studies on civilian populations are suggesting that between 10% and 30% of persons with a mTBI may develop some long-term residual deficits postinjury. Particularly in older persons (55 and up), a TBI may place that person at higher risk for the development of Alzheimer's or Parkinson's disease.[24]

In the twenty-first century the incidence of identified mTBI has risen greatly due to the recognition of the possibility and probability of neurobehavioral deficits after what was once referred to as a "mild concussion." This occurred in many sports, especially football, although other sports certainly put the athlete at risk for concussion or brain injury due to a single or repetitive blows to the head.

The other persons at extreme risk are military personnel who are in combat areas in which the use of explosives (bombs, grenades, land mines, mortar/artillery shells) is commonplace. In fact, brain injury has become known as the signature wound of the wars in the Middle East. The use of improvised explosive devices (IEDs) increased exponentially in the wars in Afghanistan and Iraq. With this, a new etiology of brain injury, *blast injury*, began to be studied as it was realized that the mechanism of injury was different from other blows to the head and that the symptoms described by the soldiers were somewhat the same and somewhat different from other types of trauma. Military medical personnel also realized with further study that the frequent accompanying disorder called *posttraumatic stress disorder*, or PTSD, was complicating the deficits experienced due to the blast injury itself.

The brain injury that results from a blast can be more complex than that caused by a motor vehicle accident or a sports injury. The injury results from the complex pressure wave generated by the blast. This pressure results from an instant rise in the atmospheric pressure around the body that is much higher than tolerated by humans. It is called a blast overpressurization wave. This is followed rapidly by blast-underpressurization, which creates a relative vacuum effect. These extreme pressure differences result in both stress and shear wave forces as the waves hit the body of anyone near the blast.[9]

There are four basic mechanisms of injury to the persons around the blast[9]:
- Primary blast injury—the explosion itself resulting in the overpressurization wave. It dissipates quickly, causing the most injury to those closest to the explosion.
- Secondary blast injury—the injury caused by energized fragments, perhaps resulting in penetrating brain injuries.
- Tertiary blast injury—the injury resulting from being thrown from the area of the blast.
- Quatermary blast injury—results from significant blood loss or from inhalation of toxic gases.

Even though the rate of TBI related to blast exposure is high given our recent military conflicts, the research to definitively differentiate effects on the brain of blast injury from the types of TBI experienced by the civilian population has been difficult to do. The frequency of injury from only the primary blast is low, so there are confounding etiologies. The modeling, for obvious reasons, must be based on animal models and, thus, is confounded by the difference in size and shape of the human head versus those of the research animals. There has been little consensus among researchers as to which computational or physical model is best to use to scale the differences.[50] There have been differences found in measures of white matter integrity[57,58] and neural activation during response inhibition using magnetic resonance imaging.[23] One study comparing victims of primary blast injury with a group injured through blunt force trauma found blast injury resulted in greater hypometabolism in the right superior parietal region. These patients showed significantly greater difficulty on measures of attentional control, possibly indicating involvement of the parietal-frontal attentional network.[39]

CHRONIC TRAUMATIC ENCEPHALOPATHY

A neuropathologic condition known as **chronic traumatic encephalopathy (CTE)** has been linked to repetitive instances of mild TBI. Historically, late-life behavioral changes in boxers were described and the term *punch drunk* was the given descriptor; later, in 1937, the term *dementia pugilistica* was used to designate the symptoms of cognitive, motor, and behavioral changes seen in boxers.[51] Upon further study of brain injury, particularly related to sports injuries, it became apparent that the disease was not limited to only the sport of boxing. Case studies also began to be reported of nonathletes who experienced repetitive brain injury from different causes (e.g., domestic abuse, head-banging behavior, injury during seizure activity) and later began to exhibit the described symptoms. The term chronic traumatic encephalopathy was introduced in the middle of the twentieth century.

Descriptions of symptoms of CTE include a wide spectrum of changes in behavior, cognition, and motor skill. Problems with attention, memory, and executive function are noted in most cases. In 2008 an organization called the Sports Legacy Institute formally affiliated with the Boston University School of Medicine in a multidisciplinary research initiative to study all aspects of CTE.[51] The clinical criteria for diagnosis in a living patient are not yet agreed on. The pathology of CTE, however, has begun to be described through autopsy studies. CTE is reported to be characterized by a distinctive pattern of progressive brain atrophy with accumulation of tau neurofibrillary and glial tangles, microvascular pathology, neuroinflammation, and degeneration of white matter, among other pathologic changes.[17,14] The Boston University research found that the location and distribution of the tau deposits help distinguish CTE from some of the other well-known neurodegenerative disorders such as Alzheimer's disease and Parkinson's disease.[61] In CTE the tau tangles tended to form in an irregular distribution pattern in the frontal and temporal areas of the cortex, clustered in dense patches in the depths of the sulci and in the more superficial layers of the cortex. Also important was the finding that beta-amyloid deposits, which are a hallmark sign of Alzheimer's, were observed in fewer than half of the brains of persons with CTE. Thus at the time of this writing, the confirmation of CTE can only be done postmortem.

THE ROLE OF THE SLP

In any patient with any degree of cognitive-communicative deficit after a TBI, the SLP is a critical part of a rehabilitation team. Although the involvement with the patients with mild TBI may be brief (but important), the most successful rehabilitation of patients with moderate to severe TBI is known to be intensive and long term in nature. Much of what is done to overcome the resulting deficits in attention, memory, reasoning, and problem solving, which are the basis of the difficulty in communication, involves training the individual to self-monitor the use of strategies that enable adaptation of his or her external and internal environment to compensate for weaknesses. Follow-up with patients who have had success in vocational and social life after TBI has shown that the ability to incorporate these strategies and adapt them to new challenges seems to be key.[55]

Synopsis of Clinical Information and Applications for the Speech-Language Pathologist

- Aphasia is an acquired disorder of language caused by focal brain damage that can affect any of the four modalities: listening, speaking, reading, and writing.
- The most common etiology of aphasia is CVA, or stroke, which occurs when the arterial distribution to a part or all of the perisylvian language cortex is interrupted. This interruption by a stroke is caused by occlusion of an artery or by hemorrhage resulting from arteriovenous malformation, aneurysm, or trauma.
- Aphasia may also be found after focal lesion caused by trauma, abscess from brain infection, or brain tumor.
- Brain tumors, which primarily arise from neuroglia, are classified according to their origin. Tumors are also graded from I to IV according to the tumor's tendency to spread.
- The most popular aphasia classification system is the Boston classification, which includes Broca's, Wernicke's, conduction, global, anomic, transcortical motor, transcortical sensory, and mixed transcortical aphasias. Each type has a characteristic profile relative to comprehension, fluency, repetition, reading, and writing.
- The aphasias classified well by the Boston system are also relatively consistent with the site of the lesion, although many questions still exist concerning the traditional localization, especially in conduction aphasia. Anomic aphasia does not localize damage well because storage and retrieval of words seem to be widely diffused in the brain.
- Subcortical damage to parts of the basal ganglia, thalamus, and internal capsule has been found to result in particular patterns of communication difficulty consistent with aphasia.
- The SLP is a critical member of the rehabilitation team for persons with aphasia, providing the most complete evaluation and setting treatment goals and plans.
- Some advances have been made in the use of pharmacologic treatment in aphasia, but the drugs

Continued

Synopsis of Clinical Information and Applications for the Speech-Language Pathologist—cont'd

studied have always been found to be most effective when combined with behavioral treatment provided by speech pathology.

- Central disturbances associated with aphasia are agnosia, apraxia, alexia, and agraphia. Alexia is a disorder of reading imposed on literate individuals after brain damage. The classic aphasias have associated reading deficits. Two other classifications exist: alexia without agraphia and alexia with agraphia. Psycholinguistic classifications of reading deficits also have been made: deep dyslexia, surface dyslexia, and phonologic alexia.
- Agraphia is a deficit in producing written language.
- Cognitive-communicative disorders are communication disorders related to damage to the nondominant hemisphere or diffuse brain damage. Communication deficits associated with right

hemisphere damage, dementia, and TBI are classified as cognitive-communicative disorders.

- The communication deficit associated with right hemisphere damage is primarily related to extralinguistic deficits rather than the true linguistic deficits such as problems with word retrieval, syntax, comprehension, reading, and writing. Attention has a major effect on the communicative effectiveness of these patients.
- Patients with right hemisphere damage have difficulty with distinguishing relevancy, integrating and interpreting context cues, inhibiting impulsive responses, maintaining topic maintenance and efficient expression, grasping figurative language, and producing and responding to emotional responses.

CASE **STUDY**

A 61-year-old man noticed a "stutter" and difficulty expressing himself soon after a stressful situation. His dysfluency became more obvious over the next 2 years, and his wife began to notice that he had difficulty with auditory comprehension as well. Audiometric testing revealed only a mild bilateral high-frequency hearing loss. Evaluation at this 2-year mark found normal performance on "bedside" neurologic examination of memory, calculations, general information, and copying of geometric figures. Speech was described as hesitant with occasional literal and verbal paraphasic errors and a marked tendency to add extra syllables to words (palilalia). Comprehension testing found him needing extra repetitions to perform even one-step commands presented verbally, but he could readily follow complex written commands. On the Boston Diagnostic Aphasia examination (Fig. 10-7) he did have some difficulty with reading but only at the complex paragraph level. Writing was hesitant and contained numerous spelling errors (Fig. 10-8, *A*). Repeat evaluations were done over the next 2 years, showing a pattern of progressive

deterioration of auditory comprehension, speech intelligibility, and writing. Reading comprehension was slower to deteriorate, but by 4 years after onset, he could comprehend only some single words written to try to aid communication. His wife reported mild forgetfulness at home, and he showed impaired visual memory and learning on neuropsychologic testing. He remained well groomed and socially appropriate with recognition of examiners who worked with him.

Questions for Consideration

1. This patient is an example of what condition discussed in this chapter?
2. Computed tomographic scans of this patient showed generalized cortical atrophy and ventricular enlargement. If more definitive imaging such as MRI had been available, what would it likely have shown as the focus of the atrophy?
3. The long-term retention of the ability to copy geometric figures and draw a clock would speak to the intactness of which part of the brain?

FIGURE **10-7**

Connected-speech elicitation picture (commonly referred to as the cookie theft picture) from the Boston Diagnostic Aphasia Examination. (Reprinted from Goodglass, H., Kaplan, E., & Barresi, B. [2001]. *The assessment of aphasia and related disorders* [3rd ed.]. Philadelphia: Lippincott, Williams & Wilkins.)

FIGURE **10-8**

Writing samples from four administrations of the paragraph writing subtest of the Boston Diagnostic Aphasia Exam describing the cookie theft picture (see Fig. 10-7 above). Samples **A** and **B** were done 2 months apart, approximately 2 years after the first symptoms of difficulty with speech were first noted by the patient. Sample **C** was done 1 year after **B** and sample **D** 1 year after **C**.

REFERENCES

1. Adamovich, B. L. B., & Henderson, J. A. (1990). Traumatic brain injury. In L. L. LaPointe (Ed.), *Aphasia and related neurogenic language disorders*. New York: Thieme.
2. Alexander, M. P., & Naeser, M. A. (1988). Cortical-subcortical differences in aphasia. In F. Plum (Ed.), *Language, communication and the brain*. New York: Raven Press.
3. Ball, A. L., Griffith, N., & Al-Fwaress, F. (2006). Constraint-induced aphasia treatment in patients with chronic language impairment after stroke. *Neurology, 66*(Suppl. 2), A324–A325.
4. Barwood, C. B. (2012). Improved receptive and expressive language abilities in nonfluent aphasic stroke patients after application of rTMS: An open protocol case series. *Brain Stimulation, 5*, 274–286.
5. Beauvois, M. F., & Derousne, J. (1979). Phonological alexia: Three dissociations. *Journal of Neurology, Neurosurgery and Psychiatry, 42*, 1115–1124.
6. Benson, D. F. (1979). *Aphasia, alexia, and agraphia*. New York: Churchill Livingstone.
7. Bogousslavsky, J., Rehli, F., & Uske, A. (1988). Thalamic infarcts: Clinical syndromes, etiology, and prognosis. *Neurology, 38*, 837–848.
8. Brain Injury Association of America. (2011). Retrieved from. http://www.biausa.org/about-brain-injury.html definitions, February 3, 2016.
9. BrainLine. (2012). Blast injuries and the brain. Retrieved from Brainlinemilitary http://www.brainlinemilitary.org/content/2010/12/blast-injuries-and-the-brain.html.
10. Carroll, L. C. (2014). Methodological issues and research recommendations for mild traumatic brain injury: The WHO Collaborating Centre Task Force on Mild Traumatic Brain Injury. *Journal of Rehabilitation Medicine, 36*(43), 113–125.
11. Centers for Disease Control and Prevention (2014). Injury prevention and control: traumatic brain injury. Retrieved from http://www.cdc.gov/traumaticbraininjury/data/rates.html.
12. Cherney, L. R., Patterson, J. P., Raymer, A., Frymark, T., & Schooling, T. (2008, October). Evidence-based systematic review: Effects of intensity of treatment and constraint-induced language therapy on individuals with stroke-induced aphasia. *Journal of Speech, Language and Hearing Research, 51*, 1282–1299.
13. Coltheart, M., Patterson, K., & Marshall, J. C. (Eds.). (1980). *Deep dyslexia*. London: Routledge and Kegan Paul.
14. Coughlin, J. W. (2015, February). Neuroinflammation and brain atrophy in former NFL players: An invivo multimodal imagining pilot study. *Neurobiological Disorders, 74*, 58–65.
15. Cummings, J. L., & Benson, D. F. (1992). *Dementia: A clinical approach* (2nd ed.). Boston: Butterworth-Heinemann.
16. Damasio, H. (1981). Cerebral localization of the aphasias. In M. T. Sarno (Ed.), *Acquired aphasia* (pp. 27–50). New York: Academic Press.
17. Daneshvar, D. G., Goldstein, L. E., Kiernan, P. T., Stein, T. D., & McKee, A. C. (2015). Post-traumatic neurodegeneration and chronic traumatic encephalopathy. *Molecular and Cellular Neurosciences, 66*(Part B), 81–90.

18. Davis, A. (1993). *A survey of adult aphasia and related disorders.* Englewood Cliffs, NJ: Prentice-Hall.

19. de Boissezon, X., Peron, P., de Boysson, C., & Demonet, J. F. (2006). Pharmacology of aphasia: Myth or reality? *Brain and Language, 102,* 114–125.

20. Dejerine, J. (1891). Sur un cas de cecite verbal avec agraphie, suivi d'autopsie. *Mémoires de la Société de Biologie, 3,* 197–201.

21. Denny-Brown, D., & Ritchie Russel, W. (1941). Experimental cerebral concussion. *Proceedings of the Royal Society of Medicine, 34,* 691–692.

22. Elsner, B. K. (2013). Transcranial direct current stimulation (tDCS) for improving aphasia in patients after stroke [Review]. *Cochrane Database of Systematic Reviews, 6,* 1–45.

23. Fischer, B. L., Parsons, M., Durgerian, S., Reece, C., Mourany, L., Lowe, M. J., et al. (2014). Neural activation during response inhibition differentiates blast from mechanical causes of mild to moderate traumatic brain injury. *Journal of Neurotrauma, 31,* 169–179.

24. Gardner, R. C., & Yaffe, K. (2015). Epidemiology of mild traumatic brain injury and neurodegenerative disease. *Molecular and Cellular Neuroscience, 66,* 75–80.

25. Gervits, F., Ash, S., Diloyan, M., Morgan, B., Coslett, H., Grossman, M., & Hamilton, R. (2015). Transcranial direct current stimulation for primary progressive aphasia. *Neurology, 84*(Suppl. P1.212).

26. Goodglass, H., & Kaplan, E. (1983). *The assessment of aphasia and related disorders* (2nd ed.). Philadelphia: Lea & Febiger.

27. Gorno-Tempini, M. L., Hillis, A. E., Weintraub, S., Kertesz, A., Mendez, M., Cappa, S. F., et al. (2011). Classification of primary progressive aphasia and its variants. *Neurology, 76,* 1006–1014.

28. Gorno-Tempini, M. L., Dronkers, N. F., Rankin, K. P., Ogar, J. M., Phengrasamy, L., Rosen, H. J., et al. (2004). Cognition and anatomy in three variants of primary progressive aphasia. *Annals of Neurology, 55,* 335–346.

29. Hagen, C., Malkmus, D., & Durham, P. (1979). Levels of cognitive functioning. In *Rehabilitation of the head-injured adult: Comprehensive physical management.* Downey, CA: Professional Staff Association of Rancho Los Amigos Hospital.

30. Haines, D. (2006). *Fundamental neuroscience for basic and clinical applications* (3rd ed.). Philadelphia: Churchill Livingstone.

31. Halpern, H., Darley, F. L., & Brown, J. R. (1973). Differential language and neurologic characteristics in cerebral involvement. *Journal of Speech and Hearing Disorders, 32,* 162–173.

32. Joanette, Y., Goulet, P., & Hannequin, D. (1990). *Right hemisphere and verbal communication.* New York: Springer-Verlag.

33. Kertesz, A. (2006). Western Aphasia Battery-Revised (WAB-R). Toronto, Ontario, Canada, Pearson Canada Assessment, Inc.

34. Kertesz, A., Lau, W. K., & Polk, M. (1993). The structural determinants of recovery in Wernicke's aphasia. *Brain and Language, 44,* 153–164.

35. Kirshner, H. S. (1995). *Handbook of neurological speech and language disorders.* New York: Marcel Dekker.

36. Langlois, J. A., Rutland-Brown, W., & Thomas, K. E. (2005). The incidence of traumatic brain injury among children in the United States: differences by race. *Journal of Head Trauma Rehabilitation, 20*(3), 229–238.

37. Lichtheim, L. (1895). On aphasia. *Brain, 7,* 433–484.

38. Luria, A. R., Naydin, V. L., Tsvetkova, L. S., & Vinarskaya, E. N. (1969). Restoration of higher cortical functions following local brain damage. In P. J. Vinken, & G. W. Bruyn (Eds.), *Handbook of clinical neurology. Disorders of higher nervous activity: Vol. 3.* Amsterdam: North Holland.

39. Marshall, I., & Newcombe, F. (1973). Patterns of paralexia: A psycholinguistic approach. *Journal of Psycholinguistic Research, 2,* 175–199.

40. Mendez, M. F., Owens, E. M., Reza Berenji, G., Peppers, D. C., Liang, L. J., & Licht, E. A. (2013). Mild traumatic brain injury from primary blast vs blunt forces: Post concussion consequences and functional neuroimaging. *Neurorehabilitation, 32,* 397–407.

41. Mesalum, M. M. (2003). Primary progressive aphasia—a language-based dementia. *New England Journal of Medicine, 349,* 1535–1543.

42. Mesulam, M. M. (1982). Slowly progressive aphasia without generalized dementia. *Annals of Neurology, 11,* 592–598.

43. Mesulam, M. M., & Weintraub, S. (2014). Is it time to revisit the classification guidelines for primary progressive aphasia? *Neurology, 82,* 1108–1109.

44. Mozaffarian, D., Benjamin, E. J., Go, A. S., Arnett, D. K., Blaha, M. J., Cushman, M., et al. (2015). Heart disease and stroke statistics: 2015 update. A report from the American Heart Association. *Circulation, 131,* e29–e322.

45. Myers, P. S. (1999). *Right hemisphere damage.* San Diego: Singular Publishing Group.

46. Nadeau, S. F., & Rothi, L. G. (2001). Rehabilitation of subcortical aphasia. In R. Chapey (Ed.), *Language intervention strategies in aphasia and related neurogenic communication disorders* (4th ed.). Philadelphia: Lippincott Williams & Wilkins.

47. Parrish, C. R., Roth, C., Roberts, B., & Davie, G. (2009). Assessment of cognitive-communicative disorders of mild traumatic brain injury sustained in combat. *SIG 2 Perspectives on Neurophysiology and Neurogenic Speech and Language Disorders, 19,* 47–57. http://dx.doi.org/10.1044/nnsld19.2.47.

48. Pattee, C., Von Berg, S., & Ghezzi, P. (2006). Effects of alternative communication on the communicative effectiveness of an individual with a progressive language disorder. *International Journal of Rehabilitation Research, 29,* 151–153.

49. Porch, B. E. (1971). Porch Index of Communicative Ability. *Administration, scoring and interpretation (rev. ed.)* (Vol. II). Palo Alto, CA: Consulting Psychologists Press.

50. Radanovic, M., & Scaff, M. (2003). Speech and language disturbances due to subcortical lesions. *Brain and Language, 84,* 337–352.

51. Reid, M. W., & Velez, C. S. (2015). Discriminating military and civilian traumatic brain injuries. *Molecular and Cellular Neuroscience, 66,* 123–128.

52. Riley, D. R., Robbins, C. A., Cantu, R. C., & Stern, R. A. (2015). Chronic traumatic encephalopathy: Contributions from the Boston University Center for the study of traumatic encephalopathy. *Brain Injury, 29*(2), 154–163.

53. Rosenbek, J. C., LaPointe, L. L., & Wertz, R. T. (1989). *Aphasia: A clinical approach.* Boston: College Hill Press.

54. Ross, E. (1981). Aprosodia: Functional-anatomic organization of the affective components of language in the right hemisphere. *Archives of Neurology, 38*, 561–569.

55. Schuell, H. M. (1965). *Minnesota Test for Differential Diagnosis of Aphasia.* Minneapolis: University of Minnesota.

56. Schutz, L. E. (2007). Models of exceptional adaptation in recovery after traumatic brain injury: A case series. *Journal of Head Trauma Rehabilitation, 22*, 48–55.

57. Simmons-Mackie, N. S. (2014). Conversation therapy for aphasia: A qualitative review of the literature. *International Journal of Language & Communication Disorders, 49*, 511–526.

58. Taber, K. H., & Hurley, R. A. (2013, Winter). Update on mild traumatic brain injury: Neuropathology and structural imaging. *Journal of Neuropsychiatry and Clinical Neuroscience, 25*(1), 1–5 .

59. Taber, K. H., Hurley, R. A., Haswell, C. C., Rowland, J. A., Hurt, S. D., Lamar, C. D., & Morey, R. A. (2014). White matter compromise in veterans exposed to primary blast forces. *Journal of Head Trauma Rehabilitation, 30*(1), E15–E25.

60. Taber, K. W. (2006). Blast-related traumatic brain injury: What is known? *Journal of Neuropsychiatry and Clinical Neurosciences, 18*, 141–145.

61. Tanridag, O., & Kirshner, H. S. (1985). Aphasia and agraphia in lesions of the posterior internal capsule and putamen. *Neurology, 35*, 1797–1801.

62. Tompkins, C. A. (1995). *Right hemisphere communication disorders: Theory and management.* San Diego: Singular Publishing Group.

63. Wasserman, J. K., Perry, J. J., Sivilotti, M. L., Sutherland, J., Worster, A., Emond, M., et al. (2015). CT identifies patients at high-risk for stroke after TIA/non-disabling stroke: A prospective, multi-center cohort study. *Stroke, 46*, 114–119.

64. Wicklund, M. R., Duffy, J. R., Strand, E. A., Machulda, M. M., Whitwell, J. L., & Josephs, K. A. (2014). Quantitative application of the primary progressive aphasia criteria. *Neurology, 82*, 1119–1126.

65. Ylvisaker, M., & Szekeres, S. F. (1994). Communication disorders associated with closed head injury. In R. Chapey (Ed.), *Language intervention and strategies in adult aphasia* (3rd ed.). Baltimore: Williams & Wilkins.

11

Pediatrics: The Developing Brain

An examination of infant behavior is an examination of the central nervous system.

Arnold Gesell and Catherine S. Amatruda,
Developmental Diagnosis, 1947

KEY **TERMS**

allocortex
apoptosis
asymmetrical tonic
  neck reflex (ATNR)
bite reflex
cortex
ectoderm
embryo
fetal period
forebrain
  (prosencephalon)
gag reflex
Galant reflex
growth cone
hindbrain
  (rhombencephalon)
induction
mesocortex
mesoderm
midbrain
  (mesencephalon)
mitosis
moro reflex
neocortex
neural plate

neural tube
neuroprogenitor
neuroprogenitor cells
notochord
obligatory
positive support reflex
primary neurulation
prone
rooting reflex
secondary neurulation
segmental rolling
  reflex
spina bifida
suckling reflex
supine
swallowing reflex
symmetrical tonic
  neck reflex
synaptic stabilization
teratology
tongue reflex
tonic labyrinthine
  reflex (TLR)
vesicles

CHAPTER **OUTLINE**

Introduction

This text is unlike many in neuroanatomy in that it starts the student studying the anatomy of the brain by learning the brain structure, function, and disorders using adult models. This approach was used initially and continues into the 6th edition for two reasons. First, many students come into the study of speech-language pathology or audiology knowing little about the brain and sometimes little about the anatomy of the rest of the body as well. As you can certainly agree by now, the number of terms that must be mastered in neuroanatomy is intimidating, and then one must try to understand how all those parts work together to produce movement, sensation, emotion, and thought. The study of embryology throws one immediately into learning how a structure was formed but not necessarily what it does and how it is related to the other structures developing simultaneously. This text is organized so that the student with little knowledge can learn the structures and their location and function and relationship to others first and then learn how they evolved after conception.

The second reason this approach was used is that students assigned to study this depth of material are adults or at least 18 years of age. As adults, we are much more familiar with the movement patterns and cognitive processes of a more mature nervous system than we are of the system we have just or several years ago left behind—that of the young child. Thus it may be much easier to identify with the examples of various functions and, perhaps, effects of injury on function.

Your particular instructor may choose to have you do this part of the text first rather than following the organization of the text; this, of course, is also fine and is in fact fairly typical. At whatever point you are when you are studying the next part of the text, may you find the miracle of the development of this complex nervous system of ours fascinating!

Development of the Nervous System

The embryologic development of the nervous system is an intriguing sequence of events occurring over a brief period. The spinal cord and brain (with the exception of the cerebellum) reach development of their full number of neurons by the 25th week of gestation. This includes the billions of cells of the cerebral cortex, both the neurons and the neuroglial cells.

Dendrites of the neuronal cells begin to develop a few months before birth but are quite primitive in the newborn. In the first year of life dendritic processes develop on each cortical neuron to establish the startling number of connections each nerve cell makes with other neurons. The average number of connections that a single cell will make is within a range of 1000 to 10,000.

EARLY DEVELOPMENT

During the second week after conception, the blastocyst that has been formed from mitosis of the zygote is embedded in the uterus. As this process takes place, the inner cell mass changes and produces a thick, two-layered plate called the embryonic disk. At the beginning of the third week, this mass is referred to as the embryo with the embryonic period lasting through the eighth week.[11] Many embryologists divide the embryonic period into 23 stages called the Carnegie stages,[13] but this depth of detail is beyond the scope of this chapter. The ninth week after fertilization until term (or 38 weeks after the last normal menstrual period) is known as the fetal period.

During the embryonic period, three primary germ layers that give rise to the tissues and organs begin to form at the beginning of the third week. These are the ectoderm, mesoderm, and endoderm. The mesoderm gives rise to muscle, connective tissues, cartilage, bone, and blood vessels, whereas the endoderm forms the linings of the digestive and respiratory tracts. The embryonic ectoderm gives rise to the epidermis and the nervous system. From these few dozen cells of the ectoderm of an almost infinitesimal weight comes the approximately 800-gram brain of the child at birth. Most, although not all, of the neuron cells will complete their cell division before birth.[9]

Also during the third week a cellular rod called the notochord develops. The notochord defines the primitive axis of the embryo and gives it some rigidity. The vertebral column segments will form from the mesoderm around the notochord. Important to embryonic development is a function known as induction, essentially meaning that the proper development of one structure of the nervous system is dependent on the proper development of its neighbors. The notochord is important in induction as it directs the overlying ectoderm to thicken and form the neural plate. The neural plate eventually gives rise to the central nervous system (CNS).

On the eighteenth day of development the neural plate begins folding in along its axis to form a neural groove with neural folds along each side. These folds move together and begin to fuse, with fusion occurring first in the middle and then progressing cranially and caudally. Closure at the cranial end is more rapid than at the caudal end. This fusing of the neural folds forms what is called the neural tube (Fig. 11-1), which then separates from the surface ectoderm. The closure of the neural tube is complete by the end of the fourth week.

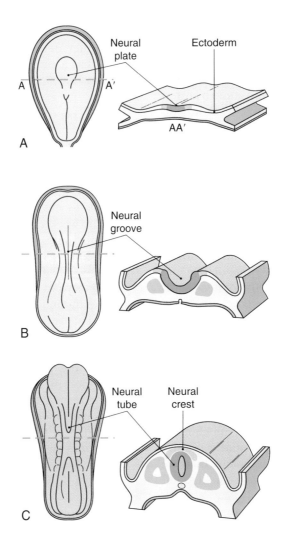

FIGURE **11-1**

Early development of the human nervous system. Drawings on the left are external views; cross-sections are shown on the right. (**A**) Neural cells develop from ectoderm (skin-to-be) cells to form the neural plate. (**B**) The plate folds in to form the neural groove. (**C**) Further folding inwards forms the neural tube. (From Stokes, M. [2012]. *Physical Management in Neurological Rehabilitation* [3rd ed.]. Edinburgh: Mosby Ltd.)

When the neural tube is formed, three layers that consist of four "zones" appear for a brief period. These zones give rise eventually to important adult derivatives. The zones and eventual derivatives are as follows[9]:

- Ventricular zone (VZ): first to appear; contains rapidly dividing neuroprogenitor cells. At least three classes of these cells have been found in the human VZ:[2]
  - Radial glial cells, expressing only glial markers
  - Multipotent precursor cells coexpressing glial and neuronal markers
  - Committed neuronal precursor cells
- Marginal zone: contains few cell bodies; mostly consists of processes of the cells making up the ventricular zone and eventually invaded by axons from the intermediate zone. Becomes layer 1 of the adult cortex

- Intermediate zone: latest to appear and formed between the ventricular and marginal zones; contains immature postmitotic cells migrated from the ventricular zone. Some of their processes will find their way to the marginal zone.
- Subventricular zone: forms between the ventricular and intermediate zones and contains progenitor cells that do not migrate further. They eventually become the macroglial cells of the CNS and some specialized cells of the brainstem and forebrain.

As the neural tube is rising from the ectoderm, the mesodermal layer of the embryo is forming longitudinal columns that soon divide into paired cubelike structures called somites (see Fig. 11-1). Eventually 42 to 44 pairs of somites develop. They form distinct surface elevations on the embryo. These somites differentiate into muscle, bone, and connective tissues (i.e., nonneural tissue).

A cross section of the developing embryo (see Fig. 11-1) shows another activity occurring as the neural folds fuse during the fourth week of development. Some of the neuroectodermal cells that lie along the crest of the neural folds break away from the other cells and migrate to the sides of the neural tube. These cells form the neural crest. The neural crest soon separates into two parts that migrate to the right and left dorsolateral aspects of the tube, where they will give rise to various important structures in the peripheral nervous system (PNS) and to the ganglia of the autonomic nervous system. The dorsal root ganglia of the spinal nerves are derived from the neural crest, as are parts of the ganglia of cranial nerves V, VII, IX, and X. In addition to these ganglion cells, the neural crest also is responsible for Schwann cells and cells forming the meninges of the brain and spinal cord.

At the beginning of the fourth week, the embryo is almost straight, and temporary openings called neuropores appear at the cranial and caudal ends of the tube (see Fig. 11-1). These openings close by the end of the fourth week, and a longitudinal folding at the head (midbrain flexure) and the tail (cervical flexure) areas occurs, giving the embryo a characteristic C-shaped curve. Also during this time, four brachial or pharyngeal arches develop in the head area. Primary derivatives of the first arch are the bones of the jaw, as well as the muscles of mastication. The second, third, and fourth arches primarily give rise to the muscles and cartilages of the face, larynx, and pharynx. Figure 11-2 shows a 5-week-old embryo depicting some of these structures.

As the cranial and caudal ends of the neural tube begin to become more differentiated, cells from the neuroectoderm called **neuroprogenitor cells** begin to flourish. They migrate and differentiate to form specific areas of the brain. By the end of the fourth week of development, the neural tube is closed. After closure, an enlarged rostral region develops containing three subdivisions of the brain. The portion of the neural tube cranial to the fourth pair of somites develops into the brain. A narrow region caudal to the fourth pair of somites develops into the primitive spinal cord (Fig. 11-3).

How the neural tube matures into the mature central nervous system is regulated by a process called neurulation. Haines[9] described two types of neurulation. **Primary neurulation** is the process that forms the brain and the spinal cord through the lumbar vertebrae. **Secondary neurulation** is the process by which the caudal neural tube (and eventually the caudal neural plate) gives rise to the sacral and coccygeal vertebrae. Problems with neural development during the primary or secondary neurulation process lead to dysraphic defects (defects of fusion). A condition called anencephaly can result from a defect of primary neurulation. With this there is

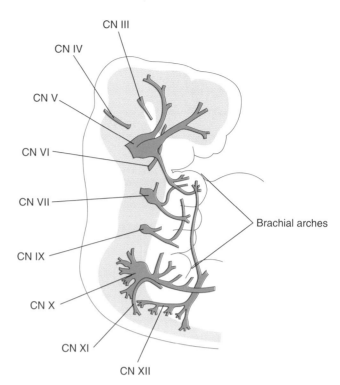

FIGURE 11-2

Schematic drawing of a 5-week-old embryo shows distribution of most of the cranial nerves, especially those supplying the pharyngeal arches. (From Moore, K. L., Persaud, T. V. N., & Torchia, M. G. [2016]. *The Developing Human*: Clinically Oriented Embryology [10th ed.]. Philadelphia: Elsevier.)

FIGURE 11-3

External view of the brain at the end of the fifth week. Primitive spinal cord can be seen inferior to the hindbrain. (From Moore, K. L., Persaud, T. V. N., & Torchia, M. G. [2016]. *The Developing Human*: Clinically Oriented Embryology [10th ed.]. Philadelphia: Elsevier.)

a failure of the anterior neural tube closure. This results in an unformed brain with the skull perhaps not present, and facial deformities. A birth defect related to a defect of secondary neurulation may occur in spinal cord embryologic development and is known as **spina bifida** (Fig. 11-4). In this condition the posterior neural tube fails to completely close, resulting in a cleft of the lower spinal cord. Although not typically fatal, spina bifida may

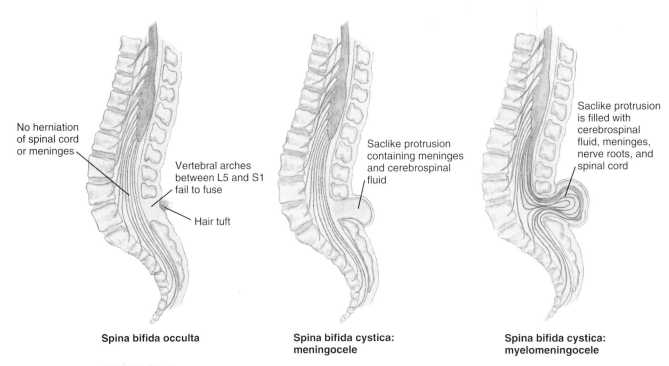

No herniation of spinal cord or meninges

Vertebral arches between L5 and S1 fail to fuse

Hair tuft

Saclike protrusion containing meninges and cerebrospinal fluid

Saclike protrusion is filled with cerebrospinal fluid, meninges, nerve roots, and spinal cord

Spina bifida occulta

Spina bifida cystica: meningocele

Spina bifida cystica: myelomeningocele

FIGURE **11-4**
Three forms of spina bifida. (From James, S., & Ashwill, J. [2013]. *Nursing Care of Children* [4th ed.]. St. Louis: Saunders.)

be accompanied by other CNS defects, especially hydrocephalus. Environmental factors as well as the presence of other CNS insults can result in neurocognitive deficits in addition to the motor impairment in these children.[5]

Embryology of the Peripheral Nervous System

The PNS develops mostly from neural cells and is summarized below:

Neural Elements
Neurons of:
- Posterior root ganglia
- Paravertebral (sympathetic chain) ganglia
- Prevertebral (preaortic) ganglia
- Enteric ganglia
- Parasympathetic ganglia of cranial nerves VII, IX, and X
- Sensory ganglia of cranial nerves V, VII, VIII, IX, and X

Nonneural Elements
- Schwann cells
- Melanocytes
- Odontoblasts
- Satellite cells of peripheral ganglia
- Cartilage of the pharyngeal arches
- Ciliary and papillary muscles
- Chromaffin cells of the adrenal medulla
- Pia and arachnoid of the meninges

- Some of the sensory cells in these ganglia arise from placodes.

Embryologic development of the neural tube forms the cells that arise from the lateral edge of the neural plate, detach, and move laterally to the neural tube. This neural crest gives rise to most of the PNS, as well as to a number of other structures. This early development of the nervous system is illustrated in Figure 11-1.

The PNS also arises from specialized epidermal cells called placodes that are found in the developing head region of the embryo. These cells join neural crest cells, and together placodes and neural crest cells form the ganglia of cranial nerves V, VII, VIII, IX, and X (Fig. 11-5).

Spinal Cord

The spinal cord develops from caudal portions of the neural tube (see Fig. 11-1). The neural canal of this region becomes the central canal of the spinal cord. Neuroblasts that give rise to the spinal cord neurons are produced between the fourth and twentieth week of development by a proliferation in the ventricular layer lining the neural canal. These cells migrate peripherally to form four longitudinal plates. These plates will become the gray matter of the spinal cord. Within this gray matter development a pair of anteriorly located cell masses, which constitute the *basal plate* and a pair

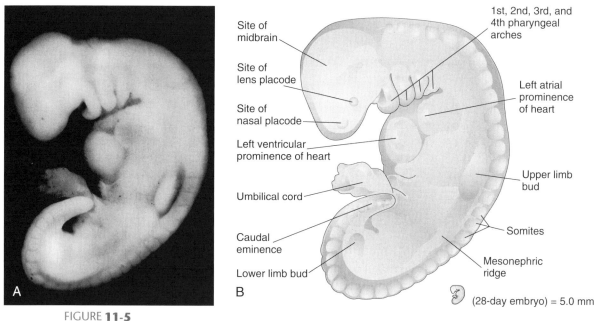

FIGURE **11-5**

A, Lateral view of an embryo at Carnegie stage 13, approximately 28 days. The rostral and caudal neuropores are closed. **B,** Drawing indicating the structures shown in **A.** The embryo has a characteristic C-shaped curvature, four pharyngeal arches, and upper and lower limb buds. (**A,** From Nishimura, H., Semba, R., Tanimura, T., & Tanaka, O. [1977]. *Prenatal development of the human with special reference to craniofacial structures: An atlas.* Washington, DC: National Institutes of Health.)

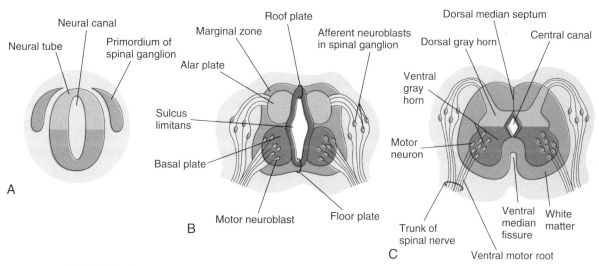

FIGURE **11-6**

Development of the spinal cord. **A,** Transverse section of the neural tube of an embryo of approximately 23 days. **B** and **C,** Similar sections at 6 and 9 weeks, respectively. (From Moore, K. L., Persaud. T. V. N., & Torchia, M. G. [2016]. *The Developing Human*: Clinically Oriented Embryology [10th ed.]. Philadelphia: Elsevier.)

of posteriorly located masses, which constitute the *alar plate*, will be formed. The basal plate develops into the anterior, or ventral, horn of the spinal cord, and the alar plate becomes the posterior, or dorsal, horn of the spinal cord (Fig. 11-6).

The lateral walls of the developing spinal cord thicken differentially into zones. The marginal zone gradually becomes the white matter of the cord as axons grow into it. A shallow groove, called the sulcus limitans, develops on the lateral walls of the developing cord. This groove divides the dorsal lamina, or alar plate, from the ventral lamina, or basal plate. The alar plate or dorsal part of the spinal cord is later associated with afferent (sensory) functions and the basal plate or ventral part of the spinal cord with efferent (motor) functions.

Until the third month of development, the spinal cord extends the entire length of the developing vertebral column. At this time the dorsal (sensory) and ventral (motor) roots of the spinal cord extend laterally from the spinal cord and unite in the intervertebral foramina to form the spinal nerves. The vertebral column elongates at a more rapid rate than the spinal cord, thus making the spinal cord shorter than the vertebral column. At birth the end of the cord, called the conus medullaris, is located at the level of the third lumbar vertebra. In the adult it is located approximately between the first and second lumbar vertebrae. As the differential growth of the two structures takes place, the nerve roots located between the conus medullaris and the intervertebral foramina elongate. The lumbar, sacral, and coccygeal nerve roots are directed downward at an angle to reach their targeted exit point at the associated vertebral foramina. This elongated bundle of nerve fibers is known as the cauda equinus (horse's tail).

Development of the Meninges

Embryologically, the meninges develop from the neural crest and the mesoderm, which eventually develop into the CNS. Both the neural crest and the mesoderm form the primitive meninges.

Development of the Ventricles

The development of the ventricle system illustrates brain growth from the neural crest and neural tube. By about the third week of development, the nervous system consists of a tube that is closed at both ends and is somewhat hook shaped. The cavity of this tube, the neural canal (see Fig. 11-1), eventually gives rise to the ventricles of the adult brain and the central canal of the spinal cord.

Embryology of Cortical and Subcortical Structures

During the fourth week of gestation the neural folds expand and fuse to form three primary brain vesicles. These are the hindbrain, or rhombencephalon; midbrain, or mesencephalon; and forebrain, or prosencephalon. The central canal of the neural tube dilates into

a rudimentary ventricular system, and in the thin roof of the ventricles the choroid plexus develops to produce cerebrospinal fluid (CSF). By about the sixth week of development these divisions have further divided, and significant brain development can be noted. The rhombencephalon divides into the myelencephalon, which later becomes the medulla oblongata, and the metencephalon, which is the future pons and cerebellum. The midbrain or mesencephalon does not divide. The prosencephalon divides into the diencephalon and the telencephalon. The diencephalon later becomes the thalamic complex and the third ventricle (Fig. 11-7). The optic cup, which eventually becomes the optic nerve and retina, also rises from the diencephalon division.

At approximately the third month of development the telencephalon divides into three parts. All the structures of the brain are present, though in quite immature versions, by the end of the third trimester of gestation (Fig. 11-8). The rhinencephalon will contain the olfactory lobes. The second division, the striatal area, is the site of the groups of neuronal cell bodies known as the basal ganglia or basal nuclei. Only in higher vertebrate and human development does the third division of the telencephalon takes place. This division is the suprastriatal structure called the neopallium. This is what is seen as the cerebral hemispheres and what is called the cortex. Figure 11-9 outlines the primary brain vesicles and the ensuing derivational pattern.

The smooth surface of the hemispheres begins to convolute at approximately 20 weeks of gestation, and by week 24 gyri and sulci gradually appear. The first sulcus to appear is the lateral sulcus with its floor, the insula, gradually covered by further development and enfolding. This folding in of the cortical tissue allows this outer layer of neurons to increase greatly, eventually reaching an approximate dimension of 2300 cm^2 without the brain becoming too large for the skull.

We have discussed previously the fact that the cerebral cortex and some subcortical areas are stratified into layers. The cortex begins to stratify into layers and at approximately 6 months of gestation the demarcation of the cortex into layers or lamina is present. The allocortex, or archicortex, which is found primarily in the limbic system cortex, is composed for the most part of three layers. The mesocortex is found as transition cortex between the archicortex and the neocortex. The mesocortex contains three to six layers and is found in regions such as the insula and the cingulate gyrus. The neocortex, or isocortex, of the cerebral hemispheres is composed of six layers. All six layers can be microscopically differentiated early in development, but the final differentiation of the outer three layers is not complete until middle childhood.

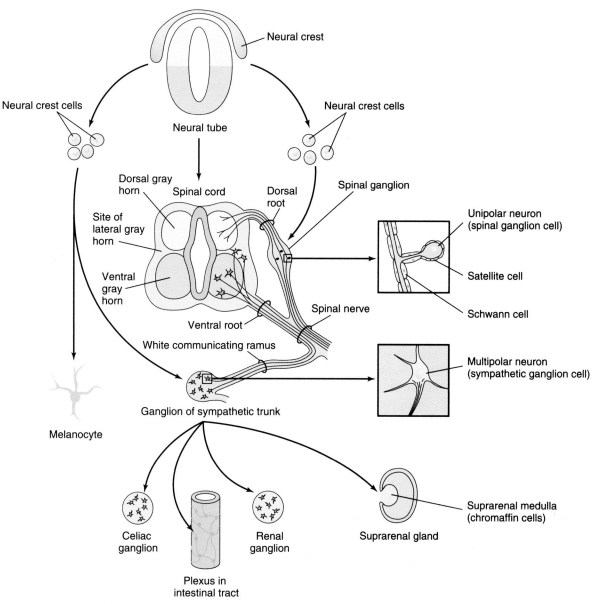

FIGURE 11-7

Diagrammatic sketches of the brain vesicles indicate the adult derivatives of their walls and cavities. The rostral part of the third ventricle forms from the cavity of the telencephalon. Most of this ventricle is derived from the cavity of the diencephalon. (From Moore, K. L., Persaud T. V. N., & Torchia, M. G. [2016]. *The Developing Human*: Clinically Oriented Embryology [10th ed.]. Philadelphia: Elsevier.)

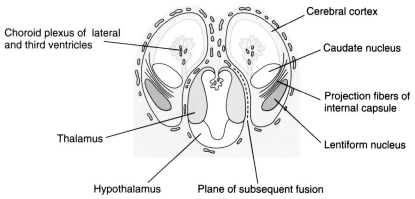

FIGURE 11-8

At 11 to 12 weeks of gestation, rudimentary structure of nearly all the parts of the brain are present. (From Moore, K. L., Persaud T. V. N., & Torchia, M. G. [2016]. *The Developing Human*: Clinically Oriented Embryology [10th ed.]. Philadelphia: Elsevier.)

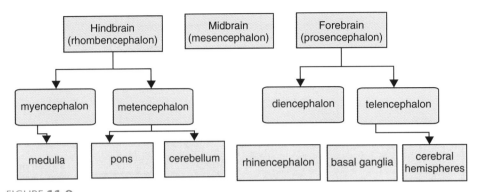

FIGURE **11-9**
Derivatives of the three primary brain vesicles.

Neuronal Migration in the Cerebral Cortex

As all cells in the developing embryo do, neurons migrate from their place of "birth" to where they will eventually function as part of a system. During the formation of the neural tube, neuroprogenitor cells or neuroblasts have begun DNA replication and mitosis, arising in the ventricular zone at the surface of the lateral ventricles. As cells divide and multiply, they cluster at the ventricular surface, thickening the walls of the tube. As they undergo their last division, they start to migrate away from the ventricular surface. At least two types of progenitor cells are active: (1) neuroblasts, which will become neurons; and (2) glioblasts, which will generate astrocytes, oligodendrocytes, and radial glial cells. The embryo will typically produce almost twice as many neurons as will eventually be found in the mature brain. This genetically programmed cell death, or **apoptosis**, is an active cell process and occurs naturally in many areas of the brain through protein synthesis.[9]

Neurons in complex vertebrate nervous systems migrate somewhat differently than in simpler nervous systems. The specific mechanisms of this neural migration are not yet totally understood, and the complex details of the processes that are understood are beyond the scope of this text. The primary modes of migration as presented by Nadarajah and colleagues[12] is briefly summarized here. The student who wishes to explore this further is directed to this article and to the work of Cooper.[1]

The development of the stratification of the cortex is an "inside-out" pattern of development. Neurons that start migrating first go the shortest distance and the later ones migrate through the earlier ones. We previously mentioned zones created in the neural tube. In corticogenesis with the migration of neurons, there are also created what are called *plates* with the preplate,

subplate, and, finally, the cortical plate most often mentioned.

Nadarajah and colleagues[12] employed time-lapsed photography to study the movement of neurons as they position themselves in the developing neocortex. They affirmed two distinct modes of migration for pyramidal neurons, which are excitatory projection neurons:

- Somal translocation: All of the immature neurons are bipolar with a leading process radially oriented toward the pial surface while the other process remains attached initially to the ventricular zone surface. In somal (or perikaryal) translocation, the neuroblasts detach from the VZ. Through a process called nucleokinesis the soma (cell body which contains the nucleus) is transported from the ventricular surface to the pial surface. Nucleokinesis involves a caging of the nucleus by microtubules and the centrosome of the cell. The alternating elongation and contraction of the microtubules move the nucleus and the cell outward to the pial surface. This appears to be the prevalent migratory method of early born cortical neurons.[8]

- Glia-guided locomotion: Figure 11-10 shows the embryologic development of the layers of the cortex as they are formed by glia-guided locomotion. In the very early stages, as outlined earlier, the cerebral new growth is relatively thin, and this kind of guidance is not typical.[12] However, as the cerebral vesicles begin to thicken, neurons migrate primarily by traveling along processes of radial glia that seem to form a scaffolding for them to be guided along. The formation of the cortex of the cerebellum is formed in similar manner. Figure 11-11 is a frame from a movie made at Hatten Laboratories using high-contrast optics.[6] This frame pictures a granule neuron of the cerebellar cortex migrating through glia-guidance. (The website link to the moving images is found in the reference list.[10]) In glia-guided migration, the nucleus will remain in the posterior part of the cell. An adhesion junction forms beneath the nucleus and

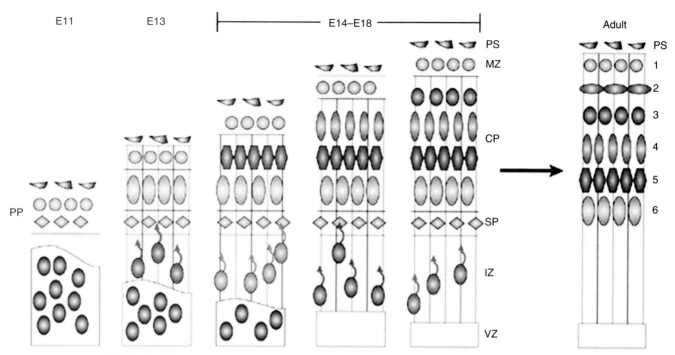

FIGURE **11-10**

Key developmental stages of development of the neocortex of the radial component of the formation of the neocortex of a mouse brain. The mouse brain is used extensively in research on brain development as its embryology is similar to human development. This embryologic time period here represents around 6-18 weeks in human gestation. Migration along radial glia is shown as vertical bars. E = Embryologic day. At E11 the preplate (PP) is established by a postmitotic wave of neurons that has migrated from the ventricular zone (VZ) to the pial surface (PS). By E13 a second postmitotic neuronal wave has migrated through the intermediate zone and split the PP into the marginal zone (MZ) and subplate (SP), creating the cortical plate (CP). During E14-E18 subsequent waves of neurons expand the CP in an inside-out fashion, as each wave of neurons passes its predecessors to settle underneath the MZ. In adulthood, the SP degenerates, leaving behind the six-layered neocortex. (From Gupta, A., Tsai, L-H., & Wynshaw-Boris, A. [2002]. Life is a journey: A genetic look at neocortical develop *Nature Reviews Genetics, 3*, 342–355.)

FIGURE **11-11**

A granular neuron cell of the cerebellar cortex migrating and guided along a radial glial process. (From Gasser, U. E., & Hatten, M. E. [1990]. Central nervous system neurons migrate on astroglial fibers from heterotypic brain regions *in vitro, Proc Natl Acad Sci* 87: 4543–4537.)

a leading process of the cell radiates out toward the direction of migration. The neuron moves by release and reformation of the adhesion junction, moving it along the glia scaffolding it is traveling along.

There are two essential proteins identified as critical to normal formation of the cerebral and cerebellar cortices as well as the hippocampus. The first identified was an extracellular protein called Reelin expressed by the *RELN* gene on chromosome 7q22. This was discovered through histochemical studies of what was called the reeler mouse mutant, a phenotype that had been used in research since the 1950s.[4] Research on Reelin led to the discovery of an intracellular adaptor protein called the Dab1 protein.[3] Dab1 is critical to the signal transduction of Reelin during neuronal migration. Research has also identified Reelin as a multifunctional protein and critical to neuron growth, maturation, and synaptic activity in adult brains.[3] The chemical and genetic signaling that directs the migration of neurons and determines where they are to go is, again, much beyond the scope of this text, but these two proteins can be remembered as critical to the process. The reeler mouse is a mouse with mutations of Reelin expression and has frequently been used as a model to continue advancing research on disorders of neural migration.

MAKING CONNECTIONS

After making their way to the targeted region of the neocortex, the young neurons must establish connections with other neurons and become integrated into neural networks. To do this they develop an axon and also dendrites. The dendrites will eventually form dense arbors of connections near the vicinity of the cell body.[14] Dendritic spines develop and become the site of many of the synaptic contacts onto dendrites. These spines form at different rates in different parts of the brain with the maximal rate occurring at about 6 months after birth.[9]

The axon of each neuron cell contains on its tip a structure called a growth cone. It is from the site of the growth cone that the axon elongates and extends out into the surrounding neural tissue, guided by tropic factors or molecules that send it toward a particular target. Also influencing the axon are trophic factors, which help maintain its metabolism.[9] The axon may branch, and each branch will also contain a growth cone. Some branches established will not ever become innervating connections. On those that do, the growth cone becomes a presynaptic terminal and the target neuron membrane begins to express the necessary postsynaptic mechanism, such as neurotransmitter receptors and second messenger molecules. Although many synapse connections will be made during this period of development, many are later lost or they are replaced by other connections. According to Haines,[9] for synaptic stabilization to take place there must be: (1) signal generation by a presynaptic cell, possibly the neurotransmitter required by the adult synapse; (2) a means for the postsynaptic cell to respond to the signal; and (3) a retrograde signal from the postsynaptic cell to the presynaptic cell to tell it which contacts should remain in maturity. There is competition for synaptic space and the advantage in the developing brain especially is given to the contact used most frequently.

CRITICAL PERIODS

The study of abnormal embryonic development is called teratology. Teratogens are defined as any environmental factor that can produce a permanent abnormality in structure or function, restriction of growth, or death of the embryo or fetus.[7] Commonly the causes of congenital abnormalities are divided into two categories: (1) genetic factors, such as chromosomal abnormalities, and (2) environmental factors, such as medications, drugs, maternal conditions, and chemicals. There are several factors on which the effect an environmental agent will have on a developing embryo depend. A fundamental concept of teratology is that certain stages of embryologic development are more vulnerable to teratogens than are other stages. The most critical period for the growth of a particular organ is the period of most rapid cell division for that particular tissue or organ. Thus the critical period varies depending on the organ of concern. For brain development, the most critical period is from 3 to 16 weeks.[11] Major anomalies occur during the third and fourth week as the neural tube and the neural crest form. The fetal period is also quite susceptible to teratogens, such as alcohol, and future cognitive development may be affected, resulting in some degree of intellectual disability. When labeling an agent or condition as a teratogen, other factors have to also be taken into consideration, such as the route, length, and dose of exposure. Table 11-1 lists some environmental teratogenic agents or conditions that are known to cause CNS deficits given the appropriate timing and condition of exposure or occurrence during brain development.

Primitive Reflexes of the Newborn

The speech-language pathologist, especially those in public schools or centers primarily working with a young child population, must understand the primitive reflex profile to discern whether dysarthria, primitive reflexes, or other speech, language, or cognitive problems exist in a child. An understanding of the Moro reflex and the symmetrical and asymmetrical reflexes (Figures 11-12, 11-13, and 11-14) as well as the other primitive reflex patterns of infants helps the speech-language pathologist understand the development of these reflexes into more permanent movement patterns. Furthermore, the speech-language pathologist also learns how primitive communication patterns such as cooing (as related to the emergence of reflex patterns and then more advanced movement patterns) and random sound productions of the newborn infant lead to speech sound development.

Diagnosis of Neurologic Disorder with Primitive Reflex

The neurologic examination of the newborn with suspected cerebral damage has in recent years relied heavily on the concept of a primitive reflex profile. Primitive and postural reflexes follow an orderly

TABLE 11-1	
Agents or Conditions That Can Be Teratogenic to CNS Development	
AGENT OR CONDITION	**ADDITIONAL CONSIDERATION**
Radiation	
Infectious Agents	
Chickenpox (varicella)	During first 20 weeks
Rubella	
Toxoplasmosis	
Thermodisruptions	
Hyperthermia	Body temperature of ≥102° F
Hypothermia	Body temperature of ≤95° F
Exposure to Toxic Metals	
Lead	>20 μg/dL
Mercury	>3 μg/dL
Lithium	Avoid during first trimester. No breast feeding if taking Lithium
Chemical Exposure	
PCBs	Exposure to airborne level of >0.0001 mg/m³
Toluene	Exposure to >375 mg/m³ more than 8 hours/day
Maternal Conditions	
Diabetes	
Iodine deficiency	
Maternal phenylketonuria (PKU)	
Folic acid deficiency	
Maternal Habits/Intake	
Alcohol abuse	Best practice is to abstain throughout pregnancy
Tobacco (nicotine)	
Marijuana	
Cocaine	
LSD	
Thalidomide	
Warfarin	
Angiotensin-converting enzyme inhibitors	
Statins	
Isotretinoin (Accutane, Retin A)	

Data from Gilbert-Barness, E. (2010). Teratogenic causes of malformation. *Annals of Clinical and Laboratory Science, 40,* 99-114.

FIGURE **11-12**
The Moro reflex is elicited by dropping the head. The reflex is pathologic in the presence of a persistent symmetrical abduction and upward movement of the arms with fingers splayed, followed by flexion of the arms in clasp manner as the child's back arches.

FIGURE **11-13**
Symmetrical tonic reflex. The symmetrical tonic neck reflex is elicited by passively extending and flexing the neck five times. The reflex is pathologic in the presence of obligatory arm extension or leg flexion with neck extension for more than 60 seconds. (Modified from Capute, A. J., Accardo, P. I., Vining, E. P. G., & Rubenstein, J. E. [1978]. *Primitive reflex profile.* Baltimore: University Park Press.)

FIGURE **11-14**
The asymmetrical tonic neck reflex (ATNR) is elicited by turning the head to each side
for 5 seconds. This movement is repeated five times to each side. The reflex is pathologic
in the presence of obligatory extension and flexion of limbs for more than 60 seconds.
(Modified from Capute, A. J., Accardo, P. I., Vining, E. P. G., & Rubenstein, J. E. [1978].
Primitive reflex profile. Baltimore: University Park Press.)

sequence of appearance and disappearance, beginning in the fetal period and extending through the
first years of life. The reflexes are mediated at a
subcortical level. First described by Rudolph Magnus (1873-1927), who received a Nobel Prize for his
efforts, these reflexes can help determine degrees of
prematurity or suggest neurologic dysfunction. If a
normal reflex pattern does not appear on schedule,
or if a reflex pattern persists beyond the age at which
it normally disappears, the newborn or infant is considered at risk for cerebral injury or other neurologic
involvement. Some pediatric neurologists assert that
neurologic abnormalities at birth predict a diagnosis
of minimal cerebral dysfunction at later ages, but others have found a limited association between neonatal
abnormalities and neurologic signs, particularly at 1
year and beyond.

Despite questions about the reliability of prediction
for a diagnosis of minimal neurologic abnormality, the
careful evaluation of early primitive reflexes and later-
evolving postural reflexes provides a basis for diagnosis
and therapy of disturbed motor function. Examination can usually provide a locomotor prognosis, indicating when and how a child with cerebral palsy will
walk. Table 11-2 summarizes the primitive and postural

TABLE 11-2
Primitive and Postural Infantile Reflexes of the First Year

REFLEX	RESPONSE
Asymmetrical tonic neck reflex	Infant extends limbs on chin and flexes on occiput side when turning head
Symmetrical tonic neck reflex	Infant extends arms and flexes legs with head extension
Positive support reflex	Infant bears weight when balls of feet are stimulated
Tonic labyrinthine reflex	Infant may retract shoulder and extend neck and trunk with neck flexion; tongue thrust reflex may occur
Segmental rolling reflex	Infant may roll trunk and pelvis segmentally with rotation of head or legs
Galant reflex	Infant arches body when skin of back is stimulated near vertebral column
Moro reflex	Infant may adduce arm and move it upward, followed by arm flexion and leg extension and flexion

reflexes of the first year. Although the speech-language pathologist may be more interested in the neurologic status of oral and pharyngeal reflexes, an understanding of the primitive and postural reflexes is essential in the assessment of the neurologic maturity of a child suspected of cerebral injury.

A notable lack of consensus exists on the definition of the stimulus and response in the widely tested primitive reflexes. In addition, no agreement has been reached on how the responses change with time and growth. Seven reflexes are reviewed in this chapter. They are commonly assessed by neurologists and pediatricians and are typical of the first year of life, with the peak development at approximately 6 months. Testing during this peak time avoids assessing the transitory neurologic signs of the newborn but is sufficiently early to allow a neurologic diagnosis before 1 year of age. These seven reflexes also appear to be predictive of later motor function in the child. Of the many infantile reflexes described by neurologists in the literature, these are the most studied.

ASYMMETRICAL TONIC NECK REFLEX

The **asymmetrical tonic neck reflex (ATNR)** probably is the most widely known of the early body reflexes. The reflex was shown to be universally present in the healthy infant by the outstanding child development specialist Arnold Gesell (1880-1961). When the healthy child is **supine**, he or she may lie with the head turned to one side. The extremities on that side (the chin side) are extended, with a corresponding flexion of the contralateral extremities on the opposite (occiput) side. This position is described as the fencer's position.

To test for the presence of the reflex, the child is placed in a supine position. Observations are made of active head turning and subsequent movement of the extremities. The head is then passively turned through an arc of 180 degrees to each side for 5 seconds. This maneuver is repeated five times on each side. Consistent changes in muscle tone in the extremities generally define the presence of the reflex. A clearly positive response is visible extension of extremities on the chin side and flexion on the occiput side when the head is passively turned. If extension of the extremities on the chin side and flexion on the occiput side last more than 30 seconds, the response may be called **obligatory**.

If the response is found beyond the eighth or ninth month, it is indicative of possible cerebral damage and poor motor development and suggests that the cortical control of upper motor neurons is not on schedule

and that motor behavior is still controlled at subcortical levels. Obligatory tonic neck reflexes persisting into the second year and beyond usually are incompatible with independent standing and walking; they may disappear later, however, and the child may learn to walk alone. The ATNR may be seen in various types of cerebral palsy, predicting brain injury, but it is not useful for distinguishing between spastic and dyskinetic types. This reflex suggests brain injury only and is in no way completely diagnostic for cerebral palsy or its subtypes. The ATNR can reemerge after a catastrophe such as cardiac arrest and also may be present in progressive disease. It has little or no effect on the development of speech and shows little relation to the oral and pharyngeal reflexes. Elicitation procedures for the ATNR are illustrated in Figure 11-14.

SYMMETRICAL TONIC NECK REFLEX

The **symmetrical tonic neck reflex** is analogous to the ATNR, but the head is manipulated in flexion and extension in midline rather than turned laterally. The resulting responses are differences between upper and lower extremities rather than right-left differences in extremities. The normal reflex is an extension of the arms and flexion of the legs if the head is extended in midline. Flexion of the head has the opposite effect; the arms flex and the legs extend.

The technique of eliciting the reflex is to first get the child to flex and extend his or her neck. The neck is then passively extended and flexed. This is repeated five times each for extension and flexion. If the reflex sign is absent at 5 to 6 months or persists into the second year, it is a symptom of motor abnormality. The symmetrical tonic neck reflex does not appear to elicit any associated oral or pharyngeal reflexes (see Fig. 11-13).

POSITIVE SUPPORT REFLEX

Magnus saw the **positive support reflex** as necessary for support of erect posture. When the balls of the feet are stimulated, opposing muscle groups contract to fix the joints of the lower extremities so that they bear weight. To test the reflex, the infant is suspended around the trunk, below the armpits, with the head in midline and slightly flexed. The child is bounced on the balls of the feet five times. The feet are then placed in contact with the floor, and the degree to which the infant can support his or her weight is assessed. The positive support reflex is seen in fetal life and is considered abnormal if it persists beyond 4 months. A persistent strong response has been associated with spastic

FIGURE **11-15**
The positive support reflex is elicited by suspending the child so that the balls of the feet can be bounced on a flat surface. The reflex is pathologic if the child remains on his or her toes and cannot move out of the position for 60 seconds or more. (Modified from Capute, A. J., Accardo, P. I., Vining, E. P. G., & Rubenstein, J. E. [1978]. *Primitive reflex profile.* Baltimore: University Park Press.)

quadriparesis. The positive support reflex does not appear to elicit associated oral or pharyngeal reflexes (Fig. 11-15).

TONIC LABYRINTHINE REFLEX

The tonic labyrinthine reflex (TLR) is associated with the changes in tone related to different postures. The position of the extremities changes with respect to the position of the head in space because of the orientation of the labyrinth of the inner ear. The TLR is tested in both supine and prone positions.

To test in the prone position, the child is held in prone suspension. The head is extended approximately 45 degrees below the horizontal plane. Changes of posture and tone in the extremities are evaluated, with special attention to the shoulder area. When the head is flexed, a normal response involves protraction of the shoulders or flexion of the lower extremities. Consistent tone changes should be present in at least one upper and lower extremity for the reflex to be considered present (Fig. 11-16).

In testing the TLR in the supine position, support is placed between the shoulders so that the head is extended at 45 degrees. Position and tone of the shoulders are assessed. Active neck flexion and grasp in midline are elicited. If the flexion and grasp responses are not noted, the head is flexed with the back supported and the midline grasp is sought again (see Fig. 11-16).

The normal response is shoulder retraction if the head is in extension. Trunk and leg extension accompanies shoulder retraction. Neck flexion results in shoulder protraction in 5 seconds and the disappearance of an extension posture.

An abnormal TLR may be accompanied by extensor hypertonia, and a persistent abnormal response may prevent the infant from rolling over normally. A pathologic response may make the legs so rigid that when the child is pulled to a sitting position, he or she will stand instead. The TLR is sometimes present in healthy children, but it is more common in children with pathologic conditions. Of the reflexes reviewed, it is the only one that may be routinely associated with oral reflexes. With the head extended 45 degrees, a reflex or tongue thrust may occur in the child with cerebral palsy.

SEGMENTAL ROLLING REFLEX

The healthy newborn shows a log-rolling response reflex associated with the activity of turning over. It is primarily a neck-righting reflex action. This early rolling response develops into a segmental rolling reflex in which turning of the head produces a reaction in which the infant attempts to undo the applied rotation by twisting the body at the waist, allowing one segment of the body to turn at a time. This corkscrew reaction allows the infant to roll over with a minimum of effort because only one segment of the body moves at a time. Abnormal

FIGURE **11-16**
A, The tonic labyrinthine reflex (TLR) is elicited by placing support between the shoulders to extend the head 45 degrees. The head is flexed 45 degrees. The reflex is pathologic if severe extensor thrust or opisthotonos occurs. **B,** Extension and flexion. (Modified from Capute, A. J., Accardo, P. I., Vining, E. P. G., & Rubenstein, J. E. [1978]. *Primitive reflex profile.* Baltimore: University Park Press.)

responses are indicated by perseveration of a simple log-rolling response in which head rotation produces the simultaneous turning of the upper and lower extremities with no segmental control. The response is seen in motor-handicapped children with cerebral palsy.

To test the segmental rolling response, the child is placed in the supine position. The response is tested in two maneuvers. First, the child is rotated from the head; second, the child is rotated from the legs. For head rotation, the child's head is first flexed to approximately 45 degrees and then slowly rotated so that the shoulders are turned. The rotation is observed. The child's head is usually rotated with one hand on the side of the face near the chin and the other hand on the occiput of the head. When the child is rolled to the right, the examiner's left hand is the face hand and the right is the occiput hand. When the child is rolled to the left, the position of the examiner's hands is reversed (Fig. 11-17).

To test the leg response, one leg of the child is flexed at the hip and knee. The examiner holds the flexed leg below the knee, and the child is rotated to turn the pelvis toward midline. Rotation patterns are then observed (Fig. 11-18). Rotation responses have not been associated with oral or pharyngeal reflexes.

GALANT REFLEX

The Galant reflex is an arching of the infant's body when the skin of the back near the vertebral column is stroked. The arching is usually forward, toward the stimulation. Arching in the other direction indicates the child is attempting to evade the stimulus. The responses may vary from total absence of response to an exaggerated hip flexion. In the majority of newborns the response is present bilaterally; unilateral responses have been reported in athetoid cerebral palsy. The response normally disappears by 2 months of age but persists in athetosis beyond that time. The Galant reflex is thought to be associated with delay of trunk stabilization and head control in athetoid cerebral palsy. Persistence of the response beyond 6 months is assumed to interfere with sitting balance. No association with oral or pharyngeal reflexes has been reported (Fig. 11-19).

MORO REFLEX

The Moro reflex, along with the ATNR, is one of the best-known and best-studied reflexes of child neurology. It is present in almost all newborns except for small premature babies. With sudden head lowering, a rapid and symmetrical abduction and upward movement of the arms occurs. The hands open, and gradual adduction and flexion of the arms occur. The lower limbs also show extension and then flexion.

Some debate has taken place about whether the Moro response and the startle response are continuous patterns. Both responses appear in the newborn, so they are thought to be discontinuous. The Moro usually reaches a peak at 2 months and diminishes by 4 months. A persistent reflex has been associated with cerebral palsy and intellectual disability.

FIGURE **11-17**
The segmental rolling reflex (with rotation of the head) is elicited by rotating the head to turn the shoulders and by rotating the legs (see Fig. 11-18) to turn the pelvis. The reflex is pathologic if the child is obliged to roll in a log-rolling manner and cannot inhibit the reflex. (Modified from Capute, A. J., Accardo, P. I., Vining, E. P. G., & Rubenstein, J. E. [1978]. *Primitive reflex profile.* Baltimore: University Park Press.)

FIGURE **11-18**
Segmental rolling reflex: rotation of the legs. (Modified from Capute, A. J., Accardo, P. I., Vining, E. P. G., & Rubenstein, J. E. [1978]. *Primitive reflex profile.* Baltimore: University Park Press.)

FIGURE **11-19**
The Galant reflex is elicited by stroking the back in the lumbar region with a blunt object. The reflex is pathologic in the presence of persistent curvature of the back and elevation of the hips. (Modified from Capute, A. J., Accardo, P. I., Vining, E. P. G., & Rubenstein, J. E. [1978]. *Primitive reflex profile.* Baltimore: University Park Press.)

To test for the Moro reflex, the child is held in the examiner's arms, well supported at the head, trunk, and legs. The examiner suddenly lowers the child's head and body in a dropping motion (see Fig. 11-12).

The most significant aspect of the stimulus is the quality of suddenness. Primitive and postural reflexes sometimes reinforce more circumscribed reflexes, but no evidence exists that the primitive Moro reflex tends to reinforce oral and pharyngeal reflexes in children with cerebral palsy. The persisting Moro reflex is much less valuable to the neurologist as a sign of cerebral injury than is the ATNR.

In summary, persisting infantile primitive and postural reflexes have been a classic sign of CNS dysfunction. In particular, they have been extremely useful in the early diagnosis of cerebral palsy. Infantile reflex behavior also has been incorporated in motor treatment programs for children with cerebral palsy. An important fact for the speech-language pathologist is that the primitive and postural body reflexes, with some exceptions, appear to have limited influence on oral and pharyngeal reflexes. Although these neonatal and early reflexes are important in assessing delayed development of motor function before age 12 to 18 months, they are of only limited use in the pediatric neurologic examination for the older child. The more conventional neurologic signs of altered muscle tone and abnormal muscle stretch and superficial reflexes, as well as the results of objective neurodiagnostic tests, are of equal value in making a diagnosis for the examining pediatric neurologist.

Oral and Pharyngeal Reflexes

Over the past half century, study of the normal infant reflexes and their relation to brain disease has promoted speech-language pathologists and others interested in the management of cerebral palsy to consider another set of reflexes—the oral and pharyngeal reflexes. Table 11-3 summarizes the major oral reflexes. Some speech specialists have assumed that abnormal oral and pharyngeal reflexes play a significant role in the speech development of the child with cerebral palsy who is dysarthric or is likely to develop dysarthria with the onset of speech. Absent or persisting reflexes, they argue, are predictive of dysarthria. Neurologists are more likely to argue that when the oral and pharyngeal reflexes are integrated into a spontaneous feeding pattern, they become more diagnostically and prognostically significant in neurologic disease. Similarly, speech-language pathologists are beginning to question whether the isolated artificially elicited reflexes of the first few months of life have as much diagnostic and prognostic importance in speech performance as do the dysphagic symptoms commonly seen in many children with cerebral palsy.

The type, number, and reliability of abnormal oral and pharyngeal reflexes found in those with cerebral palsy vary from study to study. Research strongly suggests that little or no correlation exists between the presence and number of abnormal oral and pharyngeal reflexes and the severity of dysarthria in cerebral palsy, as defined by a measure of articulation proficiency.[10] In

TABLE 11-3
Infantile Oral Reflexes

REFLEX	STIMULUS	AGE OF APPEARANCE	AGE OF DISAPPEARANCE
Rooting	Perioral face region is touched	Birth	3-6 months
Suckling	Nipple in mouth	Birth	6-12 months
Swallowing	Bolus of food in pharynx	Birth	Persists
Tongue	Tongue or lips being touched	Birth	12-18 months
Bite	Pressure on gums	Birth	9-12 months
Gag	Tongue or pharynx being touched	Birth	Persists

fact, the dysphagic symptoms—disordered biting, sucking, swallowing, and chewing—are slightly better predictors of articulation proficiency than is an elicited set of neonatal oral and pharyngeal automatisms. The correlation, however, between speech impairment and dysphagic symptoms is not particularly strong. This limited relation between speech and dysphagia strongly implies that motor control for speech and the feeding reflexes may be mediated at different levels in the nervous system. Evidence indicates that the feeding reflexes are mediated at the brainstem level and that voluntary speech is controlled at the cortical, subcortical, and cerebellar levels, with the prime voluntary pathways for speech being the corticobulbar fibers. Brainstem reflex pathways apparently subserve only vegetative and reflex functions and are inactive during the execution of normal speech. Therefore early motor speech gestures are probably not directly related to the development of motor reactions in feeding during infancy and childhood, even though some of the motor coordinations and refinements in speech acquisition are analogous to some of the biting and chewing gestures in feeding.

Even though early oral motor behavior in feeding may only have a limited resemblance to actual motor patterns for speech, management programs to improve muscle function and coordination in eating have been initiated as a possible prophylactic measure for future dysarthria. The assumption of these programs is that any improvement in motor activity of the oral musculature gained through feeding therapy might conceivably result in improvement in speech performance because the parallel activities of speech and feeding have muscles in common. At the very least, feeding therapy is likely to make eating faster and easier. This, of course, is an important consideration in the total management of the child with cerebral palsy, one that should not be overlooked by speech-language pathologists and neurologists. In fact, dysphagia may be just as disturbing as dysarthria in the young person with cerebral palsy. Direct motor training of the muscles during speech, rather than feeding

training, appears to be the most effective method for improving the dysarthria because cortically mediated speech activities drive the muscles at a more rapid and coordinated rate than do brainstem-mediated feeding activities.

Despite the controversy about oral reflexes and speech in diagnosis, management, and prognosis, a description of six commonly tested oral pharyngeal reflexes is offered for the speech-language pathologist who wants to consider this aspect of disturbed oral motor functions in the cerebrally injured infant or child. In the typical infantile oral motor evaluation, eliciting each of these infantile automatisms artificially one by one is best to determine whether they are absent or abnormally persisting. Next, the spontaneous functions of mastication and deglutition in the feeding act should be assessed to determine how these neonatal reflex behaviors have become integrated into a more complex and voluntary oral-pharyngeal pattern of feeding. Infantile mastication and deglutition use the six cranial nerves (V, VII, IX, X, XI, XII) important for future speech, so evaluation of early feeding allows cranial nerve assessment for the child who is too immature to cooperate in standard cranial nerve testing.

ROOTING REFLEX

If the perioral facial region is touched, two responses in combination make up the rooting reflex. The side-to-side head-turning reflex usually is elicited by gently tapping on the corners of the mouth or cheek. The response is the head alternately turning toward and away from the stimulus, ending with the lips brushing the stimulus. Occasionally the response occurs without the stimulus when the infant is hungry.

This activity usually precedes any actual suckling. The side-to-side head-turning response is present in the term baby and premature infant. The reflex usually disappears by 1 month of age and is replaced by the direct head-turning response, a simple movement of

FIGURE **11-20**
The rooting reflex is elicited by stimulating the cheek lateral to the mouth. From birth, the infant normally turns the head toward the stimulus and then grasps the stimulus in the mouth. The reflex is pathologic if it is absent in infants from any cause or if it persists beyond the fourth month.

the head toward the source of stimulation. The source is grasped with the lips and sucked. In the direct head-turning response, if the stimulus is applied to the corners of the mouth, the bottom lip usually lowers and the head and tongue orient toward the stimulus. The direct head-turning response is established at 1 month and disappears by the end of the sixth month of life. Persistence beyond a year may suggest cerebral injury, and asymmetry of response indicates damage to one side of the brain or facial injury. The cranial nerves involved in the reflex are V, VII, XI, and XII. The reflex is mediated by the pons, medulla, and cervical spinal cord (Fig. 11-20).

SUCKLING REFLEX

If a finger or nipple is placed in the infant's mouth, bursts of suckling behavior occur interspersed with periods of rest. The suckling reflex is integrated at birth, but within 2 or 3 months the action develops more purpose, and jaw activity is incorporated into the pattern. Involuntary suckling may disappear between 6 months and 1 year. Persistent suckling beyond 1 year suggests brain injury. The reverse, the inability to suckle, may also be an early sign of cerebral injury. The cranial nerves involved in suckling are V, VII, IX, and XII. The reflex is mediated at the pons and medulla (Fig. 11-21).

SWALLOWING REFLEX

The swallowing reflex develops after the suckling reflex is integrated into a total feeding pattern. Suckling activities produce saliva, which accumulates in the reflexogenic area of the pharynx. The swallowing reflex is triggered, and swallowing may be observed by visible upward movement of the hyoid bone and

FIGURE **11-21**
The suckling reflex is elicited by putting the index finger 3 to 4 cm into the mouth of the infant. From birth, the infant normally engages in rhythmic sucking of the finger. The reflex is pathologic if it is absent or exaggerated or if it persists beyond the fourth month.

thyroid cartilage of the larynx. The upward movement of the thyroid cartilage of the larynx may also be palpated during the swallow. Separating suckling and swallowing is sometimes difficult because a swallow may precede a suck or follow a first or second swallow. The act of deglutition involves muscles of the mouth, tongue, palate, and pharynx and depends on a highly coordinated movement pattern. Cranial nerves V, VII, IX, X, and XII are involved in the act of swallowing. An immature swallow with tongue thrusting is sometimes seen until approximately 18 months of age. A mature swallow is present afterward. The reflex is mediated at the level of the brainstem in the medullary reticular formation. Disturbances in swallowing are frequent manifestations of neurologic deficits in the infant and child, and they comprise the most important sign of neurologic disorder among the feeding reflexes.

TONGUE REFLEX

This reflex may be considered part of a suckle-swallow reaction in which the tongue thrusts between the lips. If lips or tongue are touched, cranial nerve XII predominates. Excessive thrusts beyond 18 months are abnormal. The tongue reflex is mediated at the medulla.

BITE REFLEX

Moderate pressure on the gums elicits jaw closure and a bite response. The bite reflex is present at birth; in the normal infant it disappears by 9 to 12 months, when it is replaced by a more mature chewing pattern. The reflex may be exaggerated in the brain-injured child and may interfere with feeding and dental care. Its persistence inhibits the lateral jaw movements of chewing seen in the spontaneous mastication pattern. A weak response is seen with brainstem lesions, and corticobulbar lesions exaggerate the response. Cranial nerve V innervates the reflex, which is mediated at the low midbrain and pons.

GAG REFLEX

A stimulus applied to the posterior half of the infant tongue or on the posterior wall of the pharynx causes rapid velopharyngeal closure. This primary action is

FIGURE **11-22**
The gag reflex is elicited by stimulating the posterior half of the infant's tongue with a tongue blade or stimulating the posterior pharyngeal wall. The reflex is present from birth and is pathologic when absent or exaggerated.

accompanied by mouth opening, head extension, and depression of the floor of the mouth with elevation of the larynx and diaphragm. This gag reflex is present at birth and continues throughout life. The gag serves as a protective mechanism for the esophagus. Brain-damaged children often show a hyperactive gag. In the severely motor-involved child, the gag may be difficult to elicit. In the ataxic child, the gag is sometimes hypoactive. Cranial nerves IX and X innervate the gag, and the reflex is mediated at the level of the pons and medulla (Fig. 11-22).

Synopsis of Clinical Information and Applications for the Speech-Language Pathologist

- During the second week after conception, the embryonic disk embeds in the uterus; it is referred to as the embryo from the third to the eighth week and beginning at the ninth week is called the fetus.
- During embryologic development of the brain, the ectoderm becomes the epidermis and nervous system.
- During embryologic development of the brain, the mesoderm becomes the muscles, connective tissues, cartilage, bone, and blood vessels.
- During embryologic development of the brain, the endoderm becomes the linings of digestive and respiratory tracts.
- The ectoderm thickens and forms a neural plate that gives rise to the CNS.
- Neural folds fuse to form the neural tube, which separates from the ectoderm.

- Four zones are briefly formed within the lining of the neural tube. Important adult derivatives will develop from these zones.
- The neural tube closes by the fourth week, regulated by a process called neurulation.
- The neural crest is formed from the sides of the neural tube to eventually form parts of the PNS and autonomic nervous system, including spinal nerves, cranial nerves, Schwann cells, and cells that form the meninges of the brain and spinal cord.
- The neural folds expand and fuse to form the three primary vesicles: rhombencephalon, mesencephalon, and prosencephalon. Further divisions take place with the exception of the mesencephalon.
- At 20 weeks' gestation, the brain begins to convolute from a smooth surface.
- At 24 weeks' gestation, the gyri and sulci are formed.

Continued

Synopsis of Clinical Information and Applications for the Speech-Language Pathologist—cont'd

- The neural crest and mesoderm are primitive meninges.
- Cortical neuroprogenitor cells replicate their DNA and divide in the ventricles and migrate in an inside-out pattern to various parts of the pial surface of the neocortex; this migration results in the stratification of the cortex.
- The two primary means of neural migration are somal translocation and guidance along the processes of radial glia.
- Reelin and Dab1 have been found to be critical for normal formation of the neocortex, cerebellar cortex, and hippocampus.
- Young neurons send out an axon with a growth cone on the tip. Dendritic processes also extend from the neurons. The axon's growth cones are guided by tropic molecules to particular targets, synapsing on spines of dendrites, establishing early cortical networks.
- Teratology is the study of abnormal embryonic development.
- Teratogens are environmental agents or conditions that may induce developmental interruptions after exposure to the mother.

- Genetic factors affecting development include chromosomal abnormalities.
- Environmental teratogens may include drugs, infections, medications, and chemicals.
- The most critical period for growth of a particular organ is the period of most rapid cell division; critical periods vary depending on the organ.
- The critical period for brain development is from 3 to 16 weeks' gestation.
- Major problems may occur during the third or fourth week as the neural tube and neural crest form.
- Major infantile reflexes in the developing child are the asymmetrical tonic neck reflex, symmetrical tonic neck reflex, positive support reflex, TLR, segmental rolling reflex, Galant reflex, and the Moro reflex.
- Oral reflexes in the developing child that appear at birth include rooting, suckling, swallowing, tongue, bite, and gag; the gag reflex persists throughout life, but the others usually disappear by 6 to 18 months of age.
- Swallowing is controlled by the integration of functions of central nerves V, VII, IX, X, and XII; it requires coordination but not in a form as intricate as speech.

REFERENCES

1. Cooper, J. (2013). Cell biology in neuroscience: Mechanisms of cell migration in the nervous system. *Journal of Cell Biology, 202,* 725–734.
2. Corbin, J. G., Gaiano, N., Juliano, S. L., Poluch, S., Stancik, E., & Haydar, T. F. (2008). Regulation of neural progenitor cell development in the nervous system. *Journal of Neurochemistry, 106,* 2272–2287.
3. D'Arcangelo, G. (2014). Reelin in the years: Controlling neuronal migration and maturation in the mammalian brain. *Advances in Neuroscience, 2014.* article ID 597395. Retrieved from http://www.hindawi.com/journals/aneu/2014/597395/.
4. D'Arcangelo, G., Miao, G. G., Chen, S. C., Soares, H. D., Morgan, J. I., & Curran, T. (1995). A protein related to extracellular matrix proteins deleted in the mouse mutant reeler. *Nature, 374,* 719–723.
5. Dennis, M. L., Landry, S. H., Barnes, M., & Fletcher, J. M. (2006). Critical review: A model of neurocognitive function in spina bifida over the life span. *Journal of the International Neuropsychological Society, 12,* 285–296.
6. Edmondson, J. A., & Hatten, M. E. (1987). Glial-guided neuron migration in vitro: A high-resolution time-lapse video microscopic study. *The Journal of Neuroscience, 7,* 1928–1934.
7. Gilbert-Barness, E. (2010). Teratogenic causes of malformation. *Annals of Clinical and Laboratory Science, 40,* 99–114.
8. Gupta, A., Tsai, L-H., & Wynshaw-Boris, A. (2002, May). Life is a journey: A genetic look at neocortical development. *Nature Reviews Genetics, 3,* 342–355.
9. Haines, D. E. (2006). *Fundamental neuroscience for basic and clinical applications* (3rd ed.). Philadelphia: Elsevier.
10. Love, R. J., Hagerman, E. L., & Tiami, E. G. (1980). Speech performance, dysphagia, and oral reflexes in cerebral palsy. *Journal of Speech and Hearing Disorders, 45,* 59–75.
11. Moore, K. L., & Persaud, T. V. N. (1993). *Before we are born: Essentials of embryology and birth defects* (4th ed.). Philadelphia: W. B. Saunders.
12. Nadarajah, B. A., Alifragis, P., Wong, R. O., & Parnavelas, J. G. (2003, June). Neural migration in the developing cerebral cortex: Observations based on real-time imaging. *Cerebral Cortex, 13,* 607–611.
13. O'Rahilly, R., & Müller, F. (2001). *Human tetralogy and embryology* (3rd ed.). New York: Wiley Liss.
14. Stiles, J. A., & Jernigan, T. L. (2010). The basics of brain development. *Neuropsychological Review, 20,* 327–348.

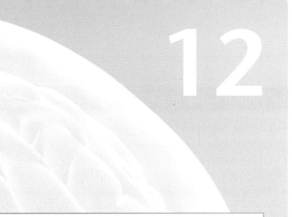

12

Pediatric Clinical Speech Syndromes

When I was born I was so surprised, I didn't talk for a year and a half.

Gracie Allen

Relation of Reflexes, Brain Development, and Speech Development

The development and progression of the reflexes presented in the preceding chapter help the speech-language pathologist (SLP) understand the way early speech and language development occurs in progression after reflexes are in place and as they mature. Once many of the reflexes are extinguished as the child's brain develops, pleasure sounds, cooing, babbling, and eventually phonemic development occurs, as previously discussed. Neurolinguistic theory postulates that the developing brain ontogenetically allows the child to form the eventual sounds that comprise that individual's phonemic system. This is attributable to brainstem development and other relevant neurologic systems (central nervous system and peripheral nervous system).

Reflexes develop first, and a delayed or persistent reflex should trigger a red flag to the SLP that the development of phonemes may be interrupted and subsequently the morphemic and perhaps pragmatic systems for that child.

ASSESSING MASTICATION AND DEGLUTITION

In the infant or child at risk for neurologic injury, the clinical evaluation of neural control of the oral and pharyngeal activities involved in chewing and swallowing allows the SLP to estimate the motor potential of those muscles, which ultimately fall under the control of higher nervous centers devoted to the production of speech. The fact that speech and feeding are mediated at different levels within the nervous system implies that evaluation of chewing and swallowing predicts future muscle activity in speech in only a limited manner. Only gross estimates of muscle potential for speech can likely be derived from any nonspeech examination because of the semiautonomous control of the muscles for the dual function.

In addition to gross estimation of muscle function in mastication and deglutition, however, the infantile oral motor examination of the cranial nerves for speech permits the SLP and neurologist to observe signs of possible neurologic disorder that may not be readily apparent in other motor behaviors. Mastication and deglutition, as relatively complex motor behaviors in the repertoire of infant motor activity, are highly sensitive to neurologic dysfunction. Dysphagia may be an early and even sometimes isolated sign of brain injury. This kind of examination, being somewhat enjoyable to an infant or child (with the exception of those hypersensitive to oral touch), may be a way to begin to assess the child's motor control for speech if the child is uncooperative for more traditional speech evaluation techniques. SLPs are also becoming highly valued for their expertise in helping evaluate the child whose feeding/swallowing ability is questioned. We often can help rule out a neurologic disorder in a child who has sensitivity or behavioral issues manifested in problems with oral intake.

Modified Feeding

Examination of chewing and swallowing is best accomplished through the technique of modified feeding. In the preverbal child, this technique can replace the more traditional procedures of the adult speech cranial nerve test, which requires a level of maturity not yet developed in the infant and very young child. By selectively placing small morsels of solid food in different locations in the oral cavity of the child, an examiner can judge the integrity of the bulbar muscles and the brainstem neural pathways innervating these muscles. Healthy children from birth to 36 months respond well to the technique, which may also be used with motor-handicapped children with oral motor involvement well beyond 3 years of age. In the healthy child, spontaneous feeding emerges from the neonatal oral and pharyngeal reflexes and reaches its full maturity at approximately age 3 years. Experiences with solid foods provide a gradual refinement and integration of movements of the lips, tongue, palate, and pharynx for chewing and swallowing.

When testing the infant or motor-handicapped child without sitting balance, the child should be placed in a chair in which the body and head can be well supported (e.g., a tumble-form chair) or in the primary caregiver's or clinician's lap in a well-supported position. In the child with some sitting balance, placement in a relaxed sitting position with adequate head support is preferred. See Chapter 7 for a summary of the cranial nerves.

Cranial Nerve VII

Placement of a small food bolus on the lower lip in midline and observation of the child's oral reaction to it provide evidence of the ability to use the muscles of the lip and lower face purposefully. Pursing the lips during rooting and sucking indicates intact facial movement. Lack of a smiling response may suggest severe bilateral facial muscle involvement. The healthy baby smiles to a human face at 2 to 4 months of age. A sober expression and sluggish grin must be carefully evaluated as possible neurologic signs of a bilateral corticobulbar system involvement ultimately affecting the paired nerves of cranial nerve VII. An asymmetric smile with a unilateral flattening of the nasal fold on one side of the face may be associated with unilateral paresis. This sign is not as obvious in the infant and young child as it is in the adult. Lack of lip tonicity may be present, and lip seal may not be maintained. In the brain-damaged child, drooling may result from the poor lip seal.

Cranial Nerve XII

The child with cerebral injury often is unable to shape, point, and protrude the tongue in retrieving food from the lower lip by licking. The lack of tongue protrusion is common in both spastic and athetoid children. In the brain-injured infant, the tongue often will not cup, even during crying. Neither will the tongue thin, nor will the tip elevate with precision. This inability to produce any fine tongue movements suggests motor involvement of both the intrinsic and the extrinsic tongue musculature.

Unilateral or bilateral atrophy of the tongue may be seen in young children, and this loss of muscle bulk suggests lower motor neuron disease. However, fasciculations are rarely seen in the tongue muscles of infants.

Excessive tongue thrust, sometimes called the tongue reflex, is common in children with severe brain damage. It is particularly common in athetosis, and it may be associated with orthodontic problems and excessive drooling. In addition, occasional wavelike involuntary movements are seen in the body of the tongue, mimicking the involuntary movements of the limbs and trunk in extrapyramidal athetosis.

Cranial Nerve V

When confronted with a small food bolus on the lips or tongue, the young child begins the total act of deglutition by initiating voluntary mastication. The aim of the evaluation at this point is to determine whether the bolus of food can be pulverized and whether the particles of food can be selectively manipulated to be transported to the back of the oral cavity. With a large food bolus, the tongue is usually elevated, so the bolus is placed between the tongue surface and the anterior hard palate and crushed. Smaller boluses of food are crushed between the hard palate and tongue, and the tongue directly begins a wavelike, peristaltic movement, carrying the food to the pharynx. If the food bolus is large, the tongue often acts in a whiplike fashion to propel the food laterally between the molars for grinding and pulverization. Observation of the vigorous tongue actions confirms the integrity of the neural control of the tongue. Disorders involving neurologic integrity of the tongue and jaw innervation often limit cerebrally damaged children to eating only diced or liquefied food.

Adequate biting and vigorous anterior-posterior movements of the mandible plus lateral grinding action of the jaws assure the SLP that cranial nerve V

innervation is intact and that muscles innervated from the pons are functional. On the other hand, an exaggerated and too-powerful bite may be a manifestation of an abnormal jaw reflex, suggesting an upper motor neuron lesion above the level of the pons. In older children with brain damage, a firm tap on the lower jaw may elicit a clonus, suggesting a hyperactive jaw reflex. If the lower jaw deviates to one side on opening or during mastication, pterygoid muscle weakness may be present on the side of deviation. In athetosis the jaw may become a major articulator, producing the motor power for elevating a poorly controlled tongue in achieving tongue tip–alveolar ridge contact and other tongue-elevation gestures.

Integration of Cranial Nerves V, VII, IX, X, and XII

When the food bolus is well masticated, the final involuntary stage of deglutition is initiated. The nasopharynx is closed by the muscles of the soft palate and the pharyngeal constrictors. Cranial nerves IX and X produce this closure. Saliva or the food bolus is pushed through the palatal fauces, into the pharynx, and onto the esophagus in a peristaltic wave. Muscles of the soft palate, the pharyngeal constrictors, and muscles of the tongue and larynx work in intricate coordination to propel the food bolus to the esophagus. In one sense, swallowing becomes the ultimate integration of the nervous mechanisms to be used later in motor expression of speech.

Speech, however, requires more intricate coordination of muscles than do chewing and swallowing. This fine coordination is accomplished through increasing cortical and cerebellar control of the pontine and bulbar muscles. Certain other complex motor adjustments are seen in speech but are not seen in chewing or swallowing. As an example, the grooved fricative /s/ requires finer motor control than is seen in mastication. To produce an adequate /s/, a central groove in the tip and blade of the tongue must be formed, with the sides of the tongue firmly anchored between the lateral dentition. This specific tongue configuration, common to speech, is not seen in brainstem-mediated functions. Intricate coordination of intrinsic and extrinsic tongue muscles is needed for the grooved fricatives. These fine motor configurations are not present in feeding. Thus assessment of mastication and deglutition in a preverbal child suspected of neurologic impairment is most appropriate, but when speech emerges, the evaluation should be based on the motor control for phonemes, syllables, words, and sentences assessed in the traditional articulation test format and on the results of a standard oral examination that includes assessment of the speech cranial nerves (see Chapter 7).

The actions of the cranial nerves for speech and the corticobulbar system, which activate the cranial nerve nuclei, can be assessed in infancy through observation of chewing and swallowing. All the nervous action of the bulbar muscles is integrated into the single act of feeding in infancy.

Developmental Motor Speech Disorders

Early cerebral injury to speech mechanisms of the developing brain results in conditions classified as **developmental motor speech disorders**. Included in a classification of the motor speech disorders are the developmental dysarthrias, developmental anarthrias, and developmental apraxias of speech. **Developmental dysarthria** is a speech disorder resulting from damage to the immature nervous system; it is characterized by weakness, paralysis, and/or incoordination of the speech musculature. **Developmental anarthria** refers to a complete lack of speech as a result of profound paralysis, weakness, and/or incoordination of the speech musculature. The diagnosis usually implies that useful speech will not develop because of the severity of the oral motor involvement. **Developmental apraxia of speech** is an impaired ability to execute the appropriate movements of speech voluntarily in the absence of paralysis, weakness, and incoordination of the speech muscles.

The term *childhood dysarthria* implies a neurologic or neurogenic speech deficit caused by a dysfunction of the motor control centers of the developing central and/or peripheral nervous systems. Disturbances are in the areas of strength, speed, steadiness, coordination, precision, tone, and range of motion or movement in the speech muscles. Apraxia is considered a motor planning disorder of speech, whereas dysarthria is associated with a partial disturbance of the speech mechanism involving motor movements. Anarthria usually is associated with a total lack of speech as a result of severe to profound motor disturbances.[20]

Certain types of developmental dysarthria have been well studied; other types have received less attention in the speech pathology literature. The developmental dysarthrias found in the various forms of cerebral palsy, for instance, have been extensively studied for many years, whereas research on the dysarthrias of childhood muscular dystrophy is much less common. The speech signs commonly observed in the developmental dysarthrias are seen in Table 12-1.

Table 12-2 shows the major differences between dysarthria and apraxia from the point of muscle movements and range of motion as seen in many childhood motor disturbances such as cerebral palsy.

TABLE 12-1

Major Developmental Motor Speech Disorders

DISORDER	SPEECH SIGNS
Developmental apraxia of speech	Disorder in selection and sequencing of articulatory movements, with oral apraxia sometimes present; comprehension intact; expression poor; occasional nonfocal neurologic signs
Developmental Dysarthrias of Cerebral Palsy	
Spastic dysarthria	Bilateral corticobulbar involvement; dysphagia; articulation disorder; hypernasality; slowed rate; loudness, pitch, and vocal quality disturbances; slow, stiff, and abrupt movements; increased muscle tone; muscle rigidity
Dyskinetic dysarthria	Athetosis (usually); dysphagia; hypernasality; articulation disorders; prevocalizations; loudness, pitch, and vocal quality disturbances; involuntary and often uncontrolled movements; often slow and writhing movements
Ataxic dysarthria	Articulation and prosodic disorders; unequal stress, loudness, and pitch; speech has an explosive, scanning quality
Mixed dysarthria	Often a combination of spastic and dyskinetic dysarthrias

TABLE 12-2

Differences between Apraxia and Dysarthria

APRAXIA	DYSARTHRIA
Sound substitutions not on the target sound	Sound distortions usually related to the target sound
Inconsistent errors; motor planning	Inconsistent speech sound substitutions from coordination problems
Often vocal or nonvocal groping behaviors	Groping for sound production precision is not noted verbally or nonverbally
Motor planning and execution difficulties	Motor disturbances causing distortions and not planning difficulties

TABLE 12-3				
Classification of Cerebral Palsy				
TYPE/ LESION AREA	FUNCTION	SUBDIVISIONS	CLINICAL SIGNS	LIMB INVOLVEMENT
Spastic Pyramidal tract	Skilled movements of limbs and digits Innervation of motor neurons for flexor movements of the limbs	Corticospinal tract Corticobulbar tract	Interrupts motor information of the brainstem and spinal cord Weakness or paralysis of various muscles Upper motor neuron lesions	Paraplegia (lower extremities versus upper extremities), diplegia (lower extremities more than upper extremities) Quadriplegia (lower and upper extremities); hemiparesis (left or right side of body) or monoplegia (only one lower extremity)
Dyskinetic Basal ganglia	Refer to Table 2-1 for the basal ganglia system Related to motor speech functioning Automatic execution of learned motor movements	Preferred term is basal ganglia–related pathways and subcortical nuclei	Either akinesia or lack of movements or dyskinesia or involuntary excessive movements; breathiness, roughness, hoarseness, tremor; exaggerated jaw movements; lip retrusion	Dyskinetic dysarthria (athetosis); choreoathetosis; dystonia; tremor, rigidity; upper extremity, lower extremity, neck, and trunk involvement
Ataxic Cerebellum	Coordination of movements of the upper and lower extremities as well as at all stages of speech production; sensory input from larynx and articulators and speech processing	Inferior peduncle Middle peduncle Superior peduncle	Ataxia Sometimes diplegia	Upper extremities Lower extremities Trunk

CEREBRAL PALSY

Developmental dysarthria is most commonly seen in children diagnosed as having cerebral palsy. **Cerebral palsy** is a neurologic condition caused by injury to the immature brain; it is characterized by a nonprogressive disturbance of the motor system. Many associated problems often are seen, such as intellectual disability, hearing and visual impairments, and perceptual problems produced by the infantile cerebral injury. Cerebral palsy is considered a major developmental disability.

Cerebral palsy has been variously classified, but most experts currently accept three major categories of clinical motor disorders: spasticity, dyskinesia, and ataxia. By far the most common type of dyskinesia is athetosis.

Table 12-3 presents a classification of the forms of cerebral palsy. As in adult disorders, spasticity implies a lesion in the pyramidal system, dyskinesia implies a lesion in the basal ganglia, and ataxia denotes a lesion

in the cerebellar system. However, syndromes are often not as clear-cut in the child as they are in the adult. Many children with cerebral palsy show a mixed picture. For instance, a child whose clinical picture is primarily athetoid, with typical slow, writhing movements of the limbs, grimaces of the face, and involuntary movements of the tongue and muscles of respiration, may also display hypertonic muscles and the upturning toe of the classic Babinski sign. The structural closeness of the neural pathways in the relatively small infant brain no doubt produces such mixed clinical pictures.

Children with cerebral palsy may also be classified according to **topologic involvement**. Common topologic pictures are hemiplegia, diplegia, and quadriplegia (see Table 12-3). **Monoplegia**, **triplegia**, and paraplegia occasionally are seen. Children may also be classified by etiology. Common causes are **prematurity**, **anoxia**, kernicterus, birth trauma, and infection. Approximately 1 to 2 out of every 1000 schoolchildren have some form of

Causes of Cerebral Palsy

Prenatal brain damage may result from:
- Impaired migration of new brain cells with the following risk factors:
  - Maternal infection, e.g., cytomegalovirus (CMV), HIV, meningitis, toxoplasmosis, rubella
  - Toxins
  - Drugs
  - Radiation exposure
- Prematurity and low birth weight with the following risk factors:
  - Low-grade infection of mother's urinary-genital tract
  - Alcohol and drug abuse, cigarette smoking
  - Poor maternal nutrition
  - Multiple fetuses
- Trauma to mother

Perinatal brain damage may result from:
- Increased pressure on brain during delivery
- Impaired circulation to the fetal brain
- Poor respiration
- Low birth weight

Postnatal brain damage may result from:
- Physical trauma
- Infection
- Respiratory distress
- Cerebrovascular disorders

cerebral palsy. Of the three major types, spasticity is the most prevalent, athetosis is next, and ataxia is the least common. Box 12-1 displays a summation of the major causes of cerebral palsy in children.

Developmental dysarthria is a major problem in the population with cerebral palsy, with 75% to 85% of the children showing obvious speech problems. Dysarthria may be complicated in some children by intellectual disability, hearing loss, and perceptual disorders. Despite complicating factors, the two major dysarthrias—spastic dysarthria and dyskinetic dysarthria of athetosis—in cerebral palsy can be differentiated. Spasticity and athetosis cannot be identified by articulatory errors alone; however, when vocal and prosodic features are incorporated into perceptual judgments of speech, the two clinical types become distinct, just as spastic and hyperkinetic types are distinct among adult dysarthrias.[22,33]

Spastic Cerebral Palsy

Spastic cerebral palsy is characterized by hypertonic reflexes. With this type of reflex, when a muscle contracts, the opposing muscle stretches abnormally, thus excessively increasing muscle tone.[24] That muscle group becomes rigid; movement therefore becomes extremely difficult. According to Owens et al.,[24] these muscle movements can be described as laborious, jerky, and unusually slow. These children often exhibit infantile patterns of the rooting reflex that involve the tongue, lips, and mandible. The movement is toward the site of the stimulation. These reflexes usually become absent after the child reaches the age of 2 to 4 months.

Spastic Hemiplegia

According to Love, children born with upper and lower extremity involvement on one side (hemi) exhibit signs of clasp-knife spastic paresis.[20] Spastic hemiplegia usually is caused by damage to the corticospinal tract, with the possibility of corticobulbar involvement. Cranial nerve XII, the hypoglossal nerve, usually is also involved, with the tongue showing contralateral deviation from the affected side on protrusion. Both dysarthric speech and dysphagia typically resolve after a brief period.

Phonologic development often is delayed in these children and is accompanied by a language delay and cognitive disturbances. Love indicated that children with right hemiplegia display a shift of language centers from the left to the right hemisphere.[20] Therefore visual spatial development, usually from the right hemisphere, is often expected to be compromised.

Spastic Paraplegia and Diplegia

Spastic paraplegia, which affects the lower extremities without involvement of the upper extremities, is uncommon in children. When it does occur, speech production usually is within normal limits without significant cognitive impairments.

Spastic diplegia usually involves all four extremities but the lower extremities display more involvement than the upper extremities, differentiating it from quadriplegia. Children with diplegia often display mild dysarthria with articulatory involvement only, but others with more severe dysarthric signs often display respiratory, laryngeal, palatal, and pharyngeal impairments in addition to articulation problems. Some dysphagia and drooling may also be present. Not all children with this diagnosis have cognitive difficulties.

Love stated that flexion and adduction of the hips in diplegia also include "scissoring or crossing of the legs during walking, producing a 'scissors gait,' a widely known clinical sign of child spasticity" (p. 45).[20] These children sometimes also display toe walking because of hamstring and Achilles tendon involvement.

Spastic Quadriplegia

Spastic quadriplegia usually displays equal involvement of both upper and lower extremities with severe involvement of the legs and arms and floppiness of the neck. In this condition both the corticospinal and corticobulbar tracts are affected. These children also display major problems with respiration, articulation, and laryngeal movements as well as compromised palatal and pharyngeal musculature. This type of spastic cerebral palsy usually has the highest incidence of intellectual disability or developmental delay.

Table 12-4 summarizes the speech performance parameters found in children with spastic and athetoid cerebral palsy.

Most of the research trials and literature on treatment of spastic cerebral palsy concerns the relief of limb spasticity. The National Institute of Neurological Disorders and Stroke[4] lists various types of treatment modalities used for spasticity in cerebral palsy including surgical procedures such as muscle/tendon lengthening or release and selective dorsal rhizotomy (SDR), which is a more complex surgical procedure in which selected overactive nerves are severed at the base of the spinal column. SDR is used only when more conservative treatments have not worked to relieve severe spasticity and associated pain. Drug treatments are also used, including the drug baclofen, which is a muscle relaxant; it is delivered via an implantable pump to the area surrounding the spinal cord; this procedure is more likely to be used on children over age 4 years who have severe spasticity. Local injection of botulinum toxin (Botox or Neuronox)[17] combined with splinting and physical therapy for stretching is also effective for children who have some movement control. The effectiveness of the injection wanes over time, usually around 3 months. Research into stem cell therapy for cerebral palsy is also being initiated through the National Institutes of Health but is in the early stages of research, and no large-scale clinical trials have been done to date.

Athetoid Cerebral Palsy

The most common of the dyskinetic syndromes of cerebral palsy is athetoid cerebral palsy. It is much less common than spastic cerebral palsy. Love reported that only approximately 5% of the total cerebral palsy population of children would be considered "pure" athetoid, whereas 10% would be diagnosed as dystonic athetosis.[20]

Slower motor development and hypotonia are the first signs of motor difficulties in athetoid children. Sitting balance is either delayed or not developed at all. One of the most prevalent signs is the absence of the Moro and the tonic neck reflexes.

TABLE 12-4
Speech Performance in Spastic and Athetoid Cerebral Palsy

RESPIRATION	PHONATION	RESONANCE	ARTICULATION	PROSODY
Rapid rate	Poor pitch control	Hypernasality	Spastic slightly superior to athetoid	Reduced variations in intensity, frequency, and timing
Abdominal breathing	Poor loudness control	Nasal emission	Articulation development systematic but delayed	Voice commonly monotone through utterance
Reverse or paradoxical breathing in athetoid cerebral palsy	Monotone	Poor intraoral breath pressure	Motor complex sounds more difficult	Slowed rate
Limited upper thorax expansion	Breathiness	Varying types of velopharyngeal inadequacy	Athetoid cerebral palsy incorporates wide range of movement of articulators	No formal studies of prosody
Flared lower ribs	Poor adduction/ abduction of vocal folds	Inconsistency of velopharyngeal closure	Also uses jaw as major articulator	
Poor tidal air control	Varying tension of vocal folds	Incoordination of velar musculature	Adults show oral motion rates 50% slower than normal	
Increased subglottal pressure	Generalized laryngeal immobility; poor timing of voice and respiration		Athetoid cerebral palsy shows some out-of-class substitution; spastic cerebral palsy does not	

Reprinted from Love, R. G. (1999). *Childhood motor speech disability* (2nd ed.). Boston: Allyn and Bacon.

In certain cases hypertonic athetosis progresses to a mixed type, usually spastic athetoid. In general, all four limbs are involved; a different presentation is rare. Speech problems usually are present along with swallowing difficulties and drooling. Severely affected motor movements of the upper and lower extremities usually correlate to the severity of the speech disorder present (see Table 12-4).

Ataxic Cerebral Palsy

Love reported that ataxic cerebral palsy is the most uncommon of the palsy syndromes.[20] Dyssynergia that translates into incoordination of the upper and lower extremities typically is present. The most identifying sign is, as Fenichel[12] stated, a staggering, somewhat lurching, wide gait pattern. Disturbed balance usually is another sign of ataxic cerebral palsy. The child with ataxic cerebral palsy is often looked on as clumsy and awkward. Muscles are hypotonic and gait does not seem to have directional control. Ataxic cerebral palsy usually involves damage to the cerebellum. The cerebellum controls and monitors balance and proprioceptive information from muscles, including rate of movement, force of movement, and directional control of movement. With ataxia, feedback from the cerebellar peduncles is lacking, thereby causing incoordination, and hence difficulty in walking.

Table 12-5 summarizes the major differences among spastic, athetoid, and ataxic cerebral palsy, including characteristics and areas of damage to the brain.

TABLE 12-5

Differences among Spastic, Athetoid, and Ataxic Cerebral Palsy

TYPE	CHARACTERISTICS	DAMAGE AREA(S)
Spastic	Spasticity: hypertonic Rigidity Stretch reflex Slow movements; laborious Presence of infantile reflexes	Pyramidal tract
Athetoid	Involuntary writhing movements	Extrapyramidal tract
	Uncoordinated volitional movements	Basal ganglia tracts
Ataxic	Poor balance Poor direction control in gait Rate dysfunction in gait	Cerebellum

Adapted from Owens, R. E., Metz, D. E., & Haas, A. (2003). *Introduction to communication disorders: A lifespan perspective* (2nd ed.). Boston: Allyn and Bacon.

CHILDHOOD SUPRABULBAR PARESIS

An isolated paresis or weakness of the oral musculature is sometimes seen in children without major motor signs in the trunk or extremities. This condition results in a form of developmental dysarthria and associated problems. Described by the neurologist Worster-Drought,[34] this condition usually affects the corticobulbar fibers that innervate cranial nerves X (vagus) and XII (hypoglossus). The etiology has been attributed to agenesis or hypogenesis of the corticobulbar fibers, but this theory has not been verified. The muscles of the lips, pharynx, palate, and tongue are involved to varying degrees. The dysarthria is marked by misarticulations and hypernasality. The individual may have a history of dysphagia and occasional laryngeal involvement and drooling.

This condition is called congenital childhood suprabulbar palsy because involvement generally is confined to the muscles innervated by the corticobulbar fibers. Paresis of the trunk and limbs is not present as in the child with obvious cerebral palsy. The condition is brought to the attention of the SLP or neurologist because of an isolated dysphagia or dysarthria. Muscles of the oral mechanism are involved, but no other obvious neurologic signs are present in the motor system. Box 12-2 lists neurologic signs seen in the dysarthric syndromes of congenital and acquired suprabulbar paresis of childhood.

MUSCULAR DYSTROPHY

Next to cerebral palsy, muscular dystrophy is the childhood neurologic disorder most likely to present a

BOX 12-2

Dysarthria in Suprabulbar Paresis Syndrome of Childhood

Congenital Signs

Articulation disorder
Hypernasality
Lip, tongue, palate, and pharynx paresis
Isolated paresis (in some cases)
Possible agenesis of corticobulbar fibers
Drooling

Acquired Signs

Articulation disorder
Hypernasality
Lip, tongue, palate, and pharynx paresis
Some facial rigidity

developmental dysarthria. The most common type of muscular dystrophy is the pseudohypertrophic type, also called Duchenne dystrophy. **Duchenne dystrophy** is associated with a sex-linked recessive gene, occurs primarily in males, and usually is manifest by the third year of life. During early development, motor milestones are often delayed and a retrospective study using parent report found that language milestones were also frequently delayed.[10] These early delays in language milestones were found to be associated with later cognitive impairments. Duchenne MD is marked by a characteristic progression of muscle weakness starting in the pelvis and trunk and eventually involving all the striated muscles, including those of the speech mechanism. The visceral muscles usually are spared. Enlargement of the calf muscles and occasionally other muscle groups accounts for the term **pseudohypertrophic**. Infiltration of fat and connective tissue produces the pseudohypertrophic effect.

In the later stages of the disease a flaccid dysarthria may appear, marked by articulation disorder and voice quality disturbances. Often the articulation disorder is mild, with only one or two phonemes in error. Dystrophic patients show reduced oral breath pressure and vocal intensity. They do not sustain phonation as well as healthy children do, and they show serious involvement of the muscles of speech. Rate of tongue movement and strength of the tongue are poor. Retracting and pursing the lips as well as pointing and narrowing the tongue are noticeably disordered actions, and phonemes requiring tongue and lip elevation often are in error. A broadening and flattening of the tongue is sometimes seen in advanced cases. Respiratory and laryngeal muscles are also weakened, affecting respiratory and phonatory performance. Despite weakness, labial phonemes generally are produced more accurately than are tongue-tip consonants. Box 12-3 presents the speech and physical signs in the developmental dysarthria of pseudohypertrophic muscular dystrophy. Several uncommon childhood dysarthrias associated with lower motor neuron disorders are surveyed by Love.[20]

Childhood Apraxia of Speech

The following definition of childhood apraxia of speech (CAS) was adopted by the American Speech-Language-Hearing Association (ASHA) in 2007:[8]

CAS is a neurologic childhood (pediatric) speech sound disorder in which the precision and consistency of movements underlying speech are impaired in the absence of neuromuscular deficits (e.g., abnormal reflexes, abnormal tone). CAS may occur as a result of known neurologic impairment, in association with complex neurobehavioral disorders of known or unknown origin, or as an idiopathic neurogenic speech sound disorder. The core impairment in planning and/or programming spatiotemporal parameters of movement sequences results in errors in speech sound production and prosody.

It has been difficult to establish incidence and prevalence of CAS because we do not as yet have clear diagnostic criteria nor do we have adequate standardized test procedures for establishing its presence.[21] In 1997 Shriberg et al.[27] estimated that CAS occurs in 1 to 2 per 1000 children in the population. A study using data gleaned from reports of children referred for speech disorders estimated 3.4% to 4.3% of the children referred were given a diagnosis of CAS.

PATHOPHYSIOLOGY

This motor speech disorder can be congenital or acquired; it occurs in children with known neurologic etiologies such as intrauterine stroke, infections, or trauma and may also occur as part of a complex neurobehavioral disorder such as those caused by genetic or metabolic disorders. Because CAS without comorbidities is rare, it is often difficult to separate from the other disorders present. Idiopathic cases in which no associated neurologic disorder or injury could be identified have been reported, however.

A genetic basis for CAS has been investigated with particular emphasis on the study of the KE family in London. Research on 30 members of four generations of this family found that almost half the members of the family had a significant communication impairment.[14] The disorder was first presented as a grammar-specific

---

BOX 12-3

Developmental Dysarthria in Pseudohypertrophic Muscular Dystrophy

Speech Signs (Flaccid Dysarthria)

Articulation disorder
Reduced vocal intensity
Respiratory weakness
Articulator weakness
Broad, flattened tongue

Physical Signs

Onset: 3 to 4 years
Proximal weakness
Pseudohypertrophic calf muscles
Proximal atrophy
Hyporeflexia, except ankles
Intellectual disability (one third of cases)

disorder, but more in-depth research later revealed a severe articulatory deficit (thought to be apraxia of speech) as well as deficits in other linguistic areas and, in some members, intellect.[31] Orofacial apraxia was also found in some members. Genetic studies of this family pointed to mutations in the *FOXP2* gene on chromosome 7. There are other studies of children and family members with a speech sound disorder diagnosed in some members as CAS in which a syndrome was also present in which a gene mutation on another chromosome was identified. Research on children with galactosemia, a metabolic disorder affecting the body's processing of sugar, found an incidence of CAS in 63% of the 24 cases studied.[32]

Neither the etiology nor the neurophysiology of CAS has been identified. However, the advent of better access to safe neuroimaging studies as well as the use of event-related potentials has provided some interesting insight into neurophysiology. Liégeois and colleagues[18] used functional magnetic resonance imaging (MRI) to study the affected and unaffected members of the KE family. Tasks used were repetition and covert and overt verb generation. Imaging found more posterior and extensively bilateral activation in all generation tasks. In trying to ascertain differences in brain structure related specifically to CAS, however, the studies of the KE family members were confounded by the presence of linguistic and cognitive deficits in many of the affected members.

Kadis and colleagues[16] analyzed cortical thickness from MRI for seven regions of interest in 14 children identified with idiopathic CAS who were receiving speech therapy for the disorder and age-matched control subjects. The only consistent difference in gray matter volume was found in the left supramarginal gyrus. No significant differences were found for the typical motor-speech programming areas nor for the superior temporal gyrus, which is an area found to show differences in gray matter volume bilaterally in children with speech sound disorders not related to CAS.[25] Earlier computational neural modeling had postulated that children with CAS would experience poor feedforward control, perhaps the result of reduced somatosensory information and increased neural noise.[30] This would increase the child's dependence on auditory feedback control.

Yet another neurophysiologic approach was taken by a group at Haskins Laboratory.[26] This study involved children with CAS and a matched control group performing a picture-naming task. The pictures were varied by complexity of structure with monosyllabic and multisyllabic words used. Evoked-related potentials (ERPs) were recorded while the children performed these naming tasks. Group differences were found that

the authors hypothesize supported both prespeech phonologic processing and motor planning. The subjects with CAS showed reduced amplitude over the right hemisphere before speaking multisyllabic words compared with monosyllabic words. The time window of this reduction was thought to be consistent with phonologic encoding. The group with CAS also was found to show a later time onset of movement both in the stimulus locked and response locked conditions, regardless of the complexity of the stimulus. This suggested differences in phonetic processing (motor planning/programming). As the authors point out, this study is primarily descriptive. It does lend support to what clinicians have always suspected—that neurobiologic differences do exist in children with CAS; clinically they appear to physiologically require a longer time to prepare for speech production.

ASSESSMENT AND TREATMENT

The disordered movements of the articulators in CAS frequently result in a serious phonologic problem in the school-age child. If an apraxic disorder of the oral muscles is present in the preschool years, it may well delay the development of speech and language, and the language developmental milestones of one-word utterances, two-word combinations, and three-word sentences may be disrupted. Although a clear-cut syndrome has not yet emerged despite considerable clinical research on the topic, it is now a fairly well-accepted clinical diagnosis though accurate assessment methodology with secure sensitivity and specificity has not yet been established.

The differential diagnosis of CAS has and continues to challenge the SLP. The treatment methods that may progress the child with CAS may differ significantly from the treatment methodology used with children with articulation disorders or phonologic disorders. It is important to try to diagnose a true case of CAS as early as possible so that targeted treatment methods can be begun. A number of studies have tried to identify characteristics that would differentiate speech apraxia from other speech production disorders. Checklists have also been formulated to help identify characteristics associated with CAS, and these have been used by many clinicians with varying success. The 2007 technical report by ASHA on CAS[8] reviewed the literature on behavioral markers for CAS available to that time, finding considerable variability in subjects used and overlap with markers often present in children with speech disorders but no oral-motor involvement. The two measures that appeared to show the most sensitivity were maximal performance for multisyllabic word production and prosody.

BOX 12-4

Features of Speech Behavior That May Help Differentiate CAS from Other Disorders

- Inconsistent errors on consonants and vowels in repeated productions of syllables and words[a]
- Lengthened and disrupted coarticulatory transitions between sounds and syllables[a]
- Inappropriate prosody, especially at the word and phrase level[a]
- Poor accuracy of movements[b]
- Poor accuracy of vowel production[b]
- Slow diadochokinetic rate[c]

[a]American Speech-Language-Hearing Association (2007).[8]
[b]Strand et al. (2013).[28]
[c]Murray et al. (2015).[23]

Strand and colleagues[29] targeted the even more difficult problem of identifying motor speech impairment in younger children or in children with little verbal ability. The DEMSS (Dynamic Evaluation of Motor Speech Skill) was supported as a reliable and valid test for this purpose with the probability of correct classification based only on the DEMSS total score being greater than 90%. The dynamic aspect of the test requires assessment of the child's ability to directly imitate simple phonetic content and syllable structure while cuing is provided. Vowel accuracy, total accuracy, prosody, and consistency are the measures taken for the total.

A recent Australian study on diagnostic differentiation recruited 4- to 12-year-old children who were suspected by community SLPs to have CAS but were otherwise normally developing.[30] Two sets of diagnostic criteria from the literature were used to identify CAS with 28 of the 72 children meeting those criteria without comorbidity. A discriminant function analysis found that syllable segregation, lexical stress matches, percentage phonemes correct in a polysyllabic picture naming task, and articulatory accuracy on repetition of /pətəkə/ reached 91% diagnostic accuracy compared with expert diagnosis. They concluded that polysyllabic production accuracy combined with a thorough oral motor examination that included diadochokinesis may prove to be sufficient to reliably identify CAS and rule out structural abnormality and dysarthria, but testing on a larger unselected subject population would be a next step.

Although new research has come forth regarding signs and symptoms of CAS, a review of the current literature continues to suggest that the differentiating features listed in Box 12-4 continue to be the ones that have gained the most consensus.

Treatment of CAS is beyond the scope of this text. New treatment methodologies are being studied and presented in the clinical literature of our profession on an accelerated basis. The astute clinician will carefully research this literature for evidence-based practice methods and will perhaps contribute to the literature from her or his clinical research and practice.

In summary, childhood apraxia of speech is still controversial. Many researchers do not agree on symptomatology, causes, assessment, or treatment procedures. Our evidence base is increasing but further study into this disorder is needed before agreement is reached on how best to treat it.

Other Disorders of Speech Production

As children mature and develop from the basic oral reflex stage to more sound or articulatory development, some simply become delayed in phonologic and/or articulatory development without a neurologic motor speech component. Articulation disorders have their roots in the phonetic (sound) development that children progress through as their oral motor skills mature. These children currently are referred to as having phonologic processing disorders. Phonologic disorders have their basis in the study of phonology from a linguistic point of view. These children, now served in clinics, do not necessarily have a motor speech component that must be addressed either linguistically or neurolinguistically.

Salient differences exist between children with an articulation disorder and those with a phonologic disorder. Much is distinguished by phonetic versus phonemic errors. Phonetically, this child struggles with speech sound form and development, but phonemically the child displays problems with language-based functions of phonemes.[1] This becomes a matter of sound formation (articulation disorder) versus phonemic function (phonologic disorder). Because motor speech delay or impairment is not present, children with articulation disorders display disturbances in the neurologic processes of sound development, and children with phonologic disorders represent an impairment of the phonemic system within the language. Articulation disorders are phonetic in nature, whereas phonologic disorders are phonemic.[1]

Locke, of the University of Sheffield in England, offers a theory of neurolinguistic development to explain how an infant develops from simply recognizing faces and voices to learning his or her parent or caregiver's voice characteristics. Locke explains that "the first phase is indexical and affective" (p. 266), in which the infant is strongly oriented to a person's face and voice. The infant's second phase is "primarily affective and social . . .

TABLE 12-6

Phases and Processing Systems and Neurolinguistic Correlates

AGE OF ONSET	DEVELOPMENTAL PHASES AND SYSTEMS	NEUROLINGUISTIC AND NEUROCOGNITIVE MECHANISMS	LINGUISTIC DOMAIN
0-3 months	Vocal learning	Specializing in social understanding	Prosody and sound segment development
5-7 months	Utterance acquisition	Specializing in social understanding	Stereotypic utterances
20-37 months	Analysis and computational	Grammatical analysis skills	Phonology, morphology, and syntax
3+ years	Integration and elaboration	Social understanding and grammatical analysis	Automatic operations and expanded lexicon and sound development

Modified from Locke, J. (1997). A theory of neurolinguistic development. *Brain and Language, 58*, 265-326.

whereby its function is to collect utterances for social purposes" (p. 266) regulated by the right hemisphere. The third phase facilitates discovery and is ultimately responsible for the child's development of speech and language rule usage. The fourth and last phase is integrative in nature. This underlies Locke's idea that "children who are delayed in the second phase have too little stored utterance material to activate their analytic mechanism at the optimum (neurolinguistic) moment and when sufficient words are learned, the capability has already begun to decline" (p. 266). This could explain, from a neurolinguistic viewpoint, the delay in speech development in infants and young children. Finally, Locke suggested that "the resulting neurolinguistic resources, not being specialized for phonological operations, are minimally adequate but not optimal for development of spoken language" (p. 266). Table 12-6 outlines Locke's system including the neurolinguistic components of speech development and language capacity.[19]

A delay in neurolinguistic development can lead to speech delays and phonologic disorders. Children develop through periodic phases, as described in Table 12-6, and if an interruption (e.g., cerebral palsy, muscular dystrophy, etc.) or delay (e.g., intellectual disability, autism, etc.) occurs, speech development would either be absent or significantly altered.

DISORDERS OF FLUENCY

The World Health Organization defines stuttering as "speech that is characterized by the frequent repetitions or prolongations of sounds, syllables or words, or by frequent hesitations or pauses that disrupt the rhythmic flow of speech."[11] Many people who stutter also exhibit what we refer to as "secondary" symptoms such as facial grimaces, extremity movements, or eye blinks. Fluency disorders or stuttering has a prevalence of about 5% during early childhood. Many children, however,

recover spontaneously, leaving a prevalence across the general population of around 1%.[36]

The various theories about what causes disorders of fluency and how best to treat them in children who do not naturally develop fluent speech will be taught to you as you progress through your curriculum. Stuttering has been researched extensively by SLPs; there have always been questions about possible neurologic differences that could account for some or all of the symptomology, which, of course, can vary greatly between individuals. It is only recently that our field has had access to imaging and other techniques that can begin to try to answer that question. Neuroimaging studies are rapidly adding knowledge about brain structure and function in adults and children with fluency disorders. They suggest that subtle functional brain differences do exist, perhaps leading to the eventual discovery of a neurologic basis for stuttering.[7]

Findings from Neuroimaging Studies

Table 12-7 lists a few of the more recent neuroimaging studies and briefly summarizes the findings. All of these studies have been done on adults who stutter. As you will see, the findings vary. A limitation of most studies on adult stutterers is that it is difficult to ascertain whether the brain activity or connections discovered are related to the etiology of the disorder or are related to compensatory mechanisms that the person has developed to deal with the disfluencies. Few studies have been done on children, and there is a critical need for this type of research to pinpoint the etiology of developmental stuttering and, perhaps one day, successfully treat it early enough to prevent persistence into adulthood.

As you will learn in your later study of treatment of stuttering, external timing aids (such as pacing techniques, metronome, etc.) often induce fluency in persons who stutter. Because of this, there has been interest in the neuroanatomic support for the brain's internal timing mechanisms as well as what parts of the brain

TABLE 12-7

Selected Neuroimaging Studies on Adults Who Stutter

AUTHOR (YEAR)	SUMMARY OF FINDINGS FROM NEUROIMAGING
Sommer et al. (2002)[28]	Decreased white matter connectivity
Brown et al. (2005)[3]	Meta-analysis using Activation Likelihood Estimation method (ALE): overactivation in right frontal operculum and anterior insula; absence of activation bilaterally in auditory areas; overactivation in cerebellar vermis
Chang et al. (2009)[6]	Reduced activation *during speech perception and planning* in frontal and temporoparietal areas; increased activation *during speech production* in right superior temporal gyrus, bilateral Heschl's gyrus, insula, bilateral precentral, supplemental motor area, and the putamen
Xuan et al. (2012)[35]	Study of brain activity during resting state: altered brain activity compared with controls in areas involved in motor, language, auditory and cognitive processing; altered functional connections between the areas as well
Ingham et al. (2012)[15]	Stuttering frequency across two tasks correlated with cortical-striatal-thalamic circuit activity. Primarily highlights the variability found in functional imaging studies
Connally et al. (2013)[9]	Study of white matter tracts: reduced integrity in the 3 cerebellar peduncles as well as the left angular gyrus; greater connectivity in the corticobulbar tract

may be most responsive to external timing cues. Etchell's research on a group of adult stutterers suggested that internal timing differences account for disfluent speech and that the basal ganglia and supplementary motor connections are involved in this deficient timing.[11] There have recently been a few studies on school-age children and adolescents that do support anatomic differences in basal ganglia structures, the putamen,[2]

and the caudate nucleus.[13] Chang and Zhu[5] also found poor functional connectivity of the basal ganglia and the SMA in children who stutter. The involvement of the cerebellum and the right inferior frontal gyrus as well as the left premotor cortex was proposed by Etchell and colleagues[11] as possible primary neural structures that use external timing cues to provide compensation when there are internal timing deficits in the controlling neural network. Finally, in the largest pediatric neuroimaging study of stuttering to that date, Chang and colleagues[7] used fractional anisotropy (FA) to look at differences in white matter development in 3- to 10-year-old children (47 children who stutter [CWS] and 42 children with no stuttering [CWNS]). Lower FA values indicate poor organization of the white matter tracts in these areas with more crossing of bundles of fibers rather than coherent tracts to and from the connecting areas. It could also imply poor myelination of the fibers or poor integrity of the membranes of the cells. Studies of FA during the developmental periods of childhood and adolescence typically show increases related to development as well as to skill acquisition and training.

In this study using FA to look at stuttering, significant decreases in FA were found in CWS with the lowest values found in the left hemisphere white matter underlying large parts of the sensorimotor cortical regions (inferior frontal gyrus, premotor cortex, motor cortex, middle and superior temporal gyri, and inferior parietal areas). These areas are along the superior longitudinal fasciculus. Decreased FA in CWS was also noted in the left cerebellum and brainstem and the entire length of the corpus callosum. Though smaller than those in the left hemisphere, right-sided decreases were found in part of the inferior frontal gyrus (BA 44), the middle and superior temporal gyri, and the supramarginal gyrus. The authors posit that these lower FA values indicating white matter structural differences in CWS suggest "deficits in long-range connectivity that support efficient sensorimotor and interhemispheric integration and cortical-subcortical interaction for skilled movement control" (p. 704) and "underlie precise timing of movement" (p. 708).

Many ways of seeing into the windows of the brain of adults and now children have been made available with the advances in neuroimaging techniques making them less and less invasive. It is now up to the researchers and clinicians to design studies that will help us learn more about which brain structures are responsible for promoting fluent speech and when and why they are most vulnerable to disruption. We may then be able to prevent developmental stuttering from occurring or at least treat it so that the disorder of fluency does not follow the child into adulthood.

Synopsis of Clinical Information and Applications for the Speech-Language Pathologist

- Oral reflexes in the developing child that appear at birth include rooting, suckling, swallowing, tongue, bite, and gag; the gag reflex persists throughout life, but the others usually disappear by 6 to 18 months of age.
- Swallowing is controlled by the integration of functions of central nerves V, VII, IX, X, and XII; it requires coordination but not in a form as intricate as speech.
- Early cerebral injury of the speech mechanisms in the infant brain results in motor speech and/or swallowing disorders.
- The speech production disorders associated with brain injury include developmental dysarthria, anarthria, and apraxia of speech.
- Developmental dysarthria is characterized by weakness, paralysis, and incoordination of the speech musculature.
- Developmental anarthria is characterized by a lack of speech as a result of profound paralysis, weakness, or incoordination of the speech muscles.
- Dysarthria is characterized by a disturbance in the motor control centers of the developing brain.
- Disturbances include strength, speech, steadiness, coordination, precision, tone, and range of motion.
- Dysarthrias can be categorized as spastic, dyskinetic, ataxic, or mixed.
- Spastic dysarthria is characterized by bilateral corticobulbar involvement, increased muscle tone, slowed rate, and loudness.
- Dyskinetic dysarthria is characterized by athetosis, dysphagia, hypernasality, articulation disorder, and vocal quality disturbance.
- Ataxic dysarthria is characterized by unequal stress, articulation and prosodic disorder, disturbance of balance, and an awkward gait.
- Cerebral palsy can be subdivided into three major categories: spasticity, dyskinesia, and ataxia.
- Approximately 75% to 85% of children with cerebral palsy have dysarthria to some extent.
- Other complications of cerebral palsy include intellectual disability and hearing loss.
- Spastic cerebral palsy is characterized by hemiplegia, paraplegia, diplegia, and quadriplegia of upper and lower extremities.
- Athetoid cerebral palsy is the most common of the dyskinesias of cerebral palsy and is characterized by hypotonia and the absence of the Moro and tonic neck reflexes.

- Ataxic cerebral palsy is the most uncommon of all cerebral palsy syndromes and is characterized by disturbed balance, lurching gait, hypotonic muscles, and damage to the cerebellum.
- Next to cerebral palsy, muscular dystrophy is the most likely condition to display dysarthria. Flaccid dysarthria may appear with an articulation problem, reduced vocal intensity, respiratory weakness, and a broad and flattened tongue; one third of the cases include intellectual disability.
- Childhood apraxia of speech (CAS) is a disorder affecting the precision and consistency of movements underlying speech production.
- CAS can be related to a neurologic or neurobehavioral disorder but also may be idiopathic.
- Mutation of the *FOXP2* gene on chromosome 7 is thought to be associated with speech impairment similar to CAS. Other genetic mutations have been found to be a possible source as well.
- Neuroanatomic differences in children with idiopathic CAS are suspected and have been identified in a few studies. No consistent etiology has been identified. Poor feedforward control and differences in phonetic processing have been supported by research.
- Neurolinguistics is concerned with the underlying process of communication, including phonology, morphology, syntax, semantics, and pragmatics in regard to various aspects of brain function.
- Locke offers an explanation of the neurolinguistic components underlying speech and language development.
- Stuttering or disorder of fluency has a prevalence of about 5% in early childhood and around 1% in the general population.
- Neuroimaging studies have become more prevalent in the past few years in the study of adults and children with developmental stuttering. Studies suggest disorganized white matter connections underlying sensorimotor areas in the left hemisphere and less so in the right hemisphere. Differences in basal ganglia and supplementary motor area and cerebellum structures have been found, with deficits in internal timing mechanisms proposed.

CASE **STUDY**

H. T., a 10-year-old boy, was brought to the emergency department by his parents. H. T. was home alone with his younger sister after his parents went out with friends. After putting his sister to bed, H. T. found liquor bottles in the wet bar of the family room and some beer in the refrigerator. He consumed a fifth of vodka and two bottles of beer within 5 hours. His parents came home and found him passed out on the kitchen floor. They called 911, and H. T. was rushed to the hospital. His blood alcohol level was four times the legal limit set for an adult. The medical team revived him, and he was admitted to the hospital. A few hours later H. T. began to have several severe grand mal seizures. Seizure activity was intermittent for almost 6 hours. Magnetic resonance imaging was completed at this time. Several areas of diffuse damage appeared on the image, but the radiologist could not determine whether any particular parts of the central nervous system were affected. Imaging was ordered to be repeated. On wakening in the morning, the house neurologist on call and physical and speech therapists were summoned for an evaluation. H. T. was disoriented ×3 and had to be prompted to answer questions. Speech was slurred, with intermittent loudness and softness in voice output, reminding the staff of the drunken state he was in when brought to the emergency department. Physical therapy provided minimal assistance to have H. T. walk across the room. Gait was wide and unsteady. Both fine and gross motor skills were tremulous and unbalanced. Alternating motion rates were slow and deliberate, and H. T. often stopped and started again several times. Many phonemic errors were noted. Social Services was consulted, and history indicated that this has happened several times before but this was the first time that H. T. passed out and had seizures, according to the parents.

Questions for Consideration

1. The speech symptoms, gait, and other behaviors appear to be reminiscent of which type of dysarthria?
   Flaccid
   Ataxic
   Spastic
   Mixed
2. What primary area of the central nervous system do you think was affected in this child?
3. Will this damage resolve as in the past, or will it be more permanent this time?

REFERENCES

1. Bauman-Waengler, J. (2004). *Articulatory and phonological impairments: A clinical focus.* Boston: Allyn and Bacon.
2. Beal, D. G. (2013). A voxel-based morphometry (VBM) analysis of regional grey and white matter volume abnormalities within the speech production network of children who stutter. *Cortex, 49,* 2151–2161.
3. Brown, S., Ingham, R. J., Ingham, J. C., Laird, A. R., & Fox, P. T. (2005). Stuttered and fluent speech production: an ALE meta-analysis of functional neuroimaging studies. *Human Brain Mapping, 25,* 105–117.
4. National Institute of Neurological Diseases and Stroke. (n.d.). *Cerebral palsy: Hope through research.* Retrieved from http://www.ninds.nih.gov/disorders/cerebral_palsy/detail_cerebral_palsy.htm.
5. Chang, S. E., & Zhu, D. C. (2013). Neural network connectivity differences in children who stutter. *Brain, 136,* 3709–3726.
6. Chang, S. E., Kenney, M. K., Loucks, T. M. J., & Ludlow, C. L. (2009). Brain activation abnormalities during speech and non-speech in stuttering speakers. *Neuroimage, 46,* 201–212.
7. Chang, S. E., Zhu, D. C., Choo, A. L., & Angstadt, M. (2015, January). White matter neuroanatomical differences in young children who stutter. *Brain, 138,* 694–711.
8. American Speech-Language-Hearing Association. (2007). *Childhood apraxia of speech.* Retrieved from http://www.asha.org/policy/TR2007-00278.htm#sec1.1.2.
9. Connally, E. L., Ward, D., Howell, P., & Watkins, K. E. (2013). Disrupted white matter in language and motor tracts in developmental stuttering. *Brain, 131,* 1–11.
10. Cyrulnik, S. E., Fee, R. J., De Vivo, D. C., Goldstein, E., & Hinton, V. J. (2007). Delayed developmental language milestones in children with Duchenne's muscular dystrophy. *Journal of Pediatrics, 53,* 474–479.
11. Etchell, E. C. (2014). Behavioral and multimodal neuroimaging evidence for a deficit in brain timing networks in stuttering: A hypothesis and theory. *Frontiers in Human Neuroscience, 9,* 1–10.
12. Fenichel, G. M. (1997). *Clinical pediatric neurology: A signs and symptoms approach* (3rd ed.). Philadelphia: W. B. Saunders.
13. Foundas, A. L., Mock, J. R., Cindass, R., & Corey, D. M. (2013). Atypical caudate anatomy in children who stutter. *Perceptual and Motor Skills, 116,* 528–543.
14. Gopnik, M., & Crago, M. B. (1991). Familial aggregation of a developmental language disorder. *Cognition, 39,* 1–50.
15. Ingham, R. J., Grafton, S. T., Bothe, A. K., & Ingham, J. C. (2012). Brain activity in adults who stutter: Similarities across speaking tasks and correlations with stuttering frequency and speaking rate. *Brain and Language, 122,* 11–24.

16. Kadis, D. S., Goshulak, D., Namasivayam, A., Pulonen, M., Kroll, R., Luc, F., et al. (2014). Cortical thickness in children receiving intensive therapy for idiopathic apraxia of speech. *Brain Topography, 27,* 240–247.

17. Kim, K., Shin, J., Kwon, B., Kim, S., Jung, I., & Bang, M. (2011). Neuronox versus BOTOX for spastic equinus gait in children with cerebral palsy: A randomized, double-blinded, controlled multicenter clinical trial. *Developmental Medicine and Child Neurology, 53,* 239–244.

18. Liégeois, F., Baldeweg, T., Connelly, A., Gadian, D. G., Mishkin, M., & Vargha-Khadem, F. (2003). Language fMRI abnormalities associated with *FOXP2* gene mutation. *Nature Neuroscience, 6,* 1230–1237.

19. Locke, J. (1997). A theory of neurolinguistic development. *Brain and Language, 58,* 265–326.

20. Love, R. J. (2000). *Childhood motor speech disability* (2nd ed.). Boston: Allyn and Bacon.

21. McCauley, R. J., & Strand, E. A. (2008). A review of standardized tests of nonverbal and oral speech motor performance in children. *American Journal of Speech-Language Pathology, 17,* 81–91.

22. Meyer, L. A. (1982). *A study of vocal, prosodic and articulatory parameters of the speech of spastic and athetotic cerebral palsied individuals.* Unpublished doctoral dissertation. Nashville, TN: Vanderbilt University.

23. Murray, E., McCabe, P., Heard, R., & Ballard, K. J. (2015). Differential diagnosis of children with suspected childhood apraxia of speech. *Journal of Speech, Language, and Hearing Research, 58,* 43–60.

24. Owens, R. E., Metz, D. E., & Haas, A. (2003). *Introduction to communication disorders: A lifespan perspective* (2nd ed.). Boston: Allyn and Bacon.

25. Preston, J. L., Molfese, P. J., Mencl, W. E., Frost, S. J., Hoeft, F., Fulbright, R. K., et al. (2014). Structural brain differences in school-age children with residual speech sound errors. *Brain and Language, 128,* 25–33.

26. Preston, J. L., Molfese, P. J., Gumkowski, N., Sorcinelle, A., Harwood, V., Irwin, J. R., & Landi, N. (2014). Neurophysiology of speech differences in childhood apraxia of speech. *Developmental Neuropsychology, 39,* 385–403.

27. Shriberg, L. D., Aram, D. M., & Kwiatkowski, J. (1997). Developmental apraxia of speech: I. Descriptive perspectives. *Journal of Speech, Language, and Hearing Research, 40,* 273–285.

28. Sommer, M., Koch, M. A., Paulus, W., Weiller, C., & Buchel, C. (2002). Disconnection of speech-relevant brain areas in persistent developmental stuttering. *Lancet, 360,* 380–383.

29. Strand, E. A., McCauley, R. J., Weigand, S. D., Stoeckel, R. E., & Baas, B. S. (2013). A motor speech assessment for children with severe speech disorders: Reliability and validity evidence. *Journal of Speech, Language, and Hearing Research, 56,* 505–520.

30. Terband, H., Maassen, B., Guenther, F. H., & Brumberg, J. (2009). Speech motor development in childhood apraxia of speech: Generating testable hypotheses by neurocomputational modeling. *Folia Phoniatrica et Logopaedica, 62,* 134–142.

31. Vargha-Khadem, F., Watkins, K., Alcock, K., Fletcher, P., & Passingham, R. (1995). Praxic and nonverbal cognitive deficits in a large family with a genetically transmitted speech and language disorder. *Proceedings of the National Academy of Sciences of the United States of America, 92,* 930–933.

32. Webb, A. L., Singh, R. H., Kennedy, M. J., & Elsas, L. J. (2003). Verbal dyspraxia and galactosemia. *Pediatric Research, 53,* 396–402.

33. Workinger, M. S., & Kent, R. D. (1991). Perceptual analysis of the dysarthrias in children with athetoid and spastic cerebral palsy. In C. A. Moore, K. M. Yorkston, & D. R. Beukelman (Eds.), *Dysarthria and apraxia of speech: Perspectives on management* (pp. 109–126). Baltimore: Paul H. Brookes.

34. Worster-Drought, C. (1974). Suprabulbar paresis. *Developmental Medicine and Child Neurology, 16*(Suppl. 30), 1–30.

35. Xuan, Y., Meng, C., Yang, Y., Zhu, C., Wang, L., Yan, Q., et al. (2012). Resting state brain activity in adults who stutter. *PLoS One, 7*(1), e30570.

36. Yari, E., & Ambrose, N. (2013). Epidemiology of stuttering: 21st century advances. *Journal of Fluency Disorders, 38,* 66–87.

13

Pediatric Disorders of Language

There is in every child at every stage a new miracle of vigorous unfolding.

Erik Erikson

Brain Growth

Acquisition of speech and language is clearly tied to physical development and maturation in the infant and child, yet the exact nature of the interaction of growth and development with emerging speech is unknown. What is known, however, is that the course of speech and language development is a correlate of cerebral maturation and specialization. But a critical question still remains: What indexes of cerebral maturation are of significance to language acquisition? Clearly critical periods occur in the maturation of the brain as well as growth gradients in different brain structures. Can these critical periods be equally applied to the stages of language acquisition?

BRAIN WEIGHT

One obvious index of neurologic development is the change in gross brain weight with age. The most rapid period of brain growth is during the first 2 years of life. The brain more than triples its weight in the first 24 months. At birth, the brain is approximately 25% of its adult weight, and at 6 months it has reached 50% of its full weight. At 1 year, the average age at which the first word appears, the brain is 60% of its adult weight. Thus the brain makes its most rapid growth in the first year of life. By 2.5 years, the brain has reached approximately 75% of its full growth, and at 5 years it is within 90% of its complete maturation. Table 13-1 illustrates this increase in brain weight. It is not until 10 years of age that the brain achieves approximately 95% of its ultimate weight. By approximately 12 years, or puberty, full brain weight is reached.

The late neurolinguist Eric Lenneberg (1921-1975) argued that the accelerated curve of brain growth in the first years of life matched the course of rapid early acquisition of language of the child.[24] He further claimed that primary linguistic skills were achieved by the age of 4 or 5 years and that the ability to acquire language diminished sharply after puberty, when accelerating brain growth reached a plateau.

DIFFERENTIAL BRAIN GROWTH

Just as the total brain grows at different rates at different ages, so do its different parts, and various brain structures reach their peak growth rates at different times. For instance, brainstem divisions, such as the midbrain, pons, and medulla, grow rapidly prenatally and less rapidly postnatally. The cerebellum develops rapidly from before birth to the age of 1 year. The cerebral hemispheres, important in language development, grow rapidly early, contributing approximately 85% to total brain volume by the sixth fetal month.

TABLE 13-1

Language and Brain Growth from Birth to 12 Years

AGE	LANGUAGE MILESTONES	BRAIN WEIGHT (G)
Birth	Crying	335
3 months	Cooing and crying	516
6 months	Babbling	660
9 months	Voicing intoned jargon	750
12 months	Approximating first words	925
18 months	Early naming	1024
24 months	Making two-word combinations	1064
5 years	Kindergarten age, sentences	1180
12 years	Fully matured brain weight	1320

The differential growth of the cortex of the cerebral hemispheres is of vital importance for speech and language function because the majority of neural structures for communication are integrated there. Most cortical neurons are in place at birth, but brain growth may be measured through the development of synaptic connections and myelination. One method of establishing a schedule of cortical growth gradients in cerebral maturity is to determine what cortical areas are most developed in myelination at birth. The motor area of the precentral gyrus of the frontal lobe is the first cortical area developed at birth. It is soon followed by the somatosensory area of the postcentral gyrus of the parietal lobe. Next, quite soon after birth, the primary visual receptor area of the occipital cortex matures. The primary auditory area, Heschl's gyrus in the temporal lobe, matures last. The medial surface of the hemispheres shows the final development of the brain.

The cortical association areas lag behind the development of the cortical receptor areas that are present and active at birth. In fact, the major association areas devoted to speech and language mature well into the preschool years and even beyond. The progressive development of Broca's area and the development of Wernicke's area are related to progressive stabilization of the phonologic system. As the phonemic motor planning system matures, the auditory association system increases its ability to process longer and more complex sequences of connected phonemes. The arcuate fasciculus connecting Broca's and Wernicke's areas apparently begins myelination in the first year and continues for some time afterward.

At 1 year the normal child has a vocabulary of one or more word approximations, usually names for objects that have been seen and sometimes touched. This stage of language development requires the ability to mix neural information from the auditory, somesthetic, and visual association areas. The association area of the inferior parietal lobe is where information from the temporal auditory association areas, the occipital visual association area, and the parietal association area combines to provide the neural bases for the feat of naming that the 1-year-old child displays. The rapid growth of vocabulary in the second and third years of life therefore may well be a correlate of the maturation of this significant posterior association area in the parietal lobe, which combines information from surrounding association areas. It no doubt is a master association area, rightly named by Geschwind as the "association area of association areas."[17]

The left hemisphere is destined to serve as the primary neurologic site for speech and language mechanisms in most infants, children, and adults. The left hemisphere shows early structural differences that support later **language dominance**. The sylvian fissure is longer on the left in fetal brains, and the planum temporale on the left is larger in the majority of fetal and newborn brains. Although the temporal lobe appears well differentiated from early life, Broca's area is not differentiated until 18 months, and the corpus callosum is not completely myelinated until age 10 years. The inferior parietal lobe, the master association area, is not fully myelinated until adulthood, often well into the fourth decade.

DIFFERENTIAL BRAIN GROWTH ANOMALY: AGENESIS OF THE CORPUS CALLOSUM

The corpus callosum is defined under the category of commissural fibers; that is, it interconnects corresponding structures in the left hemisphere with the right hemisphere. The largest bundle of these fibers is called the **corpus callosum** (Fig. 13-1, *A*). Consisting of a rostrum, genu, body, and splenium, it is formed by over 190 million axons, primarily excitatory in nature, traversing from one hemisphere to the other.[39] These fibers emerge and are sculpted in developmental stages during embryonic, fetal, and postnatal periods.

Agenesis of the corpus callosum (Fig. 13-1, *B*) is a condition present at birth in which there is partial or complete absence of the corpus callosum (CC). In the general population the prevalence is 0.02% to 0.5% with 2% to 3% of patients with intellectual disability

affected.[21] As would be expected, abnormal pathways have been shown on imaging studies to develop in the brain. Despite the presence of abnormal organization, there has always been found a great variability in function and cognition of acallosal patients.

Until recently, this was assumed to be the result of compensatory strategies developed through mechanisms of neural plasticity. A recent study using in utero diffusion tensor imaging provided evidence that this may not be the primary cause of the variability. Using the DTI and streamlined tractography, white matter pathway development was studied in 20 fetuses with isolated agenesis of the CC and compared with that of 20 gestation-age matched fetuses with normally developing brains.[21] After the imaging, the researchers constructed macroscopic connectomes of the pathways in different regions. The authors wanted to try to characterize white matter architecture before occurrence of the natural rorganization that would take place early postnatally through axon refinement and pruning and then later as a result of experience-driven changes. They found that the acallosal fetal brains showed a globally altered connectivity network already present compared with the normally developing brains. Gradually increasing connectivity strength was found in aberrant pathways running anterior-posteriorly. Less network centrality was found in dense areas of connectivity like the thalamus and cingulate cortex. These findings indicated that callosal agenesis manifests itself not only in aberrant pathways that run adjacent to the medial part of the hemispheres but also in excessive structural connectivity that intensifies during gestation. This provides support for the likelihood that abnormal fiber development in children with callosal agenesis is more likely governed by genetically determined prenatal events than by compensatory mechanisms in later life.

The frequent observation of variability of function of these children combined with the results of the study outlined earlier demands that clinicians carefully assess each child with a diagnosis of agenesis of the CC, being careful to remember that there is not a "typical" developmental pattern for speech and language. There have been case studies and reports of treatments of those patients that will be helpful but each child will serve as his or her own control.

MYELINATION FOR LANGUAGE

Myelination has been considered one of the more significant indexes of brain maturation and is often a prime correlate of speech and language. Myelination allows more rapid transmission of neural information along neural fibers and is particularly critical in a cerebral nervous system dependent on several long axon

FIGURE **13-1**

Magnetic resonance imaging (MRI) images from normal and acallosal-defect subjects. (a) Sagittal image of a normal mature corpus callosum from a 15-year-old subject. R, rostrum; G, genu; B, body; S, the splenium. (b) Coronal image of a normal corpus callosum (black arrows). (c) Sagittal image showing agenesis of the corpus callosum with the medial hemispheric sulci radiating into the third ventricle (white arrow). (d) Coronal image of true agenesis of the corpus callosum with Probst bundle formation (black arrows). (e) Sagittal image showing a patient with Chiari II malformation and partial agenesis of the corpus callosum. The rostrum and splenium are absent (black arrows). (Adapted from Kamnasaran, D. [2005]. Agenesis of the corpus callosum: Lessons from humans and mice. *Clinical and Investigative Medicine 28*: 267–282.)

connections between hemispheres, lobes, and cortical and subcortical structures. Lack of maturation of myelin in language association fibers and language centers has frequently been suggested as a cause for developmental delays in language. Immaturity of myelogenesis has not been definitely proved as a demonstrable cause in speech-language delay, but the available data suggest it as a likely factor.

Myelogenesis is a cyclic process in which certain neural regions and systems appear to begin the process early and others much later. In some instances the myelogenetic cycle is short and in other cases much longer. Clear differences in rate of myelogenesis exist between different pathways. Myelination of the cortical end of the auditory projections extends beyond the first year, whereas myelination of the cortical end of the visual projections is complete soon after birth. A similar discrepancy exists between myelination of the auditory geniculotemporal radiations and visual geniculocalcarine radiations. These myelogenetic cycles appear to underlie the early visual maturity and slowly developing auditory maturity of the infant. Myelination cycles can be roughly correlated with the milestones of speech and language development, but because no behavioral way exists of assessing myelogenetic maturation in the living brain of the child with language delay, the concepts have little or no clinical utility for the speech-language pathologist (SLP).

Cerebral Plasticity

Children who have begun to develop language normally and then sustain cerebral injury, particularly to the left hemisphere, often show a loss of language skills and a significant effect on further language development, at least initially. The younger the child, however, the more quickly the language disturbance appears to resolve itself and the child appears to become grossly normal or near normal in language function. This fact is in relatively sharp contrast to the adult who sustains left cerebral injury. In adult brains, resolution of language difficulty after focal injury to the (typically) dominant left hemisphere rarely reaches the level of normality of functioning that is possible in the child.

One explanation given for this phenomenon is that the child's brain demonstrates considerable plasticity of function in that undamaged areas are capable of assuming language function. In terms of language function, **cerebral plasticity** is defined as a state or stage in which specific cortical areas are not well established because of the brain's immaturity. The brain is more plastic during the most rapid periods of brain growth, and damage to the left hemisphere before the end of the first year of life is often associated with a shift of language function to the right hemisphere. By contrast, injury to the left hemisphere after this critical period is less likely to be associated with a functional reorganization of the brain. Studies from various neurosurgical centers show that approximately one third of patients with left hemisphere damage before age 1 year continue to have language mediated exclusively by the left hemisphere.[33] In patients in whom left hemisphere dominance for language continues even in the face of damage, it is dependent primarily on the integrity of the frontal and temporal-parietal language areas. This explanation of cerebral plasticity of language mechanisms rests on the concept of a transfer of functional areas from the left hemisphere to uncommitted areas in the right hemisphere.

The period of time in which plasticity changes occur is called the *critical period*. Each area of the cortex has its own critical period; therefore a child's recovery from an injury depends on two factors: where the lesion occurred and the exact critical period for that part of the brain.[20] This critical period has many implications for language functioning in a developing child. Axonal and synaptic developments are especially vulnerable to perinatal hypoxia, malnutrition, and even environmental toxins such as air pollution, paint, and fumes.[20] When axonal and synaptic development are affected, this vulnerability has adverse consequences on cognitive and language development. Sensory and social deprivation studies have also shown that environmental stimuli can have a significant effect on development during the critical period. To this end, a longitudinal study done by investigators from the Family Life Project in North Carolina involved studying parental and household variables of 1112 families

in relation to language development findings at age 36 months.[40] Language was measured by only the receptive language measure of the Wechsler Preschool and Primary Scale of Intelligence and the expressive tests of the Preschool Language Scale, fourth edition. Thirteen covariant variables were included, typical to study of environmental factors in child development. These included parental variables (such as parental age at first birth, income, education, employment, depression, etc.) and child variables (prenatal exposure to alcohol or drugs, number of different child-care settings, geographic isolation). The research targeted interest area beyond these variables was termed *household chaos*. This included factors associated with instability and disorganization. Household disorganization (rated with five factors: household density, number of hours of TV watching, household preparation before the five scheduled visits, cleanliness of the household, and neighborhood noise level around the home). The findings of the study found the chaos factor termed *disorganization* to be the most significant predictor of delayed language development, as measured in the study, during the first 3 years of life. This was over and beyond factors of socioeconomic status and parenting frequently cited. Although development of other skills was not studied nor was more rigorous measure of language development undertaken, this study continues to reinforce what neurodevelopmental literature emphasizes about a child's *experiences* and interactions with his or her sensory and cognitive "environment." According to Castro et al.[11] environmental enrichment programs are considered to be the most effective in overcoming cognitive problems, including the delays in speech and language development. The structure, focus, and attention to the child's needs provided by these preschool and early intervention programs are supported by many studies, including this one, as critical to enhancing language and other neurodevelopmental areas, especially for children from chaotic households.

DEVELOPMENT OF LANGUAGE DOMINANCE

An overriding fact of brain functioning is that the cerebral hemispheres demonstrate asymmetry and that language is dominant in one of them. Cerebral dominance appears to be a developing function because, although anatomic differences favor the temporal lobe in the left hemisphere, strong evidence suggests that language is less fixed in the immature brain. Lenneberg[24] advanced the theory that the course of **language lateralization** follows the course of cerebral maturation. He argued that lateralization is completed by

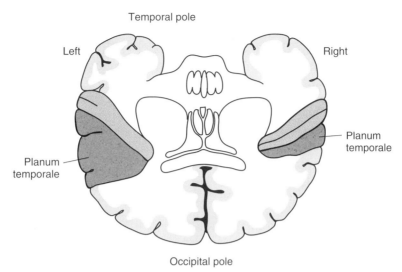

Temporal pole

Left

Right

Planum
temporale

Planum
temporale

Occipital pole

FIGURE **13-2**

Cerebral asymmetry in the planum temporale. Geschwind and Levitsky demonstrated a larger left planum temporale in 65 adult subjects, a larger right planum temporale in 11 subjects, and equal plana temporale in 24 subjects. The drawing shows an exposed upper surface of the temporal lobe with a cut made at the plane of the sylvian fissure. Note a large left planum lying behind the transverse gyrus of Heschl. On the right are two transverse gyri and a small planum. (Modified from Geschwind, N., & Levitsky, W. [1968]. Left-right asymmetries in temporal speech region, *Science, 161*, 186-187. In C. Ludlow & M. Doran-Quine [Eds.], [1979]. *The neurologic bases of language disorders in children: Methods and directions for research* [NIH Publication 79-440]. Washington, DC: National Institutes of Health Publication.)

puberty, based on the assumption that at birth the two hemispheres have equal potential for the development of language mechanisms and that gradual lateralization is associated with the period of major growth.

Current anatomic evidence suggests that the hemispheres may not have equal potentiality for language and that the left hemisphere is organized differently from the right, with speech mechanisms for language in the left.[18] The planum temporale is larger in adults, newborns, and fetuses (Fig. 13-2).[41]

Research comparing macroscopic aspects (width, height, length, and total volume of the area) of postmortem brains with structural patterns (neuronal density, axonal density, etc.) concluded that the asymmetry could not be explained by neuronal density or glial cell volume.[5] However, the findings pointed to axonal myelination as a possible explanation. Further support was provided by Galuske et al.,[16] who demonstrated a strong relation of asymmetry of the planum temporale to the organization of the clusters of neurons that characterize the area and the spacing of those clusters. These factors can be referred to as the *intrinsic microcircuitry* of the area, and area 22 of the temporal lobe is indicative of greater complexity of connections. The authors of this study concluded that this higher level of organizational complexity (increasing the area volume) could be partially attributable to use-dependent modifications that

occur during development with increasing exposure to human language. As Habib and Robichon[18] point out, however, this conclusion of exposure-dependent increase in volume is incompatible with the fact that the asymmetry is present in the neonate and even the fetus. More likely, they conclude, a genetically predetermined pattern of asymmetry exists that is further reinforced under the influence of specific environmental influences.

Cerebral dominance for language has been long associated with laterality of other functions. As long ago as 1865, Jean Bouillaud (1796-1881) suggested that language dominance and handedness were related in some way. For many years the preferred hand was believed to be contralateral to the cerebral hemisphere dominant for language. This meant that the left cerebral hemisphere was dominant for language in right-handers and the right hemisphere in left-handers. Primarily through the cortical-stimulation studies of Penfield and Roberts[32] current thinking is that the left hemisphere is almost always language dominant in right-handers, with approximately 95% of this group left-brained for language. In left-handers, approximately 50% to 70% also show language dominance in the left hemisphere.

Hand preference is a relevant but not totally reliable index in predicting language dominance. Right-handedness is a relatively universal trait and is usually associated with other preferences in laterality. Human beings also tend to prefer one foot, eye, and ear consistently. Degrees of laterality vary. Some people are more strongly right-handed than others, but true ambidexters, those who use either hand equally well, are quite rare.

Most right-handed people demonstrate ear preference, which is considered consistent with a contralateral hemisphere laterality for language in the brain. This preference can be demonstrated through **dichotic listening** tasks in which simultaneous auditory stimuli are presented to both ears at once. Listeners generally show a consistent lateral preference in recognition of stimuli in one ear over the other ear. This is called an **ear advantage**. Only 80% of right-handers show a distinct right ear advantage, so the relation to cerebral dominance for language is not always clear.

Bilingualism

Processing of language for an individual who speaks more than one language is unique. **Bilingual** individuals are capable of **code switching**. This is the ability of a bilingual speaker to shift from one language to another within a sentence or within an entire conversation. This usually occurs when both languages are used in the person's home, school, or work environment on a regular basis. According to Owens[31] this behavior is neither random nor a deficit. Sprott and Kemper[36] and others indicated that code switching is a phenomenon governed by rules and influenced by the context of the interaction. Code switching is often used as a processing tool to enhance meaning, alert a listener of a change in topic, or express humor attitudes or cultural solidarity.

Ahlsén discussed neurolinguistic distinction among three types of bilingualism: compound bilingualism, coordinated bilingualism, and subordinated bilingualism (Table 13-2).[1] Further research has indicated that most bilingual children do not know each language at exactly the same skill level. Many times, as evidenced by the SLP's experiences in the public schools, the two languages complement each other, with each language used primarily in one setting or another, such as school, work, or play.

Anecdotally, most monolingual adults who have attempted to learn another language will tell you that it is challenging and, for some, impossible to become fluent. This is yet another testament to the decreasing plasticity of the brain for language development as a person matures. Weber-Fox and Neville undertook a study using event-related potentials to look at brain maturation and performance on measures of accuracy in identifying semantic and syntactic errors in the second language.[42] They studied Chinese adults who had learned English at different maturational points (age 1-3, 4-6, 7-10, 11-13, and after age 16). Performance on tests of semantic and

TABLE 13-2

Types of Bilingualism Distinguished Neurolinguistically

TYPE	DESCRIPTION
Compound bilingualism	The first and second languages are learned concurrently before age 6 years; languages are often spoken by one parent.
Coordinated bilingualism	The second language is learned before puberty either in the home or another environment (e.g., school).
Subordinated bilingualism	The first language is dominant, and the second language is used as translation; child thinks in the first language and then translates it to the second language for speaking purposes.

Modified from Ahlsén, E. (2006). *Introduction to neurolinguistics*. Philadelphia: John Benjamins.

phrase structure judgments were compared with performance by monolingual adults on the same measures. Only the bilingual speakers who learned English after age 16 were found to be significantly poorer on this task than the monolingual speakers. The performance on phrase structure (grammar/syntax), however, was found to be sensitive to the age of acquisition of the second language; performance of those exposed before the age of 4 was similar to the monolinguals, and there was a trend for those exposed between ages 4 and 6 to perform less well. However, those who began learning English after age 6 performed significantly poorer than the monolingual subjects. Analysis of the data gathered from the associated event-related potentials (ERPs) was consistent with these findings. All groups displayed a significant N400 effect in response to semantic violations but the peak latencies in bilinguals exposed after age 16 occurred later, suggesting a slight slowing in processing. For the syntactic processing, altered ERPs were observed even with the shortest delay in exposure (1-3 years). With increased delays in exposure to the second language, the ERP data suggested reduced asymmetry in sentence type effects, indicating reduced left hemisphere specialization and, perhaps, increased right hemisphere involvement in the processing of syntax for the second language and, in this study, less accuracy.

Neurolinguists often are interested in the recovery patterns and abilities of bilingual individuals who have a neurologic infarct such as stroke or traumatic brain injury. Parallel recovery of the languages is the most common pattern experienced by these individuals.[1] Ahlsén postulated that the language used that has the most emotional ties to it is less impaired after infarct and also recovers first. Another hypothesis is that the right hemisphere is more involved in second language (L2) processing than it is with the first language (L1). This may be supported by the ERP study just discussed for those learning another language after age 3.

LANGUAGE DIFFERENCE OR LANGUAGE DISORDER?

An understanding of the difference between a language disorder and a language difference helps the student studying neurologic speech and language disorders in children. The previous discussion on bilingualism should trigger some thoughts for the student studying speech-language pathology or audiology. Is the child whose first language is not English considered disordered in English, delayed in language development in English, or just a child with a difference in his or her language systems and structures? The American Speech-Language-Hearing Association (ASHA)[4] and Silverman and Miller[35] describe these differences. A language disorder is defined as impairment in the comprehension and/or production of the language content, form, and/or usage; however, a language difference is "a variation of a symbol system . . . that reflects and is determined by shared regional, social, or cultural-ethnic factors" (p. 78).[35]

Owens stated that "a dialect within a language as well as a developing bilingualism that is affected by the influence of the first language on learning the second language is not to be considered a disorder but rather a language difference" (p. 98).[31] School systems continue to struggle with teaching children who have English as a second language (ESL) or limited proficiency in English. It is critical, however, for the SLP to try to fairly assess children who are suspected as having true language disorders in their first language. This is a difficult assignment because there are few language assessments published for the speaker of languages other than English that are available to monolingual SLPs or even to the bilingual SLP in the United States, although more are now available in Spanish.

Developing cultural sensitivity and competence would help the SLP and audiology student develop a keen awareness of cultures in general and be more prepared to deal with either language differences or disorders. The members of ASHA's Multicultural Issues Board during 2004 introduced readers to the concepts of cultural sensitivity and cultural competence.[27]

Childhood Language Disorders

To truly understand the origin of language disorders and why a child exhibits disordered linguistic behavior,

students should review the neurologic language processing structures in the central nervous system. Likewise, a review of the structures responsible for expressive language and transmitting a processed message from Wernicke's area to Broca's area through the arcuate fasciculus will help the student understand how a message is verbalized through an intricate programming of motor speech structures that allow an individual to verbalize an idea.

LANGUAGE IMPAIRMENT

In this next section of this chapter we will briefly discuss language impairment in children. By far the most prevalent childhood language abnormalities are those that are developmental rather than acquired. The term language impairment is adopted here, rather than **specific language impairment (SLI)**, which is a term that came to the forefront in the 1980s and is still in wide use in our professional literature, as well as that of education and medicine. In 2012 ASHA was asked to respond to the proposal to include the diagnosis of SLI in the new edition of the *Diagnostic and Statistical Manual of Mental Disorders* (DSM-5). Although the decision was not without controversy, ASHA recommended that the diagnosis not be included, citing debate over the robustness and validity of diagnostic criteria. ASHA maintained that the term SLI was primarily used in research rather than widely used in clinical settings. Therefore SLI is not in the DSM-5. *Language disorder* is listed under communication disorders with the criteria described as "persistent difficulties in the acquisition and use of language across modalities (i.e., spoken, written, sign language, or other) due to deficits in comprehension or production," and "language abilities that are 'substantially and quantifiably' below age expectations."[3] Historically, SLI had been defined as a language disorder that delays the mastery of language skills in children who have no hearing loss or other developmental delays.[30]

Other definitions also may have included "no evidence of lack of opportunity" as a criterion. In 2014 child language researchers and clinicians from the United States, Australia, and Great Britain made a compelling argument for the use of *language impairment* rather than SLI or language disorder. They argued that SLI has always been a diagnosis of exclusion, thereby perhaps leaving out the possibility of finding comorbidity of the language impairment and other disorders (that is, finding a language impairment, the symptoms and signs of which are outside what would be expected given the other factors). Citing other problems with defining language impairment by excluding children with lower nonverbal IQ, autism spectrum disorder, social disadvantage, and hearing loss, they recommended that professionals work to reach a consensus as to *inclusionary* criteria for the diagnosis of language impairment so that discrete language impairment could be identified even in children with these disorders.

Because this development of inclusionary criteria has not been established for clinical or research use at the time of this writing, the research cited here is primarily on children who were diagnosed with SLI. Terms found in the literature that may refer to the same disorder are *language delay, developmental language disorder,* or *developmental dysphasia* (particularly in Australia and Great Britain). According to the National Institute on Deafness and Other Communication Disorders, the disorder affects 7% to 8% of kindergarten children and its effects can persist into adulthood. This research on SLI is helpful in trying to understand the neurodevelopmental causes of difficulty with language development but may only apply to a small subset of children who are language impaired yet did not meet the strict criteria for inclusion as a child with SLI.

The familial nature of developmental language impairments has been documented, although with much variation in study design and criteria for disorder. Increased frequency of language impairment in persons with first-degree relatives affected has been found in these studies.[37,38] This finding has been strengthened by twin studies showing increased concordance in monozygotic twins compared with dizygotic twins, strongly suggesting genetic influence. Genetic variability related to both ASD and language impairment was one of the principle interests of a large study published in 2014.[8] The study identified two novel chromosome locations: 15q23-26 and 16p12. Further study found 15q to be specific to oral language impairment. Certainly the research in genetic basis for language impairment will continue, perhaps one day helping us identify those most at risk for language delay or impairment so that intervention could be initiated early in that child's life.

NEURAL BASIS OF LANGUAGE IMPAIRMENT

A search of the literature regarding any neurologic basis for language disorders that appear to be developmental or not strongly related to an identifiable accompanying disorder reveals few studies. This is perhaps because of the complexity of language development itself, with the importance of genetic and environmental factors acknowledged and well accepted. With the advent of neuroimaging techniques safe for use with children, there have been studies of brain function attempted in the past few years but little consistency has been found.[25] Liégeois and colleagues summarized selected studies in a 2014 review.[25] For this study, the authors reviewed more than 2000 abstracts and articles published between 2008 and 2013. Criteria excluded duplicate studies, studies with children with brain injury, studies with no imaging, and studies in which magnetic resonance imaging (MRI) data included no quantitative analysis. The level of evidence for the five studies used was classified as Level III-2 (a concurrent study with comparative controls) by the Australian classification criteria.[29] Their report noted the variability of inclusion criteria and diagnoses in these studies with one study using adults identified with language impairment as children and continuing to score low on language assessments. Structural imaging studies were included in four of the five cases. Three of these four focused on children. Even in such a small number of subjects, there was great variability with studies of gray matter finding increase in some temporal lobe areas in some subjects while another found decrease. Study of subcortical structures such as the caudate nucleus found similar contrary results. Studies of white matter using fractional anisotropy (FA) also found contradictory results in different subjects. Two functional imaging studies with language impairment were reviewed with both finding hypoactivation of the posterior superior temporal gyrus. In the summary of findings the authors caution that given the heterogeneity of the studies, any consistency found must be considered speculative but there was converging evidence suggesting possible neural correlates for language impairment. These were:

- Morphologic reductions in the superior temporal gyrus and sulcus in either hemisphere, suggesting a role for intact auditory processing during typical language development
- Reduced activity in the left posterior superior temporal gyrus, consistent with the morphologic reductions, again suggesting abnormal auditory processing as a factor in poor language development
- Reduction in FA in the superior longitudinal fasciculus

The primary summary of the findings of this review study stated that cortical and subcortical anomalies had been found in a wide network supporting language function with little consistency across studies except in the superior temporal gyri. At this point in research, there is much variability in neuroimaging approach and too much heterogeneity in participant groups to assist the research clinician in devising novel interventions targeted at the underlying pathology.

LANGUAGE IMPAIRMENT IN CHILDREN WITH EPILEPSY

Epilepsy is a neurologic disorder in which the activity of the nerve cells is disrupted causing seizures which result in abnormal behaviors. A seizure is defined as abnormal electrical activity in the brain with the two main types being either generalized (involving both sides of the brain) or partial (focal) beginning in one part of the brain (and perhaps spreading to generalize). The two main types of generalized seizures are *grand mal* and *petit mal*. Recurrent seizures indicate a seizure disorder or epilepsy. Epilepsy can be idiopathic and there does appear to be some genetic influence. It also is often associated with neurologic disorders of childhood like cerebral palsy, abnormal cortical development, or hippocampal sclerosis. Brain injury often will result in the development of a seizure disorder, and infections that affect the brain can also cause the onset of epilepsy.

The abnormal surges in electrical activity that occur during seizures may disrupt neuronal connections and interfere with the development of new connections. Obviously a seizure disorder could delay or impair language development in a child. Children with epilepsy are often diagnosed with language impairment, learning disability, and, sometimes, intellectual disability. About 40% of children with epilepsy have accompanying deficits in attention and may have attention-deficit/hyperactivity disorder. Language outcome is dependent on the presence of comorbidities, the age of onset, the success of seizure control (usually with drugs), and the type and severity of the disorder.

A recent study on children with a focal seizure disorder in the left hemisphere demonstrated language difficulty and may also have contributed to helping us understand normal language development. A group of children, aged 4 to 12 years, who had focal seizures of the left hemisphere were compared with a matched group of healthy children on an auditory decision task and studied with functional MRI (fMRI).[12] The researchers identified eight regions of interest in the perisylvian area and performed component analyses on these. In the healthy children the analysis suggested the existence of two functional networks that could be activated and synchronized to accomplish the language task. The *ventral network or stream* (implying white matter connectivity) was described as consisting primarily of Brodmann areas 45 and 47 in the frontal lobe as well as anterior and middle temporal lobe areas nodes; these areas were found to be tightly synchronized during language tasks in healthy subjects. A *dorsal network or stream* consisted primarily of Brodmann area 44, the angular gyrus, and a middle temporal node. For the dorsal activations there was also found a tight network synchrony between inferior parietal areas in general, and inferior frontal and temporal areas (mirroring the connections of the arcuate fasciculus).

This study thus supported the functional separation of language systems in the typically developing child. In these children both networks were recruited during the experimental task. The children with focal epilepsy, however, overall showed failure to recruit the ventral network, particularly in the younger children, and this was associated with poorer language performance. The study did not find, as predicted, less functional connectivity in the children with epilepsy compared with the healthy control subjects but did find poor activation of the ventral language network or stream. This ventral network is implicated in semantic processing of sentences and semantic decision making and thus is critical for auditory processing and comprehension. At least for this study, the poor language performance on testing highlights the importance of the ventral network for normal language development and the effect of childhood epilepsy on its continued maturation.

Landau-Kleffner Syndrome

An important but rare cause of acquired language impairment is **Landau-Kleffner syndrome (LKS)**, which is usually associated with sudden onset of difficulty with language development in children for whom the etiology initially may not be clear. The clinical picture in this group is extremely varied. The age of onset of the disorder is generally between 3 and 7 years.[15] The onset of the language disturbance lasts from a few hours or days to more than 6 months. The presence of clinical seizures is reported in only 75% to 80% of the children with the syndrome. It is important in diagnosis to have the electroencephalogram (EEG) done while the child is sleeping because the seizure activity most often occurs during slow-wave sleep and may be missed with a routine EEG done on an awake child.[15] The presence of sudden regression or slowing of language development with no known etiology should be a red flag for the presence of subclinical seizure activity, and this testing should be pursued to rule it out. LKS usually affects understanding of spoken language more than expressive, although both expressive and receptive deficits may be present. Recovery is also varied; one study followed eight children for 10 to 28 years and found full recovery in four, mild residual language impairment in one, and moderate language impairment in four.[28] Adults who appear to have recovered well may still report some difficulty with auditory processing. A brief article by Alpern[2] in *The ASHA Leader* provides discussion of LKS as well as a link to a video case study for those interested in further exploration of LKS.

LANGUAGE IMPAIRMENT IN CHILDREN WITH INTELLECTUAL DISABILITY

Cognitive deficits limit language development, and the linguistic skills of the developmentally delayed child are generally poorer than those of the cognitively normal child of equivalent chronologic age. Language development in the majority of developmentally delayed children proceeds on a slower but normal course until early adolescence, when development reaches a plateau. Some have argued that, as in other children, their language development is paced by cerebral maturation. The lack of development of adequate speech and language in **intellectual disability** often serves as one of the earliest and most sensitive signs of an abnormality in development of the nervous system for the pediatric neurologist and SLP. Table 13-3 outlines the major language characteristics of children with developmental delay.

Language delay and generalized intellectual disability have various causes. Neurologic factors delay or arrest myelinization (maturation), which would inevitably cause brain tissue to remain undeveloped. Certain biologic factors, such as genetic or chromosomal abnormalities, maternal infections in the first trimester of pregnancy, chemical or lead toxicity, metabolic malfunctions, and complications from pregnancy or delivery may also cause intellectual disability and a delay of speech and language development. Table 13-4 illustrates causes and consequent syndromes that lead to arrested cognitive and language development.

The practicing SLP or the student of speech-language pathology should keep uppermost in her/his mind that a child with developmental delay should always be assessed for language impairment. There is an expectation that language development will mirror cognitive development. The child whose language or speech development significantly lags behind their cognitive development, given no other

TABLE 13-3

Language Characteristics of Developmentally Delayed Children

LANGUAGE PARAMETER	CHARACTERISTICS
Phonology	Primitive forms
	Similar to preschoolers no matter the age of the child
Morphology	Preschool developmental characteristics
	Often uses the incorrect form of a free or bound morpheme
Syntax	Short sentence lengths
	Simple sentences lacking complexity
	Lack of clauses and compound sentence structures
Semantics	Concrete thinking; little abstract language comprehension or expression
	Lack of understanding of inferences
	Simple meanings of words noted
Pragmatics	Misunderstands gestures
	Lack of the use of gestures for getting a point across
	Poor turn taking
	Lack of asking for clarification increases miscommunications
	Usually does not initiate topics
Receptive language	Poor comprehension
	Heavily relies on context to understand information presented

Modified from Owens, R. E., Jr. (2004). *Language disorders: A functional approach to assessment and intervention* (4th ed.). Boston: Allyn and Bacon.

TABLE 13-4

Causal Factors of Intellectual Disability/Developmental Delay and the Accompanying Syndromes

CAUSAL FACTORS	SYNDROME OUTCOMES
Chromosomal/genetic	Fragile X
	Down syndrome
Complications of pregnancy/maternal infections	Rubella/German measles
	Syphilis
	Gonorrhea
	AIDS
Chemical/lead toxicity	Fetal alcohol syndrome
	Lead poisoning (eating lead-based paint chips is a common cause)
	Crack cocaine
Metabolic malfunctions	Phenylketonuria
	Poor maternal diet lacking vitamins and minerals
Complications of pregnancy and delivery	Skull malformation/immaturity of development
	Premature birth
	Lack of prenatal care

Data from Owens, R. E., Jr., Metz, D. E., & Haas, A. (2003). *Introduction to communication disorders: A lifespan perspective* (2nd ed.; pp. 165-166). Boston: Allyn & Bacon.

medical conditions that would affect language development specifically, should be diagnosed as having a language impairment with treatment provided by a speech-language professional.

LANGUAGE IMPAIRMENT IN NEGLECTED AND ABUSED CHILDREN

A 2012 report on maltreatment of children stated that the total number of reported cases of maltreatment of children (abuse and/or neglect) was 678,610 in the 50 states and Puerto Rico in 2012.[10] Parental interactions with the child are often a key factor in the child's overall development of language as well as other behaviors such as social skills, reading, personality development, and interactive skills with peers. This has been documented in many studies in the literature of psychology, speech-language pathology, and education. Clinicians should be able to recognize some of the signs and salient symptoms of child abuse or neglect. Understanding the causes of abuse and neglect and learning about the person who is the abuser will help the SLP work with these children.

Because of physical, emotional, or other trauma, these children are at risk for delays in language, communication, and social skills as well as psychological and emotional harm. According to Lubinski and Hudson,[26] salient signs of physical, sexual, or emotional abuse exist, and the SLP should be aware and alert for indicators of possible abuse. These signs of include extreme behavior outbursts, self-destructive behaviors, poor academic performance, and language delays. Environmental factors also play a part in the cycle of abuse or neglect. These factors may include lack of social support, poverty, and homelessness or poor-quality housing.[26] The behaviors associated with abuse or neglect and their consequences often lead to developmental milestone delays in young children which, of course, include speech and language.

Autism Spectrum Disorder

Until the **DSM-5** was released in 2013,[3] the disorder called autistic disorder was just one of five disorders listed under the classification **pervasive developmental disorders (PDD)**. This terminology had been introduced in 1980, and by the time of publication of the **DSM-IV** it had come to include (1) **childhood disintegrative disorder (CDD)**, (2) **Rett syndrome**, (3) Asperger's syndrome, (4) PDD, not otherwise specified (PDD-NOS), and (5) autism. In the DSM-5, the classification PDD had been replaced with **autism spectrum disorder (ASD)**, subsuming under this category autism, Asperger's syndrome, and PDD-NOS, collapsing them into a single diagnosis:

ASD. Rett syndrome and CDD were eliminated from this classification. Rett syndrome was eliminated because many symptoms of autism found in a child diagnosed with Rett could be diagnosed with ASD, using a specifier of "with known genetic or medical condition." CDD was taken out because of the differences between it and the other spectrum disorders, especially the severity and acuity of it as well as accompanying symptoms in other systems. It is a rare but devastating disorder from which recovery is typically minimal.

Asperger's syndrome was subsumed under ASD because there is little research evidence to separate a person diagnosed with Asperger's from one diagnosed with high-functioning ASD. In regard to PDD-NOS, the committee found that the symptoms identified were primarily subthreshold symptoms for the diagnosis of autism and were so vague as to be used in various ways in diagnosis.

Whereas in the DSM-IV there were three subdomains with communication and social interaction being separate domains, the DSM-5 collapsed these two into one. Table 13-5 describes the two domains for ASD and the criteria under each that are recognized for the diagnosis of ASD in the DSM-5.

The next Autism and Developmental Disabilities Monitoring (ADDM) report is expected to be published in 2016. This report will be based on the DSM-5 criteria. The new monitoring will be expanded to produce estimates of ASD diagnosis and services among 4-year-old children rather than 8-year-olds with the Centers for Disease Control and Prevention (CDC) noting that autism can now be reliably diagnosed by age 2.

The etiology of ASD is controversial and basically unknown. We do know that it has a strong genetic component. In recent years, fMRI has been found to be a useful tool to study neurobiologic function of people with ASD. Dichter[13] provided a comprehensive review of fMRI findings in ASD through 2011. He found that despite the heterogeneity of persons with ASD, several common themes emerged in the studies in regard to brain function. Task-based studies have been performed addressing social perception and cognition with tasks designed around such things as face processing, theory of mind (ability to infer feeling states and/or intentions), cognitive control (go/no-go tasks, task switching, etc.), communication, and reward processing. Dichter reported that fMRI findings during these types of tasks highlighted:

- Hypoactivation during social processing tasks in regions Dichter defines as "nodes" in the "social brain," including the prefrontal cortex, posterior superior temporal sulcus, amygdala, and the fusiform gyrus.
- Aberrant frontostriatal activation during cognitive control tasks, including the dorsal prefrontal cortex and the basal ganglia.

TABLE 13-5

Domains and Domain Criteria for Autism Spectrum Disorder from the DSM-5

A. Persistent deficits in social communication and social interaction across multiple contexts as manifest by at least two of the **following**:

  1. Deficits in social-emotional reciprocity, which may range, for example, from abnormal social approach and failure of normal back and forth conversation, to reduced sharing of interests, emotions, or affect, to failure to initiate or respond

  2. Deficits in communicative behaviors used for social interaction, ranging, for example, from poorly integrated verbal and nonverbal communication, to abnormalities in eye contact and body language or deficits in understanding and use of gestures, to a total lack of facial expressions and nonverbal communication

  3. Deficits in developing, maintaining, and understanding relationships, ranging, for example, from difficulties adjusting behavior to suit various social contexts, difficulties in sharing imaginative play or in making friends, to absence of interest in peers

B. Restrictive, repetitive patterns of behavior, interests, or activities as manifest by at least two of the **following**, currently or historically:

  1. Stereotyped or repetitive motor movements, use of objects or speech (such as simple motor stereotypies, lining up toys or flipping plates, echolalia, idiosyncratic phrases)

  2. Insistence on sameness, inflexible adherence to routines or ritualized patterns of verbal or nonverbal behavior (such as extreme distress at small changes, difficulties with transitions, rigid thinking patterns, greeting rituals, need to take same route or eat same food every day)

  3. Highly restricted, fixated interests that are abnormal in intensity or focus (such as strong attachment to or preoccupation with unusual objects, excessively circumscribed or perseverative interests)

Modified from Kaufman, W. E. (2012). *DSM-5: The new diagnostic criteria for autism spectrum disorders.* Retrieved from http://www.autismconsortium.org/symposium-files/WalterKaufmannAC2012Symposium.pdf.

- Anomalous mesolimbic responses to reward.
- For language tasks, findings included decreased lateralization differential, decreased synchrony in brain regions processing language, decreased automaticity of language processing, and recruitment of regions not typically demonstrated to process language.
- Functional connectivity studies tend to show decreased connectivity between frontal and posterior–temporal regions known to participate actively in processing social-affective information. Some recent studies found both local overconnectivity and distant underconnectivity of social processing regions.

Also briefly reported on by Dichter were structural MRI studies in ASD. He found reports of accelerated brain growth during early development in children with ASD and reports of large head circumference and brain volume. One longitudinal study reported a transient period of postnatal overgrowth of the brain in 70% of children with ASD before age 2; this overgrowth was not present in adolescence or adulthood. Some studies have found a link between increased white matter in the frontal lobe of children with ASD and reduced white matter later in adolescence and adulthood. This is consistent with the FA studies, which have found increased FA in brain areas associated with social processing in young children but reduced FA in adolescents and adults with ASD.

The Dichter review reported that studies of functional connectivity done during a resting state (rather than task-based study) in subjects with ASD found quite contradictory results, with some highlighting reduced connectivity between areas and others finding overconnectivity in similar areas. A 2015 study of subjects with high-functioning ASD sought to try to explain this inconsistency.[19] Resting-state functional connectivity studies were performed for both inter- and intrahemispheric connectivity. Adults with high-functioning ASD were compared with matched control subjects. No consistent pattern of connectivity was found in any of the ASD groups compared with control groups. Both increased and decreased connectivity was found. For interhemispheric connectivity, the magnitude of the distortion pattern correlated significantly with behavioral symptoms of ASD. The authors concluded that a neural characteristic of ASD may actually be idiosyncratic connectivity; they hypothesized that this diversity may result from the behavioral disconnection of the person with ASD from the social and environmental factors typically experienced by humans known to shape and regularize typical neural organization.

According to the 2010 ADDM report, the estimated prevalence of autism has increased 129% since 2002.[7] Although the data are not representative of the entire United States, the ADDM survey of 14 communities' health and special education records of 8-year-old children estimated that 1 in 68 children or 14.1 per 1000 8-year-old children has been identified with ASD (as

Risk Factors Associated with Autism Spectrum Disorder

- Genetic factors[14]
- A sibling with ASD[14]
- Certain genetic or chromosomal conditions such as fragile X or tuberous sclerosis[14]
- Prescription drugs valproic acid or thalidomide taken during pregnancy[14]
- Age of parent: Mother younger than 20 or older than 40; father older than 50; relative risk also increases with increase in age difference between mother and father[34]

defined by the DSM-IV because the DSM-5 criteria had not been published at that time). The CDC states that the critical period for developing autism occurs before, during, or immediately after birth. It is not known what causes autism, but research studies have identified some possible risk factors (Box 13-1).

Although we have not identified a cause or a cure, treatment for the associated behavior, communication, and learning deficits has improved greatly in the past few years as more programs and funding for clinical research have become available. We do not know whether the true incidence of autism has increased or whether medical and allied health professionals are just better at accurately identifying the disorder (or if it is diagnosed inappropriately in a number of cases). It is becoming clear that we must continue to search for the cause(s) and identify preventative measures if possible. Because we do not know how to prevent it, early identification and effective treatment are critical to improve quality of life for those affected.

Pediatric Traumatic Brain Injury

According to the Brain Injury Association of America, the leading cause of death and disability in children and adolescents in the United States is traumatic brain injury (TBI). The CDC finds that the two groups most at risk at the 0- to 4-year and 15- to 19-year age groups. According to the 2004 statistics, an average of 62,000 children, aged 0 to 19 are hospitalized with TBI in the United States, with motor vehicle accidents (MVAs), falls, sports injuries, physical abuse, and other types of causes cited. An average of 564,000 are seen in the emergency department with TBI and released each year. In the 0- to 4-year age group, falls were listed as the primary cause of injury. In the 15- to 19-year age group, MVAs are the most common cause of injury, with mild TBI from sports injuries also becoming more recognized. The 2004 report cited

also listed the alarming statistic that approximately 1300 children in the United States suffer severe or fatal brain injury each year as a result of physical abuse.

The mechanism of TBI was discussed in Chapter 10 with the concepts of coup-contrecoup, molecular commotion, and diffuse axonal injury introduced. The same mechanisms are at work when TBI occurs to the immature brain. Examination of early literature on pediatric TBI reveals that physicians and rehabilitation professionals knew little about the actual short- or long-term effects of injury to children of different ages. Until the advent of safe imaging methods that could be used on young children, there was a dearth of research. Although the numbers of children injured each year is large, it is difficult to find large groups of children on which behavioral studies can be designed without a well-coordinated multicenter study. Because of the nature of the mechanism of injury, there is also great heterogeneity among the potential subject groups. Nevertheless, progress has been made in research on children with TBI, altering the way brain injury is treated by medical and rehabilitation professionals.

It is true that the young brain has potential for recovery after injury that is much greater than the adult brain, and better recovery has always been expected from all but the most severe injuries. It had been commonly accepted that the earlier the injury, the better the recovery and that little residual deficit occurred. Studies in the 1980s and 1990s began to show that children with early TBI did appear to do well when language development and behavior were studied in their preschool years. However, when studies began to look at the learning profiles of children with early TBI once they reached the age when reading and other language-based learning skills were critical, the literature began to suggest that perhaps there were brain differences in these children that did not become evident or even suspected until higher level cognitive-linguistic processing and attentional skills were essential to learning.

Since 1999 there have been a number of studies looking at the effect of TBI on behavior and cognitive-linguistic processing, and a few are cited here. The student using this text will likely be able to find other studies that add knowledge to what may be happening to the young brain after TBI. It is vital that the SLP, whether serving children in medical centers, school systems, or private practice, understand the possible implications of TBI and advocate for appropriate services for these children and adolescents.

PATHOPHYSIOLOGY

An important advance in the study of the effects of TBI has been provided by research detailing the pathophysiology of injury to the immature brain. Different studies supported findings showing that the effect of injury was different in some respects in the developing brain than in the mature brain. A review and discussion of some of these differences[9] found discrepancies in biomechanical properties, aspects of homeostasis and structural and functional responses to injury when TBI to the developing brain was compared with that of the mature brain. A summary of these differences is found in Box 13-2.

Although neurodegenerative changes after TBI have been well documented in adults, there has not been much study of changes in the pediatric population. A 2014 review of original research attempting to document changes in children and youth after TBI included 16 studies that fit the authors' criteria.[23] These studies, consisting of both cross-sectional and longitudinal designs, did find evidence for long-term changes. Volume loss was found in selected brain regions. These included the hippocampus, amygdala, globus pallidus, thalamus, periventricular white matter, cerebellum, and brainstem. A decrease in overall brain volume was found in some

studies with increased cerebrospinal fluid and ventricular space. Decreased integrity in the cellular structure of the corpus callosum was noted on diffusion tensor imaging studies. The review of these studies continues to strengthen evidence that children's brains are more vulnerable to long-term effects of injury than once believed.

Although one study included children with repetitive mild TBI, the authors note critical need for this type of research on children with mild TBI or repetitive concussions.

RESEARCH ON OUTCOME

Given these differences, it is not surprising that research targeting acute intervention, long-term outcome, and treatment method is increasing. Researchers in Australia have been particularly active in research on cognitive recovery in pediatric TBI, asking whether the developmental period when the injury occurred may significantly affect recovery and whether there is a relationship between that period and the severity of the injury in regard to residual deficits. In a longitudinal study of 149 children admitted to the Royal Children's Hospital in Melbourne with brain injury, researchers were able to follow the cognitive development through IQ testing (with the revised Wechsler Intelligence Scale for Children or, for the younger children, the Bayley Scales of Infant Development) for 10 years postinjury in children injured after age 3 and for 30 months for those injured before age 3.[6,22] Groups were divided by age at onset of injury: infant (before age 3; $n = 27$); young (3; 0-7;11; $n = 53$), and old (8;0-12;11; $n = 69$). These groups were then divided by a categorization of severity of injury: (1) Mild defined as Glasgow Coma Scale (GCS) score at admission of 13 to 15, no abnormality on computed tomography (CT) or MRI, and no neurologic deficits; (2) Moderate: GCS score of 9 to 12 and mass lesion or evidence of specific injury on CT or MRI; and (3) Severe: GCS score of 3 to 8 and mass lesion or evidence of pathologic condition on CT or MRI.

Severe Injury Groups

For the young and old groups, the study found a definite relationship between age of injury and severity of injury in the case of severe TBI. Overall, low average IQ (full scale of 82-89) was found for children with TBI after 3 years of age, with performance related to the age of injury as age increased. Better outcomes were found for older children after severe injury. Severe TBI in children injured between ages 8 and 12 found significant increments (similar to adults) in performance in the first 12 months postinjury but then less improvement after a year postinjury. In contrast, flat recovery curves for acute period to 30 months postinjury were found for children

---

BOX 13-2

Structural and Functional Differences of the Immature Brain That Affect Recovery after Traumatic Brain Injury

In Infancy

- Markedly diminished shear resistance due to the following characteristics of the developing brain:
  - Increased water content of the brain tissue
  - Capillary density
  - Cerebral blood volume
  - Reduced extent of myelination
- Reduced brain protection by the immature skull sutures and reduced calcification of the skull, increasing skull elasticity
  - Mechanical load more easily transferred to the brain tissue
  - Causes more cranial distortion and more diffuse pattern of injury

Postinjury Differences Noted in Most Immature Brains versus Adult Brains

- Increased incidence of diffuse brain swelling
- Greater compromise in vasodilation (which would result in vasoconstriction and reduced cerebral blood flow)
- Increased susceptibility to excitotoxicity
  - In developing brain, blockage of N-methyl-D-aspartate receptors induces more rapid apoptosis (programmed cell death)
- Increased dopaminergic activity, altering sensitivity of neurons to excitatory input (in animal models)

injured between ages 3 and 7 with minimal recovery found in any domain (as measured by IQ testing).

Mild to Moderate Injury Groups

In the young and old groups, the IQ testing showed similar postinjury improvement for both mild and moderate severity. With mild TBI after age 3, mean IQs were in the average range (102-104), suggesting minimal effect on this aspect of recovery. Mean IQ findings for the young and old age groups with moderate severity of injury were lower but still within the average range (94-98). All showed gains above those expected in normal development during the immediate months postinjury, but then the trajectory slowed and stabilized from 12 to 30 months postinjury.

Injury in Children Younger Than Age 3

The children injured before age 3 made up a smaller cohort, and cognitive development was measured with a different instrument. Thus interpretation of the results had to be taken within a different context. They were followed for 30 months. A different, less positive pattern of recovery was suggested. Although children who sustained mild injury before age 3 continued to improve and did relatively well on the measures, children with moderate or severe brain injury during this early period of life continued to show significant decreases in global intellectual ability at all assessments (acute, 12 months postinjury, and 30 months postinjury).

Although these results need replication, the data certainly suggest that severity of injury and developmental stage when injured should be two of the factors considered significant when making decisions about follow-up for these children. Further study may elucidate whether injury during certain periods of cognitive development slows advancement and stabilization of certain skills or actually prevents growth of those skills over the long term.

For those with both risk factors—moderate or severe trauma and young age—long-term clinical follow-up and monitoring, at the least, appear warranted. It is likely that these children, especially those with severe TBI, will need intervention by skilled rehabilitation professionals over a long time to promote the best outcome possible.

What Else?

There could be many more disorders of childhood that are associated with language delay/disorder or that place a child at risk for these. Some of those for which language characteristics could be discussed but will be left to your individual research or your professor's assignment are:

- Prematurity
- Hearing loss
- Speech impairment
- Fragile X
- Fetal alcohol syndrome
- Attention-deficit/hyperactivity disorder
- Dyslexia

All of these and other conditions you may encounter in your clinical work are likely to have been found or will be found to show differences in brain development, structure, or function. SLPs should be the professionals assessing the language skills of these children and designing treatment programs. This requires the knowledge you are obtaining now in your reading and coursework as well as ongoing study of the research in the speech-language pathology literature; however, it may also require study of the literature in neurology, other medical professions, imaging, psychology, rehabilitation, and education. The foundation for evidence-based assessment and treatment is widening tremendously.

Clinical Information and Applications for the Speech-Language Pathologist

- Acquisition of speech and language is clearly tied to physical development and maturation.
- The course of speech and language development is a correlate of cerebral maturation and specialization.
- An index of neurologic development is the change in gross brain weight with age.
- Brain weight triples in the first 24 months of life.
- At 10 years old, the brain achieves 95% of its ultimate weight.
- Children born with agenesis of the corpus callosum show great variability in functional and cognitive development, which may be genetically determined. All should be individually assessed for speech and language because prediction is difficult.

- During critical periods for language development, illness and injury may affect development, but social and environmental factors may also be significant factors in normal development. Household organization and other social areas may warrant consideration.
- Bilingualism involves code switching.
- Age of exposure to a second language may be most critical for achieving adequate grammar and syntax for the new language. Delayed exposure appears to decrease left hemisphere specialization to support the new learning.
- The diagnosis of specific language impairment is not in the DSM-5 at ASHA's recommendation. In

Continued

Clinical Information and Applications for the Speech-Language Pathologist—cont'd

diagnostics, ASHA recommends that the diagnosis of language impairment be used in order not to exclude children with accompanying disorders that cannot account for the poor language development.

- Studies of children with focal left hemisphere seizures suggest tight network connectivity of a ventral stream and a dorsal stream supporting normal language development with the seizure activity interrupting activation of the ventral stream, resulting in language impairment.

- The sudden onset of language disturbance or regression without obvious etiology should be a red flag for subclinical seizure activity, possibly identifying a rare disorder called Landau-Kleffner syndrome. EEG studies should be done during sleep to best identify the seizure activity.

- Lack of or delay in speech or language development is one of the most sensitive early indicators of intellectual disability.

- SLPs need to be knowledgeable about the signs of neglect and abuse in children because these children often experience language and other developmental delays as a consequence.

- The DSM-5 lists autism spectrum disorder as a category that includes autism, Asperger's syndrome, and pervasive developmental disorder, not otherwise specified. Domains for communication and social interaction have been collapsed into one,

and it has been determined that autism can be reliably diagnosed as early as age 2.

- Autism appears to have a strong genetic component. Imaging and other types of studies find much heterogeneity in this population with continued research critical to finding the cause or causes. Individualized assessment and treatment is key.

- Traumatic brain injury occurs most often in the 0- to 4-year and 15- to 19-year age groups, with falls and MVAs the most frequent causes of injury.

- Differences in biomechanical, structural, and functional aspects of the developing brain compared with the adult brain make prediction of outcome more difficult. One large longitudinal study in Australia found a definite relationship between severity of injury and age of onset, with younger children more vulnerable to both moderate and severe levels of injury.

- There is a need for further research on the effects of TBI in children with a critical need for study of the effect, especially on learning, of repetitive mild brain injury or concussion.

- There are many childhood conditions that likely alter brain development and cause language delay or impairment. The SLP should be aware of these and of advances in research that may suggest best practice for assessment and treatment of clients with these conditions.

Case **Study**

B.W., a 5-year-old girl, began her kindergarten year at the local elementary school. Her teacher noted that B.W. was quite hyperactive and could not keep up with the children in her classroom during the simplest of activities. She would often sit alone because the other children were sometimes afraid of her outbursts and tantrums. The teacher noted that B.W.'s appearance seemed to be unusual, with widespread eyes and an almost blank, expressionless face most of the time. B.W. was easily distracted by noises or a new person coming into the room. She appeared to have attention difficulties and did not understand the simplest of abstract expressions. She often took things quite literally. The teacher referred her to the school psychologist. Results of testing revealed an IQ score of 72. Speech therapy evaluation further revealed poor sentence structures, often using only two- to

three-word phrases; difficulty with phonics; distractibility; difficulty sharing; and throwing tantrums when she was not permitted to do what she wanted. An individual education plan was written, and B.W. was placed in the self-contained special needs classroom with 2 hours a week in speech and language therapy and 2 hours a week in the elementary learning disability classroom.

Questions for Consideration

1. On the basis of this child's IQ, would she be classified as a developmentally delayed slow learner or as having mild to moderate intellectual disability?

2. Other than this classification, what are possible additional diagnoses that could be applied to this child? Would you suggest referral for any other assessments?

REFERENCES

1. Ahlsén, E. (2006). *Introduction to neurolinguistics.* Philadelphia: John Benjamins.

2. Alpern, C. (2010). Identification and treatment of Landau-Kleffner syndrome. *The ASHA Leader, 15,* 34–35.

3. American Psychiatric Association. (2013). *Diagnostic and Statistical Manual of Mental Disorders* (5th ed.). Washington, DC: American Psychiatric Publishing.

4. American Speech-Language-Hearing Association. (2004). *Communication differences vs. language disorder.* Retrieved from http://www.asha.org/NR/rdonlyres/8C3DF431-6762-46A5-BBDO-EC757E75FF6/0/v1IE_cult_comp.pdf.

5. Anderson, B., Southern, B., & Powers, R. E. (1999). Anatomic asymmetries of the posterior superior temporal lobes: A postmortem study. Neuropsychiatry. *Neuropsychology and Behavioral Neurology, 12,* 247–254.

6. Anderson, V., Catroppa, C., Morse, S., Haritou, F., & Rosenfeld, J. (2015). Functional plasticity or vulnerability after early brain injury? *Pediatrics, 116,* 1374–1382.

7. Autism and Developmental Disabilities Monitoring Network Surveillance Year 2010 Principal Investigators, Centers for Disease Control and Prevention. (2014). Prevalence of autism spectrum disorder among children aged 8 years—Autism and developmental disabilities monitoring network, 11 sites, United States, 2010. *Morbidity and Mortality Weekly Report Surveillance Summary, 63*(2), 1–21.

8. Bartlett, C. W., Hou, L., Flax, J. F., Hare, A., Cheong, S. Y., Fermano, Z., Zimmerman-Bier, B., Cartwright, C., Azaro, M. A., Buyske, S., & Brzustowicz, L. M. (2014). A genome scan for loci shared by autism spectrum disorder and language impairment. *American Journal of Psychiatry, 171*(1), 72–81.

9. Bauer, R. A., & Fritz, H. (2004). Pathophysiology of traumatic injury in the developing brain: An introduction and short update. *Experimental and Toxicologic Pathology, 56,* 65–73.

10. Brain Injury Association of America. (2015). *Brain injury in children.* Retrieved from http://www.biausa.org/brain-injury-children.htm.

11. Castro, A. J., Merchut, M. P., Neafsey, E. J., & Wurster, R. D. (2002). *Neuroscience: An outline approach.* St. Louis: Mosby.

12. Croft, L. B. (2014). Vulnerability of the ventral language network in children with focal epilepsy. *Brain: A Journal of Neurology, 137,* 2245–2257.

13. Dichter, G. S. (2012). Functional magnetic resonance imaging of autism spectrum disorders. *Dialogues in Clinical Neuroscience, 14,* 319–352.

14. Division of Birth Defects, National Center on Birth Defects and Developmental Disabilities, Centers for Disease Control and Prevention. (2015, February 24). *Facts about ASD.* Retrieved from http://www.cdc.gov/ncbddd/autism/facts.html#ref.

15. Foundation, Epilepsy (2013, September). *Landau-Kleffner syndrome.* Retrieved from http://www.epilepsy.com/learn/types-epilepsy-syndromes/landau-kleffner-syndrome.

16. Galuske, R. A., Schlote, W., Bratzke, H., & Singer, W. (2000). Interhemispheric asymmetries of the modular structure in human temporal cortex. *Science, 289,* 1946–1949.

17. Geschwind, N. (1979). Anatomical foundations of language and dominance. In C. L. Ludlow, & M. E. Doran-Quine (Eds.), *The neurological basis of language in children: Methods and directions for research* (pp. 145–157). Bethesda, MD: National Institutes of Health.

18. Habib, M., & Robichon, F. (2003). Structural correlates of brain asymmetry: Studies in left-handed and dyslexic individuals. In K. Hugdahl, & R. J. Davidson (Eds.), *The asymmetrical brain.* Cambridge, MA: MIT Press.

19. Hahamy, A. B., Behrmann, M., & Malach, R. (2015). The idiosyncratic brain: Distortion of spontaneous connectivity patterns in autism spectrum disorder. *Nature Neuroscience, 18,* 302–309.

20. Haines, D. E. (2006). *Fundamental neuroscience for basic and clinical applications* (3rd ed.). St. Louis: Elsevier.

21. Jakab, A. K. (2015). Disrupted developmental organization of the structural connectome in fetuses with corpus callosum agenesis. *Neuroimage, 111,* 277–288.

22. Jonsson, C. A., Catroppa, C., Godfrey, C., Smedler, A. C., & Anderson, V. (2013). Cognitive recovery and development after traumatic brain injury in childhood: A person-oriented, longitudinal study. *Journal of Neurotrauma, 30,* 76–83.

23. Keightley, M. S., Sinopoli, K. J., Davis, K. D., Mikulis, D. J., Wennberg, R., Tartaglia, M. C., et al. (2014). Further evidence for neurodengenerative change following traumatic brain injury in children and youth? A scoping review. *Frontiers in Human Neuroscience, 8,* 1–6.

24. Lenneberg, E. (1967). *Biological foundations of language.* New York: Wiley.

25. Liégeois, F. M., Mayes, A., & Morgan, A. (2014). Neural correlates of developmental speech and language disorders: evidence from neuroimaging. *Current Developmental Disorders Report, 1,* 215–227.

26. Lubinski, R., & Hudson, M. W. (2013). *Professional issues in speech-language pathology and audiology* (4th ed.). Independence, KY: Cengage Learning.

27. Mahendra, N. J., Ribera, R., Sevcik, R., Adler, R., Cheng, L., Davis-McFarland, E., et al. (2004). *Why is yogurt good for you? Because it has live cultures.* Rockville, MD: American Speech-Language-Hearing Association.

28. Mantovani, J. F. (1980). Acquired aphasia with convulsive disorder: Course and prognosis. *Neurology, 30,* 524–529.

29. National Health and Medical Research Council (Australia). (2009). *NHMRC additional levels of evidence and grades for recommendations for developers of guidelines.* Retrieved https://www.nhmrc.gov.au/_files_nhmrc/file/guidelines/developers/nhmrc_levels_grades_evidence_120423.pdf.

30. National Institute on Deafness and Other Communication Disorders. (2011). *Specific language impairment.* Retrieved from http://www.nidcd.nih.gov/health/voice/pages/specific-language-impairment.aspx.

31. Owens, R. E., Jr. (2005). *Language development: An introduction* (6th ed.). Needham, MA: Allyn and Bacon.

32. Penfield, W., & Roberts, L. (1959). *Speech and brain mechanisms.* Princeton: Princeton University Press.

33. Rasmussen, T., & Milner, B. (1977). The role of early left-brain injury in determining lateralization of cerebral speech functions. *Annals of the New York Academy of Sciences, 299,* 355–369.

34. Sandin, S. S., Stoltenberg, C., & Reichenberg, A. (2015, June 9). Autism risk associated with parental age and with increasing difference in age between the parents. Molecular Physiology. *Advance online publication.* http://dx.doi.org/10.1038/mp.2015.70.

35. Silverman, F. H., & Miller, L. (2006). *Introduction to communication sciences and disorders.* Eau Claire, WI: Thinking.

36. Sprott, R. A., & Kemper, S. (1987). The development of children's code-switching: A study of six bilingual children across two situations. In E. F. Pemberton, M. A. Sell, & G. B. Simpson (Eds.), *Working papers in language development* (pp. 116–134). Lawrence: Child Language Program, University of Kansas.

37. Stromswold, K. (1998). Genetics of spoken language disorders. *Human Biology, 70,* 297–324.

38. Tallal, P. R. (1989). Familial aggregation in specific language impairment. *Journal of Speech and Hearing Disorders, 54,* 167–173.

39. Tomasch, J. (1954). Size, distribution and number of fibres in the human corpus callosum. *Anatomy Record, 119,* 119–135.

40. Vernon-Feagans, L., Garrett-Peters, P., Willoughby, M., & Mills-Koonce, R. (2012). Chaos, poverty, and parenting: Predictors of early language development. *Early Childhood Research Quarterly, 27,* 339–351.

41. Wada, J. A., Clark, R., & Hamm, A. (1975). Cerebral hemispheric asymmetry in humans. *Archives of Neurology, 32,* 239–246.

42. Weber-Fox, C., & Neville, H. J. (1996). Maturational constraints on functional specialization for language processing: ERP and behavioral evidence in bilingual speakers. *Journal of Cognitive Neuroscience, 8,* 231–256.

Medical Conditions Related to Communication Disorders

I. Congenital Disorders
  A. *Cerebral palsy:* Defect of motor power and co-ordination related to damage of the immature brain
  B. *Congenital hydrocephalus:* Condition marked by excessive accumulation of fluid, dilating the cerebral ventricles, thinning the brain, and causing a separation of cranial bones; caused by a developmental defect of the brain
  C. *Craniostenosis:* Contraction of the cranial capacity or narrowing of the sutures by bony overgrowth
  D. *Down syndrome:* Syndrome of intellectual disability associated with many and variable abnormalities, caused by representation of at least a critical portion of chromosome 21 three times instead of twice in some or all cells
  E. *Idiopathic intellectual disability:* Intellectual disability of unknown cause
  F. *Minimal cerebral dysfunction:* Syndrome of neurologic dysfunction in children usually marked by impairment of fine coordination, clumsiness, and choreiform or athetoid movements; learning disorders often associated with this diagnosis
  G. *Neurofibromatosis:* Condition in which small, discrete, pigmented skin lesions develop in infancy or early childhood, followed by the development of multiple subcutaneous neurofibromas that may slowly increase in number and size over many years

II. Vascular Disorders
  A. *Cerebral embolism:* Obstruction or occlusion of a vessel in the cerebrum by a transported clot or vegetation, a mass of bacteria, or other foreign material
  B. *Cerebral hemorrhage:* Bleeding in the brain; a flow of blood, especially if profuse, into the substance of the cerebrum, usually in the region of the internal capsule; caused by rupture of the lenticulostriate artery
  C. *Cerebral thrombosis:* Obstruction or occlusion of a vessel in the cerebrum by a fixed clot developing on the arterial wall

  D. *Pseudobulbar palsy:* Muscular paralysis from bilateral upper motor neuron lesions of the cranial nerves; often accompanied by signs of dysarthria, dysphagia, and emotional lability with outbursts of uncontrolled crying and laughing
  E. *Recurrent cerebral ischemia or transient ischemic attacks:* Temporary disruptions of the blood supply that produce specific neurologic signs; experienced as sudden, transient blurring of vision, weakness, numbness of one side, speech difficulty, vertigo or diplopia, or any combination
  F. *Subdural hemorrhage:* Extravascularization of blood between the dural and arachnoid membranes

III. Infections
  A. *Acute anterior poliomyelitis:* Inflammation of the anterior cornu of the spinal cord due to an acute infectious disease marked by fever, pains, and gastroenteric disturbances; followed by flaccid paralysis of one or more muscular groups and later by atrophy
  B. *Cerebral abscess:* Intracranial abscess or abscess of the brain, specifically of the cerebrum; a collection of pus in a localized area
  C. *Encephalitis:* Inflammation of the brain
  D. *Human immunodeficiency virus (HIV):* A virus spread through contact with certain body fluids, attacking the body's T cells which are specialized cells that help the immune system fight infection. Untreated, the number of T cells is reduced to the point that opportunistic infections and diseases can occur, signaling the onset of acquired immune deficiency syndrome (AIDS)
  E. *Jakob-Creutzfeldt disease:* Spastic pseudosclerosis with corticostriatospinal degeneration and subacute presenile dementia; characterized by slowly progressive dementia, myoclonic fasciculations, ataxia, and somnolence with gradual onset; usually fatal within a few months to years
  F. *Meningitis:* Inflammation of the membranes of the brain or spinal cord
  G. *Neurosyphilis:* Syphilis, an infectious venereal disease caused by a microorganism affecting the nervous system

H. *Sydenham's chorea:* Acute toxic or infective disorder of the nervous system, usually associated with acute rheumatism, occurring in young persons and characterized by involuntary semi-purposeful but ineffective movements; movements involve the facial muscles and muscles of the neck and limbs and are intensified by voluntary effort but disappear in sleep

IV. Trauma

A. *Penetrating head injury:* Open head injury, which causes altered consciousness and can produce fairly definitive and chronic aphasias

B. *Closed-head injury:* Injury to the head with no injury to the skull or injury limited to an undisplaced fracture; also known as nonpenetrating head injury; can produce loss of consciousness and often produces diffuse effects

V. Tumors

A. *Astrocytomas (grades 1 and 2) and oligodendrogliomas:* Less-common glial cell tumors, with a better prognosis than glioblastoma multiforme; slow growing; usually treated with surgery and radiation therapy, with an average survival rate of 5 to 6 years after surgery

B. *Glioblastoma multiforme:* Also known as malignant glioma or astrocytoma (grades 3 and 4), the most common primary brain tumor in adults; most frequent sites are frontal and temporal lobes, although tumors may occur anywhere in the brain; infiltrative and rapidly growing, with an average survival rate of approximately 1 year

C. *Meningioma:* Benign tumor arising from the arachnoid cells of the brain; slow growing and usually occurring at the lateral areas and base of the brain; generally does not invade the cerebral cortex; favorable prognosis

VI. Degenerative Diseases

A. *Dementia of the Alzheimer's type:* Progressive mental deterioration with loss of memory, especially for recent events

B. *Parkinson's disease:* Degenerative disease resulting from damage to the dopamine-producing nerve cells of the striatum and the substantia nigra; characterized by rest tremor, rigidity of muscles, paucity of movement, slowness of movement, limited range, limited force of contraction, and failure of gestural expression

C. *Wilson's disease:* Genetic metabolic disorder caused by inadequate processing of dietary intake of copper and characterized by motor symptoms, with a significant dysarthria

D. *Huntington's chorea:* Chronic progressive hereditary disease characterized by irregular, spasmodic, involuntary movements of the limbs or facial muscles; sometimes accompanied by dementia and dysarthria

E. *Friedreich's ataxia:* Hereditary disease characterized by degeneration principally of the cerebellum and dorsal half of the spinal cord; ataxic dysarthria often an accompanying sign

F. *Dystonia musculorum deformans:* Hereditary disease occurring especially in children; characterized by muscular contractions producing peculiar distentions of the spine and hip and bizarre postures

G. *Multiple sclerosis:* Inflammatory disease mainly involving the white matter of the central nervous system; characterized by scattered areas of demyelination causing impairment of transmission of nerve impulses; may cause a variety of symptoms, including paralysis, nystagmus, and dysarthria depending on the lesion sites

VII. Metabolic and Toxic Disorders

A. *Reye's syndrome:* Sudden loss of consciousness in children following the initial stage of an infection, usually resulting in death with cerebral edema (swelling) and marked fatty change in the liver and renal system; surviving children often have motor, cognitive, and speech problems

VIII. Neuromuscular Disorders

A. Progressive muscular atrophies

1. *True bulbar palsy:* Disorder caused by involvement of nuclei of the last four or five cranial nerves and characterized by twitching and atrophy of the tongue, palate, and larynx, drooling, dysarthria, dysphagia, and finally respiratory paralysis; usually a manifestation of amyotrophic lateral sclerosis

2. *Amyotrophic lateral sclerosis:* Disease of the motor tracts of the lateral columns of the spinal cord causing progressive muscular atrophy, increased reflexes, fibrillary twitching, and spastic irritability of muscles

B. Muscular dystrophy

1. *Pseudohypertrophic (Duchenne) type:* Type of muscular dystrophy characterized by bulky calf and forearm muscles and progressive atrophy and weakness of the thigh, hip, and back muscles and shoulder girdle; occurs in the first 3 years of life, usually in boys and rarely in girls

2. *Facioscapulohumeral type:* Type of muscular dystrophy causing atrophy of the muscles of the face, shoulder, girdle, and upper arms; occurs in either sex, with onset at any age from childhood to late adult

life; characterized by prolonged periods of apparent arrest

   3. *Ocular myopathy:* Type of muscular dystrophy affecting external ocular muscles, causing ptosis, diplopia, and occasional total external ophthalmoplegia; sometimes associated with upper facial muscle weakness, dysphagia, and atrophy and weakness of neck, trunk, and limb muscles

C. *Myasthenia gravis:* Disorder characterized by marked weakness and fatigue of muscles, especially those muscles innervated by bulbar nuclei

D. Congenital neuromuscular disorders

   1. *Möbius syndrome:* Congenital disorder characterized by paresis or paralysis of both lateral rectus muscles and all face muscles; sometimes associated with other musculoskeletal anomalies

IX. Other

  A. *Epilepsy:* Chronic disorder characterized by paroxysmal attacks of brain dysfunction (seizures) usually associated with some alteration of consciousness; seizures may remain confined to elementary or complex impairment of behavior or may progress to a generalized convulsion

  B. *Wernicke-Korsakoff syndrome:* Cerebral disorder characterized by confusion and severe impairment of memory, especially for recent events; patient compensates for memory loss by confabulation; often seen in chronic alcoholics and associated with severe nutritional deficiency

Bedside Neurologic Examination

1. Mental Status
   A. Orientation: person, place, time
   B. Memory and information
      1. Three objects at 5 minutes
      2. Presidents back to Kennedy
   C. Language
      1. Spontaneous speech characterization
      2. Confrontation naming
      3. Auditory comprehension (commands, yes/no questions)
      4. Repetition (words, phrases)
      5. Reading (printed commands)
      6. Writing (signature, words, and sentences to dictation)
   D. Calculations
      1. Serial 7s (count by 7s to 100)
      2. Subtract $0.43 from $1.00
   E. Visuospatial ability
      1. Clock drawing
      2. Copying of figures
   F. Insight, judgment
2. Cranial Nerves
   A. I: Smell
   B. II: Visual fields, pupillary reactions, optic fundi
   C. III to IV: Extraocular movements
   D. V: Facial sensation
   E. VII: Facial symmetry
   F. VIII: Hearing
   G. IX and X: Articulation, palatal movement, gag reflex
   H. XI: Sternomastoid and trapezius strength
   I. XII: Tongue movement
3. Motor Examination
   A. Bulk
   B. Spontaneous movements (fasciculations, tremor, movement disorders)
   C. Strength

1. Evaluation of strength on right and left
   a. Deltoid
   b. Biceps
   c. Triceps
   d. Hip flexion
   e. Knee flexion
   f. Ankle dorsiflexion
   g. Ankle plantar flexion
   D. Reflexes
      1. Evaluation of reflexes on right and left
         a. Biceps
         b. Triceps
         c. Brachioradialis
         d. Ankle
         e. Plantar
         f. Jaw
   E. Stance and Romberg
   F. Gait
      1. Spontaneous gait
      2. Tandem gait
      3. Tiptoe gait
      4. Heel gait
   G. Sensory Examination
      1. Pinprick
      2. Touch
      3. Vibration
      4. Position
      5. Stereognosis, graphesthesia ("cortical" sensory modalities)
   H. Cerebellar
      1. Finger-nose-finger
      2. Rapid alternating hand movements
      3. Fine finger movements
      4. Heel-knee-shin

Courtesy Howard Kirshner, MD, Department of Neurology, Vanderbilt University School of Medicine, Nashville, TN.

Screening Neurologic Examination for Speech-Language Pathology

I. Mental Status
   A. *General behavior and appearance:* Is the patient normal, hyperactive, agitated, quiet, immobile? Neat, slovenly? Is he dressed in accordance with peers, background, and sex?
   B. *Stream of talk:* Does the patient respond to conversation normally? Is her speech rapid, incessant, under great pressure? Is she very slow and difficult to draw into spontaneous talk? Is she discursive, unable to reach the conversational goal?
   C. *Mood and affective responses:* Is the patient euphoric, agitated, inappropriately cheerful, giggling? Or is he silent, weeping, angry? Does his mood swing in a direction appropriate to the subject matter of the conversation? Is he emotionally labile?
   D. *Content of thought:* Does the patient have illusions, hallucinations, delusions, or misinterpretations? Is she preoccupied with bodily complaints, fears of cancer or disease, or other phobias? Does she believe that society is maliciously organized to cause her difficulty?
   E. *Intellectual capacity:* Is the patient bright, average, slow, intellectually disabled, obviously demented?
   F. *Sensorium*
      1. *Consciousness:* Note whether the patient is alert, drowsy, or stuporous.
      2. *Attention span:* Note response in cerebral function test.
      3. *Orientation:* Note whether the patient can answer questions about his person, location, and time.
      4. *Memory:* Note recent and remote memory deficits disclosed during history taking.
      5. *Fund of information:* Note in history taking.
      6. *Insight, judgment, and planning:* Note in history taking.
      7. *Calculation:* Note performance on cerebral function test.

II. Speech, Language, and Voice
   A. *Dysphonia:* Neuromotor difficulty in producing voice (cranial nerve X)
   B. *Dysarthria:* Neuromotor disorder of articulation and voice
      1. Labials (cranial nerve VII)
      2. Velars and velopharyngeal closure (IX and X)
      3. Linguals (XII)
   C. *Dysphasia:* Cerebral disorder of understanding and expressing language (give aphasia-screening test)
      1. Fluent (give screening aphasia test)
      2. Nonfluent (give screening aphasia test)
   D. *Dyspraxia:* Cerebral disorder of articulation and prosody and/or disorder of oral movement
      1. Dyspraxia of speech
      2. Oral dyspraxia
   E. *Dementia:* Cerebral disorder of language or intellectual deficit
      1. Presenile
      2. Senile
   F. *Disorganized language:* Cerebral disorder of language or confusion
   G. *Dysphagia:* Neuromotor disorder of swallowing (V, VII, IX, X, and XII)

III. Cranial Nerves for Speech and Hearing
   A. *Speech* (V, VII, IX, X, XII, and XI)
      1. V: Inspect masseter and temporalis muscle bulk; palpate masseter when the patient bites.
      2. VII: Evaluate forehead wrinkling, eyelid closure, mouth retraction, whistling or puffed out cheeks, wrinkled skin over neck (platysma), and labial articulation.
      3. IX and X: Evaluate phonation, hypernasality, swallowing, gag reflex, and palatal elevation.
      4. XII: Evaluate lingual articulation and midline and lateral tongue protrusion; inspect for atrophy and fasciculations.
      5. XI: Inspect sternocleidomastoid and trapezius contours; test strength of head movements and shoulder shrugging.
      6. Test for pathologic fatigability by requesting 100 repetitive movements (e.g., eye blinks) if the history suggests myopathic or myoneural disorder.

B. *Hearing* (VIII)
   1. Evaluate for threshold and acuity, including adequacy of hearing for conversational speech.
   2. If history or preceding observation suggests a deficit, perform air-bone conduction audiometric screening.

IV. Motor System
   A. *Inspection*
      1. Take history, including initial appraisal of the motor system; inspect the patient for postures, general activity level, tremors, and involuntary movements.
      2. Observe the size and contour of the muscles, looking for atrophy, hypertrophy, body asymmetry, joint misalignments, fasciculations, tremors, and involuntary movements.
      3. Evaluate gait, including free walking, tandem walking, and deep knee bend.
   B. *Palpation:* Palpate muscles if they seem atrophic or hypertrophic or if the history suggests they may be tender or in spasm.
   C. *Strength*
      1. Upper extremities: Test biceps.
      2. Lower extremities: Test knee flexors and foot dorsiflexors if necessary and feasible.
      3. Pattern: Discern whether any weakness follows a distributional pattern, such as proximal-distal, right-left, or upper extremity–lower extremity.
   D. *Muscle tone:* Move the patient's joints to test for spasticity, clonus, or rigidity.
   E. *Muscle stretch (deep) reflexes:* Test jaw jerk (cranial nerve V afferent and efferent) as well as other muscle stretch reflexes if necessary and feasible.
   F. *Cerebellar system* (gait tested previously)
      1. Evaluate finger-to-nose, rebound, and alternating motion rates.
      2. Carry out heel-to-knee testing.

V. Sensory Examination
   A. Test superficial sensation by light touch with cotton wisp and pinprick on face.
   B. Ask if the face feels numb.
   C. Test superficial sensation on the tongue surface with swab stick unilaterally and bilaterally, anteriorly and posteriorly.

VI. Cerebral Function
   A. When the history or antecedent examination suggests a cerebral lesion, test for finger agnosia and right-left disorientation.
   B. Have the patient perform the cognitive, constructional, and performance tasks from standard aphasia or neuropsychological tests.

Data from DeMeyer, W. (1980). *Technique or the neurologic examination.* New York: McGraw-Hill.

Glossary

abducens cranial nerve VI, which supplies motor impulses to abduct the eye.

abduction movement of a body part away from the midline.

absolute refractory period the short period of membrane unresponsiveness during the passage of an action potential; another action potential cannot be generated during this time.

acceleration-deceleration injury type of injury in which the head is accelerated and then suddenly stopped (e.g., motor vehicle accident).

acquired childhood aphasia language disorder in which cerebral insult halts or disturbs normal language development in a child.

action potential (AP) buildup of electrical current in the neuron.

action tremor rhythmic, oscillatory, involuntary movement affecting the outstretched upper limbs as well as other parts of the body and the voice. Also known as essential tremor, heredofamilial tremor.

adduction movement of a body part toward midline.

adequate stimulus a mechanical, thermal, electrical, or chemical stimulus strong enough to change the cell membrane's potential.

adiadochokinesia inability to perform rapid, alternating muscle movements; see *dysdiadochokinesia*.

afferent traveling toward a center.

afferent fibers nerve fibers that carry information toward the cell body; often used to denote sensory fibers.

agnosia lack of sensory recognition as the result of a lesion in the sensory association areas or association pathways of the brain.

agraphia acquired disorder of writing caused by brain injury.

akinesia absence or lack of movements.

alexia acquired disturbance of reading caused by brain injury.

alexia with agraphia classic neurologic syndrome of reading disorder in which damage has occurred to the angular gyrus and the surrounding areas.

alexia without agraphia classic neurologic syndrome of reading disorder, usually caused by a left posterior cerebral artery occlusion in a right-handed person; the resulting infarct produces lesions in the splenium of the corpus callosum and the left occipital lobe.

allocortex the older, original part of the cerebral cortex.

alpha motor neurons neurons allowing contraction of extrafusal fibers and that have their final common path in cranial and spinal nerves.

Alzheimer's disease the most common type of dementia. Its most striking feature is progressive deterioration of cognitive functions; language disturbance is a major symptom.

amyloid plaques axonal endings associated with pathologic deposits of extracellular beta-amyloid. Found in the brain of patients with dementia of the Alzheimer's type.

amyotrophic lateral sclerosis (ALS) a progressive, fatal motor neuron disease usually involving both the upper and lower motor neuron pathways. Also known as Lou Gehrig's disease.

analgesia loss of the sensation of pain.

anastomosis a connection between two vessels; an opening created by surgery, trauma, or pathologic condition between two spaces or organs that are normally separate.

anencephaly absence of the cranial vault at birth with the cerebral hemispheres completely absent or reduced to small masses attached to the base of the skull.

anesthesia loss of feeling or sensation.

aneurysm a sac formed by the dilation of the wall of an artery, a vein, or the heart.

angular gyrus convolution in the left parietal lobe that is critical for language processing.

anion an ion carrying a negative charge as a result of a surplus of electrons.

anistrophy the property of being directionally dependent as opposed to isotrophy which means identical properties in all directions

anomia loss of the power to name objects or recognize and recall their names.

anomic aphasia an acquired disorder of language caused by brain damage in which the primary difficulty is with word retrieval.

anoxia condition marked by the absence of oxygen supply to organs or tissue.

anterior for anatomic structures, denoting before, in front of, or the front part of.

anterior horn cell cell in the ventral portion in an H-shaped body of gray matter in the spinal cord associated with efferent pathways.

anterior spinothalamic tract the uncrossed fibers of the spinothalamic tract, which carry sensations of light or crude touch.

anterograde transport of axons from the cell body toward the axon terminal.

aphasia acquired disorder of language caused by brain damage; may affect comprehension or expression of language in any modality (spoken, written, or gestural language).

aphasic alexia a disorder of reading caused by brain damage; the reading disorder is part of the overall aphasia syndrome (for example, the reading disorder associated with Wernicke's aphasia).

aphemia an obsolete term for loss of the power of speech.

apraxia a disorder of learned movement distinct from paralysis, weakness, and incoordination; results in a disturbance of motor planning.

apraxia of speech (AOS) disorder of programming the muscles of articulation in the absence of paralysis, weakness, and incoordination.

aprosodia abnormal prosody (stress and intonation pattern in speech), usually resulting from damage to the nondominant hemisphere.

aqueduct of Sylvius small tube or outlet in the midbrain connecting the third and fourth ventricles.

arachnoid mater a thin membranous covering (meninges) of the brain and spinal cord that lies between the dura mater and the pia mater.

arcuate fasciculus long subcortical association tract connecting posterior and anterior speech-language areas in the cerebrum.

areflexia lacking normal reflexive response to an adequate stimulus.

arteriosclerosis a chronic disease characterized by abnormal thickening and hardening of the arterial walls, with resulting loss of elasticity.

arteriovenous malformation (AVM) congenital morphologic defect resulting in an abnormal cluster of arteries directly connecting to veins; often enlarges over time and is at risk of rupture.

articulatory undershoot speech production error in which the active articulatory structure (often the tongue) does not reach its target completely. Often a feature of the articulation of persons with hypokinetic dysarthria.

Asperger's syndrome a developmental disorder characterized by impaired social and occupational skills; normal language (excluding pragmatics) and cognitive development; and restricted, repetitive, and stereotyped patterns of behavior, interests, and activities; often found to show above-average performance in a narrow field against a general background of deficient functioning. This disorder is no longer in the DSM as it has been incorporated under Autism Spectrum Disorders.

association fiber tracts the fiber bundles that form connections between and within the association areas of the brain.

astereognosis loss of the ability to recognize objects through touch alone; caused by brain damage.

astrocyte a type of glial cell with numerous sheetlike processes extending from its body that are thought to provide nutrients for neurons and may have some information storage function.

asymmetrical tonic neck reflex (ATNR) a reflex, normal in the newborn, that consists of extension of the arm and sometimes of the leg on the side to which the head is forcibly turned, with flexion of the contralateral limbs. Considered abnormal if found beyond the eighth or ninth month of age in a term infant.

asymmetry disproportion or inequality between two corresponding parts around the center of an axis.

asynergia lack of coordination in agonistic and antagonistic muscles that manifests as a deterioration of smooth, complex movements.

asynergy lack of coordination of agonistic and antagonistic muscles, particularly associated with cerebellar disorders.

ataxia defect of posture and gait associated with a disorder of the nervous system; sensory ataxia, associated with dorsal column dysfunction, is distinguished from cerebellar or cerebellar pathway ataxia.

ataxic cerebral palsy a relatively uncommon type of cerebral palsy resulting from damage to the cerebellum; characterized by hypotonic muscles and an ataxic gait pattern.

ataxic dysarthria the motor speech disorder associated with damage to the cerebellum and/or its pathways; characterized by irregular articulatory breakdown, prosodic changes, and often a slow rate.

athetoid cerebral palsy the most common dyskinetic type of cerebral palsy characterized by delayed motor development and involuntary, uncontrolled writhing movements.

athetosis a neurologic disorder marked by continual, slow movements, especially of the extremities.

atopognosis loss of the power to locate touch sensation correctly; usually caused by damage to the parietal lobe.

atrophy decrease in size or wasting of a body part or tissue.

attention-deficit/hyperactivity disorder a condition that usually becomes identifiable in children in the preschool to early childhood years (and may persist into adulthood) in which three types of behavior or primary symptoms may be identified: inattentiveness; impulsiveness with hyperactivity; or a combination of these with inattentiveness, impulsiveness, and hyperactivity prominent.

audition hearing.

auditory agnosia inability to recognize the significance of sounds.

auditory brainstem response (ABR) a type of electrophysiologic audiometry in which electrical activity is evoked by brief click stimuli from the eighth cranial nerve and the brainstem; allows inference of hearing and identification of the site of lesion as the cochlea, cranial nerve VIII, or the brainstem.

autism major developmental disability marked by disturbed stereotyped behavior and language patterns; echolalic verbal behavior is often present, as are neurologic signs.

autism spectrum disorder (ASD) a neurodevelopmental disorder affecting social communication and pattern of behavior. In 2013, the diagnostic criteria for ASD were changed to: (1) Demonstration in the past or the present of deficits in social emotional reciprocity, deficits in nonverbal communication for social interaction, and deficits in developing, maintaining and understanding relationships and (2) Presence of at least two types of repetitive patterns of behavior including but not limited to stereotyped or repetitive motor movements, highly restricted fixed interests, inflexible requirement for routines, or hyper or hyper reactivity to sensory input. Severity is rated based on the level of support the individual requires. Eliminated in the 2013, changes were the previously used subcategories such as Asperger's and PDD-NOS.

autoassociator network network used in simulations of behavior in which every unit in the network is connected to every other unit, with associations stored within a layer of neurons.

autonomic nervous system a part of the vertebrate nervous system that innervates smooth and cardiac muscle and glandular tissues and governs involuntary actions (e.g., secretion, vasoconstriction, or peristalsis); includes the sympathetic nervous system and the parasympathetic nervous system.

axon a straight, relatively unbranched process of a nerve cell; literally defined as "the axis."

axonal regeneration regrowth of damaged axons.

axoplasm the protoplasm of an axon.

Babinski sign a reflex movement; when the sole of the foot is tickled, the great toe turns upward instead of downward; normal in infancy but indicates damage to the central nervous system (as in the pyramidal tracts) when occurring later in life. Also known as Babinski, Babinski reflex.

basal ganglia subcortical structures, part of the extrapyramidal system, associated with motor control of tone and posture.

behavioral neurology a specialty in neurology emphasizing clinical and research skills in neurodegenerative diseases and neurobehavioral syndromes.

bilateral related to or having two sides.

bilateral innervation supply of nerves from both sides of the body.

bilateral symmetry movements on one side of the body that mirror movements on the opposite side.

bilingual the ability to understand and converse in more than one language.

bipolar cell first-order nerve cell of the retina, synapsing with the ganglion cells.

bite reflex rapid closure of the jaw and a bite response on moderate pressure to the gums; normal in infants up to 9 to 12 months of age.

border zone the limit of the cerebral area served by either the anterior, middle, or posterior cerebral arteries.

bouton a synaptic knob; from French, meaning "button."

brain scan a neurodiagnostic tool using a radioisotope to detect damaged brain tissue.

brainstem the part of the brain connecting the spinal cord to the forebrain and cerebrum; contains the medulla oblongata, pons, and mesencephalon (midbrain).

branchial of or relating to gills or to parts of the body derived from the embryonic branchial arches and clefts.

Broca's aphasia acquired adult language disorder characterized by nonfluent speech and language; usually accompanied by hemiplegia and an anterior lesion of the brain.

Broca's area major speech-language center in the dominant frontal lobe; important for expression of language.

callosal dysgenesis defective development of the corpus callosum.

capsular referring to the internal capsule.

Carl Wernicke scientific pioneer (1848-1905) who identified an auditory speech center in the temporal lobe associated with comprehension of speech.

cation a positively charged ion.

caudal situated in or directly toward the hind part of the body.

central (parietal-temporal) alexia an acquired disorder of reading and writing caused by brain damage and usually accompanied by some degree of aphasia; also known as alexia with agraphia.

central nervous system (CNS) the brain and the spinal cord structures.

central pattern generator a term given to a cluster of neurons (afferent, interneurons, and efferent) that, when stimulated, trigger a sequenced series of physical responses. In swallowing, the medullary swallowing center, with the nucleus solitarius and the nucleus ambiguus, is thought to function as a central pattern generator.

cephalic of or relating to the head; directed toward or situated on, in, or near the head.

cerebellar hemispheres the two spherical structures comprising the cerebellum.

cerebellum cauliflower-shaped brain structure located just above the brainstem at the base of the skull.

cerebral palsy a disability resulting from damage to the brain before, during, or shortly after birth and outwardly manifested by muscular incoordination and often speech disturbances.

cerebral plasticity the ability of the brain to reorganize neural pathways on the basis of new learning and experiences.

cerebrospinal fluid (CSF) clear, colorless bodily fluid produced by the choroid plexuses and contained within the subarachnoid space circulating around the brain and spinal cord before being absorbed by the arachnoid villi; cushions the central nervous system and provides nutrients.

cerebrovascular accident (CVA) interruption of the blood flow to the brain as a result of occlusive (thrombotic or embolic) or hemorrhagic mechanisms; also known as stroke.

cerebrum the major portion of the brain, consisting of two hemispheres, that contains the cortex and its underlying white matter as well as the basal ganglia and other basal structures.

childhood apraxia of speech (CAS) a developmental sensorimotor speech disorder characterized by impairment of the ability to program the positioning of the articulators and the sequencing of muscle movements for volitional speech production; also known as developmental apraxia of speech.

childhood disintegrative disorder a rare, pervasive developmental disorder on the autism spectrum in which communication and social skills develop normally until at least age 2 years (onset usually is between 3 and 4 years) followed by pronounced loss in motor, communication, and social skills.

chorea disorder characterized by irregular, spasmodic, involuntary movements of the limbs or facial muscles.

choreiform resembling chorea.

choroid plexus structures located in certain parts of the ventricle that are composed of fused ependymal and pia mater cells and associated capillaries; makes and secretes cerebrospinal fluid for circulation.

cingulate gyrus the ridge on the surface of the cerebrum located between the cingulated sulcus and the sulcus of the corpus callosum.

circle of Willis circle of arteries located at the base of the brain; serves as a vascular mechanism for collateral circulation.

circumlocution wordy and circuitous description of unrecalled terms.

clinical neurology medical discipline involving diagnosis and treatment of diseases of the nervous system.

clonus form of movement marked by contractions and relaxations of a muscle occurring in rapid succession.

cochlear duct the middle chamber of the cochlea that contains the sensory end organ of hearing, the organ of Corti; also known as the scala media.

code switching in linguistics, alternating between two or more languages, dialects, or language registers in a single conversation.

cognition the mental process of knowing, which includes aspects such as awareness, perception, reasoning, memory, and judgment.

cognitive-communicative disorders communication disorders resulting from the neurobehavioral sequelae of diffuse (as opposed to focal) brain damage, including deficits in information processing, attention, reasoning, and problem solving and memory.

cogwheel rigidity increased tone, equalized between agonist and antagonist muscles, with a superimposed cogwheel, ratchetlike resistance; often found in patients with Parkinson's disease.

colliculi little "hills" or mounds within the brain; the superior and inferior colliculi are found in the midbrain.

computed tomography (CT) x-ray imaging technique in which the brain is viewed at different depths; the various views are correlated by computer to show structural lesions of the brain.

concentration gradient ratio of solute and water across a membrane.

conduction aphasia an adult language disorder in which auditory comprehension is good but exact repetition is poor; the site of the lesion producing the syndrome is in debate, but it may interrupt the arcuate fasciculus.

confabulation verbal or written expression of fictitious experiences.

confusional state acute symptoms of mental disorganization and agitation that may accompany head trauma or other medical conditions; the language is often marked by irrelevancy and confabulation.

congenital childhood suprabulbar palsy a disorder characterized by isolated paralysis or weakness of the oral musculature without major weakness in the trunk or extremities.

constraint-induced therapy (CIT) a treatment method in rehabilitation in which the patient is forced to use the damaged modality to accomplish tasks normally performed with that modality. For example, constraining the nonparalyzed left arm and requiring activities of daily living and therapy tasks to be done with the hemiparetic right arm and hand or, in constraint-induced aphasia therapy, requiring the patient to communicate verbally rather than allowing alternative communication methods or facilitation.

constructional disturbance the inability to form a construction in space because of a cerebral deficit.

contingent negative variation (CNV) a small negative potential recorded on an electroencephalogram over the front central scalp of some subjects who perform tasks requiring close attention or who have just received a warning stimulus; also known as E wave or expectancy wave.

contralateral related to the opposite side.

contralateral innervation the supply of nerve impulses from the opposite side of the body.

convergence the exciting of a single sensory neuron by incoming impulses from multiple other neurons.

corpus callosum the largest transversal commissure between the hemispheres; it is approximately 4 inches long.

corpus striatum subcortical mass of white and gray matter in front of and lateral to the thalamus in each cerebral hemisphere; is used to refer to the putamen, globus pallidus, and caudate nucleus collectively.

cortex the outer surface layer of the brain (or other organs).

corticonuclear fibers the fiber bundle pathway in each hemisphere from the motor cortex to the nuclei of the brainstem; depending on the particular nerve, some of the fibers decussate and others travel ipsilaterally.

corticospinal tract part of the pyramidal system that descends from the cerebral cortex to different levels of the spinal cord; facilitates motor control.

cranial nerve one of 12 pairs of nerves (fiber bundles surrounded by connective tissue) that exit the brain and pass through the skull to reach the sense organs or muscles of the head and neck with which they are associated.

declarative memory memory for facts and events.

decussation crossing over or intersection of parts.

deep dyslexia an acquired reading disorder resulting from left-hemisphere brain damage and characterized by semantic errors in reading single words.

deglutition the act of swallowing.

dementia an organic mental disorder with progressive general intellectual deterioration affecting memory, judgment, and abstract thinking as well as personality changes.

dementia of the Alzheimer's type see *Alzheimer's disease.*

dendrite the short branching processes of a nerve cell; literally means "treelike."

denervation a cutting of the nerve supply by excision, incision, or blocking.

depolarization loss of the difference in charge between the inside and outside of the plasma membrane of a muscle or nerve cell caused by a change in permeability and migration of sodium ions to the interior.

dermatome the lateral wall of a somite from which the dermis is produced.

developmental anarthria diagnosis involving complete lack of speech as a result of profound paralysis, weakness, and/or incoordination of the musculature of speech.

developmental apraxia of speech a developmental disorder characterized by impaired ability to execute the appropriate movements of speech voluntarily in the absence of paralysis, weakness, or incoordination of the musculature of speech; also known as childhood apraxia of speech.

developmental dysarthria speech disorder resulting from damage to the immature nervous system; characterized by weakness, paralysis, and/or incoordination of the speech musculature.

developmental dyslexia see *dyslexia.*

developmental language disability congenital difficulty with the production and/or comprehension of language, ranging from mild delay to severe disorder.

developmental motor speech disorders a group of disorders of speech production resulting from congenital weakness, paralysis, or incoordination of the speech musculature or a congenital disorder of programming the speech musculature. See *developmental dysarthria* and *childhood apraxia of speech.*

diaphragma sella a ring-shaped fold of dura mater covering the sella turcica, in which the pituitary gland sits.

dichotic listening test situation in which simultaneous auditory stimuli are presented to both ears at the same time; ear preference (right or left) is judged by which ear first recognizes the auditory stimulus.

diencephalon the part of the forebrain between the cerebral hemispheres and the midbrain; includes the thalamus, hypothalamus, the third ventricle, and the epithalamus.

diffuse axonal injury (DAI) extensive tearing of axons as a result of traumatic shearing forces that occur when the head is rapidly accelerated or decelerated, resulting in twisting or rotational force.

diffusion tensor imaging (DTI) an MRI technique that can measure axonal organization in nervous system tissue, describing the magnitude, anistrophy and orientation of any anistrophy.

diplegia paralysis of corresponding parts on both sides of the body, with legs more impaired.

diplopia double vision.

distal away from the center of the body.

divergence dissemination of the effect of activity of a single nerve cell through multiple synaptic connections.

dorsal pertaining to the back; posterior.

dorsal column pathway major sensory pathway mediating proprioception.

Duchenne muscular dystrophy a chronic, progressive disease beginning in early childhood that affects the shoulder and pelvic girdles, causing increasing weakness and pseudohypertrophy of the muscles followed by atrophy and the establishment of a peculiar swaying gait.

dura mater the outermost meningeal layer covering the brain.

dysarthrias a group of speech production disorders caused by oral-motor weakness, paralysis, or incoordination. May be congenital or acquired.

dysdiadochokinesia the inability to perform and sustain rapid alternating movements; speech-language pathologists in particular apply this term to a motor deficit in the oral muscles; associated with cerebellar disorder syndromes; also called alternate motion rate.

dysfluency speech marked by hesitations, prolongations, and/or repetitions that interrupt the natural prosodic flow; also refers to stuttering.

dyskinesia disorder of movement usually associated with a lesion of the extrapyramidal system.

dyslexia inability to read despite the ability to see and recognize letters and a history of appropriate instruction.

dysmetria the inability to gauge the distance, speed, and power of a movement.

dysphagia difficulty swallowing.

dysprosody disturbance of stress, timing, and melody of speech.

dystonia disorder in which the limbs assume distorted static postures as a result of excess tone in selected parts of the body.

ear advantage demonstrated ear "preference" for certain stimuli. Dichotic listening studies have shown that verbal stimuli are more accurately reported when presented to the right ear than the left ear in persons who are left dominant for language. This is called the "right ear advantage."

ectoderm the outermost of the three primary germ layers of an embryo.

efferent conducting (fluid or nerve impulses) outward from a given organ or part.

efferent fibers fibers conducting a neural impulse away from a given neuron; often refers to a motor fiber, although technically it does not necessarily refer to motor impulses.

electroencephalography (EEG) procedure producing a graphic record of electrical activity of the brain as recorded by an electroencephalograph.

embryo the developing human individual from the time of implantation to the end of the eighth week after conception.

encephalitis inflammation of the brain.

encephalon the brain.

encephalopathy pathology of the brain.

endoderm the innermost of the three primary germ layers of an embryo that is the source of the epithelium of the digestive tract and its derivatives and of the lower respiratory tract.

endolymph the watery fluid in the membranous labyrinth of the ear.

enteric relating to or affecting the intestines.

enteric nervous system a division of the autonomic nervous system formed by neuronal plexuses in the gastrointestinal tract and directly affecting deglutition and digestion during swallowing.

ependymal cells glial cells that compose the lining of the ventricles (the ependyma) and the choroid plexuses. The cells function to help make cerebrospinal fluid.

epithalamus small region of the diencephalon of the brain consisting of the pineal gland, habenular nuclei, and stria medullaris thalami.

equilibrium the state of being balanced.

essential tremor organic tremor not associated with any pathologic process.

esthesiometer instrument used to assess two-point discrimination for tactile sensation.

event related potentials (ERPs) very small brain voltages generated in brain structures in response to specific sensory, motor or cognitive events or stimuli, analyzed as time-locked activity during electroencephalogram (EEG) studies

excess and equal stress a feature noted in the speech of some persons with dysarthria, especially in ataxic dysarthria, in which normally unstressed words or syllables are stressed equally with other words with the resulting prosody sounding "robotic."

excitatory postsynaptic potential (EPSP) an electrical change (depolarization) in the membrane of a postsynaptic neuron caused by the binding of an excitatory neurotransmitter from a presynaptic cell to a postsynaptic receptor, increasing the likelihood of an action potential being generated in the postsynaptic neuron.

executive functions capacities, under primary control of the prefrontal cortex, that guide complex behavior over time through planning, decision making, and response control. Common executive abilities include judgment, problem solving, decision making, planning, and pragmatics and depend on cognitive abilities such as attention, perception, memory, and language.

explosive speech loud, sudden speech attributable to damage to the nervous system.

extensor a muscle, the contraction of which tends to shorten a limb; antagonist to flexors.

exteroceptors sense receptors (as of touch, temperature, smell, vision, or hearing) excited by stimuli outside the organism.

extinction progressive reduction in strength of a conditioned response on withdrawal of the reinforcing stimulus.

extraocular adjacent to but outside the eyeball.

extrapyramidal system the basal ganglia and its interconnections.

facilitation process of making the nerve impulses easier by repeated use of certain axons.

falx cerebri the larger of the two folds of dura mater separating the hemispheres of the brain that lies between the cerebral hemispheres and contains the sagittal sinuses.

fasciculation involuntary contractions or twitches in a group of muscle fibers.

fasciculus a nerve fiber bundle forming a connection between groups of neurons in the central nervous system; also known as a tract.

feedback in control theory, a process in which some portion of the output signal of a system is passed (fed back) to the input; often used to control the dynamic behavior of the system.

feedforward system that reacts to changes in its environment, usually to maintain some desired state; exhibits response to a measured disturbance in a predefined way but does not handle novel stimuli.

fetal period the ninth week after conception until birth.

fissure a groove on the surface of the brain or spinal cord.

flaccid flabby, without tone.

flaccid dysarthria a classification of motor speech disorders associated with damage to the lower motor neuron or some part of the motor unit; marked by certain features depending on the part of the motor unit that is damaged.

flocculus small, irregular lobe on the undersurface of each hemisphere of the cerebellum that is linked with the corresponding side of the nodulus by a peduncle.

fluency disorders speech disorders that affect the natural prosody and flow of speech.

fluent/nonfluent a dichotomous classification of aphasic language on the basis of the type of conversational speech.

focal lesion an identifiable, circumscribed area of damage or injury.

foramen an aperture or perforation through a bone or a membranous structure.

forebrain the anterior of the three primary divisions of the developing vertebrate brain or the corresponding part of the adult brain that especially includes the cerebral hemispheres, the thalamus, and the hypothalamus; in higher vertebrates, is the main control center for sensory and associative information processing, visceral functions, and voluntary motor functions; also called prosencephalon.

fractional anistrophy a scale value measuring the degree of anistrophy in a diffusion process, often used in diffusion tensor imaging of white matter

fricatives a consonant sound produced by directing and continuing the restricted breath stream against one or more of the oral surfaces (hard palate, alveolar ridge, teeth, and/or lips); may be voiced or unvoiced. Examples include /f/, /v/, /s/, and /z/.

frontal alexia reading disorder known as the third alexia; associated with a lesion in the left frontal lobe; often accompanies a Broca's aphasia.

frontal lobe the anterior division of each cerebral hemisphere having its lower part in the anterior fossa of the skull and bordered behind by the central sulcus.

frontotemporal dementias (FTD) a syndrome complex, designated by the National Institute of Neurological Diseases and Stroke, marked by progressive deterioration in behavior and/or language with retention of important features of memory, unlike other dementias.

functional magnetic resonance imaging (fMRI) the use of magnetic resonance imaging to measure the hemodynamic response related to neural activity in the brain or spinal cord.

funiculi aggregates of fiber bundles (or tracts) in the nervous system as seen in the spinal cord; also called columns.

gag reflex reflex contraction of the muscles of the throat especially caused by stimulation (as by touch) of the pharynx.

Galant reflex a newborn reflex elicited by holding the child face down and stroking along one side of the spine; normal reaction is lateral flexion toward the stimulated side; should disappear by 9 months of age or before.

gamma-aminobutyric acid (GABA) an inhibitory neurotransmitter.

gamma motor neuron neurons innervating the muscle spindle; allow contraction of intrafusal fibers and increased sensitivity of the fibers to the muscle stretch reflex.

ganglia nerve cells with common form, function, and connections that are grouped outside the central nervous system.

gasserian ganglion the large, flattened, sensory root ganglion of the trigeminal nerve that lies within the skull and behind the orbit; also called trigeminal ganglion, semilunar ganglion.

genioglossus a fan-shaped muscle that arises from the superior mental spine; inserts on the hyoid bone and into the tongue; and advances, retracts, and depresses the tongue.

genu any structure of angular shape resembling a flexed knee.

Gerstmann syndrome a cluster of left parietal lobe lesion signs, including finger agnosia, left-right disorientation, acalculia, and agraphia; a developmental form of the syndrome has been described.

glial cells cellular elements, of which there are several types, that support and expedite the activity of the neurons; glial cells outnumber the neurons 10 to 1; also called neuroglial cells.

glioma general name for a tumor arising from the supportive tissues of the brain

global aphasia an acquired disorder of language caused by brain damage and characterized by severe impairment of all language modalities, comprehension, verbal and gestural expression, reading, and writing.

globus pallidus (GPi) a nucleus of the basal ganglia that receives input from the caudate and the putamen and is the main output nucleus.

glottal coup a rapid, forceful closing and opening of the true vocal folds accompanied by a short, sharp vocalization; used in oral-motor examinations to assess vocal fold movement and strength informally.

Golgi tendon organs a collection of afferent fibers located in tendons or their processes that respond to tension during muscle contraction.

graceful degradation an engineering concept adopted in explanations of neural processing in which the loss of one component of a distributed processing network results in a reduced level, but not failure, of performance.

graded potential short-lived depolarizations or hyperpolarizations of an area of membrane. These changes cause local flows of current (movement of ions) that decrease with distance. When this occurs in a receptor cell, it is called a receptor potential.

gray matter the grayish substance of brain and spinal cord composed of neuronal and glial cell bodies, unmyelinated nerve fibers, and synapses.

gyrus an elevation or ridge on the surface of the cerebrum.

helicotrema the minute opening by which the scala tympani and scala vestibuli communicate at the top of the cochlea of the ear.

hemianopsia a visual field defect of one half of the eye field.

hemiparalysis total or partial paralysis of one side of the body that results from disease of or injury to the motor centers of the brain; also called hemiplegia.

hemiplegia see *hemiparalysis.*

hemorrhage bleeding; a profuse flow of blood.

Heschl's gyrus convolution of the temporal lobe that is the cortical center for hearing; runs obliquely outward and forward from the posterior part of the lateral sulcus.

hindbrain the posterior division of the three primary divisions of the developing vertebrate brain or the corresponding part of the adult brain that includes the cerebellum, pons, and medulla oblongata and that controls the autonomic functions and equilibrium; also called the rhombencephalon.

homeostasis the physiologic process by which the body's internal systems are maintained at equilibrium despite changes in external conditions.

homunculus caricature mapping the connections between the area of the motor or sensory cortex and the innervated body part; literally means "little man."

Huntington's chorea a progressive chorea inherited as an autosomal dominant trait characterized by choreiform movements and mental deterioration leading to dementia; accompanied by atrophy of the caudate nucleus and the loss of certain brain cells with a decrease in the level of several neurotransmitters; usually begins in middle age; also called Huntington's disease.

hyoglossus extrinsic tongue muscle involved in the retraction and depression of the tongue.

hyperalgesia increased sensitivity to pain or enhanced intensity of pain sensation.

hyperesthesia unusual or pathologic sensitivity of the skin or of a particular sense to stimulation.

hyperkinesia an abnormal, involuntary increase in muscle activity.

hypernasality the perception of nasal resonance during the production of voiced sounds, particularly vowels.

hyperpolarization increased production in potential difference across a biologic membrane.

hyperreflexia a condition in which the deep tendon reflexes are exaggerated.

hypertonia extreme tension of the muscles.

hypoalgesia decreased sensitivity to pain.

hypoesthesia impaired or decreased tactile sensibility; also called hypesthesia.

hypokinesia diminished muscle movement capacity.

hypokinetic dysarthria dysarthria caused by basal ganglia disease; most commonly associated with Parkinson's disease.

hyporeflexia diminished or absent reflexes.

hypothalamus portion of the brain that composes part of the third ventricle; critical to autonomic and endocrine function, including rage and aggression, regulation of body temperature, and nutrient intake; also exerts neural control over pituitary gland.

hypotonia muscle flaccidity; a decrease in normal muscle tone when passive movement is performed.

ideational apraxia disorder of motor planning in which complex motor plans cannot be executed, although individual motor components of the plan can be performed.

ideomotor apraxia a motor disturbance characterized by the inability to carry out motor acts on command, but some evidence is present that these motor acts can be carried out imitatively or automatically.

inferior situated below and closer to the feet than another part and especially another similar part of an upright body of a human being.

innervate to supply with efferent nerve impulses.

input fibers neural elements that make synaptic connections by synapsing onto the cell body and/or onto dendrites or dendritic spines found on the dendrites.

intellectual disability a developmental delay characterized by impaired learning, social adjustment, and maturational problems in all areas.

intention tremor a slow tremor of the extremities that increases on attempted voluntary movement and is observed in certain diseases of the nervous system (e.g., multiple sclerosis).

internal carotid arteries the inner branches, right and left, of the carotid artery that supply the brain, eyes, and other internal structures of the head; also called internal carotid.

internuncial functionally imposed between two or more neurons.

interoceptor a specialized nerve receptor that receives and responds to stimuli originating from within the body.

interstitial fluid extracellular fluid.

intervertebral foramina the openings between the vertebrae of the spinal cord through which the motor and sensory roots exit and unite to form the spinal nerves.

intrinsic neurons (interneurons) nerve cells within the central nervous system that act as a link between sensory and motor neurons.

ipsilateral on the same side.

irritability the capacity to respond to stimuli.

ischemia insufficient blood flow to brain tissue, often leading to cell death in that area.

island of Reil part of the cerebral cortex forming the floor of the lateral fissure; also known as insula.

kernicterus a form of infantile jaundice in which a yellow pigment and degenerative lesions are found in areas of the intracranial gray matter.

lacrimal related to the tears, their secretions, and the organs concerned with them.

Landau-Kleffner syndrome a pediatric disorder—first described in 1957 by Drs. William M. Landau and Frank R. Kleffner, who identified six children with the disorder—characterized by a gradual or sudden loss of the ability to understand and use spoken language. Abnormal electrical brain waves, documented by an electroencephalogram, are common, as are epileptic seizures; affected children often have hyperactivity; also called acquired epileptic aphasia.

language lateralization concept that language is not exactly alike between the two hemispheres of the brain.

language dominant the hemisphere that is the site for the major language areas and connections.

lateral a position farthest from the medial plane or midline of a body; related to a side.

lateral spinothalamic tract ascending nerve fibers originating in the spinal cord and terminating in the thalamus.

L-dopa L-3,4-hydroxyphenylalanine; synthetic dopamine that crosses the blood-brain barrier; often given to Parkinson's patients.

lesion an area of damage in the body.

ligand-sensitive channel proteins protein channels in the cell membrane that open and close in response to the presence of certain chemicals or neurotransmitters.

limb apraxia failure to perform a learned movement; may be ipsilateral or bilateral; also known as ideomotor apraxia.

limbic system interconnected nuclei in the telencephalon and diencephalon; functions include self-preservation and activities and behaviors, including emotions, sexual behaviors, memory, olfaction sensory processing; composed of the olfactory bulb, hypothalamus, amygdala, hippocampus, insular cortex, and cingulate gyrus.

localization of function a particular structure in the nervous system assigned to a specific function (e.g., Broca's area is the localized area for language expression).

long-term memory the part of memory where knowledge is stored permanently and is activated when needed (usually through cues); theoretically unlimited in capacity.

Lou Gehrig's disease see *amyotrophic lateral sclerosis*.

lower motor neurons peripheral motor neurons within the spinal cord whose axons terminate in a skeletal muscle; efferent neurons that transmit motor impulses.

magnetic resonance imaging (MRI) neuroimaging procedure in which hydrogen proteins of tissues are aligned with the magnetic field; emits a signal that is recorded in each slice (image).

magnetoencephalography (MEG) magnetic radiography depicting the intracranial fluid spaces after cerebral spinal fluid is extracted and replaced by air or gas.

magnum foramen opening in the base of the skull through which the spinal cord is continuous with the brain.

masking the drowning of a weak sound by a louder one.

mastication the chewing of food.

mechanicoreceptors Sensory receptor sensitive to mechanical stimulation such as muscles and tendons, sinuses, and hair cells of the inner ear.

medial toward the midline.

medulla oblongata also known as the myelencephalon; caudal segment of the brainstem, rostral from the foramen magnum to the pons.

meninges Membranous coverings of the central nervous system developing from the neural crest and the mesoderm layer.

mesoderm the second germ layer apparent during the third week of development of the nervous system; forms the skin (dermis), skeleton, muscles, blood, and blood vessels.

mesencephalon midbrain.

metacognition educational process that incorporates knowledge of one's abilities, the demands of the task at hand, and the effective learning strategies needed to achieve success; may be regulated by the individual involved.

microglia type of glial cell with a primarily scavenger function.

microtubules part of an axon; help carry out the process of axon transport.

midbrain the most superior of the three structures making up the brainstem; associated structures found at the midbrain level are the tectum, inferior and superior colliculi, the cerebral peduncles, and the substantia nigra.

minimal cerebral dysfunction a syndrome of neurologic dysfunction in children usually marked by impairments of fine coordination, clumsiness, and choreiform or athetoid movements; often associated with learning disorders.

mitosis a type of cell division in which a single cell produces two genetically identical daughter cells; new body cells for growth and repair are produced through mitosis.

mixed dominance inconsistency in laterality of speech and related motor functions such as hand, foot, and eye dominance in some individuals; sometimes associated with language and learning disorders.

modified feeding altered intake of food and nutrition; may include tube feedings, specialized diet plans and food consistencies, and solid and liquid restrictions.

monoloudness no variation in the loudness or volume level; static volume usually attributable to dysarthria caused by phonatory and respiratory weakness.

monoplegia paralysis of one limb.

Moro reflex infantile reflex that involves postural responses; rapid lowering of a flexed, supine head of an infant causes abduction and extension followed by flexion, of the arms.

motor association areas cortical association areas, numbered 44 to 47 in the Brodmann system, that surround the foot of the motor and premotor cortices.

motor endplate special structural enlargements of the muscle fibers at the synaptic junction.

motor fibers efferent fibers that go to the muscle and force them to contract.

motor unit a motor neuron that includes the muscle fibers it innervates.

multiple sclerosis (MS) degenerative disease of the central nervous system with no known cause; some research has linked this disease with a malfunction of the immune system; myelin degenerates but the axon remains intact; the intact axon is probably the reason for periods of remission.

multipolar cell any cell that contains more than one process (usually contains two).

muscle spindle specialized organ within a muscle; gives muscle length feedback.

muscle tone the resistance to passive movement or change of muscle length.

muscular dystrophy genetic, progressive myopathy that includes Duchenne muscular dystrophy and myotonia.

myasthenia gravis autoimmune disorder in which postsynaptic acetylcholine receptors are blocked, causing muscle weakness and fatigue.

myelin the fatty substance surrounding some axons that speeds neural transmission; the myelin-covered areas are the white matter of the brain.

myelination the process of segmental wrapping of myelin around axons; continuous myelin is interrupted by narrow gaps (nodes of Ranvier).

myelogenesis the cyclic process of laying down of myelin on certain fiber tracts.

myoclonus rapid, asynchronous movements of the limbs.

necrose to die.

necrosis cell death caused by local injury, such as loss of blood supply or disease; nonphysiologic processes; usually occurs in severe trauma.

neocerebellum the newer parts of the cerebellum phylogenetically provided by the corticopontocerebellar fibers.

neocortex theoretically, a phylogenetic division of the cerebral cortex; distinguished from the allocortex in lower animals; also called the isocortex.

neologistic jargon aphasia a temporal lobe syndrome marked by newly coined words and unintelligible utterances.

neoplasm tumor.

neural integration complete and harmonious combining of components of the nervous system.

neural tube embryologically, a hollow structure that gives rise to the central nervous system as the cells mature.

neurofibrillary tangles tangles of neurofibers common in Alzheimer's disease.

neurofilaments the fine filaments seen in neurons through an electron microscope.

neurogenesis the development of neurons from stem cell precursors.

neuroglial cells see *glial cells.*

neurolinguistics the study of the relation of communication and language regarding brain function; the manner in which the brain helps produce language and, in turn, communication.

neurology a branch of science that deals with the normal as well as the diseased or disordered nervous system.

neuron nerve cell.

neuroplasticity the capacity of neurons to adapt to a changed environment; in some cases, neuronal areas take over function(s) of damaged neurons.

neurotransmitter the substance released from an axonal terminal of a presynaptic neuron once the neuron is excited; travels across the synaptic cleft to excite or inhibit the targeted cell; examples are norepinephrine, acetylcholine, or dopamine.

Noam Chomsky twentieth-century linguist who postulated the theory of language controversy as innate versus learned.

nociceptor a receptor for pain that is stimulated by tissue damage.

Norman Geschwind early-twentieth-century pioneer in behavioral neurology.

notochord a cylindrical group of cells on the dorsal aspect of an embryo; the center of the development of the axial skeleton.

nystagmus rhythmical horizontal, rotary, or vertical oscillation of the eyeballs.

obligatory without an alternative path.

occipital lobe the posterior portion of each hemisphere that forms the posterior-lateral surface of the brain; location of visual cortex; area involved with vision.

olfaction the sense of smell.

oligodendrocyte type of glial cell that produces myelin for neurons in the central nervous system.

optic chiasm the structure located on the floor of the third ventricle composed of crossing optic nerve fibers from the medial (nasal) half of each retina.

optic disk the head of the optic nerve.

oral apraxia buccofacial apraxia; inability to program nonspeech oral movements.

organ of Corti lies against the basilar membrane in the cochlea; contains special sensory receptors for hearing consisting of hair cells and other support cells.

orthograde transneuronal atrophy process involving the large-scale death of neurons in the central nervous system in response to injury to white matter.

osmotic force the energy needed to maintain adequate body fluids and set and maintain the proper balance between the volumes of extracellular and intracellular fluids.

palilalia repeating a word or phrase with increasing rapidity as a result of neurologic damage.

palpate to examine by feeling and pressing with the palms of the hands and fingers.

parahippocampal gyrus between the collateral sulcus and the hippocampal sulcus on the inferior surface of each hemisphere; above the cingulated gyrus and below the lingual gyrus.

paralimbic areas associative areas of the cortex containing structures that form an uninterrupted girdle around the medial and basal aspects of the cerebral hemispheres; areas include the caudal orbitofrontal cortex, insula, temporal pole, parahippocampal gyrus (proper), and cingulate complex.

paralysis loss of voluntary muscular function.

paraphasia the substitution of words or sounds in words in such a way as to decrease intelligibility or obscure meaning.

paraplegia paralysis of both lower extremities and, generally, the lower trunk.

parasympathetic division pertaining to that division of the autonomic nervous system concerned with the maintenance of the body; its fibers arise from the brain and the sacral part of the spinal cord.

parasympathetic nuclei part of the autonomic nervous system; preganglionic fibers leave the central nervous system with cranial nerves III, VII, IX, and X and the first three sacral nerves; postganglionic fibers are in the heart, smooth muscles, and glands of the neck and head and the viscera in the thorax, abdomen, and pelvis regions; most of the fibers are in the vagus nerve tract.

paresis partial paralysis; weakness.

paresthesia abnormal sensation of burning, tingling, or numbness.

parietal lobe upper and central portion of each hemisphere between the frontal and occipital lobes and above the temporal lobe.

parkinsonism a disorder that manifests the symptoms of Parkinson's disease.

Parkinson's disease a slow, progressive disease characterized by the degeneration of the substantia nigra within the basal ganglia, causing a gradual decrease of the neurotransmitter dopamine; characterized by resting tremor of the hands and feet, hypokinetic dysarthria, and a masklike facial expression.

pathologic tremor a tremor caused by the structural and functional manifestations of a disease.

pattern-associator network network used in simulations of behavior that allows transformation of a pattern of activity across its input units into a pattern of activity across its output units.

peduncles very large mass (like a stalk) of nerve fibers connecting two structures in the nervous system.

perikaryon the cytoplasmic matrix surrounding a cell body in a neuron.

perilymph fluid contained in the bony labyrinth of the inner ear.

peripheral nervous system (PNS) Cranial and spinal nerves and their branches.

peristriate cortex part of the occipital lobe that receives fibers from the optic radiation; the primary receiving area for vision.

perisylvian cortex an area on the lateral wall of the dominant hemisphere for language that includes the major centers and pathways for language reception and production; see perisylvian zone.

perisylvian zone the cortex surrounding the sylvian fissure in the dominant temporal lobe; site where the major neurologic components for understanding and producing language are found (e.g., Broca's area, Wernicke's area, the supramarginal and angular gyri).

pervasive developmental disorder a disorder on the autism spectrum characterized by an impairment in the development of social interaction and social pragmatic skills as well as verbal or nonverbal communication skills and the possibility of stereotyped behaviors and interests.

phasic tone rapid contraction to a high-intensity stretch (or change in muscle length) assessed by testing tendon reflexes.

phoneme smallest meaningful unit of sound.

phonologic alexia the inability to read nonsense words, especially low-frequency words; errors are usually visual errors.

photoreceptors nerve end organs stimulated by light, as in the rods and cones of the retina.

phrenic nerves nerves arising from the cervical spinal cord that supply the diaphragm.

pia mater the innermost layer of the meninges that is vascular in nature.

Pick's disease a rare and progressive and degenerative form of dementia characterized by cortical atrophy in the frontal and temporal lobes.

Pierre Paul Broca French physician (1824-1880); localized language areas from two patients who had sustained language and motor speech losses; postulated for the first time that the left hemisphere contained the language center.

plantar relating to the sole of the foot.

plasticity the concept that in the immature brain some functional areas are not established and that unestablished areas may assume any one of a variety of functions.

plosives a class of consonant speech sounds that require a complete closure of the vocal tract followed by a quick release of air and/or acoustic sound energy; they are /p/, /b/, /t/, /d/, /k/, and /g/.

pons the part of the brainstem that lies between the medulla and the midbrain.

positive support reflex reflex that is necessary for erect posture; when the balls of the feet (bounced on a flat surface) are stimulated, a contraction of opposing muscle groups fixes the joints of the lower extremities to bear weight.

positron emission tomography (PET) imaging technique that visualizes the functioning brain by showing its activity through blood flow and glucose metabolism.

posterior directed to or situated in the back; opposite is anterior; also referred to as dorsal.

posterior alexia see *alexia without agraphia*.

postganglionic pertaining to nerve fibers in the autonomic nervous system that exit the ganglion.

postsynaptic terminal what is distal to or beyond a synapse.

postural tone the resistance striated muscles and tendons offer when stretched by a sustained, low-intensity force by a person or gravity; the recoil capability of the striated muscles and the tendons once they are fully extended by a sustained force.

potential a relative amount of voltage in an electrical field.

pragmatic communication disorder see social (pragmatic) communication disorder

praxis the normal performance of a motor act.

preganglionic pertaining to nerve fibers in the autonomic nervous system whose cell body is within the CNS (brainstem or spinal cord) with its axon extending peripherally to synapse on postganglionic neurons in the autonomic ganglia.

prematurity a state of being born after fewer than 37 weeks of gestation (birth weight is no longer considered a critical criterion).

premotor area area in the frontal lobe in front of the premotor cortex and inferior to the prefrontal cortex; responsible for sensory guidance of movement and control of proximal and trunk muscles.

presynaptic inhibition inhibitory control of afferent muscle spindles before the synapse occurs.

presynaptic terminal what is anterior to or before a synapse.

primary auditory receptor cortex found in the temporal lobe; also known as Heschl's gyrus (areas 41 and 42).

primary motor projection cortex composed mostly of precentral gyrus; voluntary control of skeletal muscles on the contralateral side of the body contained in the frontal lobe; also called the motor strip.

primary neurulation a process in which the neural tube forms from the neural plate.

primary olfactory receptor cortex areas responsible for smell, consisting of anterior olfactory nucleus, olfactory tubercle, piriform cortex, and cortical amygdaloid nucleus; only sensory fibers that do not pass through the thalamus.

primary progressive aphasia (PPA) associated with left hemisphere pathology not necessarily from acute neurologic infarct such as a stroke; may have problems in comprehension, reading, writing, naming; does not improve over time as does aphasia from stroke; deficits continue to be progressive; may be a continuous decline in language abilities over time.

primary somatosensory cortex areas 1, 2, and 3 on the postcentral gyrus; a primary receptor of general bodily sensation; thalamic radiations carry sensory data from the skin, muscles, tendons, and joints.

primary visual receptor cortex area 17 in the occipital lobe along the calcarine fissure; receives fibers from the optic tract; also known as the striate area.

procedural memory stores information from rule-based skills and is accessed through learned behaviors; also known as implicit memory.

projection neurons the axons that originate outside the telencephalon (thalamocortical fibers) projecting to the cerebral cortex and those that arise from cerebral cortex cells (corticospinal, corticopontine, and corticothalamic) and project to other downward targeted areas.

prone lying face down.

proprioception perception mediated by proprioceptors.

proprioceptors sensory nerve endings that send information regarding body movement and body positioning.

prosencephalon see *forebrain*.

prosopagnosia a visual agnosia characterized by the inability to recognize the faces of other people or one's own face in a mirror; associated with agnosia for color, objects, and place.

proximal toward the midline or center of the body.

pseudobulbar palsy muscular paralysis from bilateral upper motor neuron lesions of the cranial nerves often accompanied by dysarthria, dysphagia, and emotional lability, such as outbursts of laughing or crying.

pseudohypertrophy increase in the size of an organ or part not caused by an increase in size or number of the specific functional elements; rather, is caused by an increase in some other fatty or fibrous tissue.

pseudounipolar cell sensory neurons in the peripheral nervous system that contain a longer dendrite and a smaller axon that connects to the spinal cord.

ptosis drooping of the eyelid as a result of neurologic damage (paralysis).

putamen a part of the lenticular nucleus; a structure of the basal ganglia.

pyramidal system controls voluntary movement of the muscles for speech and all other voluntary muscles; consists of the corticospinal tract, corticobulbar tract, and the corticopontine tract.

quadriplegia paralysis of all four limbs.

radiograph see *x-ray*.

reasoning the process of evaluating information to come to a conclusion.

reflex arc a pathway leading from the receptor of a sensory stimulus to the motor response; the response is known as an automatic reflex action.

reflexes subconscious automatic stimulus response mechanisms; in human beings, reflexes are basic defense mechanisms to sensory stimulation.

relative refractory period momentary state of reduced irritation after a neural response.

regional cerebral blood flow (rCBF) a neuroimaging technique to study somatosensory pathways.

Reissner's membrane a thin anterior wall of the cochlear duct that separates it from the scala vestibuli.

resting potential the difference in potential across the membrane of a cell at rest.

resting tremor a tremor that occurs when the limb is relaxed and supported, as in Parkinson's disease.

reticulospinal tract nerve fibers that extend from the reticular formation in the brainstem to the spinal cord, contributing to functional contralateral muscle tone; helps with extensor and flexor muscle movements.

retrograde moving against the direction of flow.

retrograde transneuronal degeneration pathologic changes that occur across the axon and cell body of neurons as a result of an axonal lesion.

Rett syndrome a pervasive developmental disorder that affects cerebral gray matter; occurs in females and presents at birth; characterized by autistic behaviors, ataxic movements, and seizures.

rhombencephalon see *hindbrain*.

Romberg test a test in which the patient stands with feet together while the examiner notes the amount of body sway with the patient's eyes open and closed; also known as the body sway test.

rooting reflex a newborn reflex in which a touch to the infant's cheek or upper or lower lip causes the infant to turn toward that stimulus.

rostral toward the nasal or oral regions; superior in relation to the spinal cord and anterior in relation to the brain.

rubrospinal tracts fibers from the red nucleus to the spinal cord.

saltatory transmission the type of neuronal transmission in myelinated fibers compared with the slow transmission in unmyelinated fibers.

scalae fluid-filled columns that surround the modiolus, the hollow core of the cochlea.

scanning speech related to ataxic dysarthria; quite slow, with syllable-by-syllable pausing.

Schwann cells form and maintain myelin in the peripheral nervous system.

secondary association areas sites in which elaboration of sensation occurs; considered as extensions of the primary sensory receptor areas; also known as sensory association areas or unimodal association areas.

secondary neurulation process in which the caudal neural tube give rise to the sacral and coccygeal levels of the spinal cord; begins at approximately 3 weeks' gestation.

secretomotor stimulating secretion.

segmental rolling reflex the reflex noted when an infant rolls the trunk and pelvis segmentally with rotation of the head or legs.

selective engagement neural process in which certain neural networks are utilized for optimizing a task while others are limited in participation; primarily manifested in attention with principal cortical area involved thought to be the dorsolateral prefrontal cortex.

sensory fibers also known as afferent fibers; carry information to the central nervous system about sensations of touch, pain, temperature, and vibrations.

servomechanism control system a control device for maintaining the operation of another system.

short-term memory temporary and limited in capacity; related to working memory (the active processing to hold the information); must be continuously acted on through rehearsal or imaging or information stored here will be lost over time.

Shy-Drager syndrome condition of unknown etiology characterized by hypotension, constipation, urinary urgency, parkinsonian symptoms, cerebellar incoordination, muscle fasciculations, and leg tremors.

single-photon emission tomography (SPECT) imaging modality that uses the mechanism of the computed tomography scan but instead of detecting x-rays, it detects single photons emitted from an external tracer; radioactive compounds that emit gamma rays are injected into the subject; can scan metabolism and blood flow in the brain.

social (pragmatic) communication disorder as of 2013, a new diagnostic category in the DSM (*Diagnostic and Statistical Manual of Mental Disorders*) applied to persons with deficits in social use of language who do not demonstrate restricted interests or repetitive behaviors associated with ASD.

sodium-potassium pump related to the physiology of neurons; an ion pump that removes intracellular sodium and concentrates intracellular potassium.

soma a neuronal cell body; also called the perikaryon.

somatic pertaining to the structure of the body wall (muscles, skin, and mucous membranes).

somesthetic pertaining to the senses of pain, temperature, taction, vibration, and position.

somites mesodermal tissue that develops into the axial skeleton, dermis, and skeletal muscles.

spastic cerebral palsy congenital condition with hypertonia, hyperreflexia, and clasp-knife reflex, increased tone, and bilateral central nervous system damage.

spastic dysarthria strain-strangle, harsh voice quality; imprecise articulation, and hypernasality caused by upper motor neuron bilateral pathology; affects phonation, articulation, respiration, and resonance.

spastic dysphonia (SD) chronic phonation disorder of unknown etiology characterized by a strained voice quality with voice arrests caused by laryngeal adductor spasm; symptoms may occur in some movement disorders; also known as spasmodic dysphonia.

spasticity syndrome of hypertonus with exaggeration of stretch reflexes as a result of certain neural lesions.

spatial summation achieving an action potential involving input from multiple cells of different areas of input, usually from the dendrite.

specific language impairment (SLI) a subset condition of children with developmental receptive/expressive language disorders; possible organic involvement; language disorder must not be attributable to a more generalized condition such as hearing loss, autism, or acquired neurologic damage.

speech-language pathology the study of the diagnosis, treatment, and prevention of communication disorders, including articulation, phonology, voice, fluency, expressive and receptive language, and related disorders.

speech pathology see *speech-language pathology*.

spina bifida congenital defect of the spinal cord or the vertebral column.

spinal peripheral nerves mixed nerves (both sensory and motor) connected to the spinal cord.

spinocerebellar pathway consists of the dorsal and ventral tracts; arise from the posterior and medial gray matter of the spinal cord; dorsal ascends ipsilaterally but the ventral crosses in the cord; both terminate in the cerebellum and allow proprioceptive impulses from all parts of the body to be integrated in the cerebellum.

splenium the thickened posterior part of the corpus callosum.

split brain a condition in which the corpus callosum has been surgically divided so no information transfers between hemispheres.

stereocilia hair cell processes bent by movement.

stereognosis recognition of objects through nonvisual and tactile stimulation.

striate cortex primary visual cortex.

styloglossus the smallest of the styloid muscles arising from the anterior and lateral surfaces of the styloid process; aids in tongue retraction and swallowing.

subarachnoid space a space between the dura and pia mater layers filled with cerebrospinal fluid.

subcortical aphasia aphasia associated with either thalamic or basal ganglia lesions (subcortical structures).

subdural space region below the dura mater.

sublingual region below or under the tongue.

substantia nigra a mass of gray matter extending from the upper border of the pons into the subthalamus.

subthalamus region composed of subcortical structures of the basal ganglia located below the thalamus.

suckling reflex infant reflex that occurs when a finger is placed in the infant's mouth and bouts of sucking behavior occur; integrated at birth and develops into jaw movements after 2 to 3 months.

sulcus groove on the surface of the brain or spinal cord; also known as fissures.

summation the product of the neural impulses acting on a given synapse.

superior upper; opposite of inferior or lower.

supine lying on the back.

supplementary (secondary) motor area (SMA) motor area discovered by Wilder G. Penfield located on the ventral surface of the precentral and postcentral gyri; primary function is controlling sequential movements.

supramarginal gyrus convolution in the inferior parietal lobe surrounding the posterior end of the sylvian fissure.

surface dyslexia type of dyslexia distinguished by poor ability to use grapheme-to-phoneme conversion rules.

swallowing reflex developed after the sucking reflex is integrated into feeding; sucking produces saliva that accumulates in the pharynx, triggering the reflex; may be observed by visible upward movement of the hyoid bone and thyroid cartilage of the larynx.

Sydenham's chorea involuntary movement disorder following infection; usually occurs in children and adolescents.

symmetrical tonic neck reflex analogous to the asymmetrical tonic reflex but the head is manipulated in flexion and extension in midline rather than turned laterally; the normal execution of this reflex is an extension of the arms and flexion of the legs if the head is extended in midline.

sympathetic division that division of the autonomic nervous system concerned with preparing the body for fight or flight; its neurons arise in the thoracic and upper lumbar segments of the spinal cord.

synapse a juncture or connection; the functional contact of one neuron with another.

synaptic cleft the intervening space before and after a synapse.

synergy the cooperative action of muscles.

tardive dyskinesia uncontrolled involuntary movements of the face and tongue; often caused by excessive or long-term treatment with neuroleptic medications.

tectal pathway projects to the superior colliculi in the brainstem and the thalamus and out to many regions of the cortex; substantially involved in the ability to orient toward and follow a visual stimuli.

tectorial membrane gelatinous covering of the organ of Corti in the auditory system.

tectum roof of the midbrain; location of the superior and inferior colliculi.

temporal lobe bounded superiorly by the lateral fissure and posteriorly by the occipital lobe; the center for auditory processing in the brain.

temporal summation the additive effect of successive stimuli on one nerve, which collectively can generate a response when the individual stimuli could not.

temporal visual cortex part of the visual association cortex located within the middle and inferior temporal areas.

tentorium cerebelli one of two dural folds in the dura mater that help stabilize the brain.

teratology the study of abnormal embryology.

thalamic reticular nucleus a layer of cells enveloping the ventral thalamus whose axons are sent back into the thalamus rather than to the cortex; either facilitates or inhibits transmission of other impulses to the cortex.

thalamus two oval nodes located at the base of the cerebrum; serves as a relay station for all sensory stimulation; consists of gray matter.

thrombus A stationary blood clot along the wall of a blood vessel.

tinnitus ringing or buzzing sound heard in the ear.

tongue reflex typically a part of the suckle-swallow reaction in which the tongue thrusts between the lips; mediated at the medulla; usually disappears by 12 to 18 months of age.

tonic labyrinthine reflex (TLR) associated with changes in tone as a result of changes in head position affecting the orientation of the labyrinths of the inner ear.

tonotopic pertaining to the spatial arrangement in the auditory system determining where different sound frequencies are perceived, transmitted, or received.

topologic involvement relation of an anatomic structure to a specific body part or area.

transcortical aphasia several types of language disturbances whose causes are lesions outside the perisylvian area; repetition is always preserved.

transcranial magnetic stimulation (TMS) a noninvasive method of exciting neurons in the brain; uses weak electric current induced in the brain tissue by rapidly changing magnetic fields.

transient ischemic attack (TIA) a reversible neurologic defect (focal) lasting up to 24 hours; may indicate a risk for a stroke; may be caused by an embolism or obstruction of an artery.

transitory related to or marked by a transition; not permanent.

traumatic brain injury (TBI) diffuse brain damage that may be caused by an external force (e.g., closed-head injury from a car accident) or a penetrating force (e.g., open-head injury from a bullet wound).

tremor a purposeless involuntary movement that is oscillatory and rhythmic.

trigeminal ganglia on the sensory root of cranial nerve V in a cleft within the dura mater; gives off ophthalmic and maxillary nerves and is part of the mandibular nerve branch.

triplegia paralysis of an upper and a lower extremity and of the face or of both extremities on one side and one on the other.

uncus the hooked extremity of the hippocampal gyrus.

unilateral initiated from or affecting structures on only one side of the body.

unilateral inattention a subtle form of neglect syndrome characterized by the failure to recognize a side of the body and the space around it.

unilateral innervation indicating that the nerve supply to a particular structure comes from only one side of the body (may be ipsilateral or contralateral), as opposed to bilateral innervation, in which nerve fibers are distributed from both sides of the body.

unilateral upper motor neuron dysarthria A motor speech disorder primarily caused by unilateral damage to the upper motor neurons that carry impulses to the cranial nerves that innervate the speech musculature; the most affected speech parameter is articulation.

upper motor neurons Nerves connecting cortical motor areas with cranial and spinal nerves; composed of the direct activation pathway (DAP) and the indirect activation pathway (IAP), the DAP functions for direct voluntary and skilled movements, whereas the IAP functions to control posture, tone, and movements that support voluntary movements.

ventral toward the belly or abdomen; opposite of dorsal.

ventricular system cavities that contain cerebrospinal fluid produced by the choroid plexus located in each ventricle; the system consists of lateral ventricles and a third and fourth ventricle; connected by foramen and the aqueduct of Sylvius; found in the deepest areas of the brain.

vertebral artery supplies the brainstem and cerebellum; from the anterior and posterior spinal arteries to the spinal cord and a branch called the posterior inferior cerebellar artery.

vesicle a blister or bladder; the intracellular bladder is believed to be filled with neurotransmitter substances.

vestibulospinal tracts nerve fiber tracts that mediate cerebellar and vestibular influences on the spinal cord; facilitate reflexes and control muscle tone.

visual agnosia the inability to recognize objects by sight, usually caused by damage to the visual association area of the central nervous system.

volitional voluntary.

Wernicke's aphasia an acquired adult language disorder characterized by impaired comprehension, and fluent, paraphasic language; the patient is free of hemiplegia, and the lesion usually is in the temporal lobe.

Wernicke's area a major speech-language center in the dominant temporal lobe; important for comprehension of language.

white matter substance of the brain and spinal cord consisting of myelinated fibers and containing no neuronal cell bodies or synapses; in a freshly sectioned brain it glistens white because of the high content of lipid-rich myelin; also called the fimbria.

x-ray radiograph; film produced by radiographic imaging.

Index

Note: Page numbers followed by "*b*," "*t*," and "*f*" refer to boxes, tables, and figures respectively.

313